James B. Phipps
Dept. Botany, U.W.O.
1966

PALEOMAGNETISM

PALEOMAGNETISM

and Its Application to Geological

and Geophysical Problems

E. IRVING

Department of Geophysics

Australian National University, Canberra

JOHN WILEY & SONS, INC., NEW YORK / LONDON / SYDNEY

Library of Congress Catalog Card Number: 64–20069
Printed in the United States of America

". . . a theory may be true
even though nobody believes it,
and even though we have
no reason for accepting it,
or for believing it is true;
and another theory may be false,
although we have comparatively
good reasons for accepting it."

Karl R. Popper
Conjectures and Refutations

*(Quoted by courtesy of Professor K. R. Popper,
Routledge and Kegan Paul, and Basic Books.)*

In this book I have tried to summarize our present knowledge of paleomagnetism and to outline its relation to some other studies in the Earth sciences. Paleomagnetism is a composite subject with both geological and physical aspects, and I have written this book in a manner which may be followed by a geologist equipped with an elementary text on magnetism or by a physicist who has at hand a dictionary of geological terms.

Paleomagnetism, in common with other geophysical studies, suffers from deficiencies in the observational data available at present; but there are certain features of the data which indicate the usefulness of the results so far obtained. First, it is known that certain lavas poured out in the past few hundred years acquired a fossil magnetization accurately parallel to the direction of the geomagnetic field at the time of cooling. Second, it is known that certain very much older rocks possess a fossil magnetization of very great stability which was probably acquired when the rock was formed and which may therefore provide a record of the direction of the geomagnetic field at that time. Third, in those cases where independent studies of the same rocks have been made by different workers, the results obtained agree with one another within the expected limits of error. Finally, the paleomagnetic results impinge upon certain other areas of Earth science, particularly geology, and it is therefore possible to test their reliability by comparing them against the independent findings of geologists; it is this type of interdisciplinary testing which is needed before the bearing of paleomagnetic work on Earth history can be established on a reasonably objective basis. Numerous comparisons of this nature are recounted in this book, but these examples are only a tentative beginning to the problems of integrating paleomagnetic results with the corpus of geological knowledge.

In interpreting the data I have sought the simplest and most general explanations, inasmuch as it is fruitless to consider complex solutions until the simple ones have been found wanting. I have given consideration only to those hypotheses which can be tested * by the data at present available, or which can potentially be checked by the data which will probably be obtained in the course of the next decade.

The study of paleomagnetism has revealed phenomena which had not been previously suspected (for example, reversals of the geomagnetic field), but perhaps its greatest contribution so far has been that it provides numerical tests of hypotheses which have been formulated by workers in other subjects. As an illustration I will say a little about the hypothesis of continental drift which dates back in the geological literature for about a century. This hypothesis supposes that the continents have changed their relative positions in the past few hundred million years. Prior to the rapid developments in paleomagnetism in the past dozen years there was, so far as I am aware, no method by which the hypothesis could be firmly rejected—it made no predictions which could be rigorously tested by methods then available. Evidence (usually of a type

* By this I mean falsifiable in the sense intended by Popper in *Conjectures and Refutations*, Routledge and Kegan Paul, and Basic Books, 1963, p. 37.

related to fit and misfit arguments) was brought forward by the proponents of drift, and while this evidence was considered consistent with the hypothesis, it was similar to what had first been the basis for the formulation of the hypothesis; this "new" evidence was, by and large, only a proliferation of the type already available and which the critic had found insufficient.

Now the paleomagnetic method provides a test which is independent of any previous evidence. The test is that if the continents had *not* changed their relative positions, then the equivalent paleomagnetic poles obtained from rocks of the same age from all parts of the Earth should agree. If this agreement had been found from the observations of numerous workers on rocks of many ages in all continents, there seems little doubt that the hypothesis would have been set aside. So far as I know this was the first time the hypothesis had been exposed to a physical test which, if successful, would have disproved it. However, when the test was made on rocks from all continents, large divergences between equivalent poles were found, and these divergences occurred in a way which was roughly consistent with the hypothesis of drift. Of course this does not prove that drift occurred—it merely means that the drift hypothesis survives and merits further critical discussion. The need now is for rigorous tests of special aspects of the drift hypothesis, and in this book I have tried to show that such tests are now well in hand.

In reviewing the paleomagnetic results I have been confronted with the question of whether to include all results or only those based on detailed work. I have chosen the former course, listing the data in an appendix. I believe this list to be substantially complete, although there may be gaps because of omissions in my reading or in my private index. This appendix is much like earlier catalogues except that it is, in general, more detailed and many analyses not previously reported are included. But the results are not accepted uncritically. I have given a set of common-sense criteria (§ 5.16) for recog-

nizing results on which I believe little reliance can be placed. About 10 per cent of the results are rejected on this basis. This is the first systematic attempt to make such a selection. There will be perfectionists who will argue that my criteria are too lenient and admit data of doubtful value. However, if I have erred on the side of leniency, it is because I am aware of the number of instances in which early reconnaissance work has been corroborated by later more detailed studies.

A further problem is that of how to deal with the results which have been published during the time it has taken to prepare this book. The procedure I have adopted (which is explained in more detail in the footnote on p. 104) was to prepare an initial list of results and then to add a supplementary list at a late stage in preparation. The book is therefore up-to-date to about the end of 1963.

Referencing of previously published information has been done by author's name or, where this is cumbersome, by a number to the entry in the appendix in which the author's name is given. The bibliography is presented in a single list at the end; I have included only those paleomagnetic papers that I have read, either in the original or in the English translation, so that certain early contributions which I have not been able to locate in Australia are absent from the list.

I would like to record my gratitude to many people for their help: I am much indebted to my wife for her help in proofreading and indexing; to my assistant and colleague Martin Ward who did many of the computations; to the late Sir R. A. Fisher for his advice on statistical matters; to Professor J. C. Jaeger who has helped me greatly, not only during the preparing of this book but also previously in my work; to Professors A. L. Hales and J. W. Graham, and Dr. F. H. Chamalaun for their critical reading of the manuscript; to James Briden who was my co-worker in the studies of paleolatitude spectra described in Chapter Nine; and to Professor D. A. Brown, Dr. K. W. T. Campbell, and Dr. K. A. W. Crook for their advice on geological matters. I would like to thank all those workers who have sent me off-prints of their work and to those workers and publishers who have given their permission for the reproduction of figures and tables.

The first draft was typed by Mrs. C. Pederson and Mrs. J. C. Thorpe. The final copy was typed by Mrs. L. Nicholson and I am particularly indebted to her for this help. Finally, I would like to acknowledge with gratitude the tolerance and understanding of my wife and children, who endured, without complaint, the stresses and strains that seem to arise during authorship.

E. Irving

Canberra, Australia
June, 1964

CONTENTS

One   Introduction   1

1.1   Paleomagnetism, 1
1.2   Geomagnetism and paleomagnetism, 1
1.3   Origin of fossil magnetism, 3
1.4   Applications, 4
1.5   Field and laboratory experiments, 4
1.6   Paleomagnetic surveys, 5
1.7   Paleomagnetism, an historical study, 6
1.8   Early work, 6
1.9   Recent developments and aims, 9

Two   Magnetic properties of rocks   10

2.01   Introductory, 10
2.02   Remanent and induced magnetization, 10
2.03   Ferromagnetism, 11
2.04   Theory for single-domain particles, 14
2.05   Magnetic minerals: general points, 16
2.06   Magnetic minerals: descriptions of types, 17
2.07   Measurement of Curie points, 20
2.08   Stability of remanence, 21
2.09   Hysteresis of isothermal remanence, 22
2.10   Thermoremanent magnetization, 24
2.11   Chemical remanent magnetization, 28
2.12   Detrital remanent magnetization, 30
2.13   Viscous effects, 32
2.14   Magnetic anisotropy, 34
2.15   Stress effects, 36

Three   General features of the geomagnetic field   39

3.1   Preliminary remarks, 39
3.2   The Earth's present field, 39
3.3   Changes in the field, 40
3.4   Origin of the geomagnetic field, 42
3.5   The field of an axial geocentric dipole, 42
3.6   Paleomagnetic poles and virtual geomagnetic poles, 43
3.7   Statistical models derived from field analysis, 45
3.8   Hypothetical statistical models, 49
3.9   Comparison of models, 50

Four   Directions of magnetization and their analysis   52

4.01   Preliminary remarks, 52
4.02   Sampling schemes, 52
4.03   Fragmentary nature of the record, 53
4.04   Representation of directions, 54
4.05   Examples of NRM directions, 55
4.06   Sources of dispersion, 57
4.07   Fisher's Distribution, 58
4.08   Goodness of fit to Fisher's Distribution, 60
4.09   Statistical tests, 62
4.10   Combination of observations from rock units, 63
4.11   Angular standard deviation, 68
4.12   Paleomagnetic poles, 69
4.13   Reversals, 71

Five   The reliability of paleomagnetic observations   72

5.01   Problems, 72
5.02   Possible origins of fossil magnetism, 72

5.03 Consistency tests, 73
5.04 Study of deformed beds, 76
5.05 Study of igneous contacts, 81
5.06 Study of sedimentary features, 83
5.07 Study of jointed rocks, 86
5.08 Removal of low stability components by partial demagnetization, 86
5.09 Magnetic and thermal cleaning, 88
5.10 Special tests, 90
5.11 Magnetic "noise," 93
5.12 Red sediments, 96
5.13 Surface effects, 99
5.14 Time basis of results, 100
5.15 Repeatability of results, 101
5.16 Minimum criteria of reliability, 102

Six Paleomagnetically determined field directions 104

6.01 Preliminary remarks, 104
6.02 Cenozoic results, 105
6.03 Analysis of Cenozoic paleomagnetic poles, 109
6.04 Mesozoic results, 111
6.05 Upper Paleozoic results, 115
6.06 Lower Paleozoic results, 123
6.07 Precambrian results, 125
6.08 Analysis of mean directions, 127
6.09 Relevant hypotheses, 130
6.10 Apparent polar-wandering, 133
6.11 Axially symmetrical fields, 142
6.12 Secular variation: evidence from dispersion estimates, 146
6.13 Secular variation: evidence from TRM, 147
6.14 Secular variation: evidence from sediments, 150

Seven Reversals of magnetization 154

7.1 Introduction, 154
7.2 Examples of reversals dated stratigraphically, 155
7.3 Examples of reversals dated radiometrically, 159
7.4 Self-reversal mechanisms; theoretical aspects, 159
7.5 Observed self-reversal properties in rocks, 162
7.6 Transition zones, 168
7.7 Consistency evidence, 170
7.8 Igneous contact studies, 173
7.9 Discussion, 176

Eight Intensity of the paleogeomagnetic field 178

8.1 Introduction, 178
8.2 Methods, 178
8.3 Determinations for historic time, Western Europe, and Northern Africa, 181
8.4 Determinations for the geological past, 183

Nine Paleolatitudes and paleomeridians 185

9.01 Introduction, 185
9.02 Estimates of past position, 186
9.03 Presentation of estimates, 188
9.04 Paleoclimatic indicators, 188
9.05 Climatic zones, 190
9.06 Paleolatitude time variations for reference localities, 191
9.07 Regional variations, 196
9.08 Paleolatitude spectra, 202
9.09 Evaporites, 204
9.10 Carbonates: general, 210
9.11 Dolomite, 212
9.12 Corals, 212
9.13 Organic reefs, 213
9.14 Archeocyathinae, 215
9.15 Permian fusulinids, 217
9.16 Red beds, 220
9.17 Coal, 220
9.18 Glaciations, 224
9.19 Cretaceous paleotemperatures, 230
9.20 Desert sandstones and paleowind directions, 233
9.21 Discussion of uncertainties, 240
9.22 Paleoclimatic zones, 242
9.23 The axial geocentric dipole model, 243

Ten Special problems 245

10A Application to structural problems, 245
   10A.1 General statement, 245
   10A.2 Detection of broken ground, 245
   10A.3 Variable attitude of layers, 246

10A.4 Detection of relative rotations about vertical axes, 249
10A.5 Siletz River volcanics, 249
10A.6 Bending of Japan, 249
10A.7 Lewis thrust, 251
10A.8 The origin of the Red Sea, 251
10A.9 Alpine orogenic zone of Europe, 253

10B Paleomagnetism and paleogeographic reconstructions, 256
10B.1 Introductory remarks, 256
10B.2 Paleoclimatic aspects, 258
10B.3 Comparisons with some previous paleogeographic hypotheses, 259
10B.4 Paleomagnetism as a basis for paleogeographic maps, 265
10B.5 Some illustrations, 268

10C Paleomagnetism and stratigraphic correlation, 273
10C.1 General ideas, 273
10C.2 Use of the secular variation, 274
10C.3 Uses of apparent polar-wandering, 275

10C.4 Use of reversals, 277
10C.5 Naming problems, 280

10D Paleomagnetism and the origin and history of rocks, 280
10D.1 General remarks, 280
10D.2 Applications to igneous bodies, 281
10D.3 Applications to banded iron formation, 286
10D.4 Paleolatitudes of oil fields, 287

10E Detecting changes in the Earth's radius, 288
10E.1 Introductory, 288
10E.2 Hypotheses of an expanding Earth, 289
10E.3 Estimates of paleoradius, 290

10F Extraterrestrial paleomagnetism, 292

Appendix: Reference list of paleomagnetic results **294**

Explanatory notes, 317

References **363**

Index **385**

Symbols and Abbreviations Commonly Used

$a_{1-\mathcal{P}}$	Circle of confidence at probability $\mathcal{P}$		$\mathbf{M}_n$	Natural remanent magnetization
CRM	Chemical remanent magnetization		$\mathbf{M}_s$	Stable component of the natural remanent magnetization
$\mathfrak{D}$	Declination of magnetic field			
D	Declination of individual remanent magnetization vector		$\mathbf{M}_u$	Unstable component of the natural remanent magnetization
D_m	Declination of a mean remanent magnetization direction		N	Number of unit vectors
DRM	Detrital remanent magnetization		NRM	Natural remanent magnetization or fossil magnetization
$\mathbf{F}$	Geomagnetic field vector		oe	Oersted
F	Strength of geomagnetic field		p	Colatitude
H	Horizontal component of geomagnetic field		$\mathcal{P}$	Probability
h	Magnetic field strength		Q	Various ratios of magnetic intensity (see § 2.02)
J	Intensity of magnetization—generally referring to intensity measured in a field		S	Sampling locality
			S_r	Reference locality
H_c	Coercive force of the hysteresis cycle—B-H loop		T_C	Curie temperature or Curie point
			TRM	Thermoremanent magnetization
H_{cr}	Coercivity of maximum IRM (M_{max})—M-H loop		VRM	Viscous remanent magnetization
$H_{cr}{}'$	Coercivity of NRM or destructive field		δ	Angular standard deviation of directions from the mean direction
$\tilde{H}_p$	Peak strength of alternating magnetic field		Δ	Angular standard deviation of poles from the mean pole
			ϵ	Standard error in the mean
$\mathfrak{g}$	Inclination of magnetic field		θ	Angular displacement of unit vector from mean direction
I	Inclination of individual remanent magnetization vector			
I_m	Inclination of a mean remanent magnetization direction		θ_{63}	Circular standard deviation of individual directions from the mean
IRM	Isothermal remanent magnetization		Θ_{63}	Standard deviation of site poles from mean pole
k	Best estimate of Fisher's precision parameter κ for remanence directions		κ	Fisher's precision parameter for directions
K	Best estimate of Fisher's precision parameter K for poles		K	Fisher's precision parameter for poles
			λ	Latitude of sampling locality
$\mathbf{M}$	Remanent magnetization vector		λ_r	Latitude of reference locality
M	Intensity of remanent magnetization vector		λ'	Latitude of paleomagnetic or virtual geomagnetic pole
M_{max}	Maximum IRM		λ_p	Paleolatitude

ϕ Longitude of sampling locality

ϕ_r Longitude of reference locality

ϕ' Longitude of paleomagnetic or virtual geomagnetic pole

χ Susceptibility

ψ_p Rotation angle: angle between present meridian and paleomeridian

∂ Angle between a directional feature and the present meridian

∂_p Angle between a directional feature and the paleomeridian

PALEOMAGNETISM

CHAPTER ONE

Introduction

§ **1.1 Paleomagnetism** All rocks exhibit magnetic properties, one of which is the tendency of a rock specimen to behave as a magnet, with a north and south pole and a magnetic axis. This magnetization is a naturally occurring property, and is referred to as *fossil magnetism,* or *natural remanent magnetism,* the latter term being commonly abbreviated to NRM. *Paleomagnetism* is a loose term which is used by some workers to denote the study of this property whereas others use it to signify the property itself. In some cases the fossil magnetism was impressed when the rock was formed, its axis being along the direction of the Earth's magnetic field at that time. It may therefore serve as a fossil compass useful for determining the *direction* of the ancient geomagnetic (or *paleogeomagnetic*) field. Furthermore, its intensity depends in a complex way on the strength of the field in which it was acquired, so that, in principle, the *intensity* as well as the direction of the ancient field may be investigated. Most paleomagnetic work has however been concerned with investigating the variations in direction of the ancient field.

Paleomagnetism is composed of three elements. First, there are the geophysical aspects dealing with the time variations in the Earth's magnetic field; second, there are the physical and mineralogical aspects concerned with the origin of fossil magnetism; and third, there are the geological aspects in which paleomagnetic observations are compared with geological results. Although, in any particular context, these aspects are usually intimately connected with one another, it is convenient in this introductory discussion to consider them separately.

§ **1.2 Geomagnetism and Paleomagnetism** Most of our information about the geomagnetic field has been obtained by direct recording at magnetic observatories over the past 400 years. Paleomagnetism provides the means to extend this record back into the remote geological past. A demonstration of the paleomagnetic method is given in Figure 1.1. The directions of fossil magnetism measured by Chevallier (1925) in five rock samples taken from the 1669 lava flow of Mt. Etna [12.09] [1] are compared with the direction of the Earth's field at that time as it appears in observatory records. The rock directions are grouped around the known field direction, their average being within a degree of it. The experimental error in each determination is several degrees and the

---

[1] The numbers in square brackets refer to the appendix where further information is given.

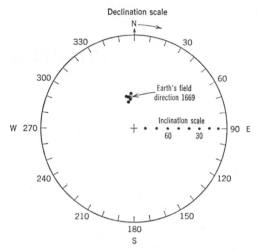

Figure 1.1. Direction of natural remanent magnetization in the 1669 lava flow, Mt. Etna, Sicily. The north-seeking directions in 5 rock samples are plotted as dots on the lower hemisphere of an equal-area net. The method of specifying directions numerically and of plotting them graphically are explained in §§ 2.02, 4.04. Data of Chevallier (1925).

small scatter is therefore not significant, so that the paleomagnetic observations provide a good statistical estimate of the field direction.

The present geomagnetic field resembles that of a *dipole* situated at the Earth's center. The lines of force of such a field run from south to north as depicted in Figure 1.2. This dipole is called the *inclined geocentric dipole,* and its axis makes an angle of 11½° with the rotation axis. It is obviously desirable to relate the paleomagnetic observations to what is known about the present field, but attempts at integration immediately encounter difficulties because of the different time scales involved; the datum in studies of the present Earth's field is a magnetic force vector **F** measured at a time which is known from observatory clocks to an accuracy of seconds, whereas the datum of paleomagnetism is a magnetization vector **M** which may reflect the ancient field direction at a time estimated from geological time scales. Therefore, it is necessary when mak-

ing these comparisons, to use some working model which expresses the long-term average behavior of the field rather than its detailed short-term behavior. The model used is that of an *axial geocentric dipole,*[2] that is, of a geocentric dipole whose axis is directed along the spin axis (Figure 1.3). The reason for adopting this model is that it is now known, from the paleomagnetic results, that for the past few million years the Earth's field *when averaged over periods of several thousands of years* has been (within the statistical errors of the determinations) like that of an axial geocentric dipole and different from that of the inclined geocentric dipole;[3] the departure of the latter from the rotational axis appears as a transient effect when viewed on the geological time scale of events. The validity of this model for earlier times however is not known with certainty but there are now many observations from diverse sources which are consistent with it. The virtues of the model are that it has considerable explanatory power and yields results of much interest for geology and geophysics. Frequent use of the model is made through-

[2] This model is set out in detail in Chapter Three.

[3] The observations relating to this fundamental point are set out in Chapter Six.

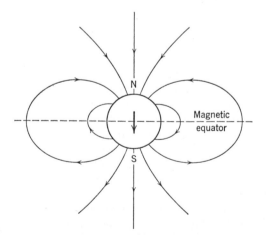

Figure 1.2. Lines of force of a geocentric dipole.

out this book and tests are made to check its validity.[4]

Some of the changes which may be expected to have affected the axial geocentric dipole field are now mentioned. These changes, which are set out schematically in Figure 1.3, are (1) the secular variation, (2) reversals of polarity, and (3) changes in attitude of the axis, which may be loosely termed polar-wandering. *Secular variation*, in the broad sense intended here, may be thought of as fluctuations of 10° or 20° about the average field direction occurring with periodicities of hundreds or thousands of years. The evidence of secular variations[5] is derived partly from direct observation of the field and partly from paleomagnetism. In the latter case the secular changes show themselves as the dispersion of the directions observed at different time levels in a rock unit. Evidence for *reversals in polarity* of the dipole axis[6] is based on the observed

occurrence of reversals in polarity of the fossil magnetism in rock units. An alternative view is that the reversals of magnetization arise from special mineralogical conditions which cause a rock to acquire a magnetization antiparallel in direction to the ambient field. Evidence for *polar-wandering*[7] is derived from paleomagnetism and also from geology, especially the study of paleoclimates in which attempts to trace the variations in the position of the Earth's paleogeographic pole have been made; this point of contact between paleomagnetism and historical geology is of fundamental importance, since it allows comparison of results from independent sources.

§ 1.3   Origin of Fossil Magnetism[8]

Most rock-forming minerals do not contribute to fossil magnetism and are referred to as the *nonmagnetic minerals*. The fossil magnetism is due to the iron oxides and sulfides present as accessory minerals which

[4] These checks which are of a diverse nature are described in various chapters and are summarized at the end of Chapter Nine.

[5] The secular variations affecting the present Earth's field are described in Chapter Three, and those affecting the ancient geomagnetic field in Chapter Six.

[6] Chapter Seven is devoted to a description of

the evidence relating to reversals of the paleogeomagnetic field.

[7] Polar-wandering is defined more exactly in Chapter Six where the paleomagnetic evidence for its occurrence is summarized.

[8] The complex problems of the origin of fossil magnetism are elaborated in Chapters Two and Five.

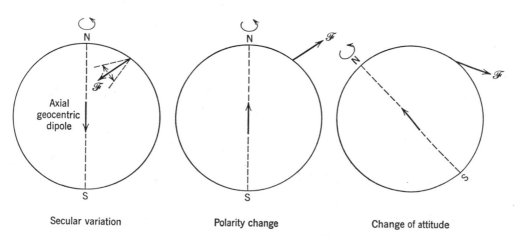

Secular variation   Polarity change   Change of attitude

Figure 1.3. Changes affecting the axial geocentric dipole. $\mathscr{F}$ are field directions averaged over several thousand years.

generally make up no more than a few per cent of the rock; they are referred to as the *magnetic minerals*.

By and large, the fossil magnetism useful for determining the direction of the ancient geomagnetic field is the product of only a small proportion of the magnetic minerals present. This is shown by the fact that the intensity of NRM is many times less than the intensity that would occur if all the magnetic material present were magnetized in a uniform direction, so that in the natural rock only a small proportion of the magnetic fraction has a preferred orientation. This means that the problem of the identification of the mineral responsible for the fossil magnetism is not simply a question of petrographic identification of the iron minerals, but of identifying magnetically the active component of the numerous magnetic phases present. The demagnetized phases may once have had a preferred orientation, but these were insufficiently stable to be retained over geological periods of time.

The mechanism by which fossil magnetism is acquired depends on the mode of formation and subsequent history of a rock. It may be acquired by cooling from high temperatures when it is called *thermoremanent magnetization* (TRM), or during the formation of iron minerals at low temperatures, when it is referred to as *chemical remanent magnetization* (CRM). It may occur in a sediment by the alignment of detrital magnetic particles when it is called *depositional remanent magnetization* (DRM).

§ 1.4   **Applications**   The third aspect of paleomagnetic work is the question of its application to certain problems, chiefly of a geological nature.[9] Paleomagnetism has made a substantial contribution to problems of stratigraphic correlation and tectonics, and is also intimately connected with paleogeography. From a knowledge of fossil magnetism it is possible to study the paleolatitude spectrum of a particular type of

[9] Chapters Nine and Ten are concerned largely with these applications.

deposit, chosen, let us say, because its accumulation is thought by some workers to have been dependent on paleoclimate. This may then be compared against the spectrum of modern deposits of similar type. A further possible course opened up by paleomagnetic work is to calculate the past positions of land masses relative to the Earth's pole and to each other; such distribution studies provide a test of the hypotheses of polar-wandering and continental drift by a method which is independent of geological evidence.

§ 1.5   **Field and Laboratory Experiments**   In the next three sections certain general points are made regarding the methodology of paleomagnetic work. Fossil magnetism is usually made up of several components of differing origins. Its properties are determined by the physical and chemical history of the rock, and by the magnetic field applied to it from the time of its formation to the time it is studied in the laboratory. The rock may have been heated or subjected to stresses, or may have undergone chemical changes, and one or all of these may have acted in conjunction with a varying magnetic field over long periods of time to produce a remanence of complex origin. The variety of conditions is so great, and so little is known about them quantitatively, that it is not yet possible either to simulate them exactly in the laboratory or to predict their effects theoretically. Consequently, arguments relating to the interpretation of paleomagnetic observations depend on there being a large body of circumstantial evidence for or against a particular point of view. In general two broad lines of enquiry may be recognized—field, and laboratory experiments.

In a *field experiment* the fossil magnetism of some geological feature is studied. Such studies are most fruitful when the origin of the feature can be surmised from geological evidence. One of the best examples (J. W. Graham, 1949) is the study of folded beds; if the remanence directions are observed to maintain a constant orientation relative to the bedding planes, then it originated prior to folding, and was not affected by stress during deformation, or by subsequent heating or chemical changes. Conversely, if the directions are parallel *in situ*, then the NRM has arisen by some process occurring subsequent to folding. It is possible in this way to obtain information about the stability of the fossil magnetism. In *model experiments* attempts are made in the laboratory to build up remanent magnetizations under controlled conditions. The two methods come together when laboratory-induced components are made to simulate the NRM so that the controlled laboratory conditions provide some broad clue to the unknown natural conditions under which the NRM arose. Although model experiments are carried out on a short time scale, and are only crude imitations of natural conditions, they are very important, since theories based on them provide a general framework of ideas within which the discussion of the origin of fossil magnetism can fruitfully proceed.

§ **1.6   Paleomagnetic Surveys**   Information is obtained as a result of surveys of the fossil magnetism of rock units. The purpose of these surveys is to obtain an estimate of the direction of the Earth's field at some known time in the past, and then to cast the result in such a form as to enable comparisons to be carried out between results for different times, and from different places.

The first step is to select for study a rock unit of known geological age and to obtain oriented samples from it. Such units comprise, say, a sequence of lavas, or sediments, or a comagmatic intrusive suite. The sampling sites usually cover a small area and the rock unit serves as a geomagnetic "observatory" at which readings were obtained at irregular intervals during the period of time spanned by the unit, and which is likely to range in the orders 10^3 to 10^6 years. The readings are related in time to those from other such rock "observatories" with the accuracies characteristic of the geological time scale.

The next step is to measure the directions and intensity of NRM. Under favor-

able circumstances a component acquired when the rock was formed is present; this is called the *primary component of the natural remanent magnetization,* or simply the *primary magnetization* (some workers use the term *original magnetization*). Subsequent to formation the primary component may decay, and further components may be added by a variety of processes; these are called *secondary components of the natural remanent magnetization,* or simply *secondary magnetization.* This may mask the primary magnetization, and one of the major technical problems is to recognize and correct for these disturbing effects. The most prominent secondary components are acquired prior to collecting samples, but sometimes noticeable components are added between collection and measurement in the laboratory; such secondary magnetization is referred to as *temporary magnetization.*[10]

The third step is to combine the observations and obtain an estimate of the mean direction of magnetization of the rock unit, in order to make comparisons between results from units of different ages and from different places. If the differences are time differences only, the means can be compared directly. If the rock units are in widely spaced locations, then direct comparisons are not possible, because of the variation of the field over the Earth's surface, and it becomes necessary, as a fourth step, to correct for this effect. The fundamental technique for doing this is that of calculating *paleomagnetic poles.* In this procedure it is assumed that the Earth's field was like that of a geocentric dipole. The use of such methods do not assume *a priori* that the field was dipolar. They are simply useful procedures for analyzing results in order to test certain hypotheses, of which those relating to the origin and reliability of the fossil directions, and the dipolar nature of the field, are the most basic.

The information from paleomagnetic surveys available to the author up to October

---

[10] The procedures for detecting secondary magnetizations are described in Chapter Five.

1963 is compiled in the appendix. This list gives the references to originals, and contains the basic data used for this book.

§ 1.7 Paleomagnetism, An Historical Study

Paleomagnetism is historical in its approach. This distinguishes it from much other geophysical work, and explains its wide application to geological problems. Studies of earthquakes, heat flow, and the Earth's gravity field relate to processes operating at present, and are of interest historically only in that they provide the end point for processes assumed to have operated in the past. In contrast the study of fossil magnetism yields results of time variations on the geological time scale, and it is this that relates it methodologically to historical geology, paleontology, structural geology, and to radiometric studies, and points the way to fruitful syntheses between these subjects in the course of time; in fact, one of the themes of this book is to show that much progress in this direction has already been made.

This historical property, which imparts such generality to the paleomagnetic method, carries with it, however, the weakness inherent in all historical studies. The situation is a familiar one in geology. For example, it is a matter of established technique to produce a description of the rock sequence in a particular region, but skill of a different order is required to reconstruct reliably the events that produce these sequences. Similarly, the surveying of a rock unit paleomagnetically is a matter of applying existing techniques, but the interpretation of the results carries the worker into the realm of the formulation of hypotheses, tests for which rest on the question of the consistency or inconsistency of data from different sources.

§ 1.8 Early Work

The great majority of observations have been published since 1930, and particularly since 1950. Prior to 1930, however, important work was done, and several studies, such as that of Chevallier (1925) on the Mt. Etna lavas, still stand as observations of great value which have rarely been bettered. A brief account of this early work is given below. No attempt is made to cover the work of all early contributors, and mention is made only of what are considered to be the more important observations and ideas. The bibliography is selective, and a more complete list may be found in Chevallier (1925) and Koenigsberger (1938).

A description of early work is given by Alexander von Humboldt (1797), who in the late 18th century carried out with his colleagues a magnetic survey of a mountain top in the Palatinate. The expedition had set out to study geology, but interest in the magnetic problem was aroused when the disturbing effect of the country rock on the compass needle was noticed. At the summit, exposures with a northerly aspect showed only south magnetic poles, and those with southerly aspect only north poles. The mountain as a whole, however, did not have a single axis, but many axes, lying in different planes. Humboldt remarked that it was not unlikely that lightning had caused the observed magnetization.

The study of these intense magnetizations occasionally found in rock exposures was continued during the 19th century by many workers. In these occurrences, variously called *punti distinti* or *points isolés*, the magnetization directions varied rapidly from point to point on the same exposure. It was generally agreed that they were due to lightning strikes. Because of their strong magnetization it is understandable that the *punti distinti* were the first paleomagnetic phenomena to attract attention. They are surface effects which fall away rapidly with depth (§ 5.13), and do not occur in all exposures. In the middle of the 19th century, instruments were developed which were sufficiently sensitive to measure the much weaker magnetization in rocks unaffected in this way and so the deeper-seated more general phenomena came to be studied.

Delesse (1849) showed that certain recent lavas were magnetized parallel to the Earth's field, the uniformity being in marked contrast to the scattered directions observed in *punti distinti*. Melloni (1853) studied the

directions of NRM of the lavas of Mt. Vesuvius and the Phlegraean Fields, which he
found were roughly parallel to the present
field, and he showed further that, when lava
specimens were raised to red heat in the
laboratory and then cooled, they acquired a
remanent magnetization parallel to the
Earth's field. This led Melloni to believe
that the NRM was acquired in the direction
of the Earth's field at the time the lavas
cooled. Folgerhaiter (1899) extended Melloni's work and made a field study of the
volcanic rocks of Latium showing that they
also were magnetized roughly parallel to the
present field.

Folgerhaiter also studied the magnetization
of bricks and pottery. He argued that if
the position of the brick or pot in the firing
kiln was known, then the remanent magnetization it acquired on cooling should provide a record of the Earth's field direction.
The azimuth is unknown, but in the case
of a pot fired on its base, the direction relative to the base should give the field inclination. Folgerhaiter's work is notable because
of his interest in *magnetic stability*. He
argued that if the bodies studied had been
moved since they were magnetized, the directions in different units would be scattered if
the magnetizations were stable. He studied
a number of bricks in a Roman wall and
found that the directions from brick to brick
were in fact scattered. He also found consistent angles of inclination relative to their
bases in some Aretine vases which had been
buried randomly some 2000 years ago. He
concluded that the remanence directions had
been little changed neither since the wall
was built, nor since the burial of the vases.
This work on magnetic stability was followed
by that of David (1904) who studied a pavement, composed of domite (a type of trachyte) slabs, in the Temple of Mercury,
which is at the summit of the Puy-de-Dôme,
and dates from the 1st century B.C. The
directions in duplicate specimens from the
same slab are in good agreement (Figure
1.4*a*). The inclinations between slabs are
similar, but the declinations are widely scattered. David also measured specimens from

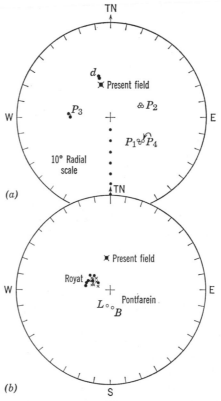

Figure 1.4. (*a*) Directions of natural remanent
magnetization in 4 flagstones (P_1 to P_4) from
pavement in Temple to Mercury. Results from
duplicate specimens from same slab are near
together. *d* are directions from supposed source
locality. Dots positive inclination, circles negative inclination. Work of David, compiled
from Bruhnes (1906). (*b*) Directions in lava
flows and underlying baked clays. Royat:
crosses give results from baked clays, dots from
lava (all with positive inclinations). Pontfarein: *B* baked clay, *L* lava. Work of David
and Bruhnes compiled from Bruhnes (1906).

a domite quarry and found directions very
close to the Earth's field with inclinations
the same as those in the slabs. He concluded
that the magnetization in this volcanic rock
had been little changed during the past 2000
years. The similarity in the inclinations in
different slabs is presumably due to the slabs
being quarried horizontally.

Folgerhaiter's work on clays baked by man
led Bruhnes and David to study material

baked by lava flows. In particular they compared, in several instances, the direction of fossil magnetism of flows with those in underlying baked clays. Two examples are given in Figure 1.4*b*. The Royat flow has downward inclination, and the Pontfarein inclination is upwards. The Royat flow is from the Petit Puy-de-Dôme, and the Pontfarein flow is in Cantal and is of Villafranchian age. It was concluded that the concordance of results showed that the magnetization of the lavas was acquired at the time of cooling, and that the magnetization of the clays dates from the time of heating by the lava. As will be seen later (§§ 5.04, 5.05) such structural tests and studies of igneous contacts, initiated over 60 years ago, still remain basic reliability tests in paleomagnetic work.

In his studies of the historical lava flows of Mt. Etna, Chevallier (1925) achieved some success in tracing the secular variations in the geomagnetic field during the past 2000 years.

We turn now to the discovery of "reversals." [11] Bruhnes and David found that the directions in the Pontfarein flow and underlying baked clay was roughly opposed to that of the present field (Figure 1.4*b*). These results initiated speculation as to the possibility that the Earth's field had reversed in sense because in all previous experimental work in the laboratory, rock specimens when heated and cooled became magnetized with the same direction and sense as the ambient field. Further evidence was produced by Mercanton (1926*a* and *b*, 1931, 1932) who argued that if the Earth's field had in fact reversed, then rock reversals should be found not only in Europe but also elsewhere. He obtained samples from Spitzbergen (Tertiary lavas), Greenland (Tertiary lavas), Iceland, Faroe Islands, Mull, Jan Mayen Land, and Australia (Tertiary and Permian lavas [7.42]), and found that some had directions in the same sense as the present field and others were roughly reversed from it. At much the same time Matayuma (1929*a* and *b*) observed similar effects in Japanese and Manchurian Cenozoic lavas [12.34]. He found that the directions of magnetization fell into two groups—one group directed close to the present field, and a second opposed in direction to the present field. He noticed that his results fell into a time sequence, rocks of early Quaternary age belonging to the second group, whereas all younger rocks belonged to the first group. Matayuma concluded "that in the earlier part of the Quaternary period the earth's magnetic field in the area under consideration was probably in the state represented by the second group, which gradually changed to the state represented by the first group."

Finally, Mercanton argued, that because of the approximate correlation of the geomagnetic and rotational axes at the present time, it might be possible from the paleomagnetic data, to test the hypotheses of polar-wandering and continental drift.

So by about 1930 several important points had been clarified. (1) Fossil magnetism was found to be a characteristic rock property. (2) Lava specimens, heated and cooled in the laboratory, became magnetized parallel to the Earth's field, so that their NRM may have originated when the lavas cooled initially, and may be parallel to the Earth's field at that time. (3) The NRM in certain Cenozoic lavas and baked clays was probably acquired in the direction of the Earth's field at the time of cooling. (4) Certain field studies, namely of igneous contacts, and of bodies that have been structurally moved at a known time, yielded vital evidence on the question of the stability of the direction of NRM over long periods of time, and thus on the usefulness of the remanence directions as indicators of the paleogeomagnetic field. (5) The direction in many recent lava flows was known to be roughly parallel to the present Earth's field, which

[11] Folgerhaiter (1899) found that some Etruscan vases of the 8th century B.C. had upward inclinations opposite in sign to the inclination of the present field in Tuscany. The inclinations however were only a few degrees, and thus do not constitute a true 180° reversal.

indicated that the field had not changed greatly in the recent geological past. (6) The directions in some older lavas in many parts of the world were roughly opposite to that of the present field, suggesting that in the more remote past the Earth's field may have reversed in polarity; the results indicated that the most recent reversal occurred in the early part of the Quaternary Period. (7) The usefulness of paleomagnetism in studying the secular variation of the Earth's field had been shown. (8) The potential application to studies of longer period variations and thus to paleogeographic problems had been suggested, although it was not until the mid-1950's that this inspired thought was put into practice.

§**1.9 Recent Developments and Aims**
The foregoing account shows a picture of slow development. The impetus which gave rise to the recent rapid development came from geomagneticians. Studies of the geomagnetic field carried out in the 1940's made it clear that no satisfactory theory of the field would be developed until much more was known about its variations in the geological past, and to obtain these a general approach became necessary with the wide-spread paleomagnetic surveying of rocks from many parts of the world. The necessary instruments were made and the statistical techniques for data reduction developed. The mechanisms by which rocks can acquire a remanent magnetization were also studied in great detail. Finally the techniques of calculating paleomagnetic poles provided an analytical tool of immense power, not only for integrating data from different parts of the world, but also for providing a numerical basis for a wide range of problems in historical geology, previous approaches to which had been qualitative. After about a century of slow sporadic growth the present day picture is one of an expanding study moving rapidly into many fields of geophysics and geology.

The ultimate aim of paleomagnetic work is to build up a picture of the time variations in the Earth's field in the geological past—an endless undertaking as yet barely begun. The data at present available are infinitesimally few compared to the number which could potentially be obtained from the rock record. Nevertheless, a promising start has been made, sufficient at least to make clear some of the potentialities and limitations of the method.

Magnetic properties of rocks

§ 2.01 Introduction This chapter contains an account of the magnetic properties of rocks with particular emphasis on those properties germane to paleomagnetic work. It is intended as an introduction to those aspects of rock magnetism which are needed for the discussion of paleomagnetic results.[1] The early sections are concerned chiefly with a very brief and qualitative description of ferromagnetism and of the magnetic minerals. The later sections are more detailed, and deal with the processes that cause remanent magnetization.

The magnetic properties of rocks have features which differ from those of the magnetic materials on which physical measurements are usually made. First the intensities of magnetization are much lower than those of iron, or the iron alloys, one reason being that the iron minerals in rocks constitute only a fraction of the whole rock. Second, in paleomagnetic work one is generally interested in magnetizations acquired in weak fields such as that of the Earth, whereas in classical ferromagnetism, the properties acquired in fields of thousands of oersteds are commonly studied. Third, there

[1] Reference may be made to Nagata (1961) for a more detailed account of the physical and mineralogical aspects of rock magnetism.

is the effect of time; in the laboratory, effects on time scales of minutes or hours are generally observed whereas the changes affecting fossil magnetism are often slow (or viscous) occurring on time scales of 10^2 to 10^8 years.

§ 2.02 Remanent and Induced Magnetism *Remanent magnetism* (or simply *remanence*) is that magnetization remaining in zero applied field; the *induced magnetization* is that induced by a field but lost when the field is removed. The total magnetic moment $\mathbf{J}_t$ of a rock *in situ* is made up of the vector sum of two components, a component $\mathbf{J}_i$ induced by the Earth's field and the natural remanent magnetism $\mathbf{M}_n$, thus

$$\mathbf{J}_t = \mathbf{J}_i + \mathbf{M}_n \qquad (2.1)$$

The intensity J_i in a weak field F is given by

$$J_i = \chi F \qquad (2.2)$$

where χ is a constant of proportionality called the *susceptibility*.

In massive lavas, and in unbanded hypabyssal intrusives and sediments, the induced component is parallel to the direction of the applied field and such rocks are said to be magnetically isotropic. But in banded sediments, layered intrusives, and foliated metamorphic rocks, the excess of susceptibility in the plane of layering to that at right angles can amount to 20 per cent or more, and the induced component is deflected from the field direction towards the axis of maximum susceptibility (§ 2.15); such rocks are said to be magnetically anisotropic.

Measurements of the permanent and induced magnetization are not carried out *in situ*, but are made in the laboratory on oriented specimens which normally have been cut to a regular shape, such as a cylinder or cube, with volume of 1 to 30 cm³. The measurements are made by *magnetometers* which survey the magnetic field of the specimen. If the measurements are made in a space in which the Earth's field has been cancelled then there is no induced component and $\mathbf{M}_n$ only is obtained. If the measurements are made with a field applied, then $\mathbf{J}_t$ is measured, and $\mathbf{J}_i$ is obtained by vector subtraction of $\mathbf{M}_n$.

For these purposes the magnetization of a rock specimen may be assumed to be concentrated at a point at or near the center of the specimen, and whose position can be calculated. This point source is called the *effective magnetic dipole*. In fact, it is never possible to describe the magnetization exactly by means of a dipole, because certain less regular components are always present. These are generally small (order of 1 per cent) and randomly directed, and are averaged out when the results from several specimens are combined. A variety of measurement techniques are available to the experimenter and reference may be made to Collinson and Creer (1960), As (1961), and Nagata and Kobayashi (1961) for details.

The direction of the effective magnetic dipole, $\mathbf{M}_n$, is specified by the angles of declination, and inclination. By convention the north-seeking direction is specified. The *declination*, D, is the angle between true north and the projection of $\mathbf{M}_n$ on the horizontal plane; it is reckoned clockwise and may have any value between 0° and 360°. The *inclination*, I, is the angle between $\mathbf{M}_n$ and the horizontal, and may have any value between $+90°$ and $-90°$, being counted positive (negative) when $\mathbf{M}_n$ is directed below

(above) the horizontal. The *intensity of magnetization*, M_n, is expressed as the dipole moment per cm³, or per gram, so that

$$\text{and} \quad \begin{aligned} M_n \text{ (volume intensity)} &= M/v \\ M_n \text{ (specific intensity)} &= M/\rho \end{aligned} \right\} \quad (2.3)$$

where M is the total moment of the specimen, v its volume, and ρ its density. Magnetic intensity is expressed in emu(cgs) called gauss. Intensities vary widely; sedimentary rocks usually have values in the range 10^{-6} to 10^{-8} emu/cm³ or less, whereas igneous rocks are more intensely magnetized, most being in the orders 10^{-2} and 10^{-4}.

In paleomagnetic work the susceptibility (equation 2.2) is expressed as the induced moment in unit field per cm³ (*volume susceptibility*) or per gram (*specific susceptibility*).

Certain ratios of magnetic intensities are used in paleomagnetic work (Koenigsberger, 1938). Although some of these refer to matters not yet discussed it is convenient to list them here.

$$Q_n = M_n/J_i = M_n/\chi F \quad (2.4)$$

$$Q_n{}' = M_n/\chi \quad (2.5)$$

$$Q_T = M_{T(F)}/\chi F \quad (2.6)$$

$$Q_{n/T} = M_n/M_T \quad (2.7)$$

Q_n is the ratio of the intensity of the natural remanent magnetization to that induced by the present field F at the collecting site. $Q_n{}'$ is similar to Q_n except the denominator is the magnetization induced in unit field. Q_T is the ratio of the total thermoremanent magnetization (§ 2.10) acquired in the field F to the magnetization induced by the same field at room temperatures.

§ 2.03 Ferromagnetism

The magnetization of a rock specimen arises from discrete sources which may be considered at three levels—atoms, domains, and mineral grains. All atoms have a magnetic moment due to the orbital motion and spin of their electrons. In most materials the magnetic moments of adjoining atoms are randomly directed in the absence of an external field so that a specimen has no net remanence. When a field is applied a magnetization is induced. In *diamagnetic* materials the susceptibility is of the order 10^{-6} and negative. In *paramagnetic* materials the susceptibility is of the same order but positive. Quartz and felspar, when pure, are diamagnetic. Olivine, pyroxene, garnet, biotite, and amphiboles are paramagnetic.

In certain other materials the susceptibility is much greater, often more than unity. It is positive, and dependent on temperature and on the strength of the applied field. In these materials the moments of adjoining atoms interact together, giving rise to *spontaneous magnetization*. The regions within which the ordering extends have dimensions of the order 10^{-4} cm and are called *magnetic domains*. The ordering is due to the presence of a very powerful intramolecular magnetic field. The energy associated with this is called the *exchange energy*. The ordering of atomic moments within a domain may follow one of three patterns (Figure 2.1). In *ferromagnetic* minerals, such as iron, the moments are parallel. In *antiferromagnetic* minerals they are arranged on two equal antiparallel sublattices so that there is no residual moment. In some other minerals, of which magnetite is an example, the moments are arranged in two unequal sublattices, so that the net magnetization is not zero; this is *ferrimagnetism*. The ordering is temperature dependent, the exchange energy working against thermal fluctuations. In ferromagnetic and ferrimagnetic minerals the spontaneous magnetization falls as the temperature increases, disappearing at the *Curie temperature* or *Curie point* T_C; above T_C the crystal is paramagnetic. In antiferromagnetic minerals the ordering is lost at the *Néel temperature* T_N, above which the crystal is paramagnetic. Certain minerals, such as hematite, possess a feeble spontaneous magnetization which is superposed on an antiferromagnetic structure and which disappears along with the antiferromagnetism at T_N; this may be due to imperfect antiparallel alignment or to a small parasitic component (Figure 2.1a and b).

The smallest magnetic mineral particles in rocks contain only one domain. The larger particles contain many domains. The boundary between domains are called *domain walls*.

Magnetic crystals have "easy" and "hard" directions. The domain moments rotate more readily into the direction of an aligning field when the latter is parallel to certain crystal axes than when it is in other directions; this is referred to as *magneto-*

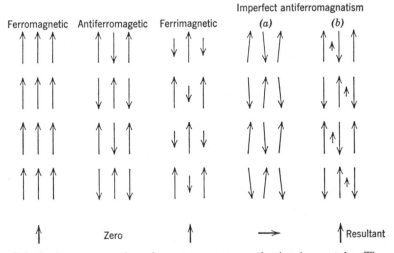

Figure 2.1. Schematic representation of spontaneous magnetization in crystals. The arrows represent the elementary moments, the resultants being given at the bottom.

crystalline anisotropy and the difference of magnetization energy between the hard and easy directions is the *magnetocrystalline anisotropy energy.* The magnetocrystalline anisotropy changes if the crystal lattice is strained, and it is sometimes convenient to recognize a *strain anisotropy,* with associated *strain energy,* which arises from lattice deformations occurring as a result of magnetostrictive changes in dimensions (see below), or to strains from external stresses, or to stresses inherited from the particle's previous history. In elongated particles, processes of magnetization tend to occur more easily along the long axis than in other directions; this is called *shape anisotropy,* which arises because of the presence of free poles, and which has an associated *magnetostatic energy* or *energy of self-demagnetization.* In zero external field the anisotropy energies will tend to align the spin direction along the axis of easy magnetization, but the spread of uniform directions throughout a whole crystal occurring under the influence of exchange energy will be inhibited by the occurrence of free poles, so that the crystal magnetizations break up into a number of domains. The positioning of the domain walls is governed by the competing exchange and anisotropy energies.

A further important effect is *magnetostriction.* In a material undergoing magnetization mechanical deformation occurs. This takes the form of expansion or contraction along certain crystallographic directions. The effect, like magnetization, itself is anisotropic in single crystals, and is due to strain arising from magnetic interaction between atoms. The magnetization of an iron crystal in a field of 1500 oe causes length changes of the order of one part in 10^{-5}, the sign of the changes depending on the direction of the field relative to the crystal axes. In paleomagnetic work, magnetostriction has been used to describe the converse effect in which the application of stress causes a change in the direction of remanence because of the stress dependence of magnetocrystalline anisotropy.

So far this discussion has been concerned only with effects within a crystal and the associated exchange and anisotropy energies. In the presence of an external field a third source of energy arises—the *mutual energy between a domain moment and an applied field.* If the two are parallel, the energy is zero; but if the field is at an angle to the domains moment, there will be a tendency for the latter to rotate into the field direction. Any particle undergoing a process of magnetization in a field will acquire a moment directed between the "easy" magnetization direction and the field. However, in a specimen composed of an assembly of grains in which the easy directions are randomly oriented, the net specimen moment will be parallel to the applied field. This is a point of fundamental importance in paleomagnetism; the magnetic properties of single crystals are anisotropic, but the effect of anisotropies is averaged out in rocks showing no preferred orientation of the shape or crystal axes.

A specimen is said to be demagnetized when the arrangement of domain moments is such that they cancel one another. This could arise from domain directions within rock particles opposing one another, or due to randomization of particle directions. There are many processes by which an isotropic demagnetized material may acquire a remanence but the essential requirement is the presence of a magnetic field, although the conditions of temperature, stress, or time, may affect the result. The simplest case is the effect of a magnetic field applied at room temperatures for periods of the order of seconds or minutes (Figure 2.2). As the field increases the magnetization in the specimen (usually referred to as the magnetic induction B being the magnetic flux density within the specimen) builds up reaching a steady value called the *saturation magnetization, J_s.* The field required to saturate is called the *saturating field, H_s.* If the field is now decreased the magnetization falls, but not along the same path, and in zero field there is a finite magnetization J_r called the *isothermal remanent magnetization* (IRM). As the field increases in the op-

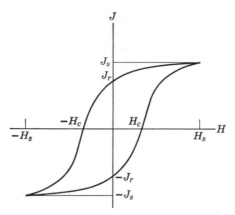

Figure 2.2. Hysteresis loop (B/H loop).

posite direction the magnetization falls, reaching zero at an applied field $-H_c$ called the *coercive force*. As the reverse field increases, the magnetization builds up again with opposite sign, reaching saturation $-J_s$ in a field $-H_s$. On repeat oscillation of the field the magnetization follows the same path, which is called the *hysteresis* (or *B-H*) *loop*.

The hysteresis loop is explained by domain theory (Figure 2.3). In the demagnetized state, the spontaneous magnetization of the domains in a crystal is arranged in a regular pattern related to the crystal axes, but with their directions cancelling one another. The application of a small field causes an increase of the resultant in a direction parallel to H by small reversible movements of the domain walls (region A); those domains, in which the spontaneous magnetization makes a small angle with H, grow at the expense of those less favourably directed. In the B region, as H increases, one domain after another swings into the most favourable directions, adjustments occurring by discrete jumps called *Barkhausen jumps*. Smooth domain wall movements also occur, so that in the B region reversible effects are present in addition to irreversible Barkhausen jumps. At C most of the domain magnetizations have turned into the preferred crystal direction nearest to that of the field. As H increases further the magnetization increases more slowly, the domain magnetizations being

pulled smoothly and reversibly around into the field direction. Saturation (E region) is reached when the alignment is complete, the magnetization J_s being equal to the sum of the moments of individual domains.

§ 2.04   Theory for Single-Domain Particles

The theory of the magnetization of an assemblage of single-domain particles given by Néel (1955) is now outlined. The magnetic particles in rocks are commonly multidomain and many workers (Néel, 1955; Verhoogen, 1959; Stacey, 1958a, 1962b; Everitt, 1962a and b) have thought it more realistic to consider their behavior in terms of domain wall movements within multidomain grains, and a discussion in these terms could be given. But there is no need for this in the present context since the concepts derived from such a discussion are similar, in essentials, to those derived from Néel's theory. The account now given is qualitative, for Néel's theory (like that for multidomain particles) is greatly simplified compared with the complex situation found in rocks.

Néel considers an elementary single-domain particle with uniaxial symmetry. The the-

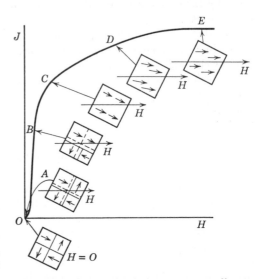

Figure 2.3. Magnetization process according to domain theory. Redrawn from Brailsford (1951), by kind permission of Methuen and Co., London.

oretical hysteresis loop for such a grain is given in Figure 2.4. When the field is parallel to the axis the path is rectangular the height being twice the spontaneous magnetization, J_s, and the width twice the coercive force H_c. On reversal of the field the direction reverses, but there is no diminution in J_s, the change occurring discontinuously. With the field perpendicular to the axis there is no hysteresis. The integrated effect of an assemblage of grains in which axes are randomly arranged is the familiar hysteresis loop (Figure 2.4c).

In the absence of any applied field the moment of a single-domain grain takes up one of the two possible axial orientations separated by a potential barrier E_r. The orientation will not be altered if E_r greatly exceeds the thermal energy (kT), k being Boltzmann's constant, and T the absolute temperature. However, for sufficiently small grain sizes and suitable temperatures, thermal agitations can cause the moment to switch positions and the intensity of magnetization of a specimen containing a large number of single-domain grains and with an initial remanent moment M_0 will, after time t, have decayed to a value M_r given by $M_r = M_0 e^{-t/\tau_0}$ where τ_0 is called the *relaxation time* of the grains. The relaxation time depends on the perturbing couples acting on the magnetic moment of the grain, the most active couple arising from elastic deformations due to thermal agitations. The magnetic moment of an assemblage of grains

will, in the absence of a field, have decayed to one-half its value ($M_r = \frac{1}{2}M_0$) after a time 0.693 τ_0, which may be thought of as the half-life of the initial remanence.

The important feature of τ_0 is its strong dependence on the ratio v/T in which v is the grain volume and T the absolute temperature. The effect of grain diameter is plotted in Figure 2.5. At room temperatures, on Néel's model, grains with diameters of 120 and 280 Å for iron and magnetite, respectively, are rendered unstable by thermal agitations, and, on the application of a weak field quickly reach equilibrium with the field. The moment acquired is called the *equilibrium magnetization* in which not all domains are aligned parallel to the field, but only a portion, which varies directly as the strength of the field for weak applied fields. Such an assemblage is said to be *superparamagnetic* (Bean, 1955). As the grain size increases the magnetization stabilizes until at diameters of 300 to 400 Å, the magnetization of magnetite at normal temperatures can, in theory, resist the effects of thermal fluctuations for geological periods of time.

Figure 2.5 shows that there is a *critical blocking diameter*, d_B, which depends on temperature, and which separates an assemblage of variable grain size into two groups; below this diameter the particle relaxation times are less than the duration of a laboratory experiment (say 10 to 60 minutes) and in the presence of an applied field particles rapidly assume an equilibrium with the field

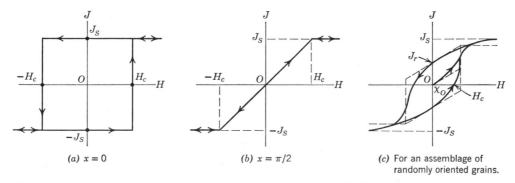

(a) $x = 0$ (b) $x = \pi/2$ (c) For an assemblage of randomly oriented grains.

Figure 2.4. Hysteresis cycle of single-domain particles (after Néel). x is the angle between the applied field and the axis of the particle.

whereas above d_B the particle moments are stable. Similarly, for a given particle diameter there is a *critical blocking temperature* T_B. Upon cooling from a high temperature, spontaneous magnetization appears at the Curie temperature T_C, and this assumes an equilibrium magnetization in the presence of a field. At a temperature T_B slightly below T_C, the relaxation time increases rapidly, the equilibrium magnetization becomes "frozen in," and subsequent changes of field direction occurring at temperatures below T_B are ineffectual in changing the direction of magnetization. This is *thermoremanent magnetization* (§ 2.11).

§ 2.05 **Magnetic Minerals: General Points** General references: Nicholls, 1955; Gorter, 1957; Nagata and Akimoto, 1961. The minerals responsible for the magnetic properties of rocks are predominantly within the ternary system $FeO-TiO_2-Fe_2O_3$ (Figure 2.6). Other relevant minerals are pyr-

rhotite and the oxyhydroxides of iron. Within the $FeO-TiO_2-Fe_2O_3$ field there are several series (described in § 2.06) of which the orthorhombic pseudobrookite series is paramagnetic and unimportant paleomagnetically.

The composition of the magnetic minerals in igneous rocks is governed by the composition of the parent magma and the physical conditions operative during cooling. Crystallization of the magnetic minerals usually occurs above the Curie point, commonly between 1100° and 800°C. The grain size, which may be expected to depend on the rate of cooling during crystallization, is variable. In volcanic rocks phenocrysts up to 0.5 mm in diameter occur, but, in general, the iron ores are matrix minerals ranging from 1 to 0.05 mm. In plutonic rocks crystals up to 1 mm or more in diameter are not uncommon.

Magnetic minerals are rarely homogenous. Several phases may be present, either as regular intergrowths which have arisen from unmixing of these series during cooling, or as

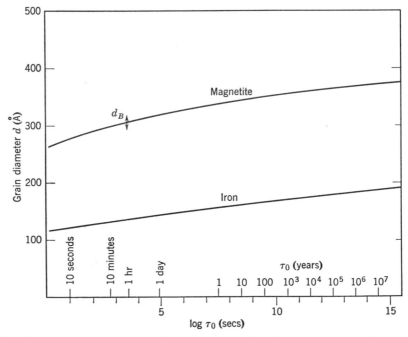

Figure 2.5. Dependence of relaxation time τ_0 on particle diameter at room temperatures for iron, magnetite, and hematite. Iron data from Néel (1955). Magnetite data from Nagata and Akimoto (1961) who assume anisotropy to be entirely magnetocrystalline. The arrows indicate the range of critical blocking diameters d_B.

less regular inclusions which have resulted from differential chemical alteration of an originally homogenous mineral. The development of intergrowths within a grain will depend on the rate of cooling through the exsolution range, which extends downwards from the crystallization temperatures. High temperature enhances ionic diffusion and, if maintained for a sufficiently long period, results in the unmixing of solid solutions into their components. Thus, the grain size and the presence of single or unmixed phases may be expected to depend on the size and type of igneous body, and on position within the body. The likelihood of preservation of homogenous minerals is greatest in the chilled margins of lava flows or hypabyssal intrusions. In the central parts of plutonic and hypabyssal intrusions the development of intergrowths is more likely than in lava flows. There is some uncertainty about the time scale of exsolution processes. It seems possible that a magnetic mineral in a cooling igneous rock may be held within the exsolution temperature for as short a period as hours or days in rapidly chilled bodies, whereas in large bodies this period may be hundreds of years or more. It is possible

that exsolution is, for the most part, completed by the time the rock has reached normal temperatures, but it has been suggested that exsolution may result from annealing on a time scale of millions of years (Kawai, Kume, and Yasukawa, 1956).

§ **2.06   Magnetic Minerals: Descriptions of Types**   *Magnetite* (Fe_3O_4) has inverse spinel structure with cell dimensions $a = 8.39$ Å and is ferrimagnetic. Although magnetite is optically isotropic it is magnetically anisotropic. The (111) direction is the easy direction of magnetization and (100) is the most difficult. The Curie point is 578°C and the saturation magnetization at room temperatures is 92 to 93 emu/g. Its theoretical density is 5.20.

Ulvospinel (Fe_2TiO_4), also an inverse spinel, has not yet been found as a natural crystal, but occurs intergrown with magnetite. Specimens prepared in the laboratory give unit cell dimensions in the range $a = 8.53$ to 8.49 Å. The theoretical density is about 4.8. It is paramagnetic at normal temperatures.

Ulvospinel-Magnetite Series or Titanomagnetites. In this series there is complete

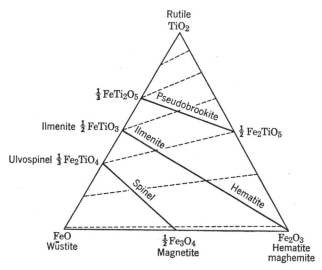

Figure 2.6.   Ternary diagrams FeO-TiO_2-Fe_2O_3 system. The broken lines are oxidation lines. Simplified and redrawn from Gorter (1957), by kind permission of Taylor and Francis, London, and E. W. Gorter.

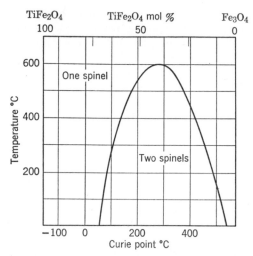

Figure 2.7. Possible form of the magnetite-ulvospinel solvus. Taken from Kawai (1959), by kind permission of N. Kawai. See also Vincent, Wright, Chevallier, and Mathieu (1957), Kawai, Kume, and Sasajima (1954a), Kawai (1956).

solid solution at temperatures in excess of 600°C (Figure 2.7). At lower temperatures there is a tendency for the two phases to exsolve. Usually exsolution lamellae form parallel to the cube faces of the more titaniferous phase. The cell dimensions increase, and the Curie point and intensity of magnetization decrease, as the proportion of ulvospinel increases, the relationships being approximately linear (Figure 2.8). The composition of naturally occurring spinels tends to be displaced in the direction of increased oxidation towards the ilmenite-hematite series. This is illustrated in Figure 2.9 where values from rock samples from Japan are given.

Maghemite and the Maghemite-Magnetite Series. Maghemite (γFe_2O_3) is a cubic mineral with cell dimensions $a = 8.35$ Å. It has an inverse spinel structure like magnetite. Maghemite inverts to αFe_2O_3 at between 200° and 700°C. The Curie point, obtained by extrapolation, is 675°C like that of αFe_2O_3, and the saturation magnetization is 83.5 emu/g, a little less than in magnetite. The theoretical density is 4.88, but the densi-

ties of natural specimens may be as low as 4. Little is known about the magnetic properties of this series.

Hematite (αFe_2O_3) is rhombohedral, $a_r = 5.427$ Å, and $\alpha = 55°16'$. The theoretical density is 5.26. At normal temperatures the saturation magnetization is between 0.1 and 0.5 emu/g. Single crystals are paramagnetic in the direction of the triad axis, but exhibit weak ferromagnetic properties in the plane normal to this axis. The origin of these properties is as yet uncertain, but they are thought to arise from a fundamental antiferromagnetism on which a feeble ferromagnetism is superposed (Figure 2.1). The Néel temperature is 675°C at which tempera-

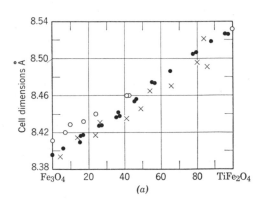

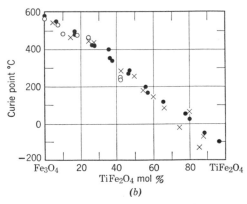

Figure 2.8. Variation of size of unit cell (*a*) and Curie temperature (*b*) in the magnetite-ulvospinel solid solution series. Values from synthetic specimens. Dots are values from Akimoto, Katsura, and Yoshida (1957), crosses from Kawai (1959), and circles from Pouillard (see Nichols, 1955).

ture the ferromagnetism is also lost. At temperatures below −15°C, called the *Morin antiferromagnetic transition,* the weak ferromagnetism disappears and there are changes in susceptibility.

Ilmenite ($FeTiO_3$) is rhombohedral with $a_r = 5.523$ and $\alpha = 54°51'$. It is paramagnetic at room temperatures. The theoretical density is 4.79.

Hematite-Ilmenite Series. The cell dimensions rise and Curie point falls steadily between hematite and ilmenite (Figure 2.10). Solid solution is complete at temperatures above 1050°C. At normal temperatures solution is restricted and the approximate form of the solvus is given in Figure 2.11. Intermediate compositions at normal temperature are represented by intergrowths of one in the other. An interesting feature of this series is that certain compositional ranges show self-reversal properties (§ 7.5).

Magnetite-Hematite Minerals. Solid solution appears to be very restricted. Partial oxidation of magnetite commonly occurs; *martite* (Fe_2O_3), which shows cubic form, is believed to be pseudomorphic after magnetite, and to represent the end-point of such oxidation.

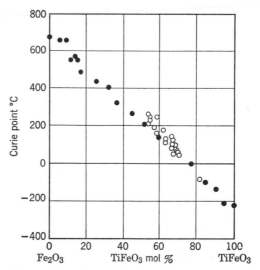

Figure 2.10. Curie points in the ilmenite-hematite series. Circles are natural minerals, dots synthetic minerals. Redrawn from Nagata and Akimoto (1961), with the kind permission of Maruzen, Tokyo, and the authors.

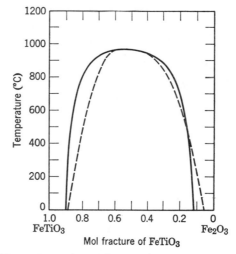

Figure 2.11. Approximate solvus curve for hematite-ilmenite series. Solid line after Uyeda (1958), dotted after Carmichael (1961).

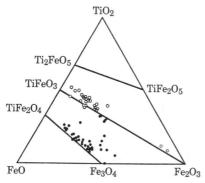

Figure 2.9. Chemical composition of naturally occurring ferromagnetic oxides in selected Japanese samples. Dots are analyses of titanomagnetites and titanomaghemites with spinel structure. Circles are minerals of the ilmenite-hematite series with rhombohedral structure. Redrawn from Nagata and Akimoto (1961), by kind permission of Maruzen, Tokyo, and the authors.

Ilmenite-Magnetite Minerals. Intergrowths of ilmenite and magnetite are common, especially in slowly cooled igneous bodies. Attempts in the laboratory to produce continuous solid solution between them without change in bulk chemical composition, have been unsuccessful, but their close association in nature indicates that solid solution may occur at magmatic temperatures, the solid phase exsolution perhaps occurring by several irreversible steps which are not reproducible in laboratory experiments.

Oxyhydroxides of Iron. There are four important species. They dehydrate to oxides at 100° to 300°C. First, αFeOOH or *geothite* which is the oxyhydroxide corresponding to hematite. Second, βFeOOH, which is paramagnetic, is a cubic body-centered mineral which changes to αFe_2O_3 on heating. Third, *lepidocrocite* (γFeOOH) is the oxyhydroxide corresponding to maghemite; it dehydrates to the spinel phase γFe_2O_3. Finally, δFeOOH is a hexagonal close-packed mineral which is strongly ferromagnetic and which dehydrates to αFe_2O_3. The α and γ forms occur naturally. The β and δ forms are synthetic.

Pyrrhotite. Of the iron sulfides only pyrrhotite shows remanent magnetization. The structure is defective in iron and should be written $Fe_{1-y}S$, but is usually written FeS_{1+x} where $0 < x \leq 0.14$. The Néel transition to the paramagnetic state is constant throughout the range and occurs at about 300°C. Below this temperature it is antiferromagnetic when $0 < x < 0.09$, and ferrimagnetic in the remainder of the range. In the ferrimagnetic range there is a temperature interval, about 20° below the Néel

transition, in which pyrrhotite is antiferromagnetic.

§2.07   Measurement of Curie Points

Sometimes a magnetic mineral assemblage has a single Curie point, but commonly two or more are present. The Curie point(s) is an important rock property and is measured by *thermomagnetic analysis*. These techniques provide information about the *whole* magnetic mineral assemblage in a specimen, not only of that portion which provides the remanence, say the NRM.

The most important method is that of *Curie*, in which the saturation magnetization J_s is measured as a function of temperature, using a magnetic balance. A small furnace, in which a specimen is heated, is placed between the poles of an electromagnet, where there is a strong field gradient. The magnetization of the specimen is measured by observing the movement it undergoes in response to this gradient. The intensity is plotted against temperatures, and a change of slope in the curve corresponds to a Curie point.

Laboratory heating often causes chemical or textural changes in magnetic minerals, and these may be detected by comparing the form of the J_s/T curve as the temperature rises with that obtained on cooling. Examples of reversible and irreversible curves are given in Figure 2.12. In the former case the

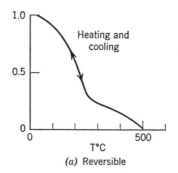
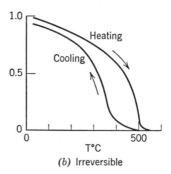

Figure 2.12.   Thermomagnetic analysis, J_s/T curves for magnetic minerals from (*a*) Mihara 1950 basalt (applied field 2400 oe) and (*b*) Odawara dacite pumice (applied field 1700 oe). Redrawn from Nagata and Akimoto (1961), with the kind permission of Maruzen, Tokyo, and the authors.

curves are indistinguishable; in the latter the cooling curve indicates a reduction in Curie point by over 100°C and a lower intensity at room temperatures. Further examples of J_s/T curves are given in Figures 7.9a, and 7.10. It is also possible to measure the susceptibility as a function of temperature a Curie point being marked by a rapid change in values (Figure 7.9b).

§ 2.08 Stability of Remanence

The question of the stability of NRM is of basic importance in paleomagnetic work. The following discussion is given with the fossil magnetism in mind, although the techniques are also applicable to synthetic remanence. The stability of NRM is, of course, its resistance to change under given conditions; fossil magnetism is useful for determining the direction of the ancient geomagnetic field only if it, or some identifiable component of it, is sufficiently stable to have withstood the forces tending to alter it during the rock's history. Stability may be studied either by field or laboratory tests, but preferably both. These tests are described in Chapter Five, but it is convenient at this point to give a brief account of the laboratory techniques.

The stability of the NRM may be judged by its resistance to steady or alternating magnetic fields, or to heat. The resistance to magnetic fields depends on the coercive force, and the resistance to heat depends on the blocking temperatures of the magnetic minerals responsible for the NRM. Generally, the coercive force and blocking temperature are not characterized by single values but by a wide range of values, and it is convenient to speak of the *coercive force spectrum* (J. W. Graham, 1953) and the *blocking temperature spectrum*.

Demagnetization by Alternating Magnetic Fields. The use of alternating magnetic field demagnetization was introduced in paleomagnetic work by Thellier and Rimbert (1954, 1955). The procedure is as follows: the intensity and direction of remanence are first measured, and the specimen is placed in an alternating field of peak intensity $\tilde{H}_p$ which is then reduced slowly to zero. The magnetiza-

tion of all domains with a coercive force less than $\tilde{H}_p$ will follow the field as it alternates. As the field is reduced, domains with progressively lower coercivities become fixed in orientations governed by the structure of the magnetic minerals: in an isotropic specimen the orientations will be random. The magnetization is then remeasured, and the process repeated using a higher value of $\tilde{H}_p$. An unwanted anhysteretic remanent magnetization [2] will be induced in the specimen, if a steady field such as that of the Earth's, is present, or if the variations in the alternating field are asymmetrical. Such effects are avoided by carrying out the demagnetization in zero field, and by filtering the current supply to the demagnetizing coil (As and Zijderveld, 1958) or by spinning the specimen (Brynjólfsson, 1957; Creer, 1959). The results of such a stepwise demagnetization may be expressed graphically, as changes in the intensity of magnetization, or as changes in the directions. (See Figure 5.16.)

Demagnetization by Heat. These methods were also introduced into paleomagnetic work by Thellier (1938). Demagnetization by heat can be carried out continuously or in steps. In the former case the intensity and direction of the specimen are measured while the specimen is heated. Measurements are taken after each increase in temperature, for instance every 25°C, and the components destroyed in the proceeding temperature interval can thus be calculated. At the blocking temperature T_B for a particular magnetic component the relaxation time of the grains becomes short compared with the time taken to make a measurement, and thermal agitations scatter the domain moments. In stepwise demagnetization the specimen is heated to a temperature T_1 (say 50°C), then cooled to room temperatures in zero field and measured. The component with blocking temperatures $T_B < T_1$ is destroyed. The procedure is repeated, heating now to a higher temperature (say 100°C), so that upon cooling in zero field, further components (those

---

[2] *Anhysteretic remanent magnetization* is the remanence acquired by a specimen in a low steady field on which is superposed an alternating field.

in which $T_1 < T_B < T_2$) are demagnetized, and so on up to the highest blocking temperature. The results of thermal demagnetization, like those for alternating fields, are expressed as changes in the intensity and in direction (Figures 5.28 and 5.17). The changes observed will be related to the spectrum of blocking temperatures.

Readily available accounts of apparatus for the thermal demagnetization of fossil magnetism, with constructional details and illustrative results, have been given by Wilson (1962c, 1961) for the continuous process, and by Irving, Robertson, Stott, Tarling, and Ward (1961) for the stepwise procedure.

Demagnetization by Steady Fields. These methods were introduced into paleomagnetic work by Johnson, Murphy, and Torreson (1948), and have been extensively used by Russian workers (Petrova, 1961; Petrova and Koroleva, 1959). The direction and intensity of a specimen is measured initially, and then it is placed in a small magnetic field (say 10 oe) with its remanence opposed in direction to that of the field. The speci-

men is then removed from the field and its magnetization measured, the process being repeated in higher fields until the intensity disappears (Figure 5.23). The strength of the field required to achieve this is called the *coercivity of NRM* or the *destructive field* (H_{cr}'). The value of H_{cr}' will depend partly on the coercivity of the domains carrying the initial remanence, and partly on the proportion of domains present whose coercivity is less than H_{cr}'. Zero remanence indicates that there are sufficient domains with a coercive force less than H_{cr}' to counterbalance those carrying the initial magnetization with a coercive force exceeding H_{cr}'.

A low value of H_{cr}' may mean that the magnetization is of low stability, and (or) that a high proportion of low coercive force domains are present. The destructive field is only a general guide to stability. A high value for H_{cr}' indicates high stability, but a low value does not necessarily mean that small stable components are absent.

§ 2.09   Hysteresis of Isothermal Remanence   Hysteresis loops of the *B-H* type

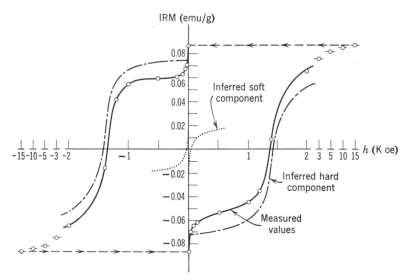

Figure 2.13. Hysteresis of IRM (*M-H* curve) in the basal plane of single crystal of hemoilmenite. The horizontal axis is broken to diminish sideways spread and to enlarge the interesting region between ±2000 oe. The measured, and inferred hard and soft component curves are indicated. Circles are experimental points. Redrawn from Carmichael (1961), with the kind permission of the Royal Society, London, and C. M. Carmichael.

(Figure 2.2) may be obtained for rock specimens, but because the field required to magnetize rocks to saturation is often high, especially in sediments, there are technical difficulties in obtaining complete *B-H* curves, and it is more convenient to study the *hysteresis of IRM* (or *M-H* curves).

If a rock is placed in a magnetic field at room temperatures and the field is then switched off, the specimen acquires a remanence, provided the strength of the field exceeds the coercive force of the softest magnetic component. Upon successive treatments in increasing fields the remanence increases to a maximum value, M_{max}, called the *maximum isothermal remanence* which is to be compared to the remanence J_r at $H = 0$ on the *B-H* loop. The field required to pro-

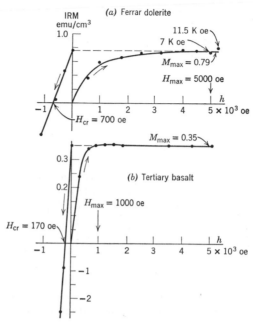

Figure 2.15. Hysteresis of IRM (*M-H* curves) in igneous rocks. (*a*) Ferrar Dolerite (data of Bull, Irving, and Willis, 1962). (*b*) Tertiary basalt of New South Wales (data of Irving, Stott, and Ward, 1961).

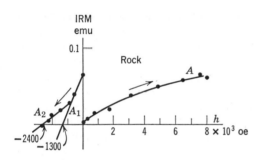

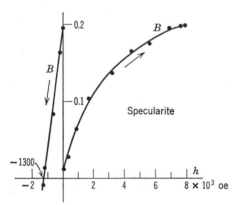

Figure 2.14. Hysteresis of IRM (*M-H* curve) in a sediment. Curve *A* is for a specimen of Torridonian sandstone. Curve *B* is for specularite grains extracted from the same rock. Intensities are measured in emu/cm³ for the rock, and in emu/gr for the extract. Redrawn from Irving (1957*a*), with the kind permission of the Royal Society, London.

duce M_{max} is called the *remanent saturating field* H_{max}. Successively increasing fields are applied in the opposite sense to M_{max} until the remanence becomes maximum in the reverse direction. The "back" field required to reduce M_{max} to zero is called the *coercivity of maximum remanence* (H_{cr}). The demagnetization curve is sometimes smooth, suggesting a more or less continuous range of coercivities, but is sometimes stepped, indicating that they are confined within defined ranges. The use of this method is illustrated by the following examples. A remanence hysteresis curve is given in Figure 2.13; the path is symmetrical about the axes so that only one-half need be shown, and this procedure is followed in Figures 2.14 and 2.15, to which the initial magnetization curves are also added.

Roquet (1947, 1954*b*) studied synthetic powders of the magnetite and hematite of the type described below (§ 2.10). Dispersed magnetite powder became saturated in a field of a few thousand oersted, and H_{cr} is 200–300 oe. Hematite powder, on the other hand, was not saturated in 30,000 oe, and H_{cr} was several thousand oersteds.

An interesting case, studied by Carmichael (1959, 1961), of two component stability of M_{max} is given in Figure 2.13. The material is hemoilmenite ($0.7FeTiO_3 \cdot 0.3Fe_2O_3$) from the Allard Lake region of Quebec, which shows a well-developed exsolution structure of hematite-rich (ilmenhematite) lamellae set in an ilmenite-rich (hemoilmenite) ground mass. The lamellae are of two sizes, the larger range from 1 to 10 mm in length, and from 5 to 20 μ in thickness, and the smaller are roughly 5 μ to 10 μ long, 1 μ wide, and 0.2 μ thick. In the experiment the field is applied parallel to the basal plane and the remanence approaches saturation in 15,000 oe. The demagnetization curve is stepped, and this is interpreted as being caused by two components with differing coercive forces, one with a value about 100 oe and the other about 1400 oe. The former is attributed to the larger lamellae, and the latter to the smaller ones whose high stability indicates that they act as single domain grains.

An example from a sedimentary rock is given in Figure 2.14. Curve A is for a very fine sandstone specimen. The rock consists of quartz and felspar fragments, much red staining material presumably hematite, and with frequent bands of detrital specular ore particles, the whole cemented by quartz. Curve B is for the black detrital particles extracted by hand-picking from the same rock. In neither case is saturation reached in 8000 oe. The demagnetization curve for the extract falls steadily with $H_{cr} = 1300$ oe. That for the specimen follows a curved path, which may be interpreted as due to two components: with A_1 of lower stability responsible for the early rapid fall and with H_{cr} equal to that for the extract, and A_2 with much higher H_{cr}, so that at 2400 oe it, and the component induced in A_1 by the field, equal zero.

Figure 2.15 gives results from igneous rocks. The Ferrar dolerite result was obtained from a specimen collected from a sill intruded into the Beacon sandstones of Antarctica. The intensity builds up to saturation rather slowly, although more rapidly than in the sediment just described. The intensity falls steadily upon demagnetization indicating the presence of a more or less continuous range of coercivities, the mean being 700 oe. This is also the case in the result from a Tertiary basalt, but the value for H_{cr} is now 170 oe, which is about the smallest value yet observed for a rock. The saturation occurs rapidly being complete in 1000 oe. These two behavior patterns are rather characteristic of igneous rocks with respectively stable and unstable fossil magnetism.

§ **2.10   Thermoremanent Magnetization** (TRM)   General references: Néel, 1955; Verhoogen, 1959; Nagata and Uyeda, 1961; Everitt, 1961b, 1962a and b; Stacey, 1963. The TRM of a rock is the remanence acquired upon cooling through a certain temperature interval in the presence of a magnetic field. The remanence acquired during cooling from the maximum Curie point to room temperature is called the *total TRM*. In this section effects are described which are observed to occur on the laboratory time scale, and which relate to igneous rocks which have cooled comparatively quickly from high temperatures. The possible effects of heating to moderate temperatures for geological periods of time, such as may occur during deep burial in the Earth's crust, are mentioned later (§ 2.13).

Dependence on Applied Field. In a weak magnetic field the intensity of TRM of igneous rocks is generally proportional to the field h (Figure 2.16). In stronger fields the TRM levels off, finally becoming saturated. This is shown in Figure 2.17 for synthetic specimens using the data of Roquet (1954a). The magnetite was prepared by reduction of hematite at 650°C. The grains were dispersed in a ceramic matrix at a concentration of about 1 per cent. The hematite was prepared by heating the precipitate formed by adding ammonia to a ferric chloride solution. The grain size in both cases is approximately 0.1 μ. The magnetite powder approaches saturation in several hundred oersteds the limiting remanence being 14.25 emu/g, which is about ⅐ the saturation magnetization. The IRM approaches saturation more slowly, needing about 1000 oe, the magnitude being the same as that for TRM. The effects with hematite are comparable, except the fields are an order of magnitude greater; the TRM is not yet saturated in 800 oe, and the IRM in 30,000 oe.

The field dependence of TRM aligned parallel to the easy directions of magnetization in single crystals of magnetite and hematite has been studied by Syono, Akimoto, and Nagata (1962) and is given in Figure 2.17c. The magnetite crystal was a 5 mm octahedron with a saturation magnetization $J_s = 98$ emu/g; it became saturated in about 100 oe, the intensity being only 10^{-3} of J_s. The hematite was a hexagonal plate $5 \times 5 \times 1$ mm with $J_s = 0.5$; its TRM in 1 oe is almost one half J_s, and about 100 times greater than the TRM acquired by the magnetite crystal in the same field. Syono and others attribute this contrast, first to the strong magnetocrystalline anisotropy of hematite which facilitates the development of a remanence in the basal plane so that the crystal acts as a single domain, and second to the much larger spontaneous magnetization of magnetite which causes the break-up of the crystal into

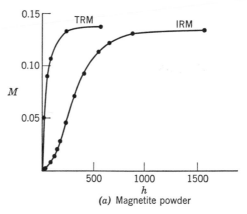

(a) Magnetite powder

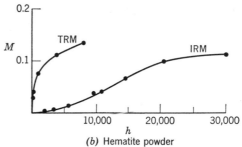

(b) Hematite powder

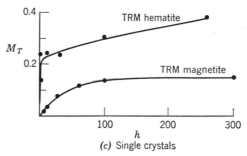

(c) Single crystals

Figure 2.17. Dependence of TRM and IRM on applied field h. (a) Dispersed magnetite. (b) Hematite powder. (c) TRM in single crystals of magnetite (in 111 direction) and hematite (in 1000 direction). M is in emu/g and h is in oe. (a) and (b) are redrawn from Roquet (1954a), by kind permission of l'Institut de Physique du Globe, and (c) is plotted from single-crystal data of Syono, Akimoto, and Nagata (1962).

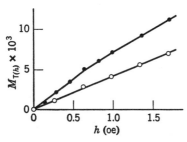

Figure 2.16. Dependence of the intensity (in emu/g) of TRM ($M_{T(h)}$) on applied field h in weak fields; results from two igneous specimens. Redrawn from Nagata and Uyeda (1961), by kind permission of Maruzen, Tokyo, and the authors.

mutually canceling domains. This result is relevant to paleomagnetism since it suggests the possibility that in a rock in which magnetite is the most abundant magnetic mineral hematite may contribute substantially to the

TRM even though it is present only in subordinate amounts (§ 7.5).

In unstressed rocks, with no preferred orientation of crystallographic or shape axes of the magnetic minerals, the direction of TRM is parallel to the direction of the applied field. An example is given in Figure 2.18; 28 specimens of coarse-grained monzonite, adamellite, gabbro, and andesite were heated to 600°C and cooled in a vertical field of 1.1 oe. The remanence directions are closely-grouped ($\theta_{63} = 2°$, $k = 1570$ (see § 4.07)) and their mean is *exactly* parallel to the field. The effects of anisotropy, in which the TRM is not parallel to the applied field, and self-reversal in which the TRM, although parallel, is opposed in sense to the field, are discussed later (§§ 2.14, 7.5).

Additive Property of Partial TRM. If, during cooling, the field is applied only between temperature interval T_1 to T_2 where $T_2 < T_C$, the field being canceled at all other temperatures, a component called the *partial TRM* is acquired. It is found experimentally that in a weak field, like that of the Earth's, the partial TRM acquired in any temperature interval depends only on the field applied during that temperature interval, and is not affected by the field applied at subsequent intervals in cooling; that is, the total TRM (M_T) is equal to the sum of all the partial TRM's acquired in each consecutive temperature interval between the Curie point and room temperature (Thellier, 1951; Nagata, 1953).

The additive property is summarized in the idealized curves (Figure 2.19). In (*a*) the partial TRM acquired in a constant and weak field over a temperature interval is plotted as a function of the mean temperature of that interval; in (*b*) the partial TRM's are plotted cumulatively, so that, upon cooling, the increment during any temperature interval is added to the components acquired in higher intervals. Experimentally, curves of type (*a*) are obtained by exposing a cooling specimen to a weak field only during a restricted temperature interval; curves of type (*b*) are obtained by applying the field from T_C to a given temperature and then canceling the field for the remainder of the cooling range.

Stability of TRM. The intensity of TRM induced by cooling in a weak field is found

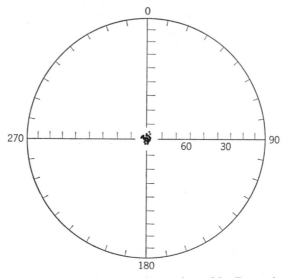

Figure 2.18. Direction of total TRM in 28 specimens from Mt. Dromedary intrusive complex. The cooling field was vertical and down. The directions are plotted as dots on the lower hemisphere of an equal-area net. Redrawn from Robertson (1963), by kind permission of the American Geophysical Union and W. A. Robertson.

to be unchanged on remeasurement after a lapse of days or weeks. TRM is also strongly resistant to demagnetization. The steady field demagnetization of total TRM (in 0.42 oe) of powders of hematite (αFe_2O_3) and magnetite is given in Figure 2.20. The remanent coercive force for hematite is 470 oe and that for magnetite 66 oe.

An example of stepwise thermal demagnetization is given in Figure 2.21. The material is a gabbro from the Mt. Dromedary intrusive complex (Robertson, 1963). The total TRM is very resistant to heating up to about 450°C, and thereafter drops suddenly to the Curie point of about 570°C. Demagnetization of total TRM by alternating fields is illustrated in Figure 2.22. The rock is a trachyte lava from the Aden Volcanics. The intensity of total TRM in a field of 0.6 oe ($M_{T(0.6)}$) is 0.85×10^{-3} emu/cm³. This is little changed in low fields but afterwards the intensity falls to a steady value $M'_{T(0.6)}$, about one half the initial intensity. The direction remains remarkably constant throughout, the circular standard deviation (§ 4.07) of the successive observations being 1°. Thus the total TRM consists of two components, a component $M'_{T(0.6)}$ of very great stability, and one of much less stability which is effectively demagnetized in 450 oe $\tilde{H}_p$. The specimen was then placed in a steady field of 300 oe which gave a magnetization, $M_{i(300)}$, about 12 times greater than $M_{T(0.6)}$. The speci-

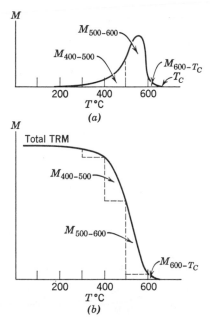

Figure 2.19. The acquisition of TRM. In these idealized curves the partial TRM's are plotted, (a) separately, and (b) cumulatively, as a function of temperature. Modified from Cox and Doell (1960).

men was again demagnetized, and $M_{i(300)}$ is lost completely after treatment in an alternating field of 300 oe $\tilde{H}_p$ equal to the strength of the magnetizing field. The component $M'_{T(0.6)}$ however is unchanged throughout, its intensity and direction being exactly the same as that before the isothermal remanence $M_{i(300)}$ was acquired.

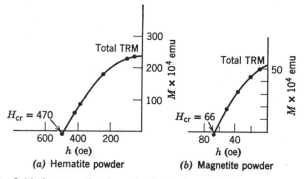

Figure 2.20. Steady field demagnetization of TRM of synthetic specimens of powdered hematite, and of powdered magnetite dispersed in a matrix. Redrawn from Roquet (1954a), with the kind permission of l'Institut de Physique du Globe.

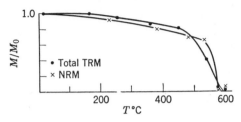

Figure 2.21. Thermal demagnetization of NRM and total TRM of Cretaceous gabbro of the Mt. Dromedary intrusive complex. The curves are normalized to unity at room temperatures. Redrawn from Robertson (1963), with the kind permission of the American Geophysical Union and W. A. Robertson.

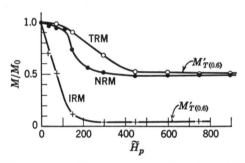

Figure 2.22. Comparison of alternating field demagnetization of IRM, NRM, and total TRM in the same sample of trachyte from the Aden volcanics. Normalized intensity is plotted against peak field strength. Redrawn from Irving and Tarling (1961), with the kind permission of the American Geophysical Union.

The component $M'_{T(0.6)}$ is magnetically independent of the IRM imposed in 300 oe.

Acquisition of TRM. Many features of the acquisition of TRM are explained by Néel's single domain theory (§ 2.04). As a rock, containing an assembly of magnetic grains, cools through its Curie point T_C it assumes an equilibrium magnetization at T_C. As the temperature falls the coercive force and the spontaneous magnetization increase, and there is a narrow range within which the relaxation time increases rapidly, freezing-in the equilibrium magnetization at the blocking temperature. On further cooling the relaxation time and coercive force continue to increase. This explains how, at

high temperatures, weak fields like the Earth's can give a preferential alignment to domains which, at normal temperatures, have coercive forces of hundreds of oersteds. Since the grain size in a rock varies, there will be a range of blocking temperatures. If the grain sizes extend down into the superparamagnetic range, the blocking temperatures extend below room temperatures. For the most part, however, the useful component of TRM is found to be acquired in the range 100°C below T_C. If, as is often the case, more than one phase is present each with a characteristic Curie point, then each phase will have an associated train of blocking temperatures dependent on the grain size spectrum within each phase. Néel's theory also explains the additive property of partial TRM. The partial TRM acquired in a temperature interval T_1 to T_2 resides in a group of domains with blocking temperatures in that interval. At temperatures below T_1, the grains responsible for this partial TRM will have long relaxation times compared to the duration of an experiment, and will be unaffected by fluctuations in the applied field. At temperatures above T_2 the relaxation time is short, and the grains follow the field fluctuations, so that the partial TRM is destroyed.

§ 2.11 Chemical Remanent Magnetization (CRM)

Many rocks contain magnetic minerals which were formed either at low temperatures by chemical processes initially, or have been subjected to secondary alteration at temperatures below their Curie point. These effects may take a variety of forms. Many sediments contain iron oxides deposited chemically, sometimes at the time of deposition, sometimes long afterwards; these may occur as identifiable crystals, or as fine powder disseminated through the rock. Metamorphic rocks commonly contain pyrrhotite, hematite, or magnetite, which may have formed at moderate temperatures. Magnetic minerals commonly undergo exsolution, and the exsolution temperature range may extend below the Curie point. Diffusion of ions within the crystal lattice may also occur at low temperature. Finally, a rock may undergo surface weathering involving, in different circumstances, oxidation, leaching, or enrichment of iron (§ 5.13).

Koenigsberger (1938) recognized that such low temperature processes may affect the magnetization of rocks, in particular, he noted the possibility of exsolution effects and the effects of chemical changes occurring in sediments after deposition. He coined the name *crystallization remanence,* which he compared to the magnetization Maurain (1901) had observed to be acquired in the cold by iron deposited electrolytically. This is a useful term to apply to remanence acquired by crystals formed below the Curie point. The term *chemical remanent magnetization* is used here to embrace all types of remanence (including crystallization remanence) which arise from changes of a chemical or physico-chemical nature occurring at temperatures below the Curie point.

Haigh (1958), Nagata and Kobayashi (1958), and Kobayashi (1959) (see also Kobayashi, 1961, for further relevant results) have shown that magnetite obtained by heating hematite powders of grain size less than 1 μ at temperatures of 270° to 340°C, for periods of hours in a reducing atmosphere and in an applied field, acquired a magnetization parallel to this field. The magnetization produced is very similar, in its demagnetization characteristics, to total TRM, but different from IRM induced in the same specimens, the latter falling off very much more rapidly (Figure 2.23). The intensity of CRM is proportional to the strength of the applied field up to fields of about 50 oe. The intensity in fields of about 1 oe is some ten times less than the total TRM.

CRM is thought to arise from a process of nucleation. In the early stages, small newly formed grains behave superparamagnetically, the spontaneous magnetization following the field. As the grain size increases, the relaxation time increases (§2.04), and the magnetization is stabilized. TRM is fixed as a result of the fall of temperature, volume being constant, whereas CRM is fixed by the increase in volume, temperature remaining constant. On this theory three stages may be envisaged in the build-up of CRM: a superparamagnetic stage with no remanence, a single-domain particle stage with remanence of high stability, and a multidomain

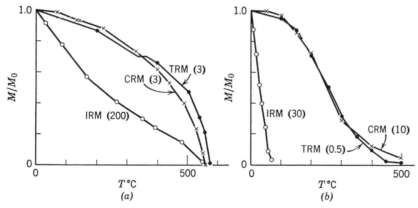

Figure 2.23. Normalized demagnetization curves for different types of remanence in magnetite prepared chemically. (*a*) Thermal demagnetization, measurements taken at room temperature. (*b*) Alternating magnetic field demagnetization. The curves are labeled CRM, IRM, and TRM indicating the mode of origin of the magnetization, respectively, chemical remanent magnetization at 340°C, isothermal remanent magnetization induced at 20°C, and total thermoremanence. The field in oersteds employed for each process is shown by the numbers in parentheses. Redrawn from Kobayashi (1959), with the kind permission of the Society of Terrestrial Magnetism and Electricity of Japan, and K. Kobayashi.

particle stage with remanence of lower stability. Further references to discussions of CRM are: Doell, 1956, 1957; Martinez and Howell, 1956; Nagata and Kobayashi, 1963; Howell, 1962.

§ 2.12 Detrital Remanent Magnetization (DRM) [3]

A small proportion of the particles which go to form a detrital sediment are usually magnetic. These particles have been derived by erosion from older rocks and may inherit a remanence from them. Under suitable depositing conditions it is possible that the moments of these particles become statistically aligned along the direction of the ambient field, and that this alignment may be fossilized in the resulting sediment. A NRM of this origin has been invoked for the glacial and postglacial varved sediments of New England (McNish and Johnson, 1938; Johnson, Murphy, and Torreson, 1948) and Sweden (Ising, 1943; Granar, 1958; Griffiths, King, Rees, and Wright, 1960), the Torridonian Sandstone (Irving, 1957a) and various late Tertiary and Pleistocene sediments of Japan (Nagata, 1953).

Alignment of magnetized detrital particles may occur during their fall through water, when the scatter of directions will depend on the degree of turbulence and the strength of the couple between particle and field. If the particles are elongated they may tend to be magnetized along their lengths, so that a systematic divergence from the field may occur if directed currents are present. Once the particle hits bottom, mechanical interaction with other particles may disturb this alignment, but if, for some reason, deposition is temporarily halted, particles resting on the surface may be insufficiently confined to prevent alignment along the field, given a sufficient period of time. In poorly sorted sediments the particles will tend to be locked together. But in sediments which are well-sorted with regard to their nonmagnetic par-

ticles, and whose magnetic particles are smaller (as is often the case in fine sandstones), the latter may be free to rotate within interstitial holes for some time after deposition while the sediment is full of water, so that continuous adjustment to the field may occur. Rotations will cease once compaction and cementation close these holes. It is convenient therefore to recognize DRM of two types: first, remanence acquired at deposition due to particle alignment during sedimentation (*depositional DRM*), and second, remanence acquired by particle rotation into the field after deposition but prior to consolidation (*post-depositional DRM*). Field observations relevant to these ideas may be obtained by studying the relation of NRM directions to sedimentary structures (§§ 5.04, 5.06).

Nagata (1953, 1962) and Stacey (1963) have considered theoretically the question of the alignment of particles in a field as they fall through water. Laboratory experiments have been carried out by Benedikt (1943), and Johnson, Murphy, and Torreson (1948) using glacial varves from New England, and by Nagata (1953) using fine sands and crushed volcanic rock. More recent studies have used Swedish and Icelandic varves, and these are now described (King, 1955; Griffiths, King, and Wright, 1957; Griffiths, King, Rees, and Wright, 1960; Rees, 1961). The material used has an average particle size of between 5 and 25 μ; that is, fine silt grade. The magnetic particles have a size distribution similar to that of the nonmagnetic particles, and there seems no need to consider the mechanical behavior of the magnetic and nonmagnetic fractions separately. The magnetic fractions consist partly of high-density particles probably of nearly pure magnetic oxide, and partly of less dense composite grains consisting of magnetic inclusions in silicate minerals. The mean sphericities range from 0.84 to 0.66.

When such sediment is redispersed in a tank and allowed to settle through still water the new sediment is magnetized so that its declination is in good agreement with that of the applied field, but the inclination, I_0, is almost

---

[3] The term *depositional remanent magnetization* has sometimes been used synonymously with detrital remanent magnetization (see, for example, Nagata, 1961).

invariably less than the field inclination $\mathcal{I}$. When the bottom is horizontal, the difference is called the *inclination error*,

$$\iota = \mathcal{I} - I_0 \qquad (2.8)$$

The error depends on the field inclination, and is a maximum of about 25° at $\mathcal{I} \simeq 60°$, falling to negligible values for low field inclinations (Table 2.1). The relationship between $\mathcal{I}$ and I_0 may be represented by

$$\tan I_0 = f \tan \mathcal{I} \qquad (2.9)$$

The data of Table 2.1 give $f = 0.4$. The inclination error is independent of grain size in the range studied. Flume experiments in running water show that it is also independent of current velocities up to 30 cm/s. The inclination error, however, varies with the dispersion observed between cores from the same experiment. If *SD* is the standard deviation of the directions of cores from the same batch, then it is found empirically that $\iota = 22.2 - 1.64\,SD°$ and so for $SD = 13°$ (values 10° or 20° are commonly observed in sedimentary rocks) ι may become negligible.

The inclination error could arise from shape effects. An elongated particle, magnetized along its length, will tend to settle flat. It was thought at first that the parameter f in equation (2.9) represented the proportion of such elongated particles present, $1 - f$ being the proportion of spherical particles, but shape analyses described above show that the elongations are insufficient, and that there is no division into elongate and spherical fractions. Consideration was then given to the question of what happens when a particle hits bottom and rolls into a hollow in the surface. The effect of particle-rolling in the direction of and away from the field averages out, but sideways particle-rolling systematically diminishes inclination. On this particle-rolling model the inclination error may be envisaged as a potential source of error in all detrital sediments, not just in those with elongated magnetic particles.

When the depositing surface is tilted, a further deviation occurs called the *bedding error* β, given by

$$\beta = I_\alpha - I_0 \qquad (2.10)$$

where I_α is the inclination observed when deposition occurs on a slope making an angle α with the horizontal. Values of β for 10° slopes are listed in Table 2.1. If the slope is downward in the direction of the horizontal component of the field, then β tends to increase the inclination and works against ι. The particle-rolling model explains the effect; for particles settling into hollows in the surface, forward rolling will tend to be more frequent and greater than backward rolling, and so the inclination is increased.

A third deviation occurs if the deposit is laid down in running water, the remanence direction being deflected by angles up to 10° in current velocities of 5–30 cm/sec, the magnitude of the effect being independent of velocity within this range. It is believed that the rotation occurs before the particle touches bottom, and prior to the acquisition of inclination or bedding errors. The most

Table 2.1 Directions of Depositional DRM. $\mathfrak{D}$, $\mathcal{I}$ are the directions of the applied field in different experiments. D_0, I_0 and D_{10}, I_{10} are the directions observed in sediment on a flat surface, and a surface tilted northwards at 10°, each result being an average of about 5 cores taken from the deposit. ι is the inclination error, and β the bedding error. The duplicate run at $\mathcal{I} = 65°$ indicates the degree of repeatability of results. Data of King (1955). Reproduced by kind permission of the Royal Astronomical Society, London, and R. F. King.

$\mathfrak{D}$, $\mathcal{I}$	D_0, I_0	D_{10}, I_{10}	$\iota°$	$\beta°$
0, 0	359, −2	356, 6	2	8
0, 10	355, 7	353, 17	3	10
0, 25	359, 16	357, 24	9	8
0, 45	0, 24	358, 39	21	15
0, 65	2, 38	358, 55	27	17
0, 65	355, 41	345, 59	24	18
0, 90	191, 80	177, 55	10	−25
180, 80	174, 47	177, 30	33	−17

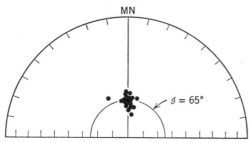

Figure 2.24. The remanent magnetization acquired by wet synthetic sediment. The applied field direction is at the intersection of the small circle of inclination −65° and the magnetic meridian MN. Specimen directions (25) are marked as dots on the upper hemisphere (negative inclinations) of an equal-area projection. Redrawn from Irving and Major (1964), with the kind permission of Elsevier Publishing Co., Amsterdam.

obvious explanation for such effects is in terms of hydrodynamic couples acting on elongated particles, but a satisfactory model based on quasispherical particles can also explain the observations (Rees, 1961).

We turn now to the laboratory studies of effects occurring after deposition. In preliminary experiments Lloyd (quoted in Clegg, Almond, and Stubbs, 1954a) crushed red Triassic marl and allowed the powder to settle in a tank. The sediment became magnetized with declination along the Earth's field, but with an inclination some 8° less than the field inclination of about 65°. He also found that sediments deposited in zero field could be magnetized by applying a weak field after deposition, provided the water content exceeded 50 per cent by weight of the deposit; this time there was no inclination error the magnetization being along the applied field and the intensity was comparable to that of the parent rock. The material used, which is quite different from the varve sediment of the previous experiments, is typical of the red bed material of paleomagnetic work.

Results from synthetic sediments are now mentioned. In these experiments an attempt is made to model the effects of penecontemporaneous slumping or reworking by animals, such as is not uncommon in sediments studied paleomagnetically. Quartz sand with mean particle diameters and magnetite were mixed dry in the proportions 200:1. The quartz grain-size varied in different samples in the range coarse silt to fine sand, and the maximum ratio of the diameters of the quartz and magnetite varied from 1 to 0.5. The samples were flooded with water and allowed to stand overnight in a weak magnetic field. In all cases the samples became magnetized parallel to the field, and this substantiates Lloyd's result for all field inclinations. An example of results obtained at a field inclination of −65° and strength 0.6 oe is given in Figure 2.24. The mean of the sample directions is along the applied field and this contrasts strongly with the inclination error of about 25° (Table 2.1) observed by King for depositional experiments at this field inclination. These results suggest that DRM in coarse silts and fine sands can occur after deposition, and without inclination error. Earlier processes, such as grain alignment during settling, or bottom-rolling, may then be irrelevant. The field observations of uniform magnetization in slump beds (§ 5.04) and the consistency between igneous and sedimentary rocks (§ 5.03) are consistent with this view.

§ 2.13   Viscous Effects   So far, this chapter has been largely concerned with effects which can be observed in the laboratory in the course of a few hours. Over longer time-spans remanence may be affected in two ways and commonly both will operate. First, the intensity of primary magnetization (say TRM or CRM) may decay in time—a process which is called *viscous demagnetization* or *viscous decay*. Second, a new magnetization may be acquired at temperatures below the Curie temperature and this is called *viscous remanent magnetization* (VRM). If the ambient field is different from that in which the primary magnetization was acquired, then both will tend to obscure the primary magnetization, because as the VRM increases and the primary component decays the latter will become less effective. Magnetic viscosity in rocks was first noticed by Thellier (1938) and has since been studied by many workers, for example Kawai and Kume (1953, 1959), Roquet (1954a), Creer (1957b), Shimizu (1960), Janovsky and Sholpo (1962).

Viscous effects are due to thermal agitations. Even at low temperatures there are energies which are sufficient to change an assembly of domains to their state of lowest energy. If a magnetic field is present it provides a bias to the directions, so that a VRM accumulates. Rocks contain a wide coercive force spectrum (§ 2.08) and particles with short relaxation times will be affected preferentially, while those with long relaxation times may remain unchanged for long periods.

The build-up of VRM in basalt and baked clay specimens over periods of years has been shown to be proportional to the logarithm of time and parallel to the field in which they were stored (Rimbert, 1958). Rimbert showed that such VRM, imposed over a period of time t in a field h, could be demagnetized in an alternating field whose rms strength is given by

$$\tilde{H}_{\mathrm{rms}} = -100 + 75 \log h + 10(2 + \log h) \log t$$

$$(2.11)$$

It is useful to distinguish two types of VRM—*normal temperature VRM* and *moderate temperature VRM* acquired by heating to moderate temperatures of the order of 100°C as may have commonly occurred in the history of many rocks.

Normal temperature VRM has been extensively studied. It occurs to a greater or lesser degree in all rocks, usually as relatively soft magnetization parallel to the direction of the Earth's field at the collecting locality, or to the axial geocentric dipole field direction, which is the average direction since the postulated last reversal of the field about 1 m.y. ago (§§ 6.02, 7.3). When the field direction changes, VRM decays and memories of components acquired in more remote time are likely to become negligible once the new

field direction has been established for hundreds or thousands of years. Extrapolation of the empirical relationship (2.11) suggests that the alternating field needed to demagnetize VRM acquired by a rock in a field of 0.5 oe applied for 1 m.y. is 106 oe. As will be seen later (§§ 5.08, 5.09) normal temperature VRM components parallel to the Earth's field can, in fact, be demagnetized in alternating fields of 100 to 200 oe, which is consistent with Rimbert's laboratory experiments.

A neat illustration of the effect of normal temperature viscous "drag" has been given by Kawai and Kume (1959). They studied samples of sedimentary rocks from the same formation at Hota in the Bôzô Peninsula, Japan, but which had been re-oriented with respect to the Earth's field at various times in their history, either by natural break-up into conglomerates, or by quarrying and incorporation into masonry. They argued that the earlier the process of re-orientation the greater viscous effects ought to be, and their observations showed this to be true. Samples from two conglomerate beds with estimated ages of 10^7 and 10^5 years were grouped close to the present field but with a significant dispersion. Specimens taken from statues and buildings several hundred years old were scattered but with their mean direction along the Earth's field. Finally, specimens from two pavements aged 50 and 3 years were found to be very widely dispersed, the latter randomly. Thus the material studied by Kawai and Kume reaches *approximate* equilibrium with the field in about 1 m.y. although the residual dispersion in the conglomerates shows that perfect equilibrium had not been achieved.

Relaxation times diminish with temperature increase (§ 2.04) and viscous effects will be enhanced. Kawai and Kume (1953) studied the build-up of VRM in specimens of rock powder held at a given temperature in a constant magnetic field. The material used was from conglomerate pebbles which did not show random directions *in situ,* and so were unstable magnetically. The temperatures applied were in the range 28° to 68°C and it was found that the magnetization built up at a rate proportional to the logarithm of time of heating, and in the course of a few days an intensity comparable in magnitude to the NRM was generated. It therefore seems likely that heating of many rock types to moderate temperatures (yet well below the Curie point of the magnetic minerals) for long periods will induce substantial VRM components; such heating could arise either during deep burial, or from igneous intrusion. As the temperature falls, due either to uplift or the cessation of igneous activity, the relaxation time increases and the VRM is stabilized. Moderate temperature VRM (which also may be thought of as a viscous type of TRM) may be expected to differ from normal temperature VRM in two respects. First, moderate temperature components will usually be directed not along the present field but along an earlier direction so that they may be difficult to recognize in the observation. Second, they may be magnetically stable and resistant to demagnetization and may be mistaken by the experimenter for the desired primary component. The study of moderate temperature VRM has yet hardly begun, and field examples have not yet been identified with certainty. It appears possible that the remagnetization of the Beacon Sandstone and the Basement Complex in South Victoria Land postulated by Turnbull (1959), and Bull, Irving, and Willis (1962) to have occurred as a result of regional heating at the time of intrusion of the Ferrar Dolerites, is of this type (Figure 7.26). A second possible example is the stable magnetization directed along the Permian geomagnetic field which Chamalaun and Creer (1963) have found to occur in Devonian sediments of Britain; it is not unlikely that this magnetization was acquired at a period of deep burial and regional heating during the Hercynian orogeny.

§ **2.14 Magnetic Anisotropy** From the paleomagnetic point of view, the important feature of remanence is its parallelism to the field in which it was acquired. In fact, this is only true for isotropic rocks. If a marked anisotropy is present the TRM is deflected away from the ambient field towards the direction of "easy" magnetization. Magnetic anisotropy may be an intrinsic property present in the rock in the unstressed state when it is called *intrinsic anisotropy,* or it may arise from strains due to external stresses when it is called *stress-induced anisotropy.* In this section intrinsic anisotropy only is considered, stress-induced anisotropy being discussed in § 2.15. Intrinsic anisotropy is potentially important in fabric analysis (J. W. Graham, 1954*b*; Granar, 1958; Hargraves, 1959; Stacey, 1960*a*; Stacey, Joplin, and Lindsay, 1960; Fuller, 1960; Balsley and Buddington, 1960; Khan, 1962; Stone, 1963), but the following remarks are concerned only with its relation to paleomagnetic work.

Each iron mineral crystal in a rock is magnetically anisotropic (§ 2.03) and if a preferred alignment of crystal or shape axes occurs the rock as a whole is anisotropic. Shape effects are the more important. For practical purposes a rock may be considered isotropic when the anisotropy is too small to deflect the remanence away from the field direction by an angle greater than the experimental error, which can be taken as 3°.

Anisotropy is measured by the variation in the values of susceptibility (Ising, 1943; Fuller, 1960; Girdler, 1961; King and Rees, 1962; Stone, 1963), saturation magnetization (Stacey, 1960*a*), and IRM or TRM in different directions in a specimen. The results are expressed in terms of a triaxial ellipsoid. The lengths of the principal axes are proportional to the maximum, intermediate, and minimum values. In order to separate preferred alignments having linear and planar form, workers have defined various ratios of the principal axes, but for present purposes the degree of anisotropy (thinking in terms of susceptibility) may be expressed as a ratio An given by

$$An = \chi_{max}/\chi_{min} \qquad (2.12)$$

An An value of 1.5 means that the maximum anisotropy exceeds the minimum by 50 per cent.

The TRM acquired by an anisotropic rock

may be expected to be deflected towards the "easy" (or maximum) direction, and the question arises—at what values of anisotropy do these effects become important? It is found experimentally that the directions of total TRM in rocks with bulk anisotropies of less than 5 per cent are directed parallel to the applied field; an example is given in Figure 2.18. The deflections of TRM in specimens showing substantial anisotropy of susceptibility are given in Figure 2.25. In this experiment the plane of maximum and intermediate susceptibility was set horizontally during cooling and the applied field was the Earth's. Specimens (S) of ferro-gabbro from the Skaergaard intrusion have inclinations deflected towards the plane of maximum susceptibility by 5°; the gabbro is strongly layered, apparently due to crystal settling. A_1 represents specimens of polycrystals from the Allard Lake hemoilmenite which became magnetized with inclinations 11° less than the applied field. Further values are for a Ludwigite (L) from Korea with aligned acicular magnetite, a single crystal (A_2) from Allard Lake, and a single crystal of specular hematite (H), in which the observed depar-

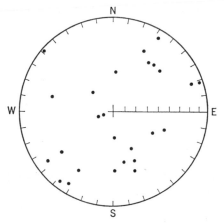

Figure 2.26. Directions of maximum susceptibility axes in specimens from several localities in the Deccan Traps of India. Plotting on lower hemisphere of an equal-area net. Compiled from Girdler (1961).

tures were 52°, 55°, and 67° respectively. The anisotropy factors increase as the departures increase and these results suggest a limit of about 5 per cent before divergences from the field become important. Anisotropies in excess of this would systematically affect the paleomagnetic results only if the principal axes were systematically aligned throughout a whole rock unit. The effect of anisotropies of approximately 10 to 20 per cent with expected deflections of 5° or 10° would be averaged out in the results of a paleomagnetic survey based on specimens from a rock unit in which preferential alignment, although perhaps present at particular localities, was absent from the unit as a whole.

Many of the igneous rocks used in paleomagnetic work have been shown to have An values of 5 per cent or less. For example, Girdler (1961) studied 26 specimens from a number of localities in the Deccan Traps and found values ranging from 3.6 to 0.8 with a mean of 1.6 per cent. The principal axes are widely scattered (Figure 2.26), and no systematic paleomagnetic effects are likely to arise in such material.

So far only the effect on TRM has been considered in which the anisotropy is present prior to the acquisition of remanence. But in many sediments (§ 2.12) and meta-

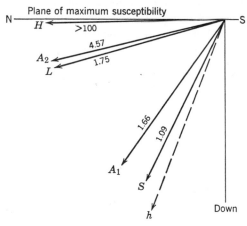

Figure 2.25. Inclination of total TRM in anisotropic specimens. h is the applied field with inclination +68°. The inclination of the total TRM is indicated by an arrow, the letters being for different rock types (see text). The value of the anisotropy factor An is given in each case. Compiled from Uyeda, Fuller, Belshé, and Girdler (1963).

morphic rocks the remanence and anisotropy may have been acquired at much the same time and at temperatures below the Curie point. DRM due to elongated particles would tend to produce a marked anisotropy, but the directions need not diverge from the field. In the varved clays of Sweden, Ising (1943) and Granar (1958) found an excess of susceptibility in the horizontal plane of 10 to 20 per cent. Howell, Martinez, and Statham (1958) found similar anisotropies in Silurian sediments. In those metamorphic rocks in which the magnetization was acquired during crystal growth it might be expected that stress would cause crystal alignment, and strong anisotropy can generally be observed (Grabovsky and Brodskaya, 1958; Daly, 1959; Fuller, 1960; Balsley and Buddington, 1960; Khan, 1962; Howell, Martinez and Statham, 1958).

§ **2.15   Stress Effects**   Rocks are subjected to stresses during their history. Stresses may arise from cooling, or from burial, or from tectonic causes. They may take the form of hydrostatic pressure or uniaxial stresses. If stress is applied concurrently with some magnetization process (for instance, TRM) it may affect the remanence produced; if applied long after the acquisition of an initial remanence it may modify it.

Hydrostatic Pressure. Kume (1962) and Girdler (1963) have reported results from experiments conducted in confining pressures of up to 10^4 kg/cm^2 which would correspond to a depth of about 30 km in the Earth. In both cases a stepwise procedure was used— the specimens were first subjected to a certain pressure in the presence of the Earth's field, then removed from the press and measured, the process being repeated for higher pressures. Kume finds that synthetic specimens of magnetite, maghemite, and hematite, which had been initially magnetized isothermally in 500 oe, showed a decrease in intensity by amounts varying from 90 to 50 per cent. The NRM of a specimen of Volvic andesite showed a decrease in intensity of 50 per cent. The decrease in all cases was similar to that observed in unstressed

specimens by demagnetization in 100 to 200 oe alternating field, suggesting that pressure affects only the least stable components. No changes of directions of magnetization were found either in the synthetic specimens or the andesite.

Girdler's experiments were carried out on material with a TRM. The specimens were partially demagnetized in alternating magnetic fields of 500 to 600 oe before and after the application of pressure, so that the results cannot be compared directly with those of Kume. Synthetic specimens of magnetite and hematite heated above the Curie temperature and cooled in the Earth's field, and igneous rocks from the Pyrénées and Ardnamurchan (gabbro and dolerite) were used. Decreases in intensity of up to 85 per cent were observed. In samples of partly oxidized Fe$_3$O$_4$ direction changes between treatment of up to about 40° occurred, the changes varying randomly between treatments. But no direction changes occurred in natural rock.

Uniaxial Stress. Experiments on synthetic specimens have been reported by Domen (1958*b*, 1962). He found that specimens of powdered natural magnetite from Sampo Mine, Okayama, Japan, when subjected to uniaxial stresses approaching 10^4 kg/cm^2 acquired a remanence perpendicular to the direction of stress. The magnitude of the moment depends on the time for which the stress is applied leveling off for application times of 5 to 10 minutes, to a magnitude of about 0.8 emu/g. The effect is also temperature dependent diminishing by a factor 5 when the experiment is carried out at temperatures of 100°C or more.

Stress effects in natural rocks at room temperatures have been studied by J. W. Graham, Buddington, and Balsley (1957), and Powell (1960). The former workers subjected a number of metamorphic rocks from the Adirondacks to uniaxial compressions of 250 kg/cm^2. The rocks are strongly anisotropic, the differences between the principal susceptibility axes usually exceed 20 per cent and commonly range up to 50 per cent or more (Balsley and Buddington, 1960). Measurements were made while the pressure was applied. Deflections of the fossil magnetization of up to 30° occurred, which, in most, but not all cases, disappeared when the stress was released.

The effect of stress on TRM may be studied in the laboratory by heating a rock specimen to a temperature above its Curie point and subjecting it to uniaxial stress during cooling in a field, then measuring the resulting direction of magnetization and comparing it with that of the field. The idea is that the history of many of the igneous rocks commonly used in paleomagnetic work is one of cooling under stress, either from loading as in the case of intrusives, or from cooling contraction prior to jointing as in lavas. Stott and Stacey (1959, 1960) studied 80 specimens of Australian rocks (dolerite, porphyry, and basalt) using uniaxial stress of 500 and 1000 kg/cm², and an applied field of 0.6 oe. The magnetic minerals in these specimens were predominantly titanomagnetites (L. G. Parry, 1960). They found that, within the experimental error, the TRM acquired was parallel to the direction of the field, and to the directions in duplicate specimens heated and cooled under the same conditions but without stress. Negative results were also obtained for IRM acquired under load in a field of 140 oe. All their samples were essentially isotropic. The observed bulk anisotropies in general did not exceed 3 per cent (Stacey, 1960a). Similar experiments by Kern (1961a) on 54 andesite and basalt specimens containing titanomagnetites as their dominant magnetic minerals gave TRM's parallel to the ambient field, the stresses applied in this case being in the range 175 to 350 kg/cm².

In contrast to the behavior of isotropic rocks, stress often has a positive effect on TRM in anisotropic rocks. Strongly anisotropic serpentine has been found to acquire TRM's under a stress of 500 kg/cm², which diverged by up to 56° from the direction of the field—0.6 oe (Stott and Stacey, 1960). Hall and Neale (1960) observed departures ranging from 1° to 8° for TRM acquired by certain Tertiary dolerite dike specimens under uniaxial stress in the range 200 to 1000 kg/cm² in a field of 1.5 oe. The directions rotated towards the plane normal to the stress axis. Finally, there are the interesting studies of the TRM acquired under uniaxial stress in anisotropic rocks made by Kern (1961a), using the Adirondack material which show the deflection of NRM isothermally (see above). Three groups of specimens were used, the first cooled with no stress, and the second and the third with different applied stress (Figure 2.27). The divergences of TRM from the field often exceeded 10°, and in one unstressed specimen was about 30°. After demagnetization in alternating magnetic fields of 300 oe the scatter was much reduced, not only for the stressed specimens, but also for those cooled without loading, and the final grouping of directions around the applied field was very good.

The conclusion from these studies is that no measurable effects on the directions of magnetization have yet been found in rocks with low anisotropy such as those used for paleomagnetic work; this applies to tests using hydrostatic pressure or uniaxial stress. Positive effects occur in strongly anisotropic rocks in response to uniaxial stress, but in cases so far studied, these are removed by partial demagnetization in moderate alternating fields. Kern (1961b and c) suggests that stress-aided magnetization affects first the domains with lowest energy barriers so that the stress-induced components are concentrated in domains with low coercive force, whereas the TRM is concentrated in domains with high coercive force, so that the former is preferentially removed by demagnetization. A comparable proposal has been made by Stott and Stacey (1960) who suggest that stress-aided VRM acquired at normal temperatures should also be preferentially removed by alternating field demagnetization.

Stress-Induced Anisotropy (Stacey, 1960b). Intrinsically isotropic specimens become anisotropic when stressed. Stacey subjected 5 specimens (Tasmanian dolerite and Permian Upper Marine latites of N.S.W.) whose natural unstressed anisotropies were very small, to uniaxial stress of 520 kg/cm², and then measured the anisotropy of saturation magnetization. An appreciable anisotropy was produced which disappeared when the stress was released. This reversible anisotropy has a negligible effect on the total TRM after stress release, as the experiments described above show. Stacey presumes that when an intrinsically isotropic rock is subjected to stress while cooling in a magnetic field it first acquires a TRM direction deflected from the field in a manner controlled by the stress-induced anisotropy; but then, on unloading, the TRM returns precisely to the field direction. All experimental results at present available are consistent with his hypothesis.

Compaction in Sediments. Vlassov, Kovalenko, and Tropin (1961) subjected synthetic sediments, which had a depositional DRM, to axial compressions. They found that the inclination in sediments with grain-sizes of about 1 μ was decreased by 6° after 400 kg/cm² compression, and by 10° after 3268 kg/cm². In sediments of grain-size 0.02 μ such compressions produced negligible effects. The decrease of inclination in the coarser sediment was attributed to rotation of elongated particles during compaction. The grain-sizes used in these experiments are very much less than those of sediments used in paleomagnetic work. The relevance to natural conditions, of results obtained by this extreme compression of wet sediment, is obscure.

Shear Distortion. Evison (1961, 1962) contends that plastic flow of rocks would alter remanence directions, but the good agreement observed over regions of continental extent (§ 5.08) appears to exclude this possibility in rocks commonly studied paleomagnetically.

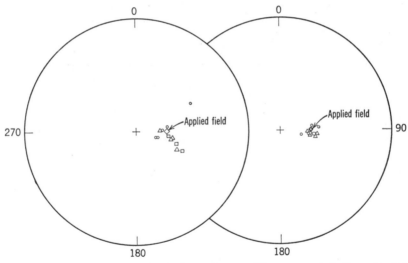

Figure 2.27. TRM directions in Adirondack specimens. The stress axis is the axis of the projection (into the page). Circles denote directions acquired under zero stress, triangles under 175 kg/cm², and squares under 350 kg/cm². (a) After cooling under given stress in an applied field. (b) Same after partial demagnetization in alternating magnetic fields of 300 oe. Redrawn from Kern (1961a), with the kind permission of the American Geophysical Union and J. W. Kern.

CHAPTER THREE

General features of the geomagnetic field

§ **3.1 Preliminary Remarks** The aim of the study of paleomagnetism is to map the variations in the geomagnetic field in the geological past, and it is useful to have some means of comparing the past and present behavior of the field. Because of the incompleteness of the geological record, the irregularities in the processes of magnetization, and the uncertainties in correlating rock beds from place to place, the paleomagnetic description of the ancient field will always be very much less detailed than the description of the present field obtained at magnetic observatories. It is necessary, therefore, when comparing the rock data with the present field, to have a model of the field which expresses the average rather than the detailed form of its variations. Such a model needs to be based on observatory data, but cast in such a form that it can be compared against paleomagnetic results. These models aim to describe the morphology of the field, and are not models of the mechanism by which the field is generated.

In this chapter a brief account of the general features of the present field and its variations over the recent past is given, and this is followed by a discussion of certain generalized models useful in paleomagnetic work.

§ **3.2 The Earth's Present Field** The geomagnetic force $\mathbf{F}$ at any place on the Earth's surface has components $\mathfrak{X}$, $\mathfrak{Y}$, and $\mathfrak{Z}$ respectively northerly, easterly, and downward. $\mathbf{F}$ is specified by its magnitude F, or the magnitude of its horizontal component $H = (\mathfrak{X}^2 + \mathfrak{Y}^2)^{1/2}$, and by the angles of *declination* (or *variation*) $\mathfrak{D}$ and *inclination* $\mathfrak{I}$. The conventions for $\mathfrak{D}$ and $\mathfrak{I}$ are the same as those for the angles used to define a direction of remanent magnetization (§ 2.02). The quantities F, H, $\mathfrak{X}$, $\mathfrak{Y}$, $\mathfrak{Z}$, $\mathfrak{D}$, and $\mathfrak{I}$ are called *magnetic elements*.

Measurements of the magnetic elements at certain observatories extend back about 400 years, although only in the last century has there been a reasonable coverage for the whole Earth. The results are displayed in maps giving the lines joining places at which elements have equal mean annual value. Lines of equal inclination are called *isoclines,* and those of equal declination are called *isogonic lines.* The zero isocline is called the *geomagnetic equator,* and is a wavy line circling the Earth close to the geographic equator. The inclination increases northward and southward from the geomagnetic equator, becoming vertical at the *magnetic dip poles.* These poles, one in northern Canada (73° N, 100° W), and one in Antarctica (68° S, 143° E), are some distance

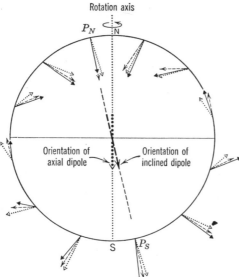

0.6 oe
·······> Theoretical field to geocentric axial dipole

- - - -> Theoretical field to geocentric inclined dipole

———> Earth's field, 1945, projected onto meridional plane

Figure 3.1. Comparison of the directions of hypothetical fields of a geocentric axial dipole and a geocentric inclined dipole with the actual observed directions. The section is through the meridional plane 70° W through the geomagnetic poles, P_N and P_S, and the geographical poles, N and S. Observation points are at geomagnetic latitudes 0°, 30°, 60°, and 90°. Redrawn from Cox and Doell (1960), with the kind permission of the Geological Society of America, and the authors.

from the geographical poles. They are not diametrically opposed, each being about 2300 km from the antipole of the other. The intensity sometimes reaches several oersted, but only locally, and these anomalies are due to concentrations of magnetic ores. The intensity of the main field reaches a maximum at the dip poles, being about 0.7 oe near the south dip pole and 0.6 oe at the north dip pole. The minimum of about 0.25 oe occurs in a region centered about 25° S, 45° W near southern Brazil.

It is customary in geomagnetism to take observations for any year from all parts of the world and subject them to spherical harmonic analysis. This shows that the field can be represented by hypothetical multi-

poles at the geocenter. The first is called the *inclined geocentric dipole*, which makes an angle of 11½° with the spin axis. The axis of the inclined geocentric dipole is called the *geomagnetic axis,* and the points where this intersects the surface are called the *geomagnetic poles.* The latitude, relative to this axis and poles, is called *geomagnetic latitude.* At present the geomagnetic poles are at 79°N, 70° W and 79° S, 110° E, and have changed little in the past hundred years. The goodness of fit of the present field to that of an inclined geocentric dipole is shown in Figure 3.1. The inclined geocentric dipole may be resolved into 3 components, one along the rotational axis called the *geocentric axial dipole* which is by far the largest, and 2 of much smaller magnitude in the equatorial plane. The resultant of the equatorial dipoles amounts to about 15 per cent of the axial dipole. During the past century there has been a decrease of 7 per cent in the Earth's dipole moment (Figure 8.3).

The higher harmonics constitute the *nondipole* or *irregular field.* The rms strength of the nondipole field at the surface amounts to about 5 per cent of the dipole field. This field is displayed in *isodynamic maps* which give contours joining places at which any of the elements of the nondipole field have equal value. There are several regions, in which the nondipole components are large, and which are surrounded by contour systems forming cells with dimensions of similar size to the continental landmasses. One notable feature is the low value of the nondipole field in the Pacific region.

§ **3.3   Changes in the Field**   Changes recognized from the observatory data are called the transient and secular variations. As will appear later, paleomagnetism has indicated the occurrence of slower variations, namely, changes in attitude of the Earth's dipole axis relative to certain landmasses (§ 6.09), and reversals in polarity of the field (Chapter Seven) which are not detectable on observatory time scales.

The *transient variations* have periodicities of the order of days. They have a negligible effect on the direction of the field and are of no paleomagnetic significance.

At any one place the geomagnetic field changes from year to year. Such changes are called the *secular variations,* and are important in paleomagnetic work. The variations at any particular place are expressed by plots of the directions observed at intervals over several hundreds of years. The range of directional changes is about 10° to 20° on either side of the average. Four examples compiled by Cox and Doell (1960) are given in Figure 3.2 in which the variations are compared with the directions of the field of the axial and inclined dipole. Two examples from the northern hemisphere show small variations with directions close to the hypothetical directions. The variation at London has been smooth and regular, forming about three-quarters of a loop, extrapolation yielding a period of 480 years. In two examples from the southern hemisphere the variations are more rapid and diverge more from the hypothetical directions.

The variations over the Earth's surface for a given time interval are shown by means of isoporic maps. An *isopor* is a line joining places at which there has been equal rate of change of a magnetic element. Maps for the past few decades show several (10 or less) isoporic foci occupying regions of comparatively rapid change (Figure 3.3). Around these are sets of oval curves covering regions of continental dimensions, and, in between, there are areas of comparatively slow change. The secular variation is a regional, not a planetary, phenomenon. It is small over the northern and western Pacific; it is less in the northern than in the southern hemisphere; and in certain areas, for instance South Africa, the changes are very rapid. When a time sequence of maps is studied the isoporic foci are seen to drift westward. This is shown by the arrows which indicate the movements of the chief foci between 1922 and 1945. From an analysis of the variation between 1909 and 1945 Bullard, Freedman, Gellman, and Nixon (1950) found a mean westerly drift of about 0.32° ± 0.07 of longitude per year. A similar change is noticeable in the behavior of the nondipole field; a time sequence of iso-

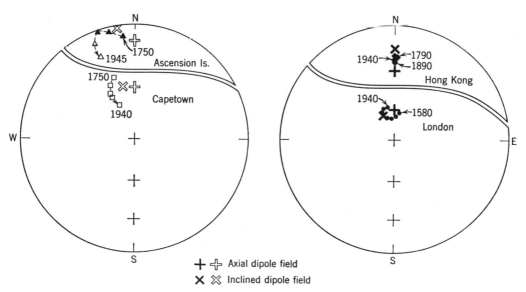

Figure 3.2. Time changes in the direction of Earth's field at four observatories. Successive observations are spaces every 40–50 years. Equal-area projection, solid symbols on the lower hemisphere, open symbols on the upper hemisphere. Redrawn from Cox and Doell (1960), with the kind permission of the Geological Society of America and the authors.

dynamic maps shows a westerly drift of the nondipole components with a somewhat slower average rate of 0.18° ± 0.02, but there is doubt as to the significance of this difference. There are also apparent, but small, north-south components and regional variations in the rate of drift.

§ 3.4   Origin of the Geomagnetic Field

The source of the field is within the Earth, probably within the core. That the Earth acts as a large magnet, and that its field was due to internal causes, was first indicated by the experiments of W. Gilbert (1600). At the end of the sixteenth century the field directions in many parts of the world were known, and for purposes of comparison Gilbert mapped the variations in the direction of the magnetic field of a *terella,* which is a piece of magnetite (§ 2.06) cut into the shape of a sphere. He found that the variations were in agreement with those on the Earth.

Early theories suggest that the field arose from the permanent magnetism of the Earth, or from some fundamental property of rotating bodies, but neither has proved tenable. Modern theories ascribe the field to motions in the highly conducting fluid core which act as a self-exciting dynamo. Such motions are likely to be mainly 2-dimensional controlled by the Coriolis force arising from rotation, and this may be the reason for the dominantly axial character of the field. The fluid motions are thought to arise from convection, the amount of heat required to drive them being small. The irregular field is considered to result from perturbations of the main field by eddies within 100 km of the core surface. The westerly drift of the irregular field is attributed to the outer layers of the core rotating less rapidly than the mantle and crust.

§ 3.5   The Field of an Axial Geocentric Dipole

The remainder of this chapter is

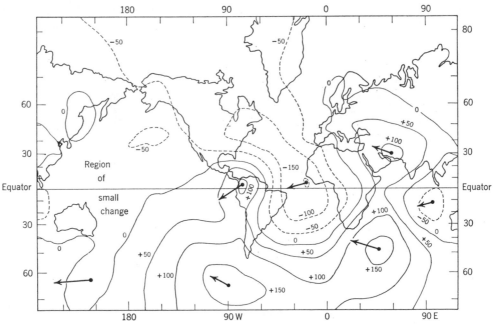

Figure 3.3. Schematic representation of secular variation and westerly drift. Isopors of the vertical component (z) for 1922 are given, numbers indicating increases in γ/3 yr. Dotted isopors indicate decreases. The origin of each arrow is the center of the chief isoporic foci for 1922 and the heads are the foci for 1945. Compiled from Vestine, Laporte, Cooper, Lange, and Hendrix (1947).

given over to an account of descriptive models. The field of a uniformly magnetized sphere, viewed at or beyond its surface, is the same as if the magnetization were that of a dipole situated at the center. This is a good approximation to the present field if the axis is taken as the geomagnetic axis (Figure 3.1). If the axis is taken as the geographic axis the approximation is less good, but it is convenient to consider this case initially, since, as will be seen later (§ 6.02), the field has approximated very closely to an axial geocentric dipole in the past few million years.

The lines of force are shown in Figure 3.4. The field is rotationally symmetrical and the elements of the field are not dependent on longitude. If $\mathfrak{M}$ is the moment of the dipole, and r the radius of the Earth, the strength of the field F at latitude λ is given by

$$F = \mathfrak{M}r^{-3}(1 + 3 \sin^2 \lambda)^{\frac{1}{2}} \qquad (3.1)$$

The field (F_0) at the equator is $\mathfrak{M}r^{-3}$ and that at the poles $2\mathfrak{M}r^{-3}$. The average magnitude of the present field at the equator is 0.31 oe giving a value for the Earth's dipole moment of 8.06×10^{25} gauss. The field direction ($\mathfrak{D}$, $\mathscr{I}$) at any place of geographic latitude λ or colatitude

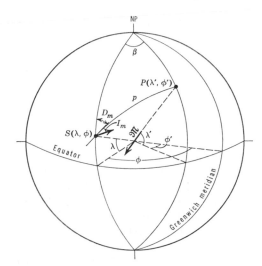

Figure 3.5. Calculation of paleomagnetic poles. The elementary dipole, $\mathfrak{M}$, is placed at the center of the sphere. NP is the north geographic pole, P the paleomagnetic pole, S the sampling locality. D_m, I_m are the co-ordinates of observed paleomagnetic direction. If $\mathfrak{D}$, $\mathscr{I}$, is an observed field direction then P is a virtual geomagnetic pole.

p is given by

$$\mathfrak{D} = 0° \qquad (3.2)$$

and

$$\mathscr{I} = \tan^{-1}(2 \tan \lambda)$$
$$= \tan^{-1}(2 \cot p)(0° \le p \le 180°) \quad (3.3)$$

The curve of (3.3) is plotted in Figure 3.9.

§ **3.6 Paleomagnetic Poles and Virtual Geomagnetic Poles** The dipole axis may be inclined to the present axis of rotation. If the axis intersects the sphere at a known point $P(\lambda', \phi')$, then the direction for any place on the sphere can be calculated. In practice the problem presents itself in reverse. The direction at a locality $S(\lambda, \phi)$ is known from observation and the need is to calculate the orientation of the hypothetical geocentric dipole relative to S. The coordinates of P are obtained from the following equations (Figure 3.5).

$$\lambda' = \sin^{-1}(\sin \lambda \cos p + \cos \lambda \sin p \cos D),$$
$$\cdots (-90° \le \lambda' \le 90°) \qquad (3.4)$$

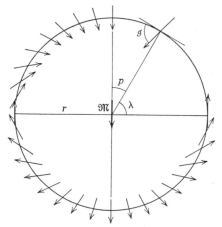

Figure 3.4. Field of a uniformly magnetized sphere. $\mathfrak{M}$ is the central dipole and the arrows give the field directions on a surface of radius r.

$$\phi' = \phi + \beta,$$
$$\cdots (\cos p \geq \sin \lambda \sin \lambda')$$
$$\phi' = \phi + 180 - \beta,$$
$$\cdots (\cos p < \sin \lambda \sin \lambda')$$
(3.5)

where $\beta = \sin^{-1}(\sin p \sin D / \cos \lambda')$,

$$\cdots (-90° \leq \beta \leq 90°) \quad (3.6)$$

D is reckoned clockwise from true north, I is positive downward, and p is obtained from (3.3). Positive latitudes lie between 0° and 90° N and negative latitudes between 0° and 90° S. Longitudes 0° to 180° E are positive and 0° to 180° W negative.

The direction used may be obtained in two physically distinct ways: they can be directions ($\mathfrak{D}, \mathfrak{I}$) of the present field, or an average (D_m, I_m) of remanence directions measured in rocks (§ 4.10). Poles calculated from directly observed fields are called *virtual geomagnetic poles* (Cox and Doell, 1960). Virtual geomagnetic poles calculated from directions

of the 1945 field observed at magnetic observatories are plotted in Figure 3.6. Poles calculated from paleomagnetic directions are called *paleomagnetic poles*, or simply *poles* where the meaning is clear from the context.[1]

[1] When poles were first calculated from rock data (Hospers, 1954a, 1955; Creer, Irving, and Runcorn, 1954) no specific name was given to distinguish them from poles obtained in other ways. In subsequent papers by various authors terms such as "ancient pole" or "geomagnetic pole" were applied, and it was clear from the context what was meant. Later (for example in Creer, Irving, and Nairn, 1959; Irving, 1959) the term *paleomagnetic pole* came into use. This is a simple name, descriptive of the method, and sufficient to distinguish poles calculated on this basis from those obtained in any other fashion. Then Cox and Doell (1960) introduced the term *virtual geomagnetic pole* to signify poles calculated not only from field directions but also poles calculated from rock data. Here the term virtual geomagnetic pole is reserved for poles calculated from field data,

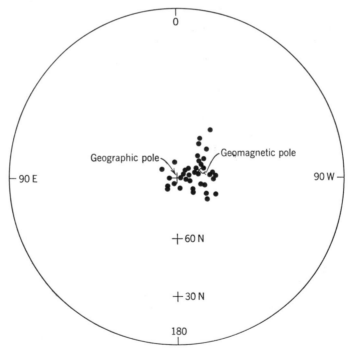

Figure 3.6. Virtual geomagnetic poles calculated from directions at observatories in 1945. The observatories cover a wide spread of north and south latitude. Redrawn from Cox and Doell (1960), with the kind permission of the Geological Society of America and the authors.

Virtual geomagnetic and paleomagnetic poles differ not only in the physical nature of the data from which they were derived, but are related to different time scales. A virtual geomagnetic pole is calculated for what is, geologically speaking, an instant in time. Paleomagnetic poles, as initially conceived, are calculated from average directions of rock units and provide information over periods of 10^3 years or more, and over 10^6 years in many cases. A further reason why a firm distinction should be made between poles calculated from spot readings of the present field and those calculated from averages of paleomagnetic directions, is that the former group around the geomagnetic pole (Figure 3.6) whereas the latter, for the past several thousand years, have grouped around the geographic pole (Figure 6.3); the paleomagnetic pole estimates the position of the geographic pole, whereas the virtual geomagnetic pole is related to the inclined geocentric dipole which is a transient effect on the geological time scale.

§ 3.7 Statistical Models Derived from Field Analysis

The model described in § 3.5 takes no account of secular fluctuations. A paleomagnetic study of a rock formation may be expected to provide information about these variations. The information will not be a continuous record such as is taken at a magnetic observatory (Figure 3.2), but will be a statistical record governed by the irregularities of depositional and magnetization processes. Models used to represent such effects should meet these requirements. They should be consistent with what is known of the present Earth's field. They should represent the statistical behavior of the field over a period (10^3 to 10^6 years) comparable to the time required for rock units to be laid down; it is impractical and unnecessary to simulate such detailed behavior for instants in time as is depicted in Figure 3.3. In addition, the models should be in a form which is directly comparable with the paleomagnetic data, so that their

and paleomagnetic pole is used for poles calculated from rock data.

validity for past geological periods can be tested.

Since the average field over the past few thousand years is that of an axial geocentric dipole (§ 6.02), variations over such periods may, in simple terms, be considered to arise from two causes—variations in the nondipole field, and wobble of the inclined dipole about the Earth's axis. Models to simulate these effects, together or separately, may be generated artificially or by analysis of the present field. The latter are considered now and the former in § 3.8. Models derived from the present field may be obtained by the analysis of field directions, or by an analysis of virtual geomagnetic poles.

Analysis of Field Directions for 1945 (Creer, 1955, 1962a, 1962b). It is supposed that the time variations of the directions of the geomagnetic field observed at a given point are comparable to the variations at a given epoch around a line of latitude passing through that point. The directions $(\mathfrak{D}, \mathfrak{I})$ are read from the 1945 geomagnetic chart at fixed intervals of latitude and longitude. The values for each geographic and geomagnetic latitude are combined into sets. In each set the $\mathfrak{X}, \mathfrak{Y}, \mathfrak{Z}$ axes (§ 3.2) are rotated into conformity carrying the direction with them. The scatter of the directions so obtained is expressed by the angular standard deviation (δ), which, for this number of data, is numerically equal to the circular standard deviation (§ 4.11).

The results are given in Figure 3.7. Curve 1 gives the values plotted against *geographical* latitude and measures the effect of both the nondipole components and the equatorial components of the inclined geocentric dipole. Curve 2 gives the values plotted against *geomagnetic* latitude and gives a measure of the nondipole components. The scatter due to the inclined geocentric dipole as measured around lines of geographical latitude is plotted in curve 3. The total dispersion (curve 1) in the northern hemisphere is less than curve 3, which at first sight seems absurd, but the inclined dipole is derived from the analysis of results from both hemispheres and is different from that which would be calculated from the northern hemisphere data alone. All three curves fall for the most part between 5° and 20°, and are latitude dependent, having higher values in low than in high latitudes.   Curves 1 and 2 show an asymmetry between hemispheres. This is to be compared with the more intense secular variation in the southern hemisphere (Figure 3.3).

It is possible that the disparity is short-lived, so that the mean, irrespective of latitude sign, will give a closer approximation to the average situation over periods of thousands of years (Figure 3.8).   This mean curve, relative to

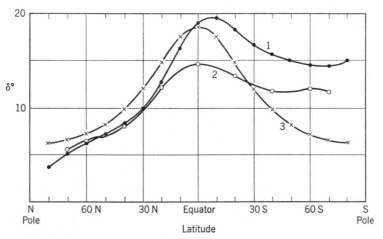

Figure 3.7. Direction dispersion as a function of latitude. δ is the root mean square deviation of 36 directions spaced every 10° of longitude along a given latitude. Curves 1 and 3 versus geographic latitude; curve 2 versus magnetic latitude. Redrawn from Creer (1962a), with the kind permission of the American Geophysical Union and K. M. Creer.

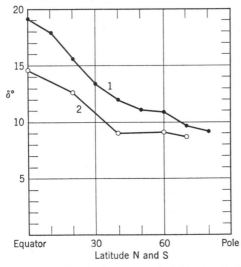

Figure 3.8. Dispersion versus latitude for 1945. Averages for both hemispheres. Compiled from Figure 3.7. Curve 1 versus geographic latitude; curve 2 versus geomagnetic latitude.

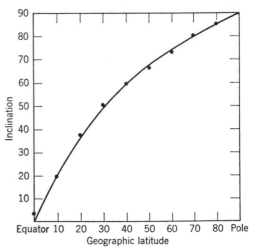

Figure 3.9. Variation of the mean inclination with latitude for 1945. The dots are the inclinations of the average direction at different latitudes, compiled from Creer (1962a). The line is the curve expected from a geocentric axial dipole field (equation 2.3).

geographical latitude, varies by a factor 2, from just under 20° at the equator to a little over 9° at the pole. The mean of the 36 directions around a line of latitude is close to that of a line of force of the geocentric axial dipole field at that latitude. Individual departures are as much as 5°, but much of this is accounted for by statistical fluctuations. However, the averages for both hemispheres are in very good agreement with equation 3.3 (Figure 3.9).

Virtual Geomagnetic Poles for Epoch 1945 (Cox, 1962). In this analysis the directions $(\mathfrak{D}, \mathcal{I})$ are read on a 10° grid of latitude and longitude from the 1945 geomagnetic chart and are used to calculate virtual geomagnetic poles. In equations 3.4, 3.5, and 3.6 the latitude and longitude (λ, ϕ) are the values for each grid intersection, the coordinates $\mathfrak{X}, \mathfrak{Y}, \mathfrak{Z}$ remaining fixed in space. Individual poles for each latitude are meaned and their dispersion estimated, either by Fisher's precision

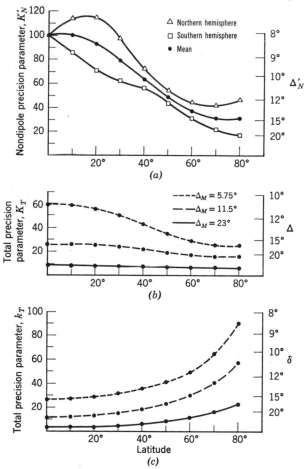

Figure 3.10. Nondipole and total precision parameters as a function of latitude. Precision is given on the left scale and root mean square deviation on the right. Geographic latitude is plotted horizontally. In (a) the nondipole precision parameter K'_N of the virtual geomagnetic poles is plotted. In (b) K_T the total precision parameter of poles is calculated using three values for the mean departure Δ_M of the mean pole and values of K_N obtained from (a). In (c) K_T is transformed to directions dispersions k_T expected at various latitudes for the three models in (b). Redrawn from Cox (1962), with the kind permission of the Society of Terrestrial Magnetism and Electricity of Japan and A. Cox.

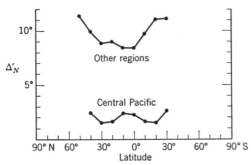

Figure 3.11. Angular standard deviation Δ'_N of virtual geomagnetic poles as a function of latitude: central Pacific compared with other regions. The values for latitudes 40° N to 30° S in the central Pacific are obtained from the grid intersections circled in Figure 3.12. The values for other regions are from all longitudes except these. Compiled from Cox (1962).

parameter K'_N, or the root mean square deviation Δ'_N calculated from equations (4.10) and (4.26), assuming the geomagnetic pole (78.6° N, 70.4° W) calculated from spherical harmonic analysis as the true pole. The mean poles (17 values for latitudes 80° N to 80° S) group closely around the geomagnetic pole, and their weighted average (weighed according to the relative length of small circles of latitude) is 78.1° N, 70.5° W which compares very well with the geomagnetic pole. The pole precision varies with both latitude and longitude. The variation with latitude is greater in the southern than in the northern hemisphere (Figure 3.10). The mean, assuming the asymmetry between hemispheres to be temporary, varies by a factor 2, from 15° (Δ'_N) near the pole to 8° at the equator. There is also a marked low pole dispersion calculated from the central Pacific region. Dispersions at the same latitude in this and other regions differ by a factor 4 (Figure 3.11). The deviations, observed at particular localities, between virtual geomagnetic poles and the geomagnetic pole are plotted on world charts (Figure 3.12). In a large area in the central Pacific, stretching eastward through Central America, and westward across Australia and Indonesia toward Ceylon, these deviations are less than 3°, and this "appears much like a window or filter through which the main inclined magnetic dipole can be seen undistorted." Also notable are the larger departures in the southern than the northern hemisphere. This may be compared with the average departure between the observed field and the *axial* geocentric dipole field, which at present is 8.5° for the northern

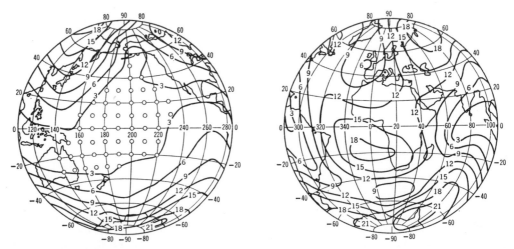

Figure 3.12. Map showing lines of equal angular distance between the geomagnetic pole and virtual geomagnetic pole for 1945 contoured at 3° intervals. Circles give datum points for central Pacific analysis (Figure 3.11). Redrawn from Cox (1962), with the kind permission of the Society of Terrestrial Magnetism and Electricity of Japan and A. Cox.

hemisphere, and 17.3° for the southern hemisphere (Cox and Doell, 1960).

§ 3.8 Hypothetical Statistical Models

Attempts may be made to simulate the secular variation by imagining the axial geocentric dipole field to be perturbed by randomly directed components at the Earth's surface, or by considering the effect of wobble of the geocentric dipole itself. More complex models may be necessary later but these are sufficient for present purposes.

Model A (Irving and Ward, 1964). Consider a geocentric dipole field of strength F perturbed by randomly directed components of constant magnitude F_d. F varies with latitude (equation 3.1) so that the dispersion of directions diminishes as the latitude increases (Figure 3.13). From an analysis of a sample of directions at a particular latitude, an estimate k of Fisher's precision parameter can be made (§ 4.07). This is given approximately by

$$k = 3\sigma^{-2} \qquad (3.7)$$

where $\sigma = F_d/F$. If $\sigma_0 = F_d/F_0$, where F_0 is the field at the equator and λ the latitude, then

$$k = 3\sigma_0^{-2}(1 + 3\sin^2\lambda) \qquad (3.8)$$

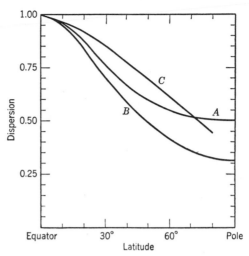

Figure 3.14. Standard deviation of field directions expected for statistical Models *A*, *B*, and *C* ($\Delta_M = 11.5°$). Values are normalized to unity at the equator.

or, more conveniently,

$$\theta_{63} = 46.8\,\sigma_0(1 + 3\sin^2\lambda)^{-\frac{1}{2}} \text{ degrees} \qquad (3.9)$$

where θ_{63} is the circular standard deviation (§ 4.07). The variation in dispersion is inversely proportional to the intensity of the dipole field. The variations of θ_{63} with latitude are plotted in Figure 3.14. The direction distributions are symmetrical about the mean.

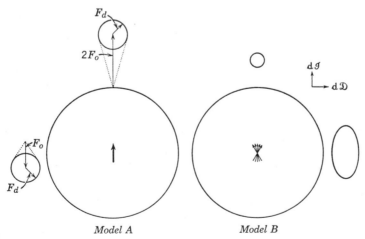

Figure 3.13. Hypothetical statistical models of the dispersion of the Earth's field. Diagrams of models *A* and *B* (see text). The circles and oval above and to the sides give a schematic representation of the field direction distributions.

Model B (Creer, Irving, and Nairn, 1959). (Figure 3.13.) Any direction observed on the Earth's surface may be represented by a geocentric dipole **m**. It is assumed that this dipole wobbles in a random fashion around the mean dipole $\mathfrak{M}$ following Fisher's Distribution with precision K. The distribution of directions observed at different latitudes will vary in form and magnitude. The observed distribution is circular at the poles, but elsewhere is an oval having semiaxes $d\mathfrak{D}$ and $d\mathfrak{I}$ in directions perpendicular and parallel to the meridians given in degrees by

$$d\mathfrak{D} = \theta_{63}(1 + 3\sin^2\lambda)^{-\frac{1}{2}} \quad (3.10)$$

$$d\mathfrak{I} = 2\theta_{63}(1 + 3\sin^2\lambda)^{-1} \quad (3.11)$$

where θ_{63} is the circular standard deviation of the oscillations of **m** around $\mathfrak{M}$ and the values $d\mathfrak{D}$ and $d\mathfrak{I}$ are the standard deviations of the declination and inclination caused by these oscillations. The oval thus defined contains 63 per cent of the directions. For large polar precision ($K > 30$), the precision of observed directions k is given by (see Creer, 1962a)

$$k/K = (1 + 3\sin^2\lambda)/(5 - 3\sin^2\lambda) \quad (3.12)$$

The curve of this equation is given in Figure 3.14.

Model C (Cox, 1962). Model B may be modified by superposing components due to the nondipole field variation on those due to the wobble of the geocentric dipole. Thinking in terms of virtual geomagnetic poles, the component of scatter due to nondipole components (K'_N) may be obtained from Figure 3.10 and scatter K_D due to an assigned mean dipole wobble can be calculated. The two together give the total pole precision K_T as follows:

$$(K_T)^{-1} = (K'_N)^{-1} + (K_D)^{-1} \quad (3.13)$$

The effect of the dipole wobble may be estimated by assigning values to the radius of the circle containing a given proportion of the mean dipole axes; if the proportion is one-half and the radius of the appropriate circle is Δ_M, then the precision K_D is given by $K_D = (67.5°/\Delta_M)^2$—see equation 4.13. The total precision of poles is given in Figure 3.10(b) taking values of the radii of the 50 per cent circles as 5.75°, 11.5°, and 23°, the middle value being the departure at present of the geomagnetic pole from the geographic pole. By a suitable transformation K_T can be expressed as the total precision parameters of the field directions at various latitudes (Figure 3.10(c)), which may then be compared with paleomagnetic observations.

§ 3.9 Comparisons of Models (Figure 3.14)

Models B and C require a variation of about a factor 3 between pole and equator. But the dispersions calculated from observations (Figure 3.8) vary by a factor 2, as model A predicts. From each dispersion value for the 1945 field it is possible to estimate, using equation 3.8, the ratio σ_0 of the perturbing field to the geocentric dipole field at the equator. This gives the mean value of 0.4. The standard deviation of individual points is 3 per cent, showing that model A is a remarkably good fit to the observations (Figure 6.33 and Table 6.4).

The purpose of these models is to allow comparisons between the present and past fields. Such comparisons are relevant to two important questions. First, there is the fundamental problem as to whether the Earth's field has always been that of a geocentric dipole; conformity to any of these models would suggest that this had been the case. In this connection the models of type A are of particular interest since they predict a relation between the mean intensity of the field, the dispersion of directions, and the mean inclination and, in principle, these are all measurable quantities so that a very powerful three-pronged approach is possible. Second, there is the question of the persistence of asymmetries. The analysis of the 1945 field shows asymmetry between hemispheres, and a marked zone of low variations in the Indian Ocean, central Pacific, and in central America. If the asymmetry between hemispheres is found also in the paleomagnetic results it would imply that this is a permanent feature of the field; if it should not occur then it would seem likely that the present asymmetry arose from statistical fluctuations in the distribution of the non-dipole sources, effects which would average out in time. The low variation in the Pacific and adjacent areas could be due to sources never developing, or to highly conductive material in the mantle in this sector which screens out short-period nondipole fluctuations.

CHAPTER
FOUR

Directions of magnetization
and their analysis

§ **4.01 Preliminary Remarks** Surveys of the directions of fossil magnetism (NRM) are generally undertaken with a view to obtaining information about the ancient field, either because such information is of interest for its own sake, or because it may relate to some geological or geophysical problem. The directions observed in a rock body never agree exactly; sometimes they are closely grouped, sometimes highly dispersed; they may form a coherent unipolar distribution, or the distribution may contain directions of variable polarity grouped about a common axis. Because of this variability, and because of the large number of observations, it is necessary for convenience of handling to condense the information in terms of statistical parameters of comparative value from which information of geophysical importance can be obtained. The number and variability of the data make it necessary to obtain average values for sets of observations; in particular, it is necessary to estimate the mean directions of magnetization of a rock unit, to provide some measure of the dispersion of observations about this mean, and to estimate the accuracy with which the mean is defined. Estimates of mean directions are the basic information needed for study of the variations in the Earth's field, and for geophysical calcula-

tions, for instance, the calculation of paleolatitude.

When considering observed directions two types of problems arise—those concerned with the description of observations from a single rock unit, and those concerned with the comparison of results from different units. In the former case a comprehensive set of techniques, developed by R. A. Fisher, are now available. The second series of problems arise because the rock units studied are rarely located in the same place and are often in different continents, so that direct comparison of results by Fisher's method is not possible and an additional technique is needed; this is the technique of calculating paleomagnetic pole positions, which has already been mentioned (§ 3.6), and which is elaborated here.

§ **4.02 Sampling Schemes** In any particular study it is usual to collect oriented samples from a set of sedimentary beds, lava flows, or intrusives, which have been recognized as units on geological grounds. Oriented samples are collected from some or all of the available exposures which are usually referred to as collecting sites or localities. Generally more than one sample is obtained at each site to check for orientation errors and to study variation within a site. Several specimens are often cut from each oriented sample in order to study variation within a sample. The term sample is also sometimes used in the statistical sense to refer to a set of data comprising *N* observations drawn from a uniform population.

The sampling schemes employed are of hierarchical type comprising 2 or more levels. One of the simplest schemes is where 1 oriented sample is obtained from each of a number of collecting sites, and 1 specimen is cut from each sample (Table 4.1). Further levels occur when several members are recognizable within a rock unit (say 5 thick composite lava members within an igneous complex), and specimens and samples are obtained from several sites in each member. Results may be presented as individual specimen observations, or combined at some higher level—for example, as averages for samples, for sites, or for the whole rock unit.

§ **4.03** **Fragmentary Nature of the Record** Although the time represented in a rock unit may be long, the record is never continuous. Exposure of the full thickness of a rock unit may occur in cliff sections, but most rock units are available for study in only a limited number of outcrops. Even if samples were obtained from all levels within a unit the record is still fragmentary, because of discontinuities in

Table 4.1

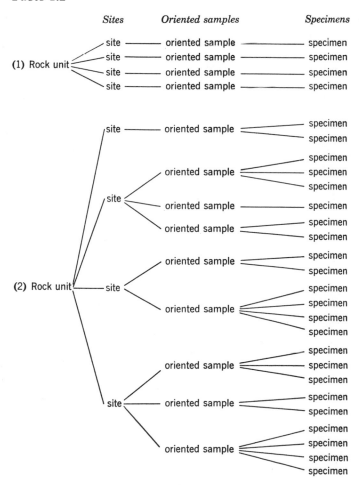

the deposition of sediments, or in igneous activity. For purposes of continuity the closest approach to ideal conditions may be expected to occur in periglacial varved clays (McNish and Johnson, 1938) and in thick sills (Jaeger and Green, 1956). Varved clays were laid down in lakes in the vicinity of glaciers. Their year-by-year banding allows samples to be taken at any one locality in a known time sequence, so that in principle, field variations can be studied in an approximately continuous fashion; there are, however, uncertainties in correlation among different collecting localities. During the cooling history of a thick intrusive sheet the Curie temperature isotherm moves inward from the margin at a rate inversely proportional to the sheet thickness (Jaeger, 1957a). A section through a sheet may therefore provide a continuous record of the field variations during the migration of this isotherm from the margin to the center. However, these situations are exceptional. The great majority of paleomagnetic observations have been obtained from sediments—particularly red beds—from lava flows, and from irregularly distributed outcrops in intrusive bodies, and the record of time variations obtained is inevitably fragmentary.

The results obtained from a series of collecting sites may be considered as *spot readings* of the field during the time taken for the unit to be laid down, since the time coverage at each site will, in most cases, be negligible compared to that of the unit as a whole. In an igneous sequence the time taken for the rock at one site (say in a lava flow) to cool through its range of blocking temperatures will be of the order of a year, during which field variations are likely to have been small compared to the errors in the method (generally not less than 3°), whereas the time taken for the whole sequence to become magnetized is to be measured in thousands of years or more. In sediments the situation is less clear, since the deposition of a thin bed may need much time, and there is the additional uncertainty as to the actual time at which the sediment became magnetized (§§ 2.12, 5.12); never-

theless the coverage at one collecting site will, in most circumstances, be short compared to that for the unit as a whole. The assumption that site means in sediments approximate to spot readings may be tested by comparing the dispersion values in sediments and igneous rocks, ideally of the same age and from the same region: the occurrence of similar values implies that the assumption is reasonable (§ 6.12). The time order of spot or site readings will often be known from superimposition of beds or igneous contact relations, but estimates of the absolute time spanned by a series of sites are likely to be uncertain.

§ 4.04   **Representation of Directions**
Each direction is represented by a vector of unit length specified by the polar coordinates (D, I), no weighting being made in favor of strongly magnetized rocks. Observations from undisturbed rocks are referred to the horizontal plane at the collecting site but results are often obtained from tilted beds and it is necessary to refer the directions to the horizontal plane at the time of formation. This usually means that the directions are rotated about the axis of strike of bedding by an angle equal to the angle of dip of the beds. Such corrections assume that the beds have attained their present attitude by simple rotation about their present strike directions, but in the case of plunging folds a correction for the fold axis tilt is also needed. These corrections may be made by calculation, or by graphical methods using the standard techniques of stereographic projections developed for structural analysis, and which have been described in other places (for example Phillips, 1955).

The strike and dip of bedding planes in sediments are estimated by measurement at each locality, or read from maps. For lavas it is estimated from measurement of flow planes, or of bedding in interleaved sediments. The amount of tilting in intrusive rocks may be estimated from the measurement of bedding planes in enclosing sediments assuming that intrusion occurred before tilting. However, most of the intrusions studied have been injected into flat-lying or gently dipping beds, and are assumed to have undergone negligible disturbance since emplacement.

The directions are plotted on Lambert's equal area projection (Schmidt net) or on a stereographic projection (Wulff net). In most cases a *polar projection* is used; the primitive is the horizontal plane, either the present horizontal at the collecting site, or the estimated horizontal at the time of formation. The directions are marked as points in such a way that the line through the point and the pole of the net make an angle D equal to the declination with the north direction and the distance of the point from the primitive is proportional to the inclination, I, according to a radial scale. Sometimes it is convenient to use the whole sphere and at other times only one hemisphere. When the inclinations are low, and both positive and negative values occur, the horizontal plane intersects the distribution, and it is convenient to use an *equatorial projection* so that the distribution occupies a more central part of the diagram. In these cases the primitive defines a vertical plane which trends either east-west or north-south, and inclination is measured as a latitude angle from the equator, and declination as a longitude angle from the vertical meridian.

§ 4.05 Examples of NRM Directions

The first example (Figure 4.1a) are observa-

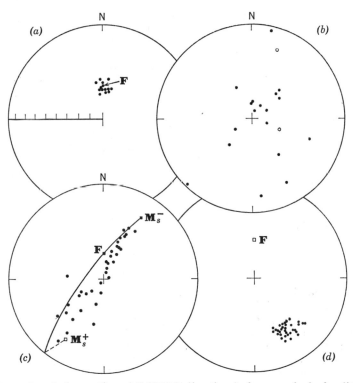

Figure 4.1. Examples of observations (all NRM directions) from a single locality. Directions with positive (negative) inclination are plotted as dots (circles) on a polar equal area net. (a) Payette Formation, Glenns Ferry, Idaho, U.S.A. [11.105]. (b) Arikee Formation, South Dakota, U.S.A.—the scatter in directions is very great ($k = 3$) [11.102]. (c) Triassic marls from Sidmouth, England—the great circle through the poles M_s-, M_s+ of the axis of stable magnetization and the direction F of the geocentric axial dipole field is marked [8.07]. Redrawn from Creer (1957b), with the kind permission of the Royal Society and K. M. Creer. (d) Cenozoic lava flow, Australia [12.45].

tions made by Torreson, Murphy, and J. W. Graham (1949) from the Payette Formation (Neogene sediments) of Idaho. Single determinations from each of 13 oriented samples gave directions which clustered around the direction of the geocentric axial dipole field (0, +62) their mean being 1, +62. Directions showing high dispersion observed by the same workers in 21 sedimentary samples of the Miocene Arikee Formation in the Badlands of South Dakota are plotted in Figure 4.1b. Figure 4.1c gives an example of a *smeared distribution* found in Triassic sediments of Sidmouth, England, by Creer (1957b). The directions are strung out approximately along the great circle passing through the geocentric axial dipole field direction and the poles $\mathbf{M}_s^-$ and $\mathbf{M}_s^+$ of the axis of stable magnetizations obtained by Clegg, Almond, and Stubbs (1954a) from Triassic sediments elsewhere in England. The observations plotted in Figure 4.1d illus-

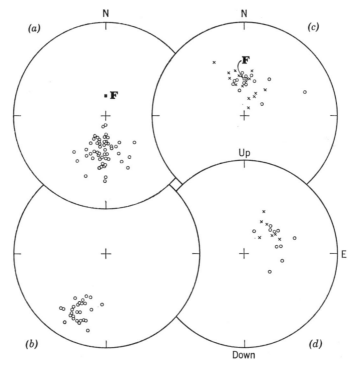

Figure 4.2. Mean site directions in the same rock unit. Each direction is the average of several samples. In (a) and (b) the inclinations are all negative and are plotted as circles on the upper hemisphere of polar equal area nets. In (c) and (d) the directions are plotted in the upper hemisphere of equal area nets, N-seeking directions as circles and S-seeking directions as crosses; (c) is a polar projection and (d) an equatorial projection. The direction of the present geocentric axial dipole field **F** is indicated by a square. (a) Tertiary lavas and intrusives of the Isle of Skye, Scotland (NRM directions)—the primitive is the present horizontal [11.012]; data of Khan (1960) replotted, by kind permission of M. A. Khan. (b) Oslo igneous complex—the directions after magnetic cleaning are corrected for low geological dips so that the primitive is the plane of "bedding" at each site as obtained from flow surfaces and adjacent sediments [7.13]. (c) Newer Volcanics of Victoria, Australia (NRM directions)—the lavas are flat-lying and the primitive is the present horizontal [12.45]. (d) Chugwater Formation, Wyoming and Colorado, U.S.A.—the NRM directions have all been corrected for a geological dip of between 8° and 28°, and the plane of the projection is the vertical E/W plane (the bedding pole at each site is upward) [8.30].

trate the close grouping often encountered in repeated observations from the same lava flow. The results, which are 34 specimen observations from 10 samples, were obtained from a flow in the Pliocene to Recent Newer Volcanics of Victoria. The mean direction is 150, +33.

The previous examples are of observations from single collecting localities. In Figure 4.2 examples are given of observation from many sites within the same rock unit. Several oriented samples were collected from each site and in some cases several specimens cut from each sample. The measured directions were combined, using the methods described in § 4.10, to give site mean directions.

Figures 4.2a and b give examples of unipolar distributions, that is, of directions grouped in a regular fashion about an average direction. The results in Figure 4.2a are the observations of Khan (1960) at 53 igneous rock sites in the Tertiary of Skye. The results in Figure 4.1b were obtained by v'Everdingen (1960) from 27 members of the Oslo igneous rock complex of Permian age. In both results the directions differ very greatly from that of the geocentric axial dipole field in the collecting region.

Figures 4.2c and d show bipolar distributions in which the site means are grouped about two directions approximately 180° apart. Such opposed magnetizations are commonly encountered. The results in Figure 4.2c were obtained from 29 sites in the Newer Volcanics of Victoria and are an example of a reversal about an axis parallel to that of the geocentric axial dipole field. The results in Figure 4.2d are from 10 localities in the Chugwater Formation (Collinson and Runcorn, 1960) which is a red bed sequence of Permian or Triassic age. At 7 localities sets of directions with opposed polarities occur, at 3 localities only positive polarities occur. The means for each 17 polarity groups are plotted and these show a reversal about an axis strongly inclined to the axial dipole field.

§ 4.06 Sources of Dispersion

The dispersion of directions arises from errors inherent in the method (which may be referred to as *paleomagnetic errors*) and also to variations in the paleogeomagnetic field. The possible sources are listed here, but discussion of them is, for the most part, delayed until later.

The objective is to obtain a sequence of spot readings spaced through the time during which the rock unit became magnetized. In each reading the paleomagnetic error may be assessed and the readings themselves then analyzed to provide information about the Earth's field. Because of the hierarchial nature of the sampling schemes, two sources of dispersion are immediately recognized—that *within-sites*, and that *between-sites*.

The dispersion of specimen or sample observations at a particular collecting site may arise from several sources:

1. there are errors in the orientation and measurement of specimens: cumulatively these are usually between 2° and 5° and generally small compared to the observed dispersion;
2. there may be errors in the alignment of the primary magnetization due to failure of rocks to become magnetized parallel to the Earth's field: possible causes for this are the inclination error and compaction in sediments (§§ 2.12, 5.03), and anisotropy in igneous rocks (§ 2.15);
3. the direction of primary magnetization may subsequently be modified by secondary components (§§ 2.13, 5.08, 5.09);
4. errors may arise because of inaccuracies in the estimates of the horizontal plane at the time of magnetization;
5. there may be a fundamental "noise" level, different for different rock types, which limits agreement between adjacent specimens (§ 5.11);
6. should the time span of the record at a collecting site be appreciable then dispersion due to field variations may be present.

The dispersion of estimated site mean directions may arise from the following sources:

7. there may be statistical effects due to the errors in determining the site mean direction (§ 4.10);

8. if errors of type (4) are present in individual samples there will be a component of scatter between-sites due to errors in the correction for relative tectonic movement between sites;

9. variations in the field direction during the time span between the magnetization of different sites may contribute a component of scatter.

Component (9) is of much geophysical interest since it estimates the magnitude of the secular variation in the past (§ 6.12).

If the components of scatter arising from these sources are each denoted by precision parameters κ_1, κ_2, etc. (precision being an inverse measure of dispersion (§ 4.07)), then the over-all precision, κ_0, of the directions in a rock unit is given to a good approximation by

$$\frac{1}{\kappa_0} = \frac{1}{\kappa_1} + \frac{1}{\kappa_2} \cdots \frac{1}{\kappa_9} \qquad (4.1)$$

§ 4.07   Fisher's Distribution   R. A.

Fisher (1953) has given a method for dealing with observations of position on a sphere. Suppose that N directions observed at the same hierarchical level (Table 4.1) are known. The direction cosines (l_i, m_i, n_i) of the ith direction (D_i, I_i), regarded as a unit vector, are

$$l_i = \cos I_i \cos D_i, \qquad m_i = \cos I_i \sin D_i,$$

$$n_i = \sin I_i \qquad (4.2)$$

Fisher suggested that individual specimen directions, when regarded as points on a sphere, will be distributed with the probability density

$$\mathcal{P}_A \, dA = \frac{\kappa}{4\pi \sinh \kappa} \, e^{\kappa \cos \theta} \sin \theta \, d\xi \, d\theta \quad (4.3)$$

where (ξ, θ) are the polar coordinates of the element of area dA, θ being the angular departure from the mean, and ξ the azimuthal angle. The density is axially symmetrical about the true mean direction, ξ being distributed uniformly through 360°. The proba-

bility of finding a point in the belt between θ and $\theta + d\theta$ is

$$\mathcal{P}_\theta \, d\theta = \frac{\kappa}{2 \sinh \kappa} \, e^{\kappa \cos \theta} \sin \theta \, d\theta \qquad (4.4)$$

The parameter κ determines the precision of points. If $\kappa = 0$ they are uniformly distributed and the directions are random; for large values of κ they are confined to a small portion of the sphere near the true mean direction. The normalizing factor in 4.3 makes the density integrate to unity over the entire sphere. The distribution is illustrated in Figures 4.3 and 4.4 for $\kappa = 5, 10$, and 50. The probability of finding a direction making a given angle with the mean is given in Figure 4.4; for example, the chances of finding a direction between 9.5° and 10.5° of the mean when $\kappa = 50$ is $\mathcal{P} = 4.08 \times 0.017 = 0.08$. The probability of finding a point in a small area dA, the normal to which makes an angle θ with the true mean direction, will be given by dA times the expression 4.3, which is plotted in Figure 4.3.

Fisher showed that the best estimate (l, m, n) of the true mean direction is the vector sum of the N individual directions (l_i, m_i, n_i), that is

$$l = \frac{\sum\limits_{n=1}^{N} l_i}{R}, \quad m = \frac{\sum\limits_{n=1}^{N} m_i}{R}, \quad n = \frac{\sum\limits_{n=1}^{N} n_i}{R} \quad (4.5)$$

where (l, m, n) are the direction cosines of the mean direction and where

$$R^2 = \left(\sum_{n=1}^{N} l_i \right)^2 + \left(\sum_{n=1}^{N} m_i \right)^2 + \left(\sum_{n=1}^{N} n_i \right)^2 \quad (4.6)$$

The declination, D_m, and inclination, I_m, of the mean direction are given by

$$\tan D_m = \frac{\sum\limits_{n=1}^{N} m_i}{\sum\limits_{n=1}^{N} l_i} \qquad (4.7)$$

and

$$\sin I_m = \frac{\sum\limits_{n=1}^{N} n_i}{R} \qquad (4.8)$$

Fisher also showed that the best estimate k of the precision is

$$k = \frac{N - 1}{N - R} \qquad (4.9)$$

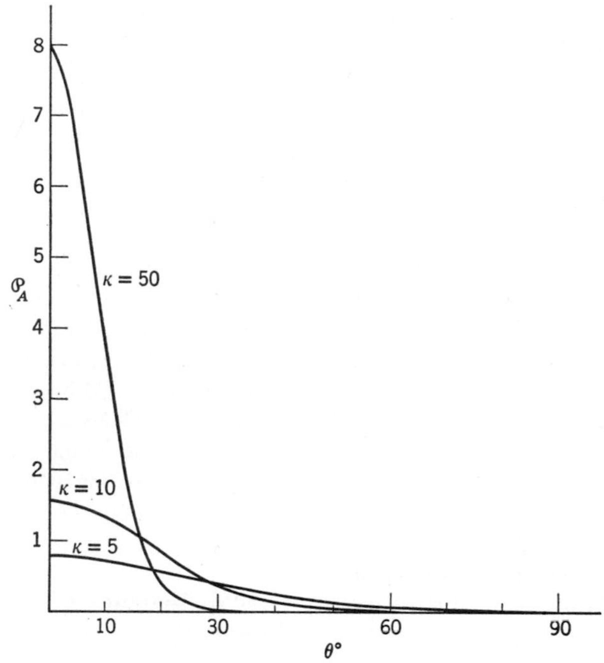

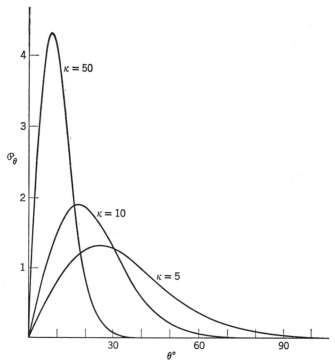

Figure 4.3.   Expression 4.3. $\mathcal{P}_A$ versus θ for 3 values of κ, calculated by M. A. Ward.

Figure 4.4.   Expression 4.4. $\mathcal{P}_\theta$ versus θ for 3 values of κ, calculated by M. A. Ward.

When the true mean is known, but the precision is not, the best estimate k' is given by

$$k' = \frac{N}{N - R \cos \vartheta} \qquad (4.10)$$

where ϑ is the angle between the true and estimated mean directions.

In order to get a picture of κ in numerical terms it is useful to study the probability of observing a direction which makes an angle θ_0 or more with the true mean (Watson and Irving, 1957). When κ exceeds 3, this is given approximately by the formula

$$\mathcal{P}(\theta > \theta_0) = e^{-\kappa(1-\cos \theta_0)} \qquad (4.11)$$

Therefore,

$$1 - \cos \theta_0 = \frac{- \log_e [\mathcal{P}(\theta > \theta_0)]}{\kappa} \qquad (4.12)$$

Values of θ_0 for 3 probability levels are plotted in Figure 4.5. When θ_0 is small these useful relationships hold:

$$\theta_{50} = 67.5k^{-\frac{1}{2}} \text{ degrees} \qquad (4.13)$$

$$\theta_{63} = 81k^{-\frac{1}{2}} \text{ degrees} \qquad (4.14)$$

$$\theta_{95} = 140k^{-\frac{1}{2}} \text{ degrees} \qquad (4.15)$$

These give the radii of the circles whose centers are the true mean and which contain respectively 50, 63, and 95 per cent of the individual directions. The second is analogous to the Standard Deviation of the Normal Distribution, and may be called the *Circular Standard Deviation*, and the third to the useful yardstick 1.96 times the Standard Deviation. Although, for a Normal Distribution, about 68 per cent of the directions lie within the Standard Deviation, for a Fisher Distribution only about 63 per cent of the directions lie within the analogous quantity.

§ **4.08   Goodness of Fit to Fisher's Distribution** (Watson and Irving, 1957) Estimates

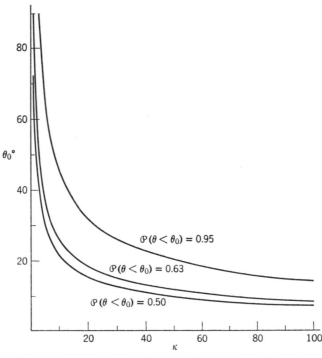

Figure 4.5. Boundaries for 3 proportions of Fisher's Distribution. These curves give the semi-vertical angle of the cone, whose axis is the mean direction, and which contains 50, 63, and 95 per cent of the individual directions in distributions; with various values of κ. Calculated by M. A. Ward.

of mean direction and precision and the statistical tests described later (§ 4.09) are only valid if the directions used for analysis obey Fisher's Distribution to a sufficient approximation. In most cases both κ and the true mean are unknown, and it is necessary to compare the data with a distribution of the form 4.3 in which $\kappa = k$, and $\hat{\theta}$, the estimate of θ, is the angle between an observed direction and the estimated mean (l, m, n). Also an estimate $\hat{\xi}$ of the azimuthal angle is needed. Values of $\hat{\theta}$ and $\hat{\xi}$ may be determined exactly by spherical trigonometry, but it is quicker, and adequate, to find them graphically. The directions are plotted on a polar projection so that (l, m, n) coincides with the center point. The angles, $\hat{\theta}$ and $\hat{\xi}$, can then be read off directly. The angles $\hat{\xi}$ should be uniformly distributed over the range 0° to 360°. To test this the statistic χ^2 is used. This is calculated from the formula

$$\sum \frac{(f_o - f_e)^2}{f_e} = \sum \frac{f_o{}^2}{f_e} - N \quad (4.16)$$

and measures the divergence between observation and expectation; f_o and f_e are the observed and expected frequencies in the intervals into which the range is divided. The degrees of freedom (d.f.) of χ^2 are decided, using the general rule—d.f. = (number of classes) − 1 − (number of constants fitted). Here only 2 constants are fitted because κ is not relevant and only two of the coordinates of the true mean are independent. To test whether the angles $\hat{\theta}$ are distributed as in equation 4.11 the ex-

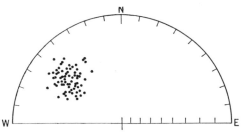

Figure 4.6. Directions of fossil magnetism in 70 specimens from one sample collected at site A9 in the Torridonian Sandstone Series. A stereographic projection is used, and the inclinations are positive. The primitive is the bedding plane, which is inclined at 12° in a direction 293° E of true N. Data of Irving (1954).

pected frequency of θ between the limits θ_1 and θ_2 is given by

$$N[e^{-k(1-\cos\theta_1)} - e^{-k(1-\cos\theta_2)}] \quad (4.17)$$

and χ^2 may be used again. An example is now given.

Directions observed in 70 specimens cut from a single oriented sample of very fine sandstone from the Diabaig Group of the Torridonian Sandstone are plotted in Figure 4.6. The observed and expected class frequencies for $\hat{\theta}$ and $\hat{\xi}$ are given in Table 4.2. The fit is excellent, χ^2 in both cases being less than expectation. The estimate k is 55.2. The dispersion is small, no observation making an angle of greater than 20° with the mean vector.

Table 4.2 Fit of Observations to Fisher's Distribution. *Table reproduced by permission of the Royal Astronomical Society.*

	Range of $\hat{\xi}$ in Degrees								
	1–45	46–90	91–135	136–180	181–225	226–270	271–315	316–360	χ^2
Observed	10	6	8	12	4	9	11	10	2.34
Expected	8.75	8.75	8.75	8.75	8.75	8.75	8.75	8.75	

	Range of $\hat{\theta}$ in Degrees						
	$0-3\frac{1}{2}$	$3\frac{1}{2}-6\frac{1}{2}$	$6\frac{1}{2}-9\frac{1}{2}$	$9\frac{1}{2}-12\frac{1}{2}$	$12\frac{1}{2}-15\frac{1}{2}$	$>15\frac{1}{2}$	χ^2
Observed	5	13	15	16	11	10	1.5
Expected	7	13.8	16.4	13.9	9.5	9.4	

§ **4.09 Statistical Tests** The first requirement is an estimate of accuracy of the calculated mean direction. Fisher showed that, at a probability level $(1 - \mathcal{P})$, the true mean of a population of N directions lies within a circular cone, whose axis is the estimated mean and whose semivertical angle, $a_{(1-\mathcal{P})}$ is given by

$$\cos a_{(1-\mathcal{P})} = 1 - \frac{N - R}{R} \left\{ \left(\frac{1}{\mathcal{P}}\right)^{\frac{1}{N-1}} - 1 \right\}$$

(4.18)

$\mathcal{P}$ is usually taken as 0.05, and the value, a_{95}, is the radius of *the circle of confidence*. Values of

$$\left\{ \left(\frac{1}{\mathcal{P}}\right)^{\frac{1}{N-1}} - 1 \right\}$$

are given in Table 4.3. These relationships are valid for small values of a:

Probable error of the mean, a_{50}

$$= 67.5/(kN)^{\frac{1}{2}} \text{ degrees} \quad (4.19)$$

Radius of the circle of confidence, a_{95}

$$= 140/(kN)^{\frac{1}{2}} \text{ degrees} \quad (4.20)$$

The circle of confidence is used for comparing an estimated mean with some direction which is known with negligible error—for instance, for comparison with the direction of the Earth's present field at the collecting site. The two directions are significantly different at level $\mathcal{P} = 0.05$ if the angle between them exceeds a_{95} and, conversely, are not significantly different if the angle is less than a_{95}. Circles of confidence are also often used to compare two mean directions, each having an associated error, which is not negligible. If the circles do not intersect, the two mean directions may be judged as differing significantly. When the circles overlap a further test is required, and is shown below.

Comparison of Mean Directions (Watson, 1956a). To test whether the true mean directions of s populations are identical, the statistic

$$\frac{2(\Sigma N_i - s)}{2(s - 1)} \frac{\Sigma R_i - R}{\Sigma N_i - R_i} \quad (4.21)$$

may be referred to the F-ratio tables with $2(s - 1)$ and $2(\Sigma N_i - s)$ degrees of freedom. It is supposed that the sample from the ith population contains N_i individual directions and has a resultant of length R_i, and that R is the length of the vector sum of resultants of all the individual directions. Large values of the statistic suggest that the assumption of identical true mean directions is false because the algebraic sum of the resultants R_i will then be much greater than the length of the vector sum, R. This test assumes that the precisions of the s populations are the same.

Table 4.3 *Values of* $\left\{ \left(\dfrac{1}{\mathcal{P}}\right)^{\frac{1}{N-1}} - 1 \right\}$ *for* $\mathcal{P} = 0.05$, N *from 3 to 100*

N	0	1	2	3	4	5	6	7	8	9
0	—	—	—	3.472	1.714	1.115	0.821	0.648	0.534	0.454
10	0.395	.349	.313	.284	.259	.239	.221	.206	.193	.182
20	0.171	.162	.153	.146	.139	.133	.127	.122	.117	.113
30	0.108	.105	.101	.098	.095	.092	.089	.087	.084	.082
40	0.080	.078	.076	.074	.072	.070	.069	.067	.066	.064
50	0.063	.062	.061	.059	.058	.057	.056	.055	.054	.053
60	0.052	.051	.050	.049	.049	.048	.047	.046	.046	.045
70	0.044	.044	.043	.043	.042	.041	.041	.040	.040	.039
80	0.039	.038	.038	.037	.037	.036	.036	.035	.035	.035
90	0.034	.034	.033	.033	.033	.032	.032	.031	.031	.031

100 — 0.031

Comparison of Precisions (Watson, 1956a). If samples of N_1 and N_2 specimens give precision estimates k_1 and k_2 then

$$\frac{k_1}{k_2} = \frac{\text{variance with } 2(N_2 - 1) \text{ degrees of freedom}}{\text{variance with } 2(N_1 - 1) \text{ degrees of freedom}} \quad (4.22)$$

assuming the two populations have the same value for k. This assumption may be tested. The right-hand side of 4.22 has the variance ratio or F-distribution. Because $1/k$ can be regarded as an estimate of the variance $1/\kappa$, distributed like that of an estimate from a sample of Normally distributed observations. Values of $F = k_1/k_2$ far from unity suggest that $k_1 \neq k_2$. For several populations, the ratio of the largest to the smallest k may be used to test the hypothesis that the precision is constant over the populations. The ratio may be referred to the tables of the maximum F-ratio.

Test of Randomness (Watson, 1956b; Vincenz and Bruckshaw, 1960). The observed directions of magnetization are often widely scattered and the question that sometimes faces the experimenter is: are the directions randomly distributed over the sphere or is there a significant mean direction? If the former is true then the data have no significance for studies of the direction of the past field. In practice, the estimate k is never zero, and this may arise from sampling fluctuations, the true value κ being zero. To distinguish this case, a test, based on Watson's argument, may be used. The resultant R of a sample of size N will approach N if the points are closely grouped, but will be small if they are not. Assuming that the points are random a value R_0 may be calculated which will exceed R with any given probability. A useful range of R_0 values is given in Table 4.4. The entry at the place corresponding to the sample size gives the value of R_0 which will be exceeded with a probability of 5 per cent in sampling from a population in which $\kappa = 0$.

§ **4.10 Combination of Observations from Rock Units** The dispersion within oriented samples, between samples from the same site, and between sites from the same rock unit are often highly variable (see for example Figures 4.1 and 4.2). Also, the number of specimen observations per sample and the number of samples per site often vary greatly, because, as an investiga-

Table 4.4 Significance Points R_0 at $\mathcal{P} = 0.05$. *Values $N = 3$ and 4 from Vincenz and Bruckshaw (1960) by kind permission of the Cambridge Philosophical Society and the authors. $N = 5$ to 20 from Watson (1956b) by kind permission of the Royal Astronomical Society and the author. $N = 21$ to 100 calculated by M. A. Ward. Correct to 2 decimal places $N < 51$, correct to 1 decimal place $50 < N > 101$.*

N	0	1	2	3	4	5	6	7	8	9
0	—	—	—	2.62	3.10	3.50	3.85	4.18	4.48	4.76
10	5.03	5.28	5.52	5.75	5.98	6.19	6.40	6.60	6.79	6.98
20	7.17	7.35	7.52	7.69	7.86	8.02	8.18	8.34	8.50	8.65
30	8.80	8.94	9.09	9.23	9.37	9.51	9.65	9.78	9.91	10.04
40	10.17	10.30	10.42	10.55	10.67	10.79	10.90	11.03	11.16	11.26
50	11.37	11.5	11.6	11.7	11.8	11.9	12.0	12.2	12.3	12.4
60	12.5	12.6	12.7	12.8	12.9	13.0	13.1	13.2	13.3	13.4
70	13.5	13.6	13.7	13.8	13.8	13.9	14.0	14.1	14.2	14.3
80	14.4	14.5	14.6	14.7	14.8	14.8	14.9	15.0	15.1	15.2
90	15.3	15.4	15.4	15.5	15.6	15.7	15.8	15.9	15.9	16.0

100 — 16.1

tion proceeds, sampling procedures may change, not necessarily in a manner which is desirable statistically, but perhaps governed by new technical advances or shortages of time available to the worker. Some authors have felt that the accuracy will be best conserved by giving unit weight to the observations from each specimen (or oriented sample) irrespective of their grouping into oriented samples (or sites). In other cases the disparity between specimens from the same site, and between sites from the same rock unit is such that the worker is inclined to treat each site mean direction as a single observation irrespective of the number of specimens or samples obtained from it. An attempt to effect a compromise between these two extreme opinions has been made in dealing with cases where the dispersions are small and rather uniform. But no general method has yet been devised for dealing rigorously with observations of unequal value.

The methods which have been used are described below. In many cases these involve much arithmetic and it may therefore be asked why they are necessary. There are two reasons. First, it is always instructive to obtain some idea as to the maximum amount of information obtainable from a given body of data, particularly as a guide to future sampling, and so that too high an accuracy will not be attributed to results. Second, the magnitude of the secular variation may, in principle, be inferred from the dispersion of directions, and the initial step in this important study is the search for an adequate statistical description of dispersions.

Repeated Use of Fisher's Method. The statistical methods described in § 4.07 may be used repeatedly on specimen observations from an oriented sample giving each unit weight to obtain means for samples, then on sample means giving each unit weight to obtain means for sites, and finally on site means giving each unit weight to obtain estimates of the over-all mean direction for the rock unit. The method is applicable to results from collecting sites scattered through an igneous body. The dispersion of site

means (being subject to effects (7), (8), and (9) enumerated in § 4.06) may provide a maximum estimate of the magnitude of the field variations during the time of formation. The method is also applicable to sediments, although the interpretation of the dispersion of site means is less clear than in the igneous case, because of the possibility that long periods of time are represented at each site, and the uncertainty as to whether or not the magnetic record parallels the sedimentary record. A comparison of values for igneous and sedimentary rocks of comparable age from the same region sheds light on this problem (see § 6.12).

This is a safe procedure. It is a common sense method which will appeal to geologists accustomed to observing the wide variations of properties encountered in a rock unit, and who are appreciative of the uncertainties in theories concerning the origin of such properties. The estimates of error obtained will be conservative estimates, and differences judged significant by this method are very likely to be physically significant. There are, however, certain disadvantages: the data are not fully utilized since not all observations are directly used in the final average; no account is taken of the errors in the site means, nor of the variability of these errors; and no allowance is made for the variation in the number of observations and of precision at different sites, too much weight being given to sites with low precision, and too little to those of high precision.

Analysis Giving Specimen Observations Unit Weight. Sometimes, particularly in studies in which numerous specimen observations are available from only a few sites, the results have been combined giving unit weight to specimen directions as if each had been drawn from a uniform population. This method assumes that each *specimen* observation is a spot-reading of the field direction, and that the dispersion between specimens from the same sample and between samples from the same site may be attributed to the secular variation; it is assumed that a specimen was laid down and became magnetized in a short time in comparison to the time scale of the secular variation, and at a time independent of that of adjacent specimens.

A comparison of methods is made in Tables 4.5 and 4.6. The first is an example of results of high and uniform precision obtained by sampling scheme (1) Table 4.1; the second gives results of variable precision obtained by sampling scheme (2). Estimates of means obtained by different weighting procedures are not appreciably different, but there are considerable differences in the

Table 4.5 Directions of Magnetization Observed at 4 Sites in the Tasmanian Dolerites (Lower to Middle Jurassic). *Directions of NRM in 17 specimens cut from 17 samples. The site numbers are those used in the original (Irving, 1963).*

	D, I	N	R	k	$a_{95}°$
Site 10 2 samples, 2 specimens	296, −78 285, −73				
Combined	290, −76	2	1.998	50	—
Site 39 7 samples, 7 specimens	75, −62 99, −75 120, −74 213, −83 157, −77 127, −87 86, −78				
Combined	107, −79	7	6.874	48	9°
Site 46 4 samples, 4 specimens	256, −80 2, −64 278, −74 347, −87				
Combined	318, −80	4	3.899	30	17°
Site 47 4 samples, 4 specimens	338, −80 321, −82 38, −80 205, −82				
Combined	340, −86	4	3.961	78	11°
Combined, unit weight to specimens	21, −88	17	16.492	32	6°
Combined, unit weight to sites	319, −86	4	3.945	54	13°

calculated errors—the values giving specimens, samples or sites unit weight increase in that order. At the site level the difference in error estimates is sometimes small (sites 1, 2, and 4, Table 4.6), since the precision of sample means exceeds that of specimen observations and compensates for the fewer units. But the estimates of the error in the mean of sites differ widely, the error obtained by giving specimens unit weight being much less than that calculated by giving sites unit weight.

By way of criticism of the method of giving unit weight to specimens, the following points are noted. Specimen observations are not randomly distributed in a stratigraphic sense but are clustered at certain levels so that the principle of random sampling is violated. The method is only justified in a statistical sense if dispersions ob-

Table 4.6　Directions of Magnetization at 4 Collecting Sites in Upper Kuttung Sediments (late Carboniferous).　*These results are from specimens partially demagnetized by heating to 300°C and cooling in zero field.*

		D_m, I_m	N	R	k	$a_{95}°$
Site 1 7 samples 23 specimens	Unit weight to specimens	154, +76	23	22.572	51	4°
	Unit weight to samples	154, +76	7	6.934	91	6°
Site 2 7 samples 21 specimens	Unit weight to specimens	171, +80	21	20.735	76	4°
	Unit weight to samples	171, +80	7	6.964	166	5°
Site 3 5 samples 15 specimens	Unit weight to specimens	256, +85	15	13.431	9	14°
	Unit weight to samples	233, +83	5	4.668	12	23°
Site 4 5 samples 18 specimens	Unit weight to specimens	201, +78	18	16.635	12	10°
	Unit weight to samples	198, +79	5	4.915	47	11°
Combined, **unit** weight to specimens		177, +80	77	72.964	19	4°
Combined, **unit** weight to samples		177, +80	24	23.378	37	5°
Combined, **unit** weight to sites (means of **samples**)		182, +81	4	3.982	164	7°

Table 4.7 Analysis of Dispersion. *Table of Watson and Irving (1957) reproduced with the kind permission of the Royal Astronomical Society.*

Source	Degrees of Freedom	Sum of Squares	Mean Square	Expectations of Mean Squares
Between sites	$2(B-1)$	$\Sigma R_i - R$	$\dfrac{\Sigma R_i - R}{2(B-1)}$	$\dfrac{1}{2}\left\{\dfrac{1}{\kappa_W} + \dfrac{\overline{N}_i}{\kappa_B}\right\}$
Within sites	$2\{\Sigma(N_i - 1)\}$	$\Sigma(N_i - R_i)$	$\dfrac{\Sigma(N_i - R_i)}{2\Sigma(N_i - 1)}$	$\dfrac{1}{2\kappa_W}$
Total	$2(N-1)$	$N - R$		

served at all hierarchial levels are constant in magnitude and have the same mean; although this may be the case in a few instances, it is generally not true. It is an arbitrary method; any desired error may be obtained by multiple sampling at a few collecting levels or by cutting many specimens from a single sample. The method is based on assumptions about deposition rates in sediments, but these are generally unknown factors. A second assumption implicit in this method is that sediments become magnetized at deposition so that a piece of rock deposited over a certain number of years has preserved within it the magnetic history of those years; there is no evidence at present in support of such an assumption.

Two-Tier Analysis (Watson and Irving, 1957). The analysis of dispersion at 2 sampling levels is now described. It is assumed that N_i observations are taken from the ith of B sites, the sites being spaced uniformly through the thickness and areal extent of a rock unit; and further that the observations within the ith site obey Fisher's Distribution with precision κ_W, and the true

Table 4.8 Data from Ferrar Dolerites (Bull, Irving, and Willis, 1962) [9.38].

Number of sites $B = 46$
Number of specimens $N = 92$ (2 per site)
Resultant of specimens $R = 88.99$
Resultant of site means $R_s = 44.86$
Resultant of specimens, site by site $\Sigma R_i = 91.20$

mean site directions vary from site to site with precision κ_B about the true over-all mean for the rock unit. The true over-all mean direction may be estimated by the vector resultant of all $(N = \Sigma N_i)$ the observations, or, by the direction of the vector resultant of B site mean directions—the estimates obtained by either method being closely similar. The problem considered here is that of estimating κ_W and κ_B, and the error in the over-all mean direction. The treatment is valid only for cases where κ_W is approximately constant, and where dispersions are small—that is, κ_W and κ_B large. It is appropriate to observations in basic igneous rocks, notably basalt flows, and dolerite sills and dykes.

Estimates k_W and k_B of κ_W and κ_B may be found by using the analysis of dispersion given by Watson (1956a). The observations are first reduced to give the lengths of the vector resultants at each of the sites, $R_1, R_2, \cdots R_B$ for instance, and the length of the resultant of all the $N = \Sigma N_i$ observations, R for instance. Table 4.7 may then be completed. Here $\overline{N}_i = (N - \Sigma N_i^2/N)/(B-1)$ and is the weighted average of the number of observations at a site. The significance of the between-site variation may be judged by an F-test. If the result is significant, estimates k_W and k_B may be found by equating the mean squares to their expectations, otherwise between-site variation may be ignored, that is, $\kappa_B = \infty$. As an example data from the Ferrar Dolerites (Table 4.8) gives the following results (Table 4.9).

Table 4.9 Analysis of Dispersion in Ferrar Dolerites

Source	Degrees of Freedom	Sum of Squares	Mean Square	Expectations of Mean Squares
Between sites	90	1.21	0.024	$\frac{1}{2\kappa_W} + \frac{1}{\kappa_B}$
Within sites	92	0.80	0.009	$\frac{1}{2\kappa_W}$
Total	182	2.01		

Thus $F = 0.024/0.009 = 2.66$, which exceeds the variance ratio at $\wp = 0.01$, so that the between-site dispersion is significant. Hence $k_W = 56$, and $k_B = 67$, which correspond to circular standard deviations θ_{63} of $10.7°$ and $9.9°$. The between-site precision freed of the effects of dispersion within sites is, of course, greater than the precision of mean site directions which is 38.

If the resultant of all the N observations is used as estimator of the direction of magnetization of the rock unit, it will be distributed approximately as Fisher's Distribution with a precision k_o given by

$$k_o^{-1} = (k_W N)^{-1} + (k_B B)^{-1} \qquad (4.23)$$

The circle of confidence may then be found from equation 4.15; for example, the Ferrar Dolerite data lead to $k_o = 1877$, so that $a_{95} = 140 k_o^{-\frac{1}{2}} = 3.2°$. If the procedure of using only the site means is followed, a slightly larger circle of confidence is obtained since the data are not so fully used, and this will particularly be so if an unequal number of observations has been taken at each site. The Ferrar Dolerite data give, by this method, $a_{95} = 3.4°$.

Comment. In most circumstances when combining numerous observations from a large rock unit it is a misuse [1] of Fisher's method to give unit weight to each specimen

[1] The author has not always been innocent in this regard (Boesen, Irving, and Robertson, 1961).

—a procedure which leads to underestimation of the radius of the circle of confidence. The values of a_{95} calculated in this way are probably too small by a factor approximately equal to the square root of the number of specimens per site, that is, by a factor of roughly 2. The use of site means as units is sound, and will rarely, if ever, be physically misleading. The more refined 2-tier analysis makes fuller use of the data, but is applicable only in favorable circumstances, where dispersions are approximately uniform from site to site. A more general procedure for weighting site results of unequal value is much needed.

§ 4.11 Angular Standard Deviation

(Wilson, 1959). In a population of N vectors the departures of individuals from the mean may be expressed by the angular standard deviation δ given by

$$\delta = \cos^{-1}(R/N) \qquad (4.24)$$

The mean direction and magnitude R of the resultant of N unit vectors are obtained as for Fisher's method (equations 4.6, 4.7, and 4.8). The angular standard deviation ϵ of the mean may be taken as

$$\epsilon = \delta N^{-\frac{1}{2}} \qquad (4.25)$$

Where the true mean is known, the deviation, δ', becomes

$$\delta' = \cos^{-1}[(R/N)\cos\vartheta] \qquad (4.26)$$

where ϑ is the angle between the true and estimated means (Cox, 1962). The method employs the analogue of the standard deviation used for distribution of points on a plane. No assumption is made about the distribution of vector densities. The results obtained by applying these formulae are indistinguishable numerically from those obtained by the use of Fisher's method when N is sufficiently large, that is $N \doteq N - 1$ (Creer, Irving, and Nairn, 1959). No allowance is made for the small size of samples so that when N is small the values of δ and ϵ will be less than the quantities θ_{63} and a_{63} (equations 4.14 and 4.18). The comparison is made in Table 4.10 in which N

is the number of igneous bodies studied, and R the resultant of their mean direction. The lower row gives results from the suite as a whole, and the upper those from a unit within the suite. In the former case the estimates are indistinguishable, in the latter they differ appreciably. Wilson's method ascribes higher precision than that of Fisher when the data are few. The amount of arithmetic work in Wilson's method is about the same as in Fisher's, the main labor in each case being the calculation of R. Runcorn (1960) has commented on Wilson's method.

§ 4.12 Paleomagnetic Poles

When results are available from rock units from the same region comparisons may be made directly using the methods just described. But results are often from different continents, and it is necessary to adopt some method of comparison based on an assumed configuration of the geomagnetic field at the time the fossil magnetism was acquired. One method is to calculate the position of the paleomagnetic pole (§ 3.6) relative to the sampling region, and to compare this with poles calculated from other rock units. Disagreement between results from the same general region indicates the magnitude of nondipole components in the paleogeomagnetic field, whereas agreement indicates that, for that region and period of time, the field was effectively that of a geocentric dipole. Agreement between results from widely separated regions shows that the field was dipolar, but disagreement indicates either a nondipolar field or that the regions have moved relative to one another since the time in question. A second method would be to reduce all the observations to a single base station. For example, the results from a region S may be reduced to base station B, situated in another part of the world, by first calculating the paleomagnetic pole P relative to S, and then the directions to be expected at B from a geocentric dipole with pole P. The directions may then be compared against the values actually observed at B. The calculations may be worked from

Table 4.10   Data from Antrim Igneous Suite, Northern Ireland. (1) *Wilson (1959)* [11.021]. (2) *Hospers and Charlesworth (1954) and Wilson (1959)* [11.018, 019, 021, 022].

	N	R	$\theta_{63}°$	$a_{63}°$	$\delta°$	$\epsilon°$
(1) Upper Basalts	6	5.72	19	$8\frac{1}{2}$	$17\frac{1}{2}$	7
(2) Combined results	65	61.63	$18\frac{1}{2}$	$2\frac{1}{2}$	$18\frac{1}{2}$	$2\frac{1}{2}$

equations 3.3 to 3.6 and Figure 3.5. In essence these two procedures are the same.

The paleomagnetic pole must not be thought of as the ancient equivalent of the geomagnetic pole. The geomagnetic dipole is the dipole which best fits the Earth's present field, and is derived by analysis of observations at stations spread over the Earth's surface for what is, geologically, an instant in time. Estimates of the paleomagnetic pole are derived from an analysis of data obtained from a single region and representative of a long time sequence. *The paleomagnetic pole is not defined for the entire Earth but relative to the sampling region only.* There are two methods, the first has been the more widely used.

Method I. A pole may be calculated from an estimate (D_m, I_m) of mean direction of a rock unit as already described (§ 3.6). The mean is not determined exactly so that the pole is also subject to error. If a_{95} is the radius of the circle of confidence around the estimated mean, and dI_m and dD_m are the associated changes in inclination and declination, then

$$a_{95} = dI_m = dD_m \cos I_m \qquad (4.27)$$

An error δI_m in the inclination corresponds by equation 3.3 to an error δp in the ancient colatitude p given by

$$\delta p = \tfrac{1}{2}a_{95}(1 + 3\cos^2 p) \qquad (4.28)$$

The error δp lies along the great circle passing through the point of observation S and the paleomagnetic pole P, and is the error in determining the distance of P from S. An error in the declination corresponds to a displace-

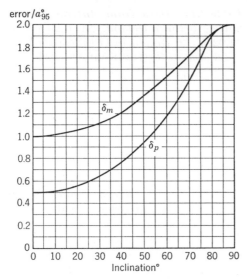

Figure 4.7. Polar errors δp and δm versus inclination I_m normalized for $a_{95} = 1°$.

ment δm from P in the direction perpendicular to the great circle PS where

$$\delta m = a_{95} \sin p / \cos I_m \qquad (4.29)$$

Graphs normalized to unit direction error, are given in Figure 4.7, from which values of sufficient accuracy for most purposes can be read. When P and S coincide, the polar error zone is circular; otherwise it is oval. In order to obtain a pole estimate of given accuracy many more observations are required when the paleolatitude of a sampling region is high than when it is low.

Method II. Each site direction may be specified by a pole. It is assumed that the *site pole* undergoes secular oscillations around the mean paleomagnetic pole in a random fashion as in Fisher's Distribution and with precision K. The position of the paleomagnetic pole for the unit may then be obtained by combining the site poles using Fisher's method. In this case the polar error zone is always circular so that $\delta m = \delta p$.

In both methods there are assumptions about the manner in which the directions are distributed. Method I assumes that the directions combined to give the mean (D_m, I_m), obey Fisher's Distribution. In Method

II it is assumed that the field variations have an oval distribution—the form varying with paleolatitude (equations 3.10 and 3.11). When sufficient data about the variation with paleolatitude of the form and magnitude of the distribution of mean site directions are available, it should be easy to decide which method is the more correct by comparing the fit of observations to Fisher's Distribution and to these equations.

The pole position is approximately the same whichever method is used, and the errors differ in detail but not in order of magnitude. Method II corrects automatically for differences in latitude and longitude of site positions, whereas Method I assumes mean coordinates for the sampling region. Since the sampling sites in a rock unit are generally spread over an area small compared to that of a continent, the error introduced from this source by Method I is small. In same cases where there are results from a formation of considerable lateral spread Method II is more applicable. For the present purposes, however, the differences are small and of uncertain physical significance, but, as more data of improved accuracy appear, increasing attention to these matters will be necessary.

Paleomagnetic Poles for Geological Periods. It is sometimes found that the poles obtained from results from rock units spread through time of the order of a geological period and situated in the same landmass agree closely. An estimate of the average position for the period and relative to that landmass may be obtained by applying Fisher's statistics to each pole determination (Tables 6.1, 6.2). This procedure of grouping results by geological periods is arbitrary, since the past behavior of the Earth's field may not be related in any simple way to the geological time divisions. For instance, there is no change in paleomagnetic properties at the Carboniferous-Permian boundary, but a break has been observed to occur some distance down in the Carboniferous sections of Europe and Australia (§ 6.05). However, at this present early stage in the development of paleomagnetic work no grouping other than one based on geology seems feasible. Eventually, however, groupings made entirely on magnetic characteristics will need to be made.

§ **4.13   Reversals** Directions with opposed polarity are often encountered in the same rock unit. If the axis of the alignment is close to the present field it is usual to refer to those directions with polarities the same as the present field as "normal," and those in which the polarities are opposite as "reversed." However, because of the slow drift of the magnetic axis, which becomes apparent in Lower Tertiary and older beds (§ 6.09), the application of these terms may be confusing. Runcorn (1956a) suggests that dipole fields with the same sense relative to the axis of rotation as the present field be termed *negative,* and fields opposed to these *positive.* This sign rule is easily remembered since the direction of rotation of the Earth and the direction of a positive field correspond to a right-hand corkscrew rule. The convention is to regard the direction as negative (positive) when the paleomagnetic pole toward which the north- (south-) seeking magnetization points is in the present-day northern hemisphere. The convention leads to ambiguities in the early Paleozoic and Precambrian but is generally suitable for comparative purposes in younger rocks.

Strictly, Fisher's statistics apply only to unipolar distributions. When both polarities occur it is usual to calculate a mean axis (irrespective of sign) by reversing one set and then applying Fisher's method. Although not rigorously correct this procedure is usually adequate.

The reliability of paleomagnetic
observations

§ 5.01 **Problems** The basic argument in paleomagnetic work is that some rocks acquire a component of magnetization, called the primary magnetization, parallel to the Earth's field at about the time the rock was formed so that, in principle, the variations in the directions of the geomagnetic field throughout geological history may be obtained from a laboratory study of the remanent magnetization of oriented rock samples of known geological age. It is the general practice to study oriented samples collected from a sedimentary or igneous rock formation, or from a set of coeval intrusives. The idea is that such a study may provide information about the average direction of the field, and the magnitude and form of the secular variation during the time in which the rock unit was laid down.

Under favorable circumstances the direction of primary magnetization may have remained unchanged, and the directions of natural remanent magnetization (NRM) are indicators of the ancient field direction, the uncertainty in the time to which the directions relate being the limits within which the geological age of the rock is known. However, the directions of NRM may not have been acquired when the rock was formed but at some subsequent time, so that the observations of direction are only of interest

if this time can be ascertained. Further possibilities are that the primary component has been masked by the imposition of secondary components of greater magnitude and different in direction, or that the primary component was not parallel to the ambient field. It is necessary, therefore, when confronted with observations of NRM to initiate enquiries directed to the following problems. At what time in the history of the rock was the magnetization acquired? Was it parallel to the ambient field? Are secondary components present? Is the magnetization stable; in particular, is it possible to recognize components of differing stability, and how did these originate? Has the rock undergone chemical or physical changes since deposition? These questions concern events long since past and relate to rocks of widely differing composition and history. The most powerful lines of approach are through field experiments (§ 1.3)—in particular, the study of the consistency of directions, laterally and stratigraphically, and between rocks of different origins, together with the study of the fossil magnetism of geological features of known origin.

§ 5.02 **Possible Origins of Fossil Magnetism** It may be useful at this point to summarize briefly the possible ways in which a rock may become magnetized, since tests of reliability have, in general, been designed to assess the reality or unreality of various hypothetical processes.

Primary components may develop in several ways. Recent lavas erupted at temperatures of about 1000°C or more acquire, on cooling, a thermoremanent magnetization (TRM) in the direction of the Earth's field (see Figure 1.1, and [12.03, 09, 32, 40, 56, and 63]). This indicates that ancient lavas and intrusive igneous rocks may have similarly acquired a primary TRM. In magnetically isotropic bodies the direction of TRM may be expected to be parallel to the ambient field, but if systematically directed anisotropies in excess of about 5 per cent occur, then the TRM may be deflected (§ 2.14). Redistribution of iron minerals or deposition of new ones may occur in the late stages of cooling and produce a component of chemical remanent magnetization (CRM), which may not be readily distinguishable from the primary TRM (§ 2.11). It is possible that cooling stresses affect the magnetization. Sediments may develop a depositional remanent magnetization (DRM) and a CRM as a result of the deposition of iron minerals, during or prior to lithification. The DRM may be subject to inclination error (§ 2.12) and to compaction effects.

Secondary magnetizations may also originate in several ways. Metamorphism will affect the primary magnetization of both sediments and igneous rocks. Local thermal metamorphism at igneous contacts may be expected to erase the primary remanence and produce a TRM parallel to the field at the time of cooling. If this time is known, and the rock unmoved, the directions in contact rocks are very useful (§§ 5.05, 7.8). Such magnetic effects may penetrate further into country rock than metamorphism, since the heat needed to remagnetize may be less than that for mineralogical changes. Regional metamorphism involving reconstitution of iron minerals by solid diffusion would obliterate an earlier magnetization and build up a new one of CRM type; if stresses cause grain alignments, as in schists or slates, the magnetization directions may be expected to be related to rock fabric and not necessarily be parallel to the ambient field.

Slow physicochemical changes not obvious geologically may cause subtle long period effects. For example, finely divided iron minerals in a superparamagnetic state may undergo a small increase in grain size by nucleation, passing into the ferromagnetic range, and so acquire a remanent magnetization (§ 2.11); this may occur several geological periods after deposition. The grain size increase may only need to be small (Figure 2.5). Red beds might be particularly susceptible to such changes. A second possibility, dealt with later (§ 7.3), is that physicochemical changes induce a reversal in polarity.

Finally, secondary magnetizations may arise from certain "blanket" effects. All rocks are subject to stresses. These may be produced by tectonic causes producing folding or faulting, and may give rise to stress-aided viscous remanent magnetizations (§ 2.15). They may be expected to be mild in flat-lying beds, but severe in highly deformed strata. All rocks are subject to the effects of thermal agitations producing viscous decay and possibly a secondary VRM (§ 2.13). Then, as a rock becomes exposed at the surface by erosion, it may be affected either by lightning, weathering, or thermal cycling through atmospheric temperature changes (§ 5.13).

§ 5.03 Consistency Tests The occurrence of well-grouped directions, divergent from the present field, indicates the absence of large viscous components imposed recently by the geomagnetic field, and of components of chemical origin due to recent weathering. The test is of broader significance if applied to results from a wide range of rock types of different origins and composition. One of the best examples is the consistency observed between red sediments, dolerite intrusions, and basalt flows in the Upper Triassic Newark Series of New Jersey (Figure 5.1, Table 5.1 [8.42]); the mean directions do not differ significantly from group

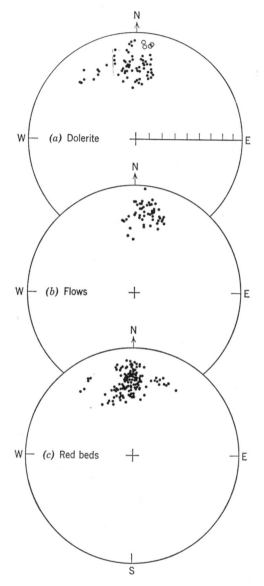

to group. The rock types represented have had different physical and chemical histories and the agreement implies that these differences have not affected their directions of magnetization. The agreement between sediments and igneous rocks indicates the absence of an inclination error in the sediments and implies that the effect of cooling stresses in the igneous bodies was negligible.

The test of consistency is enhanced if reversals are present, since if secondary components are added to a bipolar distribution the resultants of opposed groups would no longer be antiparallel (Figure 5.2). The presence of an exact reversal means that substantial secondary components are absent. The test applies to reversals arising either from reversal of the field, or from self-reversal mechanisms (§ 7.1). Commonly reversals are not exact, the addition vector needed to bring them into alignment being antiparallel to the present field. This is presumably due to viscous components imposed by the present field, and their effect can be minimized by averaging the direction irrespective of sign (§ 4.13).

Grossly inconsistent directions at a site often occur. The scatters are sometimes unsystematic (Figures 4.1b and 5.25), but in other cases the directions fall approximately along a great circle which passes through the direction of the geocentric dipole field or the present field (Figures 4.1c and 5.21).

Figure 5.1. Paleomagnetic directions in the Newark Series of New Jersey. The direction in the red sediments are those of NRM. The NRM of the igneous rocks contains viscous components directed along the present field. These have been minimized by magnetic cleaning in 150 oe(peak) alternating magnetic field and the directions after this treatment are given here. Equal-area projection. Redrawn from Opdyke (1961a), with the kind permission of the American Geophysical Union and N. D. Opdyke.

Table 5.1 Mean Directions for Different Rock Types in the Newark Series, New Jersey. *Data of Opdyke (1961a); reproduced with the kind permission of the American Geophysical Union and N. D. Opdyke.*

Rock	Sites	D_m, I_m	R	k	$a_{95}°$
Newark sediments	18	357, +24	17.63	46	5
Dolerite intrusions	6	356, +28	5.87	38	8
Watchung flows	5	9, +24	4.96	100	8
Combined	29	359, +25	28.36	44	4

These distributions are referred to as *smeared, planar* or *great-circle distributions.* The great circle which best fits the points has been called by Khramov (1958) *the circle of remagnetization.* Such distributions are generally considered to be due to the presence of 2 components: a VRM of comparatively low stability imposed recently by the Earth's field, and a more stable component which may be a TRM, CRM, or DRM. The ratio of stable and unstable components varies, producing the variation in directions (Figure 5.3). Sometimes a scatter of points about the great circle is observed and is attributed to temporary components of viscous origin imposed during storage in the laboratory. If the secondary component is due to weathering it may be of high stability as Robertson and Hastie (1962) have shown. An estimate of the direction of the stable component may be made by choosing a point on the circle of remagnetization furthest from the present field direction. This commonly used procedure carries some uncertainty since there is an element of subjectivity in the choice of the point, and, moreover, the stable direction may lie anywhere between this point and the antipole of the present field; also, it assumes that some at least of the directions are little affected by secondary components. A more favorable situation arises when the beds at different collecting sites have been tilted at different angles so that the circles of remagnetization, when plotted with respect to the bedding planes, will intersect in the direction of the stable components. This method is much to be preferred to that just described, but it suffers from the disadvantage that favorable struc-

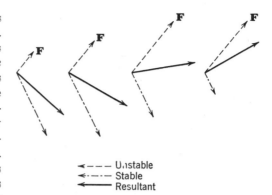

Figure 5.2. Reversals test for secondary components. Originally antiparallel sets of directions (positive P and negative N) are no longer reversed if secondary components S are added. The mean, irrespective of sign, of the resultants R, estimates the original alignment.

Figure 5.3. Origin of smeared distributions. **F** is the present field.

tural and paleomagnetic situations have so far proved rare.

Tests of consistency are at their most powerful when applied to results from many formations spread over a large area or through long time spans. Comparison is made using paleomagnetic poles. Several examples are known of consistency over regions of continental extent, and 5 examples are listed below. The first 4 illustrate agreement between rocks belonging to the same geological period. The last illustrates the consistency observed through a long time sequence.

(*a*) Results from Quaternary lavas, intrusives, and sediments from localities spread over much of the Earth (Figure 6.3). Reversals occur.

(*b*) Results from Permian beds of Europe and northern Asia spread over a distance of 6000 km and including red sediments, lavas, and intrusives, ranging in age from early to the uppermost Permian (Figure 6.10). The directions are all positive.

(*c*) Results from Triassic rocks of Europe and northern Asia, including red sediments, lavas, and intrusives, and covering a distance of 6000 km (Figure 6.9). Reversals occur.

(*d*) Results from Triassic beds of North America, including red sediments, lavas, and intrusives, spread over a distance of about 4000 km (Figure 6.9). Reversals occur.

(e) Results from late Paleozoic and Mesozoic formations of eastern Australia, from tuffs, sediments, lavas, and intrusives, ranging in age from Lower Triassic to upper Lower Cretaceous (Figure 6.31). The sampling sites are spread over a distance of 2000 km.

These results are consistent with a dipole configuration for the Earth's field for the times and places in question. They are also consistent with the assumption that the magnetizations are of primary origin. They indicate that special effects, such as inclination errors in sediments, nonalignment due to anisotropy, or effects due to stresses or secondary chemical changes, have not affected the results by an amount in excess of the statistical accuracy of the determinations. This is not to say that under every circumstance such effects will be negligible. The rocks from which the above evidence was obtained are in tectonically stable regions, and there is no geological evidence to suppose that they have undergone gross physical or chemical changes since the period of their formation.

§ 5.04   Study of Deformed Beds   These tests are based on the idea that if sections of a body, magnetized initially in a uniform direction, undergo relative movement, the dispersion of directions between different parts will be related to the degree of movement provided the forces operating during and since deformation have been insufficient to change the directions. Folgheraiter and David, at the turn of the century, appear to have been the first (§ 1.08) to exploit this idea, which is applicable to many types of deformation structures.

Bedding Tilt Test (J. W. Graham, 1949). If the remanence directions in beds of different attitudes differ *in situ* but are brought into agreement after correction for relative rotation the magnetization has been acquired prior to deformation and was not altered by it (Figure 5.4). The test may be applied to a single structure, say a fold, within an otherwise little deformed sequence, or more generally over a wide area when observations are taken at sites with differing bedding tilts. The test over a wide area is the more powerful.

Graham's results are given in Figure 5.5. The samples were collected from within a few yards of one another from a massive bed of grey sediment about 3 inches thick. Both NRM directions and bedding poles are given, related groups being indicated by letters. The bedding poles are scattered over 113° of arc and the directions over 127°.

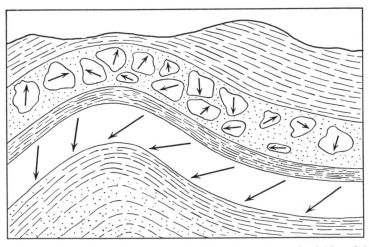

Figure 5.4.   Bedding tilt and conglomerate tests. Directions shown in fold and in conglomerate cobbles indicate a stable pre-deformation magnetization. Modified after Cox and Doell (1960).

After correction for folding the results are in good agreement with north-seeking directions to the NW with negative inclinations. The corrections were carried out by rotating directions so that all their corresponding bedding poles fell at the projection center. The good agreement between the corrected directions is contrasted with the wide scatter *in situ*. The folding is Appalachian, which means the NRM directions have remained unchanged at least since Permian time. This was the first demonstration that directions of magnetization in rocks could be retained unchanged over geological spans of time. An application of the test to tilted beds over a wide area is given in Figure 5.22. Further cases are to be found in the Appendix [1.01, 1.37, 5.34, 11.098, 11.103, 12.47] but it is unfortunate that more examples of this vital test are not available.

Conglomerate Test J. W. Graham (1949). Conglomerate beds contain cobbles derived by erosion from pre-existing beds. If the initial magnetization of the parent formation is held by the cobbles the directions *in situ* observed in different cobbles will be random, because mechanical forces will far exceed magnetic aligning forces during deposition. The observation of random directions implies that the magnetization of the parent formation is stable and predates the deposition of the conglomerate. Uniform directions from cobble to cobble imply that the magnetization of the conglomerate occurred subsequently. But such observations, although they suggest that the parent body magnetization is secondary, do not necessarily mean that this is so, since the process of conglomerate formation may itself have affected the magnetic properties. A further complication arises if the outcrop has been struck by lightning which can produce scattered directions (§ 5.13). Such an occurrence would be marked by abnormally high intensities, and can be tested by carrying out detailed studies of the dispersion of directions within cobbles, an example of which is given in Figures 5.6 and 5.7. In this instance, the conglomerate is pre-Jurassic in age and the cobbles have been derived from the nearby Precambrian Torridonian Sandstone. The dispersion within cobbles varies with rock type as is observed in the beds *in situ* (Figure 5.14). Moreover, the

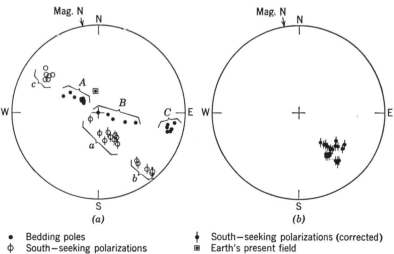

•	Bedding poles	⚬	South—seeking polarizations (corrected)
φ	South—seeking polarizations	⊡	Earth's present field
○	North—seeking polarizations		

Figure 5.5. Directions of fossil magnetism in a folded bed of the Rosehill Formation, Pinto, Maryland [4.11]. The directions are plotted on the lower hemisphere of an equal-area net, (*a*) *in situ,* and (*b*) after correction. Redrawn from Graham (1949), with the kind permission of the American Geophysical Union and J. W. Graham.

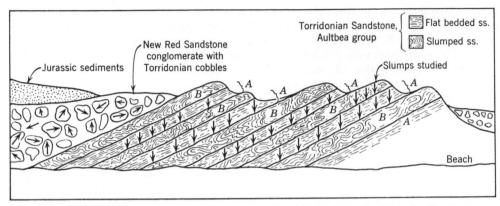

Figure 5.6. Schematic representation of results from Gruinard Bay, Rosshire, Scotland. Arrows give the directions of fossil remanence. Uniform directions in Torridonian flat-bedded sandstones (*A*) and (*B*) slumped sandstones (Figures 5.8 and 5.9) and random directions in the Torridonian cobbles of a New Red Sandstone conglomerate (Figure 5.7).

wide scatter of directions between cobbles contrasts sharply with the rather uniform directions observed in stratified beds in the same beach exposure (Figure 5.8). Thus the possibility of lightning strikes is small, and the suggestion that the magnetization of the cobbles and of the stratified beds from which they were derived predates the formation of the boulder bed, is strong. For further examples see the Appendix [1.38, 5.35, 9.30, 12.35].

Study of Slump Beds. Contorted beds, deformed before lithification when the sediment was saturated with water, provide good opportunities for studying the origin of magnetization in sedimentary rocks. A study of slump beds provides information about magnetic behavior shortly after deposition. Its weakness is that the process of slumping will affect the magnetization if not yet stabilized at this early period, so that application of results from slumps to the interpretation of observations from nearby undeformed beds is not always clear. If uniform remanence directions are found parallel to those in adjacent stratified beds, the magnetization must have occurred after slumping, but this does not mean that the magnetization is unstable. Parallel directions in slumped and enclosing undeformed beds show that no depositional inclination error is present (§ 2.13). Examples are now given

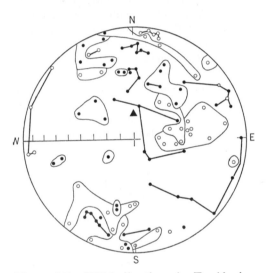

Figure 5.7. NRM directions in Torridonian conglomerate cobbles of very fine sandstone grade. Specimen directions from the same cobble are enclosed when cobbles were in beds of known New Red Sandstone age (from Gruinard Bay, Figure 5.6). Directions are linked in those cases where cobbles are from beds at Coigach, the Isle of Ewe, and Rudha Re (Rosshire), whose age is ill-defined but presumed to be New Red Sandstone. (Equalarea projection; dots give positive inclinations, circles negative inclinations.) Redrawn from Irving and Runcorn (1957), with the kind permission of the Royal Society. The triangle gives the direction of the axial geocentric dipole field.

of effects observed in certain very fine sandstones. The first is of uniform directions in slump folds with amplitudes of several meters (Figure 5.9). In this case the directions, like those in the enclosing stratified beds, diverge strongly from the present field, and the conglomerate test shows the magnetization to be stable (Figure 5.7). The precision of observations *in situ* is comparable to that in the flat-bedded layers (Figure 5.8), but after correction for deformation by rotating poles of the slump bedding to the center of the projection, the directions scatter. If, on the other hand, slump beds are found to have dispersions appropriate to the deformations and much greater than those in adjacent beds, the magnetization has originated prior to slumping, that is, virtually at the time of formation. Such a result is highly satisfactory but is rarely found. The results from a locality in the Torridonian Sandstone Series near Toscaig, Rosshire, illustrate the variability which occurs (Figure 5.10). The directions in a thin bed (*BB*) of banded very fine sandstone, rich in bands of detrital specular ore, are very closely grouped. Beneath this is a bed (*A*), about 2 m thick, of unbanded very fine sandstone in which the mean direc-

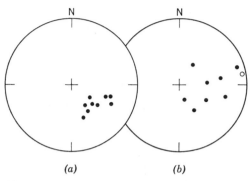

(a)   (b)

Figure 5.9. NRM directions in slumped fine sandstones from the Torridonian Sandstone Series (*B* in Figure 5.6). (*a*) Primitive is the bedding plane taken from enclosing flat-bedded strata ($k = 30$). (*b*) Gives directions corrected for slumping ($k = 6$). Equal-area projection. Redrawn from Irving (1957*a*), with the kind permission of the Royal Society.

tion is the same but the dispersion greater. Laterally, within a distance of 2 m, these beds become contorted into slump folds with an amplitude of about 1 cm, that is, of the same order as the specimen dimensions. The directions in this contorted zone are highly variable, some showing a grouping comparable to that in the massive bed, others are randomly scattered both within and between samples. No grain-size differences are observable. This result is set out numerically in Table 5.2—the sample numbers being as in Figure 5.10.

In the foregoing examples it appears that in some samples the magnetization became stabilized before slumping, but afterwards in others. This is explained by assuming variable rotation of magnetic grains after deposition. The rock is a very fine sandstone, made up predominantly of quartz and felspar ranging from 0.06 to 0.13 mm in diameter. Detrital particles of specularite (αFe_2O_3) are abundant and range in size between 0.03 and 0.07 mm, a factor 2 less than the nonmagnetic particles. A simple calculation shows that in a newly laid sand of this composition containing as much water as solid matter the spaces between the nonmagnetic particles will commonly be about the size of the magnetic grains, which will

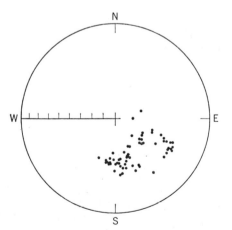

Figure 5.8. NRM directions in flat-bedded very fine sandstones of the Aultbea Group of the Torridonian Sandstone Series. Specimens spaced through a 25 m section (Figure 5.6). Equal-area projection the primitive being the bedding plane. Data of Irving (1954).

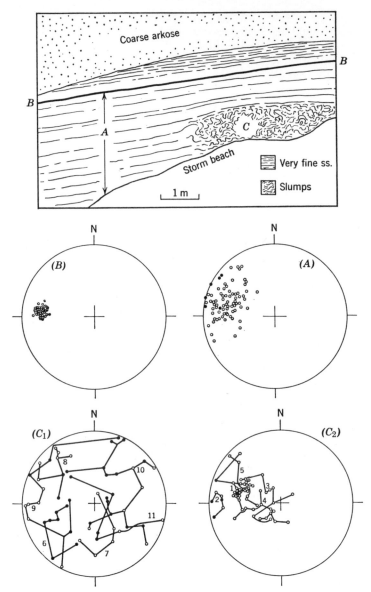

Figure 5.10. Variable dispersion of NRM directions at one locality and its relation to sedimentary features. Torridonian Sandstone Series, Applecross Group (site B44). Above is a locality sketch and below the directions are plotted on equal-area projections—the primitive being the bedding plane. (*B*) directions in specularite rich band *B–B*; (*A*) directions in flat-bedded very fine sandstones *A*; C_1 and C_2 directions in slump zone *C*. Horizontal scale is about one-half the vertical scale. In C_1 and C_2 directions in specimens from the same oriented sample are linked; this is not done in *B* and *A* to avoid confusion. Data of Irving (1954).

therefore be free to rotate into the direction
of the ambient field, so that particles, dis-
oriented during slumping, may later correct
themselves. The process is likely to be
critically dependent on relative grain sizes
and grading, and the variability of these
within a single outcrop may explain the
variable post-slumping remagnetization in
locality B44. The hypothesis is accessible
to laboratory test and experiments on synthetic sediment show that a postdepositional
magnetization, accurately parallel to the
field, is readily acquired in wet sediments of
very fine sandstone grade (§ 2.12).

§ 5.05   Study of Igneous Contacts

When molten igneous material is poured out
upon, or injected into, a pre-existing rock
which is comparatively cool, the latter is
heated, and upon cooling acquires a remanence in the same magnetic field as that in
which the outer margin of the igneous body
becomes magnetized. In some cases, when
the blocking temperatures of the country
rock are much lower than that of the igneous
material, the field in which the former becomes magnetized may be distorted by the
remanent and induced magnetization in the
latter, but, in general, the field in which both
acquire their remanence is not likely to be

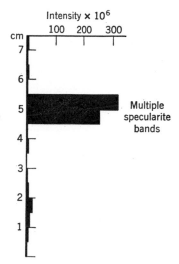

Figure 5.11. Intensity of NRM in emu/cm^3
in successive disk specimens taken every 0.5
cm through a sample containing a bedding
level (*BB* in Figure 5.10) rich in specular ore
particles. Redrawn from Irving (1957a), with
the kind permission of the Royal Society.

greatly different in direction. If the heat,
or addition of magmatic fluids, induces chemical changes, and if the temperature is not
raised to the Curie point, then the magnetization acquired by the heated country rock
may be of chemical type (§ 2.11). A further

**Table 5.2 Directions of NRM at Locality B44 Torridonian Sand-
stone Series.** *N number of specimens; D_m, I_m mean directions; k
Fisher's precision; $\theta_{63}°$ circular standard deviation. Individual directions
plotted in Figure 5.10. Data of Irving (1954, 1957a).*

	N	D_m, I_m	k	$\theta_{63}°$
Specularite layer BB 4 samples	43	277, −29	132	7
Unbanded sandstone 5 samples	78	284, −28	13	22
Slumps (C) sample No. 1	20	289, −33	28	15
2	6	270, −3	26	16
3	10	301, −67	23	17
4	12	244, −63	15	21
5	10	282, −38	14	22
6	7	233, +40	11	24
7	5	163, −53	6	33
8	8	312, 0	6	33
9	11	Effectively random		
10	19	Effectively random		
11	6	Effectively random		

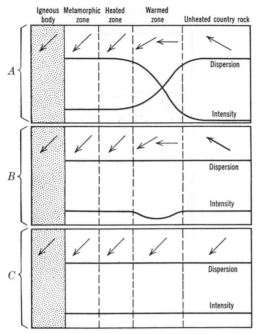

Figure 5.12. Igneous contact test. Three hypothetical cases *A, B, C,* described in the text, are given. The direction (arrows), dispersion, and intensity in each zone are indicated schematically.

possibility is that the country rock has been merely heated to temperatures of the order of 100°C so that a moderate temperature viscous remanent magnetization (VRM) is acquired (§ 2.13). In most cases, however, at igneous contacts, the magnetization will be a thermoremanent magnetization (TRM). This will be the total TRM if the temperature exceeds the highest Curie point, but only a partial TRM if the maximum temperature is less than this.

The observation of similar directions in both igneous body and baked country rock indicates that the directions are a record of the field at the time of cooling (Bruhnes, § 1.8). The test is much enhanced if it can be demonstrated that there are changes in properties with distance from the contact, corresponding to the diminishing heating effects (Everitt and Clegg, 1962).

Guided by these authors it is useful to define 3 gradational zones, which may be

expected to be present to a variable extent in most circumstances: first, a *metamorphic zone* in which extensive changes have occurred in the magnetic minerals; second, a *heated zone* in which such changes are comparatively small but in which the rock acquires a total TRM; and third, a *warmed zone* in which a partial TRM (or moderate temperature VRM) is induced so that high temperature components of primary origin may remain. Outside the warmed zone is the unheated country rock. In the most favorable case (*A* in Figure 5.12) the country rock is much older than the intrusion and consists either of sediment or of igneous material of comparatively low magnetic stability. The occurrence of high intensity at the contact, falling to low values at a distance, with parallel magnetization in contact rocks and igneous body, indicates that the magnetization both of body and contact is stable and was acquired at the time the body cooled; a further criterion is that the dispersion of directions would normally increase with distance from the contact, and that the mean directions in the baked and unbaked country rock would be different because of probable field variation during the time between its deposition and heating. If (*B*) the country rock is stable igneous material of a much greater age, its direction would normally differ from those at the contact, but there need be little change in dispersion or intensity—although a decrease in intensity may occur in the warmed zone due to directional differences in the competing primary and secondary magnetizations. The unfavorable situation (*C*) could arise should the country rock consist of stable igneous material which is only a little older than the heating body, or which, fortuitously, acquired its primary magnetization in a field parallel to that at the time of reheating. General heating during a period of regional metamorphism, deep burial, or extensive igneous activity, could also produce situation *C*.

The results in Table 5.3 were obtained by Everitt and Clegg (1962) from a 3 m Tertiary dike cutting Devonian red mudstone in Argyllshire, Scotland. At a distance of 10 cm the intensity of NRM (M_n) and maximum isothermal remanence (M_{max}) are high, indicating metamorphic changes. Beyond 36 cm, M_{max} and certain other properties remain nearly constant, but M_n falls, suggesting the presence of heated and warmed zones with magnetic changes but negligible mineralogical alteration. At distances of more than 350 cm heating effects are not felt. Study by Leng (1955) of a 2m wide Tertiary dike from Arran, Scotland, provides information nearer a contact (Figure 5.13). The country rock is Triassic red sandstone. The metamorphic zones defined by the leveling off in M_{max} values extend to 7 cm. In the final example (Figure 7.26) remagnetization through general heating, comparable to the situation in Figure 5.12c, has apparently occurred in the Basement, Beacon Sandstone, Ferrar Dolerite sequence of South Victoria Land, Antarctica; in this case the dolerite bodies are millions of times larger than the dikes in the foregoing examples. Further examples of contact studies are given in § 7.8.

§ 5.06   Study of Sedimentary Features

If a sediment acquires a magnetization at or about the time of deposition it is to be expected that it will be related to sedimentary features established at that time.

A correlation between bedding features, dispersion, and intensity at 1 outcrop is set out in Figure 5.10 and Table 5.2. The rocks

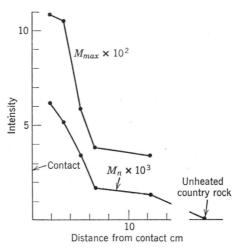

Figure 5.13. Magnetic intensities at contact of Tertiary dike with Triassic sandstone. Results of Leng (1955). M_n is intensity of NRM, and M_{max} the maximum isothermal remanence (emu/cm³).

studied are all of very fine sandstone grade. Very close grouping of directions is observed in band *BB*. This band, which varies in thickness from 1 to 3 cm, consists of between 5 and 20 per cent by volume of detrital specular ore, the remainder being quartz and felspar. The ore is concentrated in delicate laminae, 1 mm or more in thickness, which are made up almost entirely of specularite with subordinate accessory minerals. These laminae are thought to be due to a gentle winnowing action—which allowed the particle moments to become aligned in the am-

Table 5.3 Magnetization of a Tertiary Dike and Baked Contact. *d is the distance from contact, D_m, I_m is the mean of N specimens, and δ their angular standard deviation. M_n and M_{max} are the intensity of NRM and maximum isothermal remanence ($\times 10^6$ emu/g). Results of Everitt and Clegg (1962); reproduced with the kind permission of the Royal Astronomical Society and the authors.*

		d	N	D_m, I_m	$δ°$	M_n	M_{max}
Tertiary dike	Igneous	—	4	17, +55	9	—	—
Devonian mudstone	Metamorphosed	10	4	5, +52	5	2440	280,000
	Heated	35–150	14	6, +61	2.5	42	3,000
	Warmed	180	4	23, +54	5	14	2,400
	Unheated	355	4	18, +47	22	5	3,200

bient field—an effect further enhanced by magnetic coupling between particles. The directions in massive unbanded sandstones of the same grain size, but containing only about 1 per cent of evenly spread specularite grains, are much more widely scattered, but with the same mean direction. In this case apparently, there have been very few pauses in sedimentation, which allowed, in the case of band *BB*, the efficient alignment of particles on the free surface. The intensity increases by a factor of nearly 100 in passing through the band *BB* (Figure 5.11) and shows that the NRM is related to the

proportion of detrital specularite grains present.

The dispersion as a function of grain size in the Torridonian Sandstone Series is given in Figure 5.14. Dispersion is estimated from several specimen readings within each oriented sample using relationship 4.9. The results are derived from 198 samples. There is an increase of within-sample scatter with grain-size as determined from the nonmagnetic fraction. The directions in coarse-grained current-bedded arkoses laid down in turbulent water are highly scattered; those in well-sorted very fine sandstones laid

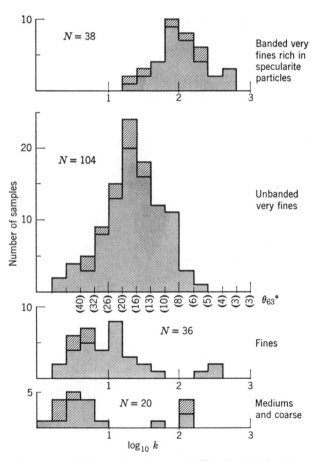

Figure 5.14. Variation of dispersion with rock type in Torridonian Sandstone Series. *N* is the number of oriented samples studied, $\Sigma N = 198$. The shaded portions refer to cobbles from conglomerates and the stippled portions to samples from the main sequence. In the second histogram values of the circular standard deviation are given in brackets. Redrawn from Irving and Runcorn (1957), with the kind permission of the Royal Society.

down in more tranquil conditions are better grouped. The relationship is that expected from a magnetization of detrital origin which has remained little altered since the time of deposition; the absence of correcting grain rotation effects in the coarse sediments is presumably due to their poor sorting. The variation of dispersion with grain size is mirrored by the variations of intensity of NRM with grain size (Figure 5.15), the intensity being roughly proportional to the precision k (Table 5.4).

Ripple marks are evidence of disturbance in newly deposited beds. Results from 19 specimens taken consecutively beneath a strongly rippled surface are given in Table 5.5. The dispersion, expressed by the circular standard deviation $\theta_{63}°$, is greater near the

Table 5.4   Median Values of the Intensity (emu/cm³ × 10⁶) (M_n) and Precision (k) in the Torridonian Sandstone Series. *From Irving and Runcorn (1957); with the kind permission of the Royal Society.*

Sandstone Type	M_n	k
Banded very fine	40	100
Unbanded very fine	11	25
Fine	7	10
Medium and coarse	3	6

ripples than at depth, although the mean directions are indistinguishable. The rock is a uniform very fine sandstone and so the effect is not related to grain size. These results may be compared with work by King

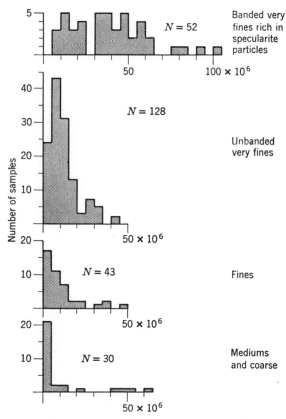

Figure 5.15. Variation of intensity of NRM with rock type in the Torridonian Sandstone Series. N is the number of samples, $\Sigma N = 254$. Intensity in emu/cm³. Redrawn from Irving and Runcorn (1957), with the kind permission of the Royal Society.

Table 5.5 **Dispersion Beneath Ripple-marks in Torridonian Sandstone.** *Data of Irving (1954).*

	N	D_m, I_m	$\theta_{63}°$
Top 3 cm	6	121, +57	18°
Bottom 6 cm	13	119, +52	10°

(1951) on the mechanical disturbance of particles on modern beaches, in which he found that movement during formation of a ripple rarely penetrated more than 4 cm, and that 1 to 3 cm was the usual depth. The greater scatter of remanence directions immediately beneath the ripples may therefore be due to the scattering of detrital particles by the water turbulence which produced the ripple.

The observed correlation of magnetic effects with sedimentary structures in the foregoing examples indicates the stability of the NRM, and, further, that it is carried by detrital specularite particles and was acquired at or soon after deposition in late Precambrian time.

§ **5.07** **Study of Jointed Rocks** The suggestion (§ 2.15) that, under stress and in the presence of a magnetic field, a rock may acquire a stress-aided magnetization concentrated in domains with low coercivity, leads to the possibility that such effects in nature may occur in rocks with irregular joint patterns; the presence of different joint directions indicates that the principal stress axes had different orientations. There are no instances of detailed studies of the relations between magnetization and joint directions, but the uniformity in magnetization directions often observed between rock bodies with greatly different joint patterns implies the absence of any correlation. An example is given in Figure 7.26 where agreement occurs among granites, cross-cutting dikes of variable strike, subhorizontal dolerite sheets with columnar jointing, and sediments with irregular fracture patterns; it seems improbable, in this particular case, that the stresses which produced the joints can have

affected the remanence directions. A further example is that given by Cox (quoted in Doell and Cox (1961a)). The directions of NRM in rock prisms radiating from the center of a pillow in a Lower Tertiary submarine flow [11.098] were found to have variable directions. After thermal cleaning at 225°C (§ 5.09) the directions became well grouped. The NRM consists of a stable component uniform in direction, and superposed components of lower stability and variable direction. The directional properties of the latter are consistent with their having originated under cooling stresses prior to their release by jointing, the underlying stable component being unaffected. But there is also the possibility that the initial scatter is due to temporary VRM components.

§ **5.08** **Removal of Low Stability Components by Partial Demagnetization** If, after carrying out several of the field studies just described, the fossil magnetism is shown to be stable, then the directions may be used as estimates of the paleogeomagnetic field. But the tests often prove negative or indecisive, and the experimenter may then either discard the result or initiate a search for underlying stable components not obvious in the NRM.

NRM is generally complex. Resolution into components may be achieved by laboratory techniques of which the most important is demagnetization (§ 2.08). Demagnetization of NRM is technically more difficult than similar studies of synthetic remanence because the intensity is lower. This type of analysis may be called *experimental analysis* to distinguish it from the statistical analysis described in Chapter Four. The spectrum of coercive forces and blocking temperatures in a rock may extend over a wide range of fields and temperatures, and different magnetization processes may affect domains from different parts of the spectrum. Since the NRM may have originated from a series of processes its various components may be distributed through the spectrum. The aim of demagnetization is the selective removal, first of components with low coercive force or low blocking temperature, and then of components with higher values, in order to investigate where, in the spectrum, the useful magnetic component resides. Examples are now given illustrating the removal of components imposed by the present field.

The first example shows the use of alternating magnetic fields (Figure 5.16). The specimen is from a latite intrusion in the Permian of Australia [7.42]. The NRM (M_n) has a direction (13, −41) and a magnitude of 14.7×10^{-5} emu/cm³. The direction is 24° from the present Earth's magnetic field **F** (12, −65) at the collecting locality. Treatment in alternating magnetic fields, increasing in steps of 30 oe, caused the directions to rotate about 100° along a great circle through M_n and **F**, progressively away from **F**, until a direction (12, +60) was reached, and there remained constant. The progressive rotation of the vector implies that a low coercivity component of magnetization, M_u, directed along **F** is being removed, and that this is completed in 210 oe. In higher demagnetizing fields the vector diminishes in magnitude without changing in direction. The NRM therefore consists of 2 components of differing stability, a component, M_u, directed along **F** and a component M_s in the direction (12, +60). The magnitudes M_u and M_s of these may be calculated since their directions are known and also the direction and magnitude of their resultant M_n. The values are $M_u = 18.0$ and $M_s = 8.1 \times 10^{-5}$ emu/cm³, the unstable magnetization of the NRM being over twice as large as the stable component.

Examples of thermal demagnetization by Wilson (1961) of baked laterite and weathered lava from the Antrim igneous suite of Northern Ireland [11.018 to 11.024] are given in Figure 5.17. The laterite underlies the lava and was baked by it. Then the lava was heavily weathered soon after extrusion. In both rocks M_n is presumably of CRM type. In the laterite M_n is 58° away from the geocentric dipole field **F** (inclination + 72°). Heating to 350°C causes rotation through 104°, in a plane containing M_n and **F**, to a direction approximately antiparallel to **F**. Further heating causes a reduction in intensity without change in direction. The

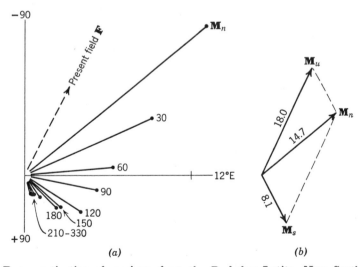

(a)   *(b)*

Figure 5.16. Demagnetization of specimen from the Berkeley Latite, New South Wales, Australia. (a) Rotation of vector directions away from the Earth's field produced by alternating field demagnetization; the field strengths (peak oe) used are marked on each vector (copyright 1961 by the University of Chicago, reproduced by kind permission of the University of Chicago Press). (b) Vector diagram of stable M_s and unstable M_u directions; magnitudes $\times 10^5$ emu/cm³. From Irving (1961).

major effect is that due to the removal of a component of magnetization $\mathbf{M}_u$ parallel to $\mathbf{F}$ in temperatures less than 350°C, and which is presumably of viscous origin imposed by the Earth's field recently. The small "tail" erased at temperatures less than 75°C is considered to be due to a temporary component $(\mathbf{M}_t)$ imposed by the Earth's field during storage after the specimen was collected. The NRM therefore consists of 3 components whose relative magnitudes may be calculated, and are (taking $M_n = 1$ arbitrary unit of intensity) $M_u = 2.9$, $M_s = 2.4$, $M_t = 0.1$. In the lava example the rotation is small (5°), the stable component predominates ($M_n = 1$, $M_u = 0.15$, $M_s = 1.1$) and there is no detectable temporary magnetization. The NRM directions in the laterite and weathered lava differ by 90°, but the stable component directions are only 6° apart, a difference which can be largely attributed to errors in

sample orientation in the field. It seems that remanence due to ancient weathering can be useful if the time of weathering is geologically ascertainable.

These results, and numerous others of similar type (see, in particular [1.63, 7.05, 7.42, 9.33, 9.46–50, 10.10, 10.15] and Cox (1961)) provide the basis of the methods now discussed.

§ 5.09   Magnetic and Thermal Cleaning

The part of the NRM of geophysical interest is the underlying stable magnetization, and it is obviously desirable to remove the unstable components; if this is achieved by alternating magnetic fields the procedure is referred to as *magnetic cleaning*, if by heat, it is called *thermal cleaning*. These procedures apply to secondary components of comparatively low stability, notably VRM's, stress-aided VRM's, partial TRM's

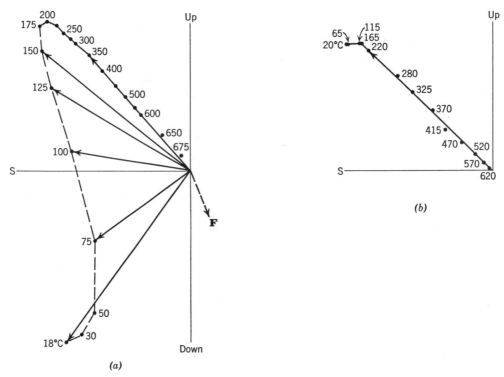

Figure 5.17. Thermal demagnetization of baked laterite (*a*) and weathered lava (*b*). $\mathbf{F}$ is the present geocentric dipole field in Northern Ireland and the directions are plotted in the plane of the meridian through $\mathbf{F}$. Each point represents the direction observed at the temperature with which it is labeled (°C). Redrawn from Wilson (1961), with the kind permission of the Royal Astronomical Society and R. L. Wilson.

acquired during secondary heating, or IRM components arising from lightning effects. They may not, in general, apply to secondary components of chemical origin, such as might arise from partial weathering and which may be of stable type.

Because of the great variability in magnetic properties the cleaning treatment required is not the same for all rocks. The question arises—what are the criteria for judging the treatment conditions necessary to minimize the effect of secondary components and yet ensure that a measureable proportion of the stable component remains? It is not sufficient simply to choose some arbitrary demagnetization field or heat treatment and submit all specimens to this. Two empirical procedures have been suggested. Some workers (As and Zidjerveld, 1958; McElhinny and Gough, 1963) use the criterion that the stable component is obtained after vector rotation stops and changes occur only in intensity (Figures 5.16, 5.17); the occurrence of an end-point beyond which rotation ceases implies that low stability components have been removed. Other workers (Irving, Stott, and Ward, 1961) use a criterion based on the dispersion of observations from several specimens from the same collecting site. The procedure is to select pilot specimens (5, for example) and study the dispersion of directions after each demagnetization step. The treatment necessary to produce minimum dispersion is selected and then applied to all specimens from the site. The idea at the base of both methods is, of course, the same, and it has been shown that its application to results from specimens from the same site gives indistinguishable estimates of the treatment required (Manwaring, 1963). The vector rotation criterion gives a value for each specimen, whereas the dispersion criterion gives an average value for each site. Both methods work well where the stabilities and directions of the two components differ sharply, and in these cases the choice of treatment conditions is not critical, provided the treatment necessary to remove the lower stability component is exceeded. But

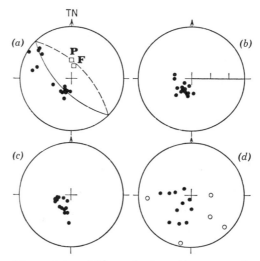

Figure 5.18. Effect of alternating magnetic field demagnetization on basalt specimens at site 5 (Yarrowvitch) in the Tertiary Basalts of New South Wales, Australia. (a) NRM, and after treatment in (b) 75, (c) 150 and (d) 750 oe(peak). In (a) **P** is the dipole field direction and **F** the present field, both on the upper hemisphere. The great circle (continuous on the lower hemisphere and dotted on the upper) through **P** and the mean direction after treatment in 75 oe is given in (a). A stereographic projection is used, dots (circles) denoting positive (negative) inclinations. Redrawn from Irving, Stott, and Ward (1961) with the kind permission of Taylor and Francis, London.

when the stability spectra of the two components overlap, or where their directions are not greatly different, or where smooth progressive vector rotations do not occur due perhaps to magnetic "noise" (§ 5.11), the problem is more difficult, and the statistical procedures in the second method are perhaps more applicable.

The example of magnetic cleaning is from the flat-lying Tertiary Basalts of New South Wales, Australia [11.094]. The directions, initially, and at 3 stages of partial demagnetization, in specimens from 1 site are plotted in Figure 5.18, and the precision in Figure 5.19. The directions are smeared toward the present field and good agreement is achieved after treatment in 150 oe; thereafter the directions scatter as the stable

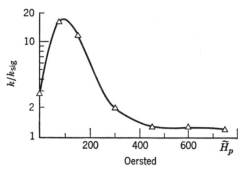

Oersted

Figure 5.19. Dispersion as a function of alternating magnetic field for Yarrowvitch basalt (Figure 5.18). k is Fisher's precision (equation 4.9) and $k_{sig} = (N-1)/(N-R_0)$ where R_0 is obtained from Table 4.4 at $\mathcal{P} = 0.05$. When $k/k_{sig} < 1$ the distribution may be considered random.

component itself is demagnetized. Minimum dispersion is achieved in a field of between 100 and 150 oe. The mean site directions (Figure 5.20) are initially widely scattered, but after partial demagnetization become closely grouped. Magnetic cleaning greatly improves the precision within- and between-sites. Other examples of magnetic cleaning may be found in the Appendix [1.42–51, 1.63–73, 1.87–89, 6.59, 6.60, 7.05, 7.11, 7.13, 7.18, 7.42, 7.43, 7.55, 7.56, 8.07, 8.29, 8.42, 8.44, 9.31, 9.32, 9.33, 9.36, 9.38, 9.40, 9.46–50, 10.09, 10.10, 10.11, 10.12, 10.15–18, 11.094, 11.110–116, 11.124, 12.48, 12.63–64, 12.68].

The example of thermal cleaning is from a study of specimens collected from 9 sites spread over a distance of 300 km in Upper Carboniferous glacial sediments of the Upper Kuttung Series in New South Wales, Australia [6.58]. The beds are variably tilted—the dips varying from 10° to 85°. The tilting occurred prior to the Triassic. The directions of NRM are smeared toward the present field by varying amounts, sometimes extensively, sometimes to a small degree. Progressive thermal demagnetization causes the distributions to condense, until at 300°C the agreement at each site is very good. Results from one site are shown in Figure 5.21. The mean site directions (Fig-

ure 5.22) initially are random ($N = 9$, $R = 3.58$) when *in situ*, and widely scattered when corrected for tilt ($R = 6.99$, $k = 4$). This indicates that large components of post-Permian age are present. The small but appreciable decrease in scatter suggests that stable pre-Triassic components occur. After heating to 300°C the *in situ* directions ($R = 6.98$, $k = 4$) are less scattered than the *in situ* NRM directions, and after correction the agreement becomes good ($R = 8.86$, $k = 57$). This demonstrates that secondary components have been removed, and that the stable magnetization was acquired prior to the Triassic.

Further cases of thermal cleaning are noted in the Appendix [5.02, 6.05–11, 6.28, 7.42, 10.10, 11.098, 11.103]. It should be mentioned that, as yet, only a small proportion of the paleomagnetic results is based on thermal or magnetic cleaning.

§ **5.10 Special Tests** This section deals with studies of certain bulk magnetic properties. Since the NRM is usually only a very small proportion of the potential remanence, the relevance of these bulk properties to the question of the reliability of the NRM as an indicator of the ancient field direction is

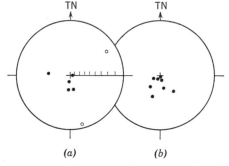

(a)   *(b)*

Figure 5.20. Mean site directions in the Tertiary Basalts of N.S.W. (*a*) NRM and (*b*) after magnetic cleaning. The NRM directions at one site were random and have no significant mean. Stereographic projection. Redrawn from Irving, Stott, and Ward (1960), with the kind permission of Taylor and Francis, London.

not always clear, but they are sometimes useful general guides.

Coercivity. The coercive force is the median point of the coercive force spectrum and high values suggest that the NRM is likely to be stable. It is, however, more usual in paleomagnetic work to measure the destructive field H_{cr}' (§ 2.08) or the coercivity of maximum IRM H_{cr} (§ 2.09). An example of the former is given in Figure 5.23. The material is glacial varved clay, and $H_{cr}' = 90$ oe. The occurrence of zero moment may not signify the destruction of the NRM, but only that the field has magnetized sufficient domains of low coercive force to produce an IRM balancing the moment of those NRM domains unaffected by the field. Petrova (1961) suggests that values of H_{cr}' in excess of about 40 oe indicate the presence of a useful natural remanence.

Values of H_{cr} in igneous rocks range from about 200 oe to over 1000 oe, and there is a broad empirical correlation between H_{cr} and stability as determined by alternating field methods: values in excess of 400 oe are generally associated with a stable NRM,

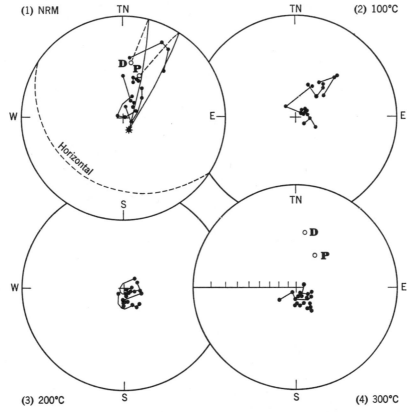

Figure 5.21. Thermal cleaning and condensation of smeared distribution in Carboniferous glacial sediments at Paterson, New South Wales. Stereographic projections are used, the plane of the projection being the bedding plane. The intersection of the horizontal with the upper hemisphere is shown by a dotted line (1). All the observed directions have positive inclinations and are marked by dots. The present (**P**) and axial dipole (**D**) field directions have negative inclinations and are marked by circles. Specimens from the same sample are linked together. The direction marked with a star in (1) is the mean direction after heating to 300°C (4). Redrawn from Irving, Robertson, Stott, Tarling, and Ward (1961), with the kind permission of the American Geophysical Union.

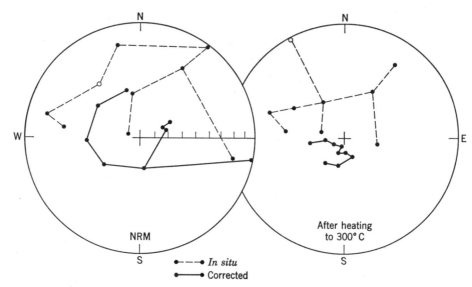

Figure 5.22. Mean site directions in glacial sediments of the Upper Kuttung Series. Equal-area projections are used, the dots (circles) denoting positive (negative) inclinations. The primitive is the horizontal plane for *in situ* directions and the bedding plane for the corrected directions.

whereas for values of 200 oe or below it is reasonable to anticipate that unstable components are present in the NRM.

Comparison of Demagnetization of NRM, TRM, and IRM. Comparison of demagnetization curves of NRM with those artificially produced is of much interest. The test is only applicable to igneous rocks or baked sediments. If the demagnetization curve of NRM is similar to that of TRM in the same specimen, the presumption that the NRM is of TRM type is strong. If, also, the direction of TRM is parallel to the ambient field, the NRM may be regarded as a reliable indicator of the direction of the Earth's field at the time the rock cooled. This test is of great power and an example is given in Figure 2.25. However, the NRM and TRM curves are usually dissimilar, the fall of intensity being more rapid in the former and may be comparable to the demagnetization curves obtained for IRM; if this is the case the need for cleaning procedures is indicated.

Ratio M_n/χ. In rocks not affected by lightning, values of about 1 or more for the ratio of the intensity of NRM to the

susceptibility are associated with NRM's of stable type, whereas values below 0.1 are usually associated with the presence of substantial unstable components. However, low values can arise because of a stable magnetization acquired in a weak field, or if there has been viscous decay without the build-up of unstable components. However, as a general guide the ratio has practical value. Some typical results are given here.

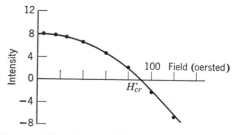

Figure 5.23. Steady field demagnetization of the fossil remanence of a sample of varved clay from Vermont, U.S.A., aged about 11,000 years. Intensity in emu/cm$^3 \times 10^5$. Redrawn from Johnson, Murphy, and Torreson (1948), with the kind permission of the American Geophysical Union and E. A. Johnson.

Magnetic Anisotropy. The reliability of observations of NRM is increased if the rock can be shown to be effectively isotropic. In addition to the anisotropy studies noted in § 2.14 a useful test is that employed by the earliest investigators (§ 1.8), namely to give a specimen a TRM in a weak magnetic field; if the direction is parallel to the applied field it is reasonable to presume that the magnetic component responsible for the NRM is itself isotropic. An example is given in Figure 2.18.

Curie Temperatures. The occurrence of Curie points only a little above normal temperatures indicates the presence of even lower blocking temperatures and of an unstable magnetization. Kawai (1955) has shown that the Azuki Tuff and Miocene sediments from the Bôsô Peninsula of Japan have a spectrum of Curie points ranging from 35° to 580°C. He found, empirically, that "of the minerals having unstable magnetization the lowest Curie point occurs generally in the range from 90°C to room temperature, whereas that of stable magnetization occurs in the range from 130° to 200°C."

The occurrence in igneous rocks of high Curie temperatures near the ideal value for magnetite and which are repeatable on cooling are sometimes associated with stable magnetization, whereas rocks with lower values not reproduceable on heating are unstable. This type of behavior has been found, for example, in the Permian latites of New South Wales [7.42].

Stress Effects. Studies of stress effects are useful guides to reliability. The demonstration of the absence of stress effects on TRM in certain isotropic rocks (§ 2.15) encourages confidence in the usefulness of the paleomagnetic results from these particular rock types.

§ 5.11 Magnetic "Noise"

Even in the most carefully conducted experiments there are usually substantial differences of a statistical nature between repeat results from the same collecting site, and it is possible that these arise from magnetic "noise" in demagnetized components. The question is relevant for the theory of the origin of dispersion, and is of practical importance for the experimenter who requires some feel as to the maximum precision to be expected in given circumstances. The hypothetical situation envisaged is set out in Figure 5.24. Except in rocks magnetized by lightning, the NRM (M_n) is always small compared to the maximum IRM (M_{max}). The small

Table 5.6 Some Values of the Ratio M_n/χ. *x is the number of determinations.* *The values are expressed as means or ranges.*

Rock Unit and Type	x	M_n/χ	Remarks
Tertiary basalts, Iceland [11.108]	$\simeq 70$	2.9	Substantially stable
Torridonian, reddish very fine sandstone, U.K. [1.01]	9	0.8–3.0	Stable
Torridonian, green siltstone, U.K. [1.01]	4	0.1–0.01	Unstable, directed along present field
Tasmanian Dolerite, Australia [9.30]	60	1.5	Stable
Ferrar Dolerite, Antarctica [9.38]	100	1.1	Substantially stable, very small unstable components present
Whin Sill Dolerite, U.K. [7.15]	5	0.9–1.7	Stable
Upper Marine Latites, Australia [7.42]	17	0.2–0.05	Very large unstable components present
EM7 Basalt, Mohole Project (Cox and Doell, 1962)	23	17.8	Stable

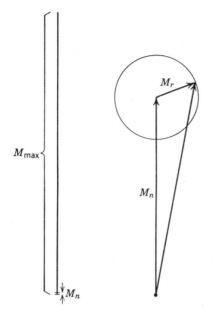

Figure 5.24. Schematic representation of the magnitudes of the fossil magnetism and maximum IRM is shown diagrammatically on the left. On the right the paleomagnetic vector is drawn 100 times bigger and the way in which the random moment M_r may impart a dispersion is indicated. Fluctuations in the magnitude of the random moment will also occur.

NRM probably arises from the alignment of domains in a small hard component of the magnetic fraction, whereas the comparatively high IRM values are probably due to a large soft component demagnetized in the natural state. It is supposed that this demagnetized component has a certain residual moment called the *random moment* M_r, which is negligible compared to M_{max} but not compared to M_n; M_r is not a remanence in the normal sense, but is the state of least energy dependent on coupling between domains and on anisotropy. In isotropic material M_r will be randomly directed from specimen to specimen and will impart a dispersion of Fisherian type to the NRM directions, and so constitute a "noise" level limiting agreement between specimens. It may be expected that this effect will be greatest in rocks whose remanence has undergone extensive viscous decay. The most convenient

circumstance to study is the dispersion between different specimens from the same outcrop of igneous rock—the whole of which acquired its primary magnetization simultaneously so that dispersion due to field variations is not present. The following discussion is developed with this instance in mind, although, in principle, the effect is a general one which may always be present to a greater or lesser degree.

There are three features of the paleomagnetic results which indicate that such a "noise" level may exist. (1) Even after careful cleaning, specimens from a single stratum nearly always show a residual dispersion greater than that due to errors in the direction determinations. (2) In igneous rocks, there is, as a general rule, a strong correlation between dispersion and magnetic instability as determined in the laboratory, the dispersion being least in stable rocks. The very large dispersion characteristic of very unstable rock is shown in Figure 5.25. Repeat measurements on the same specimen after storage in the laboratory for a period of days are inconsistent. Demagnetization

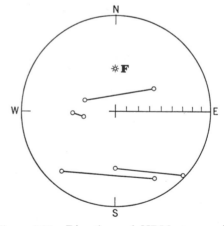

Figure 5.25. Directions of NRM at one site in the Bombo latite. This is a lava flow of Permian age [7.42]. Directions from specimens from the same sample are linked. **F** is the direction of the geocentric axial dipole field at the site. An equal-area projection is used, the primitive being the horizontal. All directions are upward.

in successively higher alternating magnetic fields causes the directions to oscillate wildly (Figure 5.26a). (3) Rock specimens subjected to severe demagnetization and later measured at normal temperatures are sometimes found to have their moments not reduced beyond a certain minimum value, called the *minimum intensity*, which may represent the state of least energy of demagnetized specimens.

The phenomenon of minimum intensity has been recognized by several workers (Irving, Stott, and Ward, 1961; Mumme, 1962b; Dickson, 1962b) using different experimental apparatus but there is likely to be much dispute as to its origin. The following remarks refer only to certain observed instances in Tertiary [11.094] and Permian [7.42] volcanics of New South Wales. In certain specimens it is found that after treatment in alternating magnetic fields, whose strength is several times greater than the coercivity of maximum IRM, the directions at each site approach a random distribution. An example from one flow is given in Figure 5.19. The intensity diminishes with increasing field but levels off to an average value at about that field in which the dispersions begin to increase. This average value is the minimum intensity, M_{min}. There are, however, fluctuations about this average, and these are associated with widely oscillating directions. The remanence within each specimen is inhomogeneous. A typical fluctuating high field curve with associated scattered directions is **given** in Figure 5.26. A comparable effect is found as a result of thermal demagnetization of the same specimens; on heating to temperatures above the Curie point and cooling in zero field, residual moments are found similar in magnitude to those obtained by field demagnetization (Table 5.7). Effects of this type are to be seen in most published curves of stepwise thermal demagnetization in which small moments are recorded after cooling in zero field from temperatures above the Curie point, but experimenters have not paid much attention to them. In the material of Table 5.7 the minimum intensity is small compared to

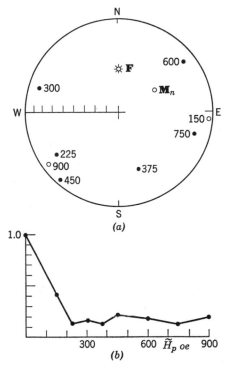

Figure 5.26. Demagnetization of Bombo latite specimen with very low stability. (*a*) Direction changes upon successive treatments in alternating fields (peak strength given by every direction). M_n is the NRM direction. An equal-area projection is used, dots (circles) indicating positive (negative) inclinations. (*b*) Demagnetization curve plotted as a ratio M/M_n of the moment after treatment in an alternating field $\widetilde{H}_p$ to the NRM; $M_n = 3.58 \times 10^{-3}$ emu/cm^3. Data of Irving and L. G. Parry (1963).

the maximum IRM, being a few parts of a per cent of this value, whereas the percentage ratio M_{min}/M_n is not small, ranging up to 14 per cent. It should be emphasized that this material is *not stable* magnetically and stable specimens behave quite differently; stable rocks, for example, the Aden trachyte (Figure 2.22), give smoothly decreasing curves, and the maximum demagnetizing field strengths available [about 1000 oe(peak) strength] do not reduce the magnetization to the minimum intensity level.

If it is assumed that the minimum intensity is an estimate of the random moment

Table 5.7   Some Magnetic Properties of the Tertiary Basalts of New South Wales. The values are averages of about 4 specimens at each of 7 sites. Minimum intensities, obtained after alternating field (ac) and thermal (th) demagnetization, are compared in the first 2 columns. The intensities of NRM (M_n) and maximum isothermal remanence (M_{max}) are in units of 10^{-3} emu/cm³. H_{cr}, the coercivity of M_{max}, is given in oersted. Data of Irving, Stott, and Ward (1961), by kind permission of Taylor and Francis, London.

	M_{min} (ac)	M_{min} (th)	M_n	M_{max}	H_{cr}
1	0.06	0.11	10.48	101.8	200
2	0.82	0.63	5.95	188.0	225
3	1.34	1.67	32.25	224.5	205
4	0.26	0.22	13.74	354.0	190
5	0.24	0.23	2.52	354.0	180
6	0.11	0.16	1.25	405.0	180
7	0.86	0.43	7.13	236.5	160

of the model in Figure 5.24 it is possible to test if its magnitude is consistent with the observed dispersion. The material chosen as an example (site 5, Figures 5.18 and 5.19, and Table 5.7) has low stability, and the NRM contains a large VRM which is removed in alternating fields of 150 oe, the intensity, M_{150}, after this treatment being 0.56×10^{-3} emu/cm³. After treatment, a dispersion remains, given by $k = 23$. If this residual scatter is due to random moments, then their most probable magnitude is given by $M_r{}^2 = 3(M_{150})^2 k^{-1}$ (equation 3.7) giving $M_r = 0.20 \times 10^{-3}$, which compares well with the observed minimum intensity of 0.24×10^{-3}. As may be expected, M_r is the lesser, since M_{min} also includes a random component derived from the demagnetization of M_{150}. To a good approximation, therefore, the dispersion remaining after removal of VRM may be accounted for by assuming the presence of randomly directed moments similar in magnitude and behavior to the observed minimum intensity.

The origin of the minimum intensity is not known. It may be due to instrumental imperfections, or may be an intrinsic rock property. The comparable values obtained by field and heat demagnetization (Table 5.7), and the consistency between M_r and M_{min} just described, suggests that the latter is the case. While instrumental imperfections may be important, there is likely to be some residual fluctuating magnetization even if the demagnetization occurs under perfect conditions. The reason is that spontaneous magnetization is lost only at the Curie point, so that the effect of alternating magnetic fields is one of rearrangement of domains, and because of statistical fluctuations and coupling between adjacent domain moments the net moment of a specimen is never likely to be zero. When cooling from above the Curie temperature in zero field, the spontaneous magnetization, as it becomes fixed at the blocking temperature, will be subject to similar effects. In anisotropic specimens the minimum moment will be aligned in the easy direction; in effectively isotropic material it will be randomly directed from specimen to specimen, or in the same specimen upon repeated demagnetization. The observed minimum intensity, and the scattered almost random directions in alternating fields whose strength exceeds the coercivity, may therefore be a result of such fluctuations, which will depend on the number and coupling of domains.

There is, as yet, no adequate theoretical treatment of this problem (see discussion by Dickson, 1962b), but the empirical correlation between dispersion and stability leads to the intuition that the minimum intensity and the observed dispersion (after cleaning) provide sufficient information for estimating the viscous decay of intensity with time, and thus the magnitude of the primary component; if this were possible, estimates of intensity of the paleogeomagnetic field become feasible by a method other than that normally used (Chapter Eight).

§ 5.12   **Red Sediments**   Extensive reconnaissance studies of sedimentary rocks in Great Britain carried out in the early 1950's (reported by Runcorn, 1957) showed that the green beds of the Diabaig Group of the Torridonian Sandstone Series, certain grey Silurian mudstones of Westmorland, green and ocher colored Devonian sediments from Caithness, and grey and buff colored sediments from the Jurassic and Cretaceous of SE England, were weakly magnetized with directions which were either highly scattered or near the present Earth's field, whereas red sediments from the Torridonian, Old Red Sandstone (Devonian), and New Red Sandstone (Triassic) had a comparatively intense remanent magnetization with closely grouped directions diverging strongly from the present field. Since that time, red beds have been extensively studied in many parts of the world, generally in preference to rocks of other colors but the origin of their magnetization is not, at present, understood, and, in any particular instance, it is not at all clear when, in the history of the rock, the fossil magnetization was acquired. These are matters of current research from which no general picture has yet emerged.

The red beds studied have been mostly in the grain-size range, siltstone, very fine or fine sandstones. The predominant nonmagnetic mineral is generally quartz, with variable proportions of felspar, clay minerals, micas, and so forth. Broadly speaking, the magnetic material occurs in four ways, two associated with the *red staining* and two with the *detrital black grains*. The proportions of these components vary widely in different formations, but generally most of the iron present is in the red staining. The black detrital grains are *specularite* (hematite α Fe_2O_3), which, in the cases so far studied, contain impurities of *magnetite* (Creer, Irving, and Runcorn, 1954; Blackett, 1956; Creer, 1957a; Irving, 1957a; J. H. Parry, 1957; Van Houten, 1961) recognizable optically, and by thermomagnetic analysis. An example of the latter shows, in Torridonian material, Curie points of 575° and 675°C, respectively magnetite and hematite, their ratio by weight being roughly 1.5 per cent (Figure 5.27). Specularite is not common in source rocks, and it seems likely that the

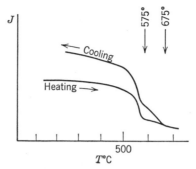

Figure 5.27. Intensity of magnetization, *J*, in 1000 oe, as a function of temperature *T* for extract of magnetic mineral from Torridonian sandstones. Extract from band *BB* Figure 5.10. Temperature scale is not linear. Redrawn from Parry (1957), with the kind permission of Taylor and Francis and J. H. Parry.

black detrital grains were derived from the oxidation of magnetite (§ 2.06) during erosion and transportation, or after deposition. The red staining is thought to be finely divided hematite or one of the oxyhydroxides of iron. It occurs, either as *interstitial dust*, which may be detrital or secondary, or as *films* or *irregular patches*, which sometimes show a secondary relationship to the detrital particles. Secondary deposits of red pigment may have been brought in by interstitial water, or may arise from the redistribution of detrital material.

The contribution of each magnetic phase to the fossil magnetism is not known, and is likely to differ greatly in different formations. In most cases each component, if magnetized to saturation, is present in sufficient quantities to produce the observed NRM, and it seems clear that the carrier of the NRM is only a small fraction of the total magnetic material present.

The magnetic properties of red beds are complicated by the fact that a very broad grain-size spectrum is usually present extending from several tens of microns down into the superparamagnetic range (Creer, 1961), so that the blocking temperatures may spread from the Curie points of magnetite and hematite down to room temperatures. Creer has determined the diameters of the superparamagnetic grains as about 20 Å.

Although alternating field demagnetization has been shown to be useful for removing unstable VRM imposed by the present field (Creer, 1959), and for reducing dispersion (Black, 1963; Gough and Opdyke, 1963) in red sediments, the maximum field strengths available in most paleomagnetic laboratories (about 1000 oe) are too weak to affect the high stability components (Opdyke, 1961a), and thermal demagnetization is necessary for study of the full range of the stability spectrum. Thermal demagnet-

ization of red beds was pioneered by Leng (1955) who showed that certain Triassic specimens could be completely demagnetized by heating to 650°C and cooling in zero field. His experimental curve (Figure 5.28) is of simple type showing a spread of blocking temperatures from 400° to 650°C, mostly in the range 600° to 650°C. An example from the Torridonian Sandstone shows a slight rise up to 500°C due to the removal of a small VRM component imposed by the present field, and thereafter a steady fall to 650°C. The curve from the Freda Sandstone member of the Keween-

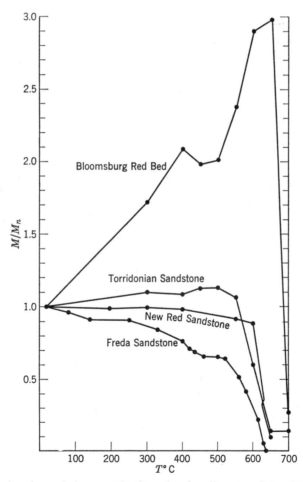

Figure 5.28. Stepwise thermal demagnetization of red sediments. Intensities M after heating are normalized to unity at room temperature. Triassic New Red Sandstone (Leng, 1955). Torridonian band *BB* [1.01] (Figure 5.10). Freda Sandstone [1.37] (P. M. DuBois, 1962). Bloomsburg Red Beds (Silurian of Pennsylvania).

awan (P. M. Du Bois, 1962) gives a range of blocking temperatures up to 450°C, then a shelf, due possibly to magnetite, and, finally, a steady and steep decline due to the blocking temperature spectrum of hematite. In these 3 examples there is little change in the remanence direction up to 600°C. In contrast, the fourth curve, from the Silurian Bloomsburg red beds, shows a spectacular increase and change in direction of about 100°, due to the removal of a component occupying the range of blocking temperatures up to 500°C and directed along the Permian field direction. The component remaining unchanged up to 650°C is due to hematite and may be the required primary magnetization. In a similar result, recently obtained by Chamalaun and Creer (1963), a component of Permian age dominates the NRM of a Devonian red bed [5.02].

Although there are many unsolved problems the very high stability of some red sediments and the good agreement between directions in red beds and igneous material of similar age from the same region (Figure 5.1) suggest that in some cases they are reliable indicators of the paleogeomagnetic field direction, either at or shortly after deposition. It is, however, very desirable in all red bed studies that there should be control observations from igneous rocks, and tests should be made for secondary components by thermal demagnetization and studies of tilted beds (§ 5.04).

§ 5.13 Surface Effects The directions of NRM in natural outcrops are often highly scattered and unrepresentative of observations on samples from the same rock unit but collected from quarries, road cuttings, or mines well below natural surfaces. Surface effects are least noticeable in regions which have been extensively glaciated in the Pleistocene, or which are now undergoing active erosion. They greatly hinder the task of obtaining reliable paleomagnetic observations in such regions as Africa, Australia, and South America, where, not only are surface effects most marked, but road-building and quarrying is less extensive than in the

more developed countries of Europe or North America. It is possible, for example, in Pennsylvania, to drive along highway cuttings and collect systematically from thousands of feet of clean fresh sequences which yield results free of surface effects; but in Australia, Africa, or South America one may drive for weeks and be fortunate to encounter more than half a dozen suitable exposures. Possible causes of surface effects are weathering, lightning, and stress effects due to thermal-cycling. Daily thermal-cycling penetrates several inches, annual cycling several feet, and these may be expected to produce viscous effects which should be corrected by partial demagnetization, and would not be distinguishable from normal viscous components. The effect of stress-cycling is not known but it would presumably enhance viscous effects.

Recent weathering presents a severe sampling problem in tropical or subtropical regions where a weathered cap tens or hundreds of feet thick may render a rock unit inaccessible to paleomagnetic study. Weathering is a process of oxidation and hydration in which iron minerals are usually changed to hematite or one of the oxyhydroxides of iron. An example of results from weathered and unweathered Cambrian sandstone is given in Figure 5.29. The directions in unweathered, compact, pinkish-brown sandstone are towards the SW with shallow negative inclinations, whereas those in recently weathered sandstones from the same formation are clustered around the present field. The weathered rock is bright red, friable, and porous, and has undergone chemical weathering in some cases to a depth of several hundred feet. The iron minerals have been reconstituted and there has been a good deal of iron enrichment. The original magnetization has been destroyed and a new one presumably of chemical origin built up. Manley (1956), Howell, Martinez, Frosch, and Statham (1960), and Robertson and Hastie (1962) have studied other cases of recent weathering. An effect of *ancient weathering* is described on p. 88.

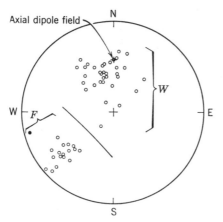

Figure 5.29. Directions of fossil magnetization in weathered (*W*), and unweathered (*F*), Elder Mountain Sandstone (Cambrian) from northern Western Australia. A stereographic projection is used and the directions are plotted as circles (dot) on the upper (lower) hemisphere. Redrawn from Irving (1959), with the kind permission of the Royal Astronomical Society.

Lightning. The outer few feet of rock surfaces are often strongly and irregularly magnetized due to lightning strikes (§ 1.8). The disturbing effect of lightning on paleomagnetic observations was pointed out by Hallimond and Herroun (1933), who advised that in order to avoid them samples should be collected from 50 ft or more beneath natural surfaces—this is now known to be an over-estimate. There have been recent studies by Matsuzaki, Kobayashi, and Momose (1954), Rimbert (1958), Domen (1958*a*), Cox (1961), Khan (1960), Russinov and Sholpo (1963), and K. W. T. Graham (1961). Graham's work on outcrops of the Robinson dike in South Africa is described below.

Clouds are generally negatively charged, and in a lightning strike electrons pass from the cloud to the ground. Each strike consists of several pulses, the current in the main stroke being of the orders 10^4 to 10^5 amps. The current takes a few microseconds to reach its peak, and about 5 times as long to decay to half this value.

The Robinson member of the Pilansberg Dike System showed close grouping of results from samples collected in deep mines (Gough, 1956). The mean direction is (14, +72) and the intensity 2.8×10^{-3} emu/cm³. In contrast, the directions in surface outcrops are highly scattered with intensities ranging up to about 400×10^{-3}. Detailed sampling was carried out over about 10 ft of outcrop, and the directions were found to be mainly in a NE/SW plane forming a circular pattern roughly concentric about the point *C* (Figure 5.30). The directions are interpreted as being due to a horizontal current flowing along the surface and into the diagram at *C*. However, this simple idea is not accurate, since specimens at similar distance from *C* have intensities which differ by a factor 10. This is explained by supposing that the current path was not straight. Demagnetization by alternating magnetic fields gave curves of IRM type, and the directions in most specimens after magnetic cleaning in several hundred oersteds rotated into the direction observed at depth. The strength of current at *C* may be calculated if the variation of intensity with applied field for this rock type is known. Graham measured this, and obtained a value of about 5×10^4 amps. This is comparable in magnitude to the currents known to be associated with lightning strike.

§ **5.14** **Time Basis of Results** In order to relate the paleomagnetically determined field variations to a reliable time basis it is necessary to know the geological age of the rocks studied and also the period at which the useful component of remanence was acquired. Good age control, either by stratigraphic or radioisotope methods, is desirable. Many paleomagnetic results have been obtained from lavas and red beds which are not precisely dated, and red bed results in particular suffer from the uncertainty as to the date at which their remanence was acquired (§ 5.12). Perhaps the most accurate time basis so far achieved is in certain igneous intrusions, which have been dated by radioisotope methods, and where there is

contact evidence indicating that the remanence was acquired during cooling. An example of this is the Cygnet Alkaline Complex of Tasmania which is intrusive into
undisturbed sediments or dolerite. Detailed
demagnetization studies of several bodies and
their hybrid and contact rocks provide a
paleomagnetic result of high reliability, the
stable magnetization being acquired at cooling (Robertson and Hastie, 1962) [10.09]).
The age of the intrusions is not well defined
stratigraphically but potassium-argon determinations on separated minerals gave these
ages: sanidine 99 m.y., biotite 99 m.y. and
hornblende 109 m.y., with an average of
104 m.y., or Cenomanian on Kulp's 1961
Time Scale (Evernden and Richards, 1962).
The mean direction of the stable magnetization is 314, −85, and this gives a reliable
estimate of the average direction of the
Earth's field in Tasmania in later Lower
Cretaceous time. Further examples may be
found in the Appendix.

§ **5.15   Repeatability of Results**   In
paleomagnetic surveys human errors occur

and the question arises as to how results
obtained by one worker agree with those
obtained by other observers studying the
same rock unit at different laboratories. By
and large the answer to this question is that
the agreement is good, but such checks are
still few in number and more are needed.

The independent surveys of the Supai
Formation of Arizona [7.51] made by Doell
(1955) at the University of California, J. W.
Graham (1955) at the Carnegie Institution,
and Runcorn (1955a) at Cambridge University, gave results in broad agreement. There
is the work of Mumme [11.124] at the University of Adelaide on the Older Volcanics
of Victoria, which is underpinned by detailed
demagnetization studies, and which confirms
the result of the earlier reconnaissance by
Irving and Green [11.093] at the Australian
National University; the means obtained by
the Adelaide and Canberra workers are, respectively, 19, −71 ($a_{95} = 9°$) and 17, −73
($a_{95} = 7°$), which are statistically indistinguishable. There is the work of Hood
[1.46–49] on the Sudbury Nickel Irruptive
which has been confirmed by the later more

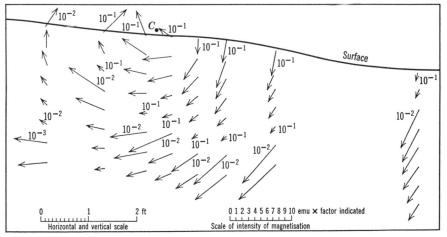

Figure 5.30. Section through an outcrop of Robinson dike in NE/SW plane. Specimen measured at intervals of about 10 per foot of core. Arrows are averages for about 5 specimens. The
intensity variation is given by the arrow lengths. The intensities decrease with depth and
the appropriate orders of magnitude are given reading from top to bottom. Redrawn from
Graham (1961), with the kind permission of the Royal Astronomical Society and K. W. T.
Graham.

extensive survey of this body by Sopher [1.87, 88].

Sometimes, however, discrepancies do occur. For example, there is a difference of roughly 5° between the results of Turnbull [9.37] and Bull, Irving, and Willis [9.38] from the Ferrar Dolerite of Antarctica. Turnbull's result is based directly on measurements of the NRM, but the later workers found small viscous components directed along the present field and removed them by magnetic cleaning. This accounts for the discrepancy.

§ 5.16 Minimum Criteria of Reliability

Before any reliance can be placed on paleomagnetic directions as indicators of the directions of the ancient field, it is necessary to demonstrate a measure of internal consistency and magnetic stability. Also, the age of the rock should be known, at least within certain broad limits. Although many results are available, consistency has not always been demonstrated, studies of stability not always made, nor the rock age defined satisfactorily. But it is impractical, at this early stage, to expect too perfect a standard. It is, however, clear that in the absence of supporting evidence a simple observation of a direction of fossil magnetism cannot, without much uncertainty, be assumed to be the direction of the ancient field, and consequently this book shall consider only those results which fulfill certain *minimum* criteria. In the appendix, results which do not fulfill these criteria, are entered in brackets; these constitute about 10 per cent of all results. The criteria are as follows.

1. *Number of Samples.* No result is considered adequate unless it is based on consistent observations from 5 or more separately oriented samples. Results based on fewer than 5 samples are considered inadequate whatever the stratigraphic distribution of samples and however many specimens were cut from them.

2. *Published Statement.* In certain cases authors have stated that they do not consider their results indicative of the Earth's field direction at the time of formation and such results are set aside.

3. *Circle of Confidence.* If the circle of confidence ($\wp = 0.05$) given in the original exceeds 25° then the result is considered inadequate, since it is felt that a mean direction which is not defined to an accuracy greater than this is unlikely to be physically meaningful.

4. *Stability.* Results from rocks whose age is Tertiary or older are not considered adequate unless there is evidence that the directions diverge significantly from the direction of the present field and that of the geocentric axial dipole field, or unless stability was demonstrated by at least one of the tests described in this chapter. Results from Quaternary rocks are not considered adequate unless there is evidence that the directions diverge significantly from the direction of the present field, or unless stability was demonstrated by at least one test.

5. *Age of the Rock.* In general, the geological age of the rock, or, in the case of baked contacts, the age of the igneous body, should be known within the limits Precambrian, Lower Paleozoic, Upper Paleozoic, Mesozoic, and Cenozoic. The ages of most of the beds studied are known very much more accurately than this. Rock ages which border these groups are regarded as satisfactory if the uncertainty on either side of the boundary does not exceed a geological period.

6. *Time of Origin of the Magnetization.* Results from rocks which are known to have acquired their magnetization long after the period of formation are not considered.

It is emphasized that these are *minimum* criteria. *It is not intended to imply that the results which satisfy them necessarily give the direction of the geomagnetic field at the time of formation of the rocks in question.* The purpose of erecting and applying these criteria is to separate off from the main body of paleomagnetic data those results which, on common sense grounds, can be regarded as of no use for the task of tracing the past history of the geomagnetic field. In general, the application of these criteria will achieve this objective, although it could be argued by perfectionists that they are too lenient so that results of doubtful value are retained. Certainly, as the subject develops more stringent criteria will have to be applied. The details relevant to the application of these criteria are given in the Appendix notes so that readers may judge these matters for themselves.

CHAPTER
SIX

Paleomagnetically determined
field directions

§ **6.01** **Preliminary Remarks** This chapter is concerned primarily with the *mean directions* of fossil magnetism in rock units and, to a lesser extent, with the *dispersion of directions* about these means. Mean directions may be expected to provide information about the past behavior of the Earth's dipole field, whereas dispersion may be expected to provide information about the secular variation of the ancient field. Occurrences of reversals of magnetization are noted, but the main discussion of these is set aside for Chapter Seven.

In this review [1] only those results are considered which fulfill the minimum reliability criteria (§ 5.16). The descriptions are given working backward in time starting with the

Quaternary. It might be thought better to proceed forward in time, beginning with results from Precambrian rocks; but generally, in these older sequences, the observational coverage is less complete, and the pattern of results more complicated than for younger rocks. It is preferable to proceed from the comparatively simple to the more complex. The account is concerned only with broad features, and is supplemented in the Appendix in which original sources are cited. The results are presented in various ways in order to display their different features. As an initial step in interpretation, the results are considered as evidence for or against certain geological and geophysical hypotheses. These arguments cannot be followed through without taking into account much geological evi-

---

[1] One problem in reviewing paleomagnetic results is that of how to deal with data that are published during the course of compilation. Some of the analyses presented in this and later chapters are based on extensive computations which cannot possibly be repeated as each new datum appears. The procedure adopted is to divide the basic data into two groups: *group A* comprising the data in the main list of the Appendix which were available to the author when compilation started (late 1961); and *group B* comprising group A together with the data in the supplementary

appendix list—data which became available between late 1961 and late 1963 when the last major revision was made. When results are presented in tables or figures it is stated whether they are based on the A or B group data. In certain other cases results are abstracted directly from previous reviews without being brought into line with the appendix data; this is done when it is felt that revision so as to include more recent data would neither change the result substantially, nor render it more useful.

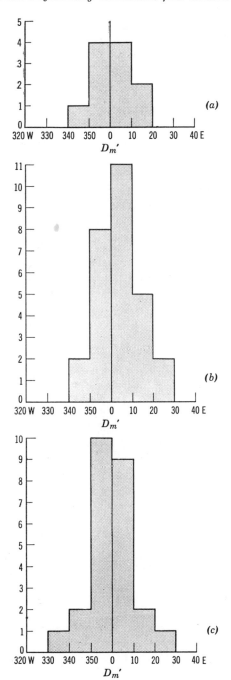

Figure 6.1. Declinations of mean directions of rock units of Quaternary and Upper Tertiary age (*B* group data). Frequency histograms of declination values (D_m') are plotted irrespective of sign obtained as follows: when $0° < D_m < 90°$, $D_m' = D_m$; when $90° < D_m < 180°$, D_m'

dence, but in this chapter the discussion is concerned only with the paleomagnetic aspects—the comparison with geological evidence being reserved for Chapter Nine.

§ **6.02** **Cenozoic Results** *The Past Few Thousand Years.* There are 11 results covering approximately the past 7000 years. They are based on studies of baked clays, periglacial varved sediments, and igneous rocks. Four results are from Europe, 3 from Asia and 1 each from Africa, Antarctica, Hawaii, and Iceland. The polarities are all negative. The mean declination is zero (Figure 6.1*a*) and the inclination is consistent with that of the geocentric axial dipole field (Figure 6.2*a*). This result is presented in an alternative fashion in Figure 6.3*a* in which the paleomagnetic poles are plotted. These cluster around the geographical pole— not the geomagnetic pole. The mean pole coincides within the errors with the geographic pole, but differs from the geomagnetic pole (Table 6.1).

Pleistocene and Plio-Pleistocene. Results are available from all continents, although those from Europe and northern Asia are the most numerous. Most results are from beds of Pleistocene age, but in some cases these range down into the Pliocene. It is not always possible to make a rigorous distinction between results from rocks of Pleistocene and Upper Pliocene age, partly because of uncertainties in dating, and partly because of the way in which the sampling has been carried out and the results reported. Younger Pleistocene beds are characterized by negative directions and older Pleistocene beds by positive directions. Both polarities occur in the Plio-Pleistocene. The declination values cluster around true north (Figure 6.1*b*) and the inclinations (Figure 6.2*a*) are roughly those to be ex-

$= 180 - D_m$; when $180° < D_m < 270°$, $D_m' = D_m - 180°$; when $270° < D_m < 360°$, $D_m' = D_m$; (*a*) gives the values for the past 7000 years ($N = 11$), (*b*) for Pleistocene and Plio-Pleistocene ($N = 28$), and (*c*) values for the Upper Tertiary ($N = 25$).

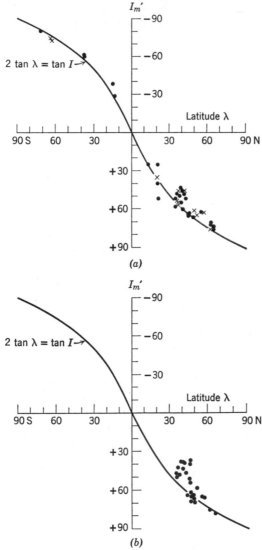

pected from the field of a geocentric axial dipole. The paleomagnetic poles cluster around the geographic pole although they are more widely scattered than those from more recent rocks (Figure 6.3b, Table 6.1). The mean pole coincides within the error with the geographic pole.

Tertiary Results. Many results are from lavas of terrestrial origin. Stratigraphic control of these is sometimes poor, and it is often not possible to assign them to a particular epoch within the Tertiary. There are also several results which include data from Quaternary beds. The results are considered under the following three headings.

Upper Tertiary. Data from rocks of designated Upper Tertiary age have been derived mainly from locations in intermediate to high northerly latitudes. Reversals of polarity without substantial changes of axis are a characteristic feature. The directions, irrespective of sign, are never very far from the geocentric axial dipole field (Figures 6.1c and 6.2b) so that the paleomagnetic poles are grouped approximately around the present geographic pole, although with more spread than in the Quaternary (Figure 6.4a, Table 6.1). In many cases, for example, in the Miocene and Pliocene results from Japan [11.066, 069] and the Miocene of France [11.005], individual results differ significantly from the geographic pole. Moreover, the mean pole is 5° from the geographic pole, an amount equal to the radius of the circle of 95 per cent confidence so that the departure borders on the significant. But there is considerable doubt as to whether the paleomagnetic results are yet sufficiently numerous or precise to detect such small changes. To a close approximation, the results from the Upper Tertiary and Quaternary show the Earth's field to have been that of a geocentric axial dipole, the approximation being more exact for younger than older rocks within this time span. This fundamental point was first made by Hospers (1954a, 1955) on the basis of fewer data, but has been borne out subsequently. Considered on the geological time scale, the divergence of the present-day geomagnetic axis appears

Figure 6.2. Inclinations of mean directions of rock units of Quaternary and Upper Tertiary age as a function of latitude λ of collecting localities (B group data). The effect of reversals is allowed for by this convention; if λ is northerly, then $I_m' = I_m$ when I_m negative, or $I_m' = -I_m$ when I_m positive, and vice-versa for southerly collecting localities. (a) Recent (11 crosses) and Pleistocene and Plio-Pleistocene (28 dots) results, (b) Upper Tertiary results (25 points). It might be noted that in this Figure and in Figure 6.1 there are 28 Pleistocene and Plio-Pleistocene results whereas 30 are listed in Table 6.1; this discrepancy arises because poles only are available for results [12.49, 50].

as a transient phenomenon. The exact correlation over the past few million years of the geomagnetic and present rotational axes and their approximate correlation over the past 20 m.y. opens up the possibility of tracing the movements of the geographical pole in the remote geological past by studying the directions of magnetization in rocks of pre-Upper Tertiary age. Results from Mt. Etna [12.09] and from Britain [12.08], each of which covers about 2000 years, average to the geocentric axial dipole field, indicating that a few thousand years are sufficient to average out the secular changes.

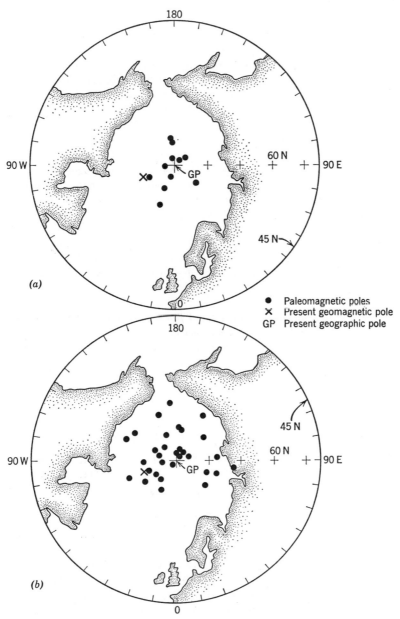

Figure 6.3. Paleomagnetic poles: Quaternary and Plio-Pleistocene (*B* group data). Polar equal-area projection north of 45° N. (*a*) Past 7000 years. (*b*) Pleistocene and Plio-Pleistocene.

This is consistent with the period suggested by the rate of the westerly drift of the field.

Lower Tertiary. Reversals of magnetization are again common in the results from beds of Lower Tertiary age, but their most important feature is, that with three exceptions (the Andean Intrusive Suite of Antarctica [11.126], the Mull Lavas [11.015], and the NW dikes of Britain [11.025]) the directions differ markedly from the direction of the geocentric axial dipole field, the departures being greatest in the results from the Deccan Traps of India. Small departures in a few individual cases have already been noted in the Upper Tertiary, but it is in the Lower Tertiary that divergences, greatly in excess of the errors, become general. The effect can be best appreciated by comparing the paleomagnetic poles (Figure 6.5) with those obtained from younger rocks (Figures 6.3, 6.4).

The consistent grouping, in the region of what is now the north coast of Asia, of 14 determinations from Europe and northern Asia, is notable. Two internally consistent results from Australia diverge from this group. The results from the Deccan Traps of India, which may in part be of Upper Cretaceous age, form a group some 50° from the present pole, and 60° from the European determinations. The large internal scatter in the Deccan results may be due to undetected partial instability (the specimens have not been magnetically or thermally cleaned), to the long time span represented, or to the fact that most of these determinations are based on results from few rock levels so that the secular variation may not have been averaged out in each instance. Two results from North America are inconsistent, the divergent result from the Eocene Siletz Volcanics [11.098] being notable. The latter is unlikely to be due to the failure to average out the secular variation, since it is based on a study of 8 flows spaced through a thick sequence. But the sampling region is in an orogenic belt, and there is the possibility that tectonic rotation of the area is responsible for the divergence (§ 10A.5).

Cenozoic Undifferentiated. Results from beds whose position within the Tertiary is uncertain, or which include levels of both Upper and Lower Tertiary age, or Tertiary

Table 6.1 Mean Paleomagnetic Poles for Upper Tertiary and Quaternary. *The A values refer to the main appendix lists, and B values include the results in the supplementary lists. N is the number of poles combined, K is Fisher's estimate of precision, $\theta_{63}°$ is the circular standard deviation, and $a_{95}°$ the circle of confidence ($\mathcal{P} = 0.05$).*

		N	Mean	K	$\theta_{63}°$	$a_{95}°$
1. Recent (past 7000 years approximately)	A	10	89, 18W	125	7	4
	B	11	88, 51W	124	7	4
2. Pleistocene and Plio-Pleistocene	A	29	88, 138W	62	10	3
	B	30	88, 144W	62	10	3
1. and 2. combined	B	41	89, 123W	71	10	3
3. Upper Tertiary	A	22	85, 128W	37	13	5
	B	25	85, 129W	41	13	5

* These are the appendix numbers of the values averaged: (1A) 12.04, 08, 09, 15, 32, 40, 41, 43, 54, 56; (1B) 12.04, 08, 09, 15, 32, 40, 41, 43, 66, 68; (2A) 12.01, 02, 03, 10, 11, 19, 20, 29, 30, 31, 33, 34, 37, 38, 39, 42, 45, 47, 48, 49, 50, 51, 54, 55, 57, 58, 59, 63, 64; (2B) as 2A and 12.65; (3A) 11.002, 005, 006, 011, 032, 041, 042, 043, 051, 052, 054, 055, 058, 059, 062, 066, 069, 077, 104, 106, 107, 108; (3B) as 3A and 11.115, 116, 123.

and Quaternary age, are plotted in Figure 6.4*b*. There is a general grouping around the present pole but 6 poles [11.027, 046, 092, 096, 113, 125] depart significantly from it.

§ 6.03 Analysis of Cenozoic Paleomagnetic Poles

The directions in Quaternary and Upper Tertiary rocks conform approximately to those of an axial geocentric dipole field, the poles from different regions agreeing

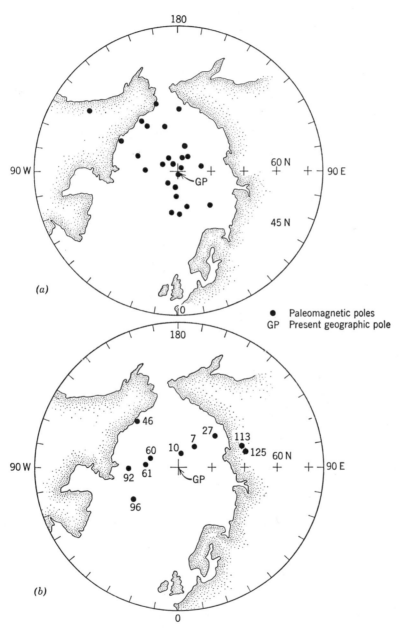

Figure 6.4. Paleomagnetic poles: Upper Tertiary (*B* group data). Polar equal-area projection north of 45° N. (*a*) Upper Tertiary. (*b*) Cenozoic undifferentiated. Individual poles being numbered as in the Appendix.

well with one another. But in the Lower Tertiary the results from different regions no longer agree, although internal consistency of results from the same region is (with the exception noted) preserved. An informative procedure for comparing results within and between regions is to plot frequency histograms of the separation of poles taken two at a time, first from the same and then from different regions. Poles from the same unit of geological time are used,

the unit being chosen sufficiently long to allow correlation of the unit as a whole from region to region. For the period in question the time units used are Quaternary and Plio-Pleistocene, Upper Tertiary, and Lower Tertiary. For the internal comparison, if n poles have been obtained from such a time unit within one region, there are $\frac{1}{2}n(n-1)$ pole pairs. For the external comparison, if $n_1, n_2, \cdots, n_m$ poles are known from m continents, the number of

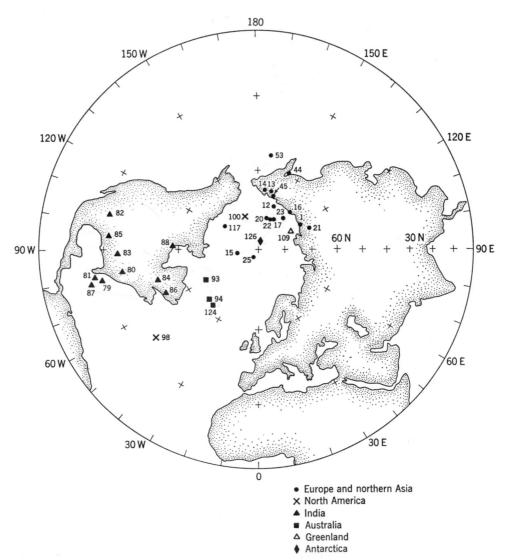

Figure 6.5. Paleomagnetic poles: Lower Tertiary (*B* group data). Polar equal-area projection of the northern hemisphere. Poles labeled as in the **Appendix**.

pole pairs is $\frac{1}{2}[(\Sigma n)^2 - \Sigma n^2]$. In the first case an estimate is obtained of the amount of apparent polar-wandering (§ 6.09) as viewed from one region during a known span of time, and this should agree with the external comparison if polar movement only has occurred, but will not agree if there has been relative movement between regions.

An ideal region for these purposes is a land area whose various parts have undergone little relative movement since the period of time in question. Relative movement, in this context, means translation or rotations; tilting of beds, for which allowance is always made (§ 4.04), or epeirogeny have no effect. Paleomagnetic results from an orogenic belt may be expected to reflect its deformation, but protected blocks within such belts may be unaffected. The Colorado Plateau seems to be an example of the latter, since results obtained from Carboniferous and Triassic beds are conformable with those from beds of similar age east of the Rockies (§§ 6.04, 6.05). All that is needed here is a broad grouping along predominantly geographical lines, and these are the divisions adopted: Europe and northern Asia, Japan, peninsular India south of the Himalayas, Africa, Australia, North America, South America, Antarctica, Greenland, and the islands of Iceland, Hawaii, and Samoa. Japan and peninsular India are considered separately from the remainder of Eurasia; Japan is in an active tectonic region, and India (and Arabia) is alien geologically to the remainder of the continent. The question of where to place China and the orogenic belts of eastern Asia in this scheme does not yet arise since no data which fulfill the minimum reliability criteria are yet available from this region.

As a more complete paleomagnetic coverage in time and space is achieved, a more detailed subdivision of the Earth into structural units will be necessary. This type of analysis is likely to be most informative for Mesozoic and Cenozoic times, since as older periods are considered the effects of tectonic movements within each region may become increasingly important.

For the Quaternary and Plio-Pleistocene the variations within and between regions are indistinguishable, the separation of pole pairs being generally less than 20°; for the comparison within regions, 17 per cent exceed 20°, and for that between regions, 16 per cent exceed this (Figure 6.6). For the Upper Tertiary the agreement within regions is about the same, 24 per cent of the values exceeding 20°, but the agreement between regions is less good, 38 per cent of the pole pairs being more than 20° apart. In the Lower Tertiary the results within continents are in fair agreement (32 per cent exceed 20°), but between continents the separations range up to 80°, and 87 per cent exceed 20°.

§ 6.04 Mesozoic Results (Table 6.2)
There are comparatively few results from Cretaceous rocks. In the Jurassic many studies have been made of rocks from the southern continents, but the northern hemisphere is poorly served. Triassic results are predominantly from Europe and North America.

Cretaceous (Figure 6.7). Fourteen results satisfy the minimum reliability conditions. With one exception [10.04], which is based on very restricted sampling, the directions diverge from the axial geocentric dipole field. There are 7 poles forming a good group from North America [10.11, 12, 17, 18] and the U.S.S.R. [10.05, 06, 14]. Two poles from Australia [10.09, 10] with good stability and age control are over 50° from this group. There are 2 results from Africa and 1 from Madagascar. Of the African results 1 [10.16] is based on limited sampling, but the other [10.15] is derived from detailed studies; both results are from rocks whose ages are not precisely fixed and which may range down into the Jurassic. There is a single result from Japan [10.07]. Although the results are few, the agreement between regions is less good than that within (Figure 6.6d).

Jurassic (Figure 6.8). Studies of sediments in Britain and the U.S.A. have yielded unsatisfactory results; only those from the

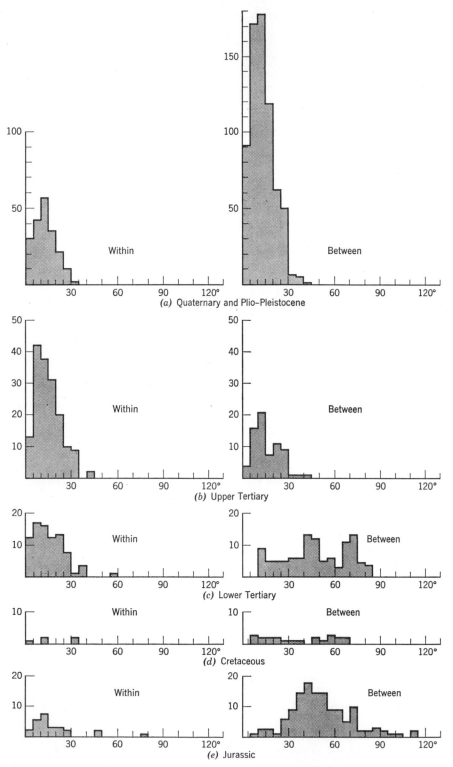

Figure 6.6. Analyses of paleomagnetic poles (*A* group data). The variation of pole separation within and between different regions are given for various time spans. The height of each col-

112

Lower Liassic sands of England [9.07], which contain a reversal of magnetization, fulfill the minimum reliability conditions, and in these the scatter is great. Concordant results from studies of Alpine sediments [9.13, 9.14] are notable (Figure 6.8*b*).

The paleomagnetic results from the southern continents (in which for these purposes India is included) are among the most important yet obtained, and are of great significance for the geological history of these regions. Most of them have been obtained from dolerites and basic lavas which are extruded upon or intruded into beds of the "Gondwana" sequences. The latter are flat-lying or subhorizontal and over most of

Figure 6.6 (*Continued*)

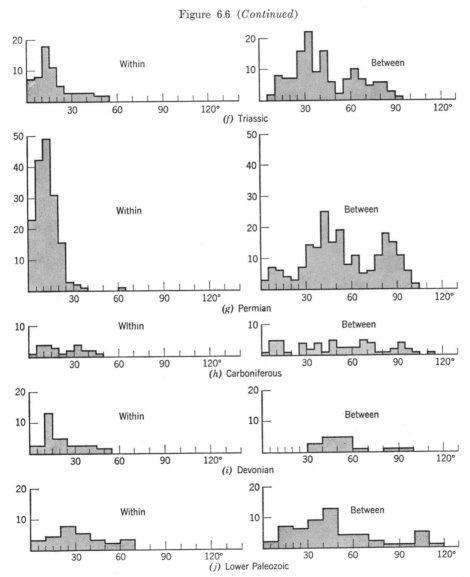

(*f*) Triassic

(*g*) Permian

(*h*) Carboniferous

(*i*) Devonian

(*j*) Lower Paleozoic

umn represents the number of occurrences of arc angles between pole pairs in the ranges indicated on the horizontal scale. In (*a*) the vertical scale is one-half that in the other figures. The interval is 5° in (*a*) to (*h*), and 10° in (*i*) and (*j*).

their outcrop have not been subjected to intense tectonic movements. The age of the igneous rocks is not always well defined stratigraphically, but, in the South American and South African occurrences, an Upper Triassic to Lower Jurassic age has been suggested, whereas for the Indian, Australian, and Antarctic occurrences a Jurassic age is favored by workers in the respective areas. A somewhat greater age therefore would be indicated for the former group.

Recent radiometric measurements have confirmed these ages for the South African, Australian, and Antarctic occurrences, and the paleomagnetic evidence from these is thus referred to a good time basis. All results, except that from India, are based on detailed stability studies. There are several determinations from South and Central Africa [9.24 to 27, 9.46 to 51], 1 each from India [9.23] and South America [9.36, 53], 4 from Antarctica [9.37, 38, 42, 56], and

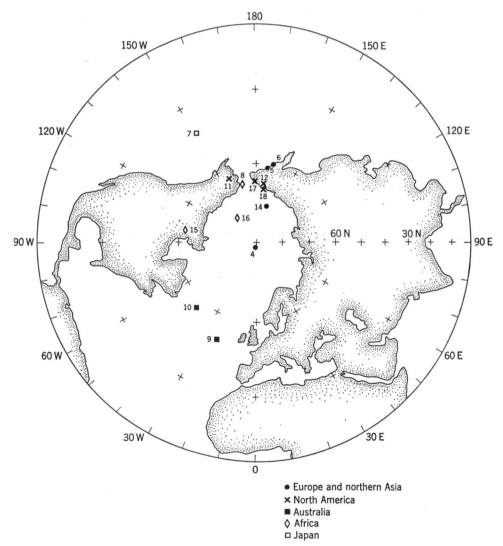

Figure 6.7. Paleomagnetic poles: Cretaceous (*B* group data). Polar equal-area projection of the northern hemisphere. Poles labeled as in the Appendix.

5 from Australia [9.28, 29, 30, 32, 33]. Reversals occur in the Serra Geral Lavas (South America) and in the Karroo Dolerites (South Africa), and these may correlate with the reversal in the Lower Liassic sands of England. The Rajmahal Traps (India), Tasmanian Dolerites (Australia), and Ferrar Dolerites (Antarctica) all have negative directions, which may be due to their being somewhat younger than the South American and African occurrences. The 5 concordant results from Australia have been obtained from intrusive bodies whose ages, determined radiometrically, range from Lower to Upper Jurassic. Results have also been reported from the Jurassic to Cretaceous Sylhet Traps of India which show directions in 2 groups [9.44, 45] not antiparallel to one another; this internal inconsistency may be due to tectonic rotations.

The pole results from the southern continents show this feature: except for the Sylhet Traps (whose age relations are in any case poorly defined) the poles are consistent within those regions from which more than 1 result is available but differ widely from region to region (Figure 6.8a). They are, moreover, inconsistent with those from Europe and northern Asia. This is made clear in Figure 6.6e in which it is seen that the poles from the same region agree in much the same way as is observed in the Cenozoic (45 per cent of the pole separations exceed 20°), whereas between regions separations of 40° are common (96 per cent exceed 20°). Particularly notable is the divergence between the poles from the Tasmanian [9.30, 31] and Ferrar Dolerites [9.37, 38] which appear to be contemporaneous; the range of ages obtained from K-Ar work being 168 to 143 m.y. and 163 to 147 m.y., respectively, their means being indistinguishable.

Triassic (Figure 6.9). Triassic beds have been studied over wide areas in the eastern and western United States. A group of 7 poles show excellent agreement, several of which (those from the Chugwater [8.30] and Moenkopi [8.31] Formations and the Newark Series [8.42]) are based on detailed work. An eighth result [8.41] is some distance from the main group, but is based only on a preliminary study at one locality. There are numerous results from Europe and northern Asia and with one exception [8.41] the set of poles from North America fall to the west of these, the mean of the two sets differing by 30° of longitude and 24° of arc. A single result from Africa [8.26] and a pair of concordant poles from Australia [8.28, 29] fall in the same general region but differ by 50° from the northern hemisphere determinations. Positive and negative directions occur commonly in Triassic beds, good examples of reversals being observed in the Keuper Marls [8.06, 07] and in the Chugwater Formation (Figure 4.2d). The agreement of poles (Figure 6.6f) within regions is good, the differences between pole pairs rarely exceeding 30° (32 per cent exceed 20°). The differences between regions are greater and 89 per cent exceed 20°.

§ 6.05   Upper Paleozoic Results (Table 6.2)   *Permian* (Figure 6.10). The most characteristic and well-established feature of Permian results is that, with the exception of certain beds in the uppermost Permian of the U.S.S.R. [7.22 to 23], the directions of magnetization are all positive (Table 7.3). The directions observed in flat-lying and gently tilted rocks, covering much of Permian time in northern Europe and northern Asia, give a remarkably consistent grouping of poles. They include results from many detailed studies of which that made on the igneous complex of the Oslo region [7.13] is the most comprehensive. Results from the Italian Alps [7.19, 20] and the Pyrénées [7.21, 55] fall to the west of the main group and may be due to anticlockwise tectonic rotations relative to northern Europe (§ 10A.8). The poles from North America are to the east of those from Europe and northern Asia; the means of the two sets differ by 46° of arc and 59° of longitude. A single result from Greenland falls near those from Europe. There are 2 discordant results from Africa which, however, are not based on any stability evidence (other than that the directions diverge from the present field) and need reinvestigation. Two concordant results from Australia [7.42, 43] which are based on detailed demagnetization studies (Figure 5.16) are about 80° and 90° respectively from the European and North American determinations. The agreement of poles within regions is good (Figure 6.6*g*), pole pairs rarely disagreeing by more than 20° (12 per cent exceed 20°), whereas the agreement be-tween regions is poor (93 per cent exceed 20°). The two peaks in the histogram at 40° to 55° and 80° to 90°, correspond to the sys-tematic divergence of the European and North American results and the divergence of the Australian poles from these.

Carboniferous (Figure 6.11). Four re-sults from beds of Mississippian and Penn-sylvanian age from widespread localities in North America are in close agreement. Ex-

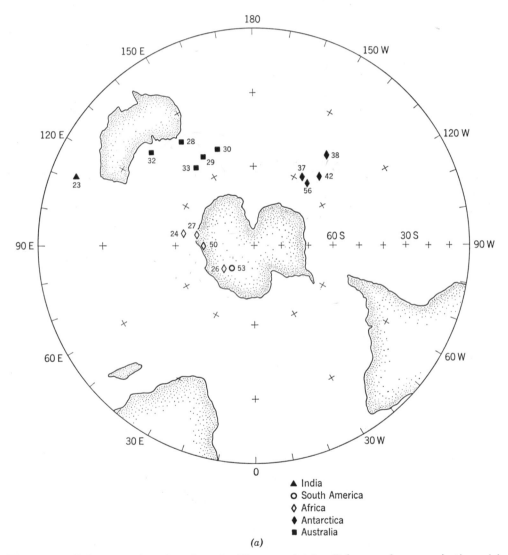

(*a*)

Figure 6.8. Paleomagnetic poles: Jurassic (*B* group data). Polar equal-area projections (*a*) above, of the southern hemisphere giving results from the southern continents and India, and (*b*) across, of the northern hemisphere giving all results. Poles numbered as in the Appendix.

cept for observations at one site in the Barnett Formation [6.63] all directions are positive. In contrast, results from Europe and the Siberian Platform, and from Australia show a large internal scatter. The results from the former region are the more numerous. One notable feature is that beds of uppermost Carboniferous age (Stephanian of western Europe [6.04], the Upper Carboniferous of the Ukraine [6.42], and the Upper Kuttung varvoid sediments of Aus-

tralia [6.58]) have positive polarity indistinguishable in direction from those observed in Permian beds in their respective regions.

Most results from Europe and Siberia give poles falling in a broad zone to the east and south of those from North America although three [6.13, 14, and 55] fall near those from that continent. The means for the European and Siberian poles is 17° of arc from that for the North American poles, the difference of longitude being 19°—

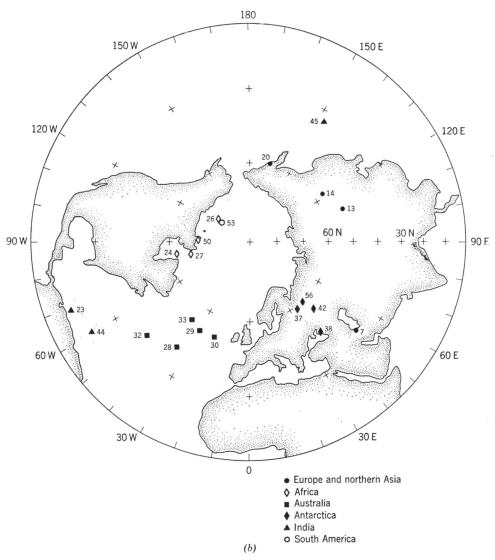

(b)

Figure 6.8 (*Continued*)

much less than in the Permian. Several results from Europe are based on detailed studies (for instance [6.11, 32]) and it is these that show a divergence from the North American results. The relative ages of the European and Siberian rocks are not always clear, but there is an indication of a general northeasterly shift of the pole during the Carboniferous.

The most notable feature of the Australian results is that the youngest beds (the Upper Kuttung glacial sediments) have steep inclinations as if laid down in high latitudes. Beneath the glacial levels the directions [6.59, 60] provide a transition to the low or intermediate inclinations observed in Devonian beds. This transition cannot be due to partial magnetic instability since the demagnetization evidence of stability is strong and those directions, giving a pole near the present pole, have positive polarity opposed to that of the present field. The

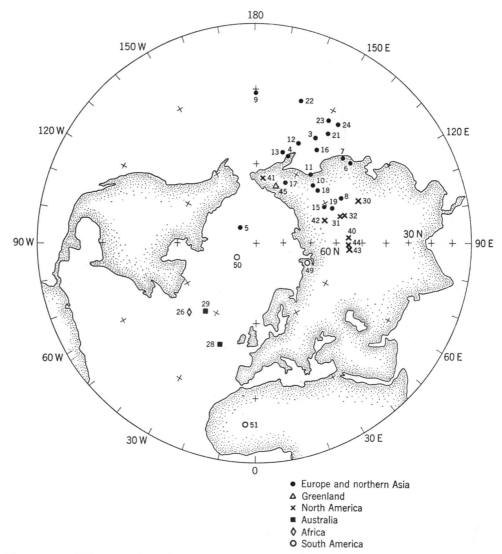

Figure 6.9.   Paleomagnetic poles: Triassic (*B* group data). Polar equal-area projection of the northern hemisphere. Poles numbered as in the Appendix.

relative ages of the beds from which the Australian results were obtained are based on superimposition evidence, and the direction of polar drift is shown in Figure 6.11. The poles diverge strongly from those obtained from the Northern Hemisphere, the divergence in the Upper Carboniferous, being about 90°.

The results from Europe-northern Asia and Australia indicate that during the Carboniferous the Earth's field relative to these regions changed considerably, becoming stabilized in the uppermost Carboniferous in a direction that remains little changed until the late Permian. Such changes are not apparent in the results from North America, which suggest that the field relative to that region has remained approximately constant in direction and not greatly different from the Permian; the similarity of the Carboniferous and Permian directions in North America may also indicate remagnetization

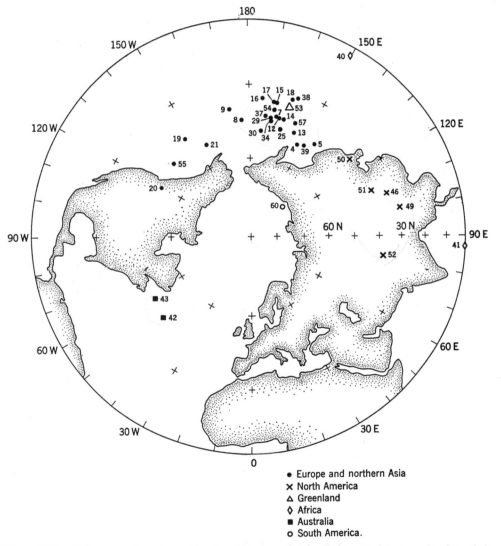

Figure 6.10. Paleomagnetic poles: Permian (*B* group data). Polar equal-area projection of the northern hemisphere. Poles numbered as in the Appendix.

in the later period. Considering the results as a whole (Figure 6.6*h*), the agreement within regions is less good than that observed in younger periods (50 per cent of pole pairs diverge by more than 20°) but the agreement between regions is again poor (78 per cent diverge by more than 20°).

Devonian (Figure 6.12). Extensive studies of rocks, ranging in age from Lower to Upper Devonian, and in locations spreading from Wales to Central Siberia give scattered results. One set of poles obtained from western Europe [5.05, 06], the Russian Platform [5.10, 16] and Siberia [5.31, 46] lie in what is now the North Pacific with a grouping comparable to that observed from Permian rocks (Figure 6.10). A second set [5.04, 41] lie just north of what is now Australia and it may be noted that certain results from the Silurian [4.07, 14], Ordovician [3.02, 05, 10], and Cambrian [2.15, 16, 28] of the U.S.S.R. also fall in this general region (Figures 6.13, 6.14, 6.15). The cause of this dual grouping of Devonian

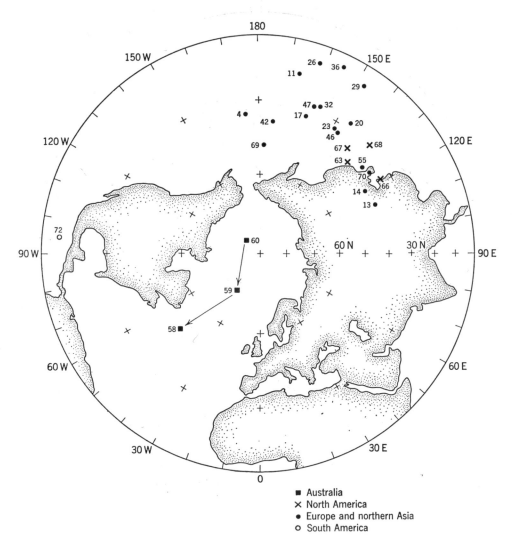

Figure 6.11. Paleomagnetic poles: Carboniferous (*B* group data). Polar equal-area projection. Poles numbered as in the Appendix.

poles from Europe and northern Asia is unknown but two possibilities bear discussion. The first is that the results reflect a variation in the field during the Devonian, the first set representing the older field direction which continues down into the Lower Paleozoic. This implies that the first set were obtained from older rocks—a point that might be difficult to test since many of the beds are continental deposits making stratigraphic correlation over such large distances difficult. The second possibility is that the fossil magnetizations giving the first set of poles—that in the North Pacific—have been acquired during the Permian and that the second group represent the true Devonian field. That remagnetization in the Permian has occurred in certain circumstances has been confirmed by the recent work of thermal demagnetization on specimens from the Old Red Sandstones of Britain [5.02] whose NRM was positive like the Permian directions from this region (Table 7.3). Many of the poles in the first set however are based on results from beds of mixed polarity, and in the Okler

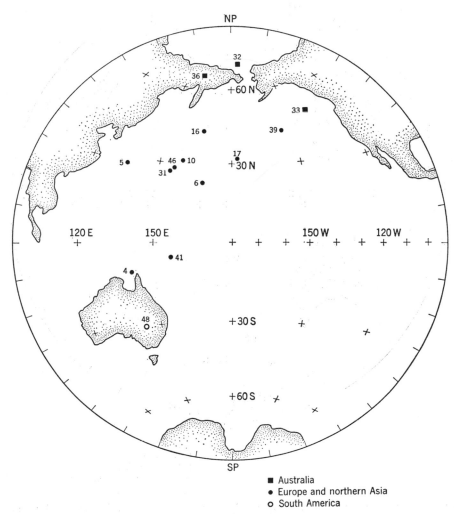

Figure 6.12. Paleomagnetic poles: Devonian. Equatorial equal-area projection. Poles numbered as in the Appendix.

Series ([5.40] see §7.6) transitions between positive and negative directions have been traced. It is difficult therefore to explain the first set entirely on the basis of secondary magnetization by the positive Permian field. Very many more results with good stability control and related to an accurate time base are needed before an adequate discussion of this curious problem can be given.

The determinations from Australia, including one [5.32] based partly on results from rocks from uppermost Silurian age, diverge from the European and Siberian results by distances of the order of 40°, which is much less than that found in the Carboniferous, Permian, and Triassic. A single pole result from South America [5.48] lies in Australia. There are no results from North America fulfilling the minimum reliability criteria. The comparison within and between regions (Figure 6.6*i*) shows that the

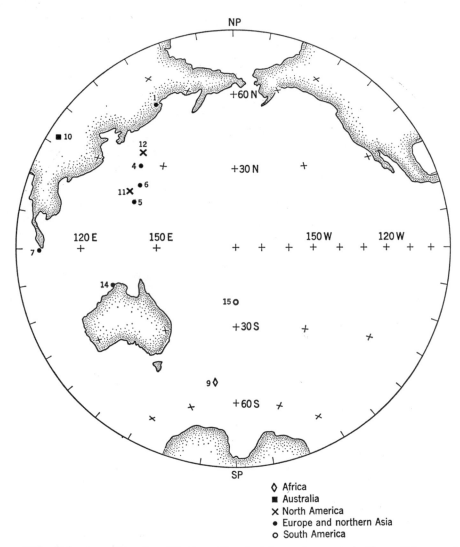

Figure 6.13. Paleomagnetic poles: Silurian. Equatorial equal-area projection. Poles numbered as in the Appendix.

agreement within is appreciably better than that between, although this analysis is subject to the uncertainties noted above.

§ 6.06 Lower Paleozoic Results (Table 6.2)

Few results have been obtained from Lower Paleozoic beds, and those that are available have been derived from surveys of a preliminary nature. The results are scattered, there being poor agreement both within and between continents (Figure 6.6).

Silurian (Figure 6.13). Seven results from Europe and northern Asia, one from Aus-

tralia, and two from North America give poles which fall in the same general region. There is one result from South America [4.15] and one from South Africa [4.09].

Ordovician (Figure 6.14). Rocks of this age have been less studied than those of any other. Of five results from the U.S.S.R. [3.01, 02, 04, 05, 10], three give poles which are close together. The single result from North America [3.06] falls in the same general area.

Cambrian (Figure 6.15). There are 5 results from Europe and northern Asia giving

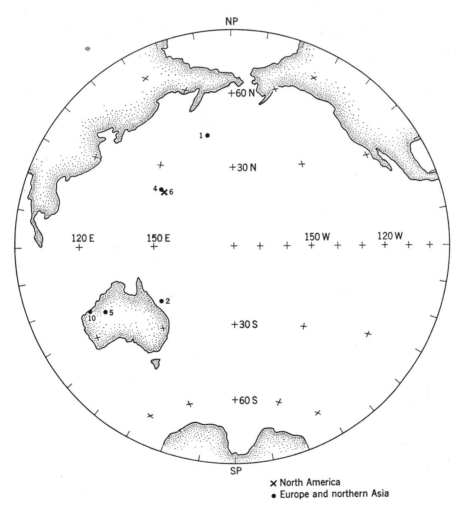

✕ North America
● Europe and northern Asia

Figure 6.14. Paleomagnetic poles: Ordovician. Equatorial equal-area projection. Poles numbered as in the Appendix.

Table 6.2 Average Paleomagnetic Poles for Various Regions. *The A values refer to the main appendix lists and the B values include the results in the supplementary lists. If there are no B values this means that no new data have become available during the writing of this book. N is the number of individual pole results, the appendix reference number of the values used being given in the footnotes. K is the precision of poles. $a_{95}°$ is the circle of confidence ($\mathcal{P} = 0.05$) which is not given if N < 5. Parentheses around poles emphasize that the result is based on a single determination only.*

Tertiary Results

Region		Upper Tertiary				Lower Tertiary			
		N	Mean	K	$a_{95}°$	N	Mean	K	$a_{95}°$
Europe and northern Asia	A	14 [a]	83, 140W	30	7	14 [c]	76, 150E	53	6
	B	16 [b]	83, 143W	34	6	—	—	—	—
Japan	A	4 [d]	84, 62W	35	—	—	—	—	—
	B	5 [e]	85, 53W	46	11	—	—	—	—
Peninsular India	A	—	—	—	—	10 [f]	38, 83W	30	9
Australia	A	—	—	—	—	2 [g]	65, 70W	—	—
North America	A	3 [h]	88, 117W	210	—	2 [i]	—	—	—
Arctic regions—Iceland	A	1 [j]	(89, 5E)	—	—	—	—	—	—
Antarctica	B	[k]	—	—	—	1 [l]	(86, 178E)	—	—

[a] [11.002, 005, 006, 011, 032, 041, 042, 043, 051, 052, 054, 055, 058, 059].
[b] Same as in footnote [a] with [11.115, 116].
[c] [11.001, 012, 013, 014, 015, 016, 017, 020, 021, 022, 023, 025, 044, 045].
[d] [11.062, 066, 069, 077].
[e] Same as in [d] with [11.123].

[f] [11.079, 080, 081, 082, 083, 084, 085, 086, 087, 088] in part Upper Cretaceous.
[g] [11.093, 094].
[h] [11.104, 106, 107].
[i] [11.098, 100] discordant values see § 10A.5.
[j] [11.108].
[k] Cenozoic lavas of undefined age available [12.55].
[l] [11.126] in part Upper Cretaceous.

Mesozoic Results

Region		Cretaceous				Jurassic				Triassic			
		N	Mean	K	$a_{95}°$	N	Mean	K	$a_{95}°$	N	Mean	K	$a_{95}°$
Europe and northern Asia	A	3 [a]	72, 168E	19	—	4 [b]	58, 105E	7	—	19 [c]	50, 146E	27	7
Japan	A	1 [d]	(42, 151W)	—	—	—	—	—	—	—	—	—	—
India	A	[e]	—	—	—	1 [f]	(13, 69W)	—	—	—	—	—	—
Africa	A	—	—	—	—	4 [h]	71, 85W	74	—	1 [j]	(53, 44W)	—	—
	B	[g]	—	—	—	10 [i]	69, 97W	36	8	—	—	—	—
Australia	A	2 [k]	54, 33W	—	—	5 [l]	47, 34W	61	10	2 [m]	53, 28W	—	—
North America	A	2 [n]	67, 171W	—	—	—	—	—	—	8 [p]	59, 106E	33	10
	B	3 [o]	69, 177W	120	—	—	—	—	—	—	—	—	—
South America	A	—	—	—	—	1 [q]	(83, 112W)	—	—	3 [s]	—	—	—
	B	—	—	—	—	1 [r]	(78, 126W)	—	—	—	—	—	—
Arctic regions—Greenland	A	—	—	—	—	—	—	—	—	1 [t]	(38, 163E)	—	—
Antarctica	A	—	—	—	—	3 [u]	52, 40E	132	—	—	—	—	—
	B	[v]	—	—	—	4 [w]	54, 40E	148	—	—	—	—	—

[a] [10.04, 05, 06].
[b] [9.07, 13, 14, 20].
[c] [8.03, 04, 06, 07, 08, 09, 10, 11, 12, 13, 15, 16, 17, 18, 19, 21, 22, 23, 24].
[d] [10.07].
[e] See "Tertiary Results" in this table.
[f] [9.23].
[g] Result [10.15] may be relevant.
[h] [9.24, 25, 26, 27].
[i] See [9.51].
[j] [8.26].
[k] [10.09, 10].

[l] [9.28, 29, 30, 32, 33].
[m] [8.28, 29].
[n] [10.11, 12].
[o] [10.11, 12, 18].
[p] [8.30, 31, 32, 40, 41, 42, 43, 44].
[q] [9.36].
[r] [9.53].
[s] Discordant results.
[t] [8.45].
[u] [9.37, 38, 42].
[v] See "Tertiary Results" in this table.
[w] [9.37, 38, 42, 52].

scattered poles. The European results include one [2.09] from Cambrian Barrandian porphyrites of Czechoslovakia. Two other Barrandian results [2.08, 14] are from beds whose age may extend beyond the limits of the Cambrian. Two results from North America [2.19, 23] fall in the same region. Two preliminary results from Australia are 40° or so away from the main group [2.17, 18].

§ 6.07 Precambrian Results (Figure 6.16). Many studies of Precambrian beds have been made. The results from North America and Europe and northern Asia are the most numerous. There are preliminary

results from Australia (3 results), India (3 results), and South America (1 result). There are 3 results based on detailed work from Africa. The following discussion is confined to those results based on detailed studies. Other results are given in the Appendix.

Results from the Upper Keweenawan [1.40] give a pole not greatly different from that obtained from Cambrian beds in North America (Figure 6.15). Numerous observations are available from late Precambrian sediments of Arizona [1.20] and the Belt Series of Montana and British Columbia [1.32]. The localities are spread over a distance of 1500 km. The mean poles for each

Table 6.2 **Average Paleomagnetic Poles for Various Regions** (Continued)

Upper Paleozoic Results

Region		Permian				Carboniferous				Devonian			
		N	Mean	K	$a_{95}°$	N	Mean	K	$a_{95}°$	N	Mean	K	$a_{95}°$
Europe and northern Asia	A	17 [a]	43, 166E	69	4	13 [c]	30, 151E	14	11	24 [e]	31, 158E	30	5
	B	20 [b]	43, 166E	78	4	16 [d]	32, 151E	15	10	10 [f]	25, 161E	11	15
Africa	A	2 [g]	—	—	—	—	—	—	—	—	—	—	—
Australia	A	2 [h]	45, 52W	—	—	3 [i]	—	—	—	3 [j]	65, 165W	19	—
North America	A	5 [k]	38, 105E	34	13	4 [l]	36, 132E	128	—	—	—	—	—
South America	B	1 [m]	(74, 130E)	—	—	1 [n]	(8, 95W)	—	—	1 [o]	(31, 37W)	—	—
Arctic regions—Greenland	A	1 [p]	(38, 163E)	—	—	—	—	—	—	—	—	—	—

[a] [7.04, 05, 07, 08, 09, 12, 13, 14, 16, 17, 18, 24, 28, 34, 37, 38, 39].
[b] Same as [a] with [7.15, 57, 54].
[c] [6.04, 11, 13, 14, 17, 20, 23, 26, 29, 36, 42, 46, 55].
[d] Same as [c] with [6.47, 69, 70].
[e] [5.02, 04, 05, 06, 07, 08, 09, 11, 12, 13, 14, 15, 17, 18, 19, 20, 23, 24, 25, 26, 27, 28, 29, 30].
[f] [5.04, 05, 06, 10, 16, 17, 31, 39, 41, 46] using different weighting from [e].
[g] [7.39, 40] discordant results.

[h] [7.41, 42].
[i] [6.58, 59, 60] transition sequence.
[j] [5.32, 33, 36].
[k] [7.46, 49, 50, 51, 52].
[l] [6.63, 66, 67, 68].
[m] [7.60].
[n] [6.72].
[o] [5.48].
[p] [7.53].

Lower Paleozoic Results

Region		Silurian				Ordovician				Cambrian			
		N	Mean	K	$a_{95}°$	N	Mean	K	$a_{95}°$	N	Mean	K	$a_{95}°$
Europe and northern Asia	A	6 [a]	25, 132E	10	22	3 [c]	15, 148E	5	—	5 [e]	03, 18W	6	(33)
	B	6 [b]	18, 131E	9	23	4 [d]	05, 140E	5	—	6 [f]	08, 24W	5	(33)
Africa	A	1 [g]	(51, 11W)	—	—	—	—	—	—	—	—	—	—
Australia	A	1 [h]	(32, 97E)	—	—	—	—	—	—	2 [i]	35, 159W	—	—
North America	A	2 [j]	26, 139E	—	—	1 [k]	(20, 153E)	—	—	2 [l]	12, 9W	—	—
South America	B	1 [m]	(19, 0)	—	—	—	—	—	—	—	—	—	—

[a] [4.01, 02, 03, 05, 06, 07].
[b] [4.01, 04, 05, 06, 07, 14] adopting a more conservative weighting than in [a].
[c] [3.01, 04, 05].
[d] Same as [c] with [3.10].
[e] [2.02, 03, 09, 15, 16].
[f] Same as [e] with [2.28].

[g] [4.09].
[h] [4.10].
[i] [2.17, 18].
[j] [4.11, 12].
[k] [3.06].
[l] [2.19, 23].
[m] [4.15] note age uncertainty.

agree very well, and this supports the geological hypothesis that the two series were laid down at approximately the same time, and indicates that subsequent tectonic movements have not greatly altered their relative positions, although the Rocky Mountain orogenic belt intervenes between them.

The directions in the lower beds [1.02] of the Torridonian Sandstone Series differ from those in the upper levels [1.01], the change being an axis transition and not a reversal. The lower group has negative directions, whereas the upper group is characterized by serial reversals about an axis which is approximately constant in direction. Studies of the Longmyndian sediments of England [1.03] give directions similar to those in the Upper Torridonian. The poles for the Keweenawan, Beltian, and Arizona sediments, and those for the Upper Torridonian and the Longmyndian fall near the present-day equator in the mid-Pacific.

It is unfortunate that only 5 results from the Precambrian are from radiometrically dated rocks. There are excellent results from South Africa [1.06, 07, 63]—one from the

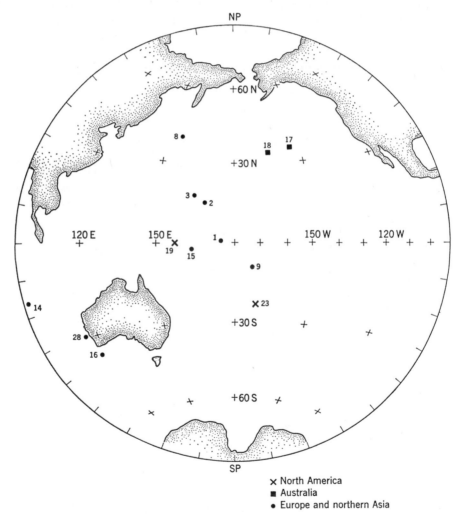

Figure 6.15. Paleomagnetic poles: Cambrian. Equatorial equal-area projection. Poles numbered as in the Appendix.

Bushveld Gabbro (1920 ± 130 m.y.), 1 from the Pilansberg Dikes (1290 ± 180 m.y.), and two from the Great Dike of Rhodesia (2150 m.y.). The results are in broad agreement, indicating that during this long time span the Earth's field relative to Africa did not change greatly. The time of emplacement of the Sudbury Nickel Irruptive [1.49] is considered to lie within the limits 1200–1800 m.y., that is, within the time range of the Bushveld and Pilansberg intrusives. The pole for the Sudbury intrusives is 70° away from the South African determinations. The Beltian results are to be related to a radiometric age of 750 m.y. and their pole falls near the South African determinations derived from rocks of approximately twice this age.

In several cases the relative ages of pairs of rock units are known. The Baraga County Dikes of Michigan [1.34] are overlain by Keweenawan sediments [1.40] in localities near to those sampled for paleomagnetic work. The pole from the former therefore relates to a time earlier than that from the latter, the sense of change with time being indicated in Figure 6.16*b*. The two distinct directions observed in the Torridonian Sandstone Series provide two poles [1.01, 1.02], the direction of change being determined by superimposition. A further pair of poles whose relative ages are known with some certainty are those from the Sudbury Nickel Irruptive [1.49] and the Beltian [1.32]. The change in this and the previous two pairs is approximately the same, both in direction and magnitude, and there is the possibility that they reflect a contemporaneous change in the Earth's field.

§ 6.08 Analysis of Mean Directions

The time variations in the results for each region are now considered. For comparative purposes these changes may be expressed in one of three ways: (1) as changes of directions relative to the present geocentric axial dipole field; (2) as movements of the paleomagnetic pole relative to the sampling region (apparent polarwandering); or (3) as changes of latitude and rotations of the sampling region. An account of

the first of these, based mainly on the work of Blackett, Clegg, and Stubbs (1960), is now given. The second is discussed in § 6.09 and and the third in Chapter Nine.

The mean direction (D_m, I_m) of a rock unit at a collecting locality may be compared with the direction $(\mathfrak{D}_m, \mathscr{I}_m)$ of the Earth's field over the past several thousand years, that is, with the direction of the geocentric axial dipole field (§ 6.02). The simplest procedure is to plot the directions from a given region and this is done for western Europe in Figure 6.17. The method suffers from the disadvantage that no correction is made for the differences in the position of collecting localities. Nevertheless a systematic shift of the directions with time, from NNE with positive intermediate inclinations, to north with positive steep inclinations, is clear.

A further procedure is to calculate the differences, ΔI_m and ΔD_m, between the components of the directions D_m, I_m and $\mathfrak{D}_m$, $\mathscr{I}_m$.

$$\Delta I_m = I_m - \mathscr{I}_m \qquad (6.1)$$

for negatively polarized rocks, and

$$\Delta I_m = -I_m - \mathscr{I}_m \qquad (6.2)$$

for positive polarizations. The angle ΔD_m, called the *rotation*, is of paleogeographical interest since it defines the angle between the present and paleomeridian (Figure 6.19); it is subsequently denoted by the symbol ψ_p and its value is obtained as follows:

$$\left.\begin{array}{l} \text{if} \quad 0° < D_m < 180° \\[4pt] \qquad \psi_p = D_m \quad \text{or } D_m - 180° \\[8pt] \text{or} \\[8pt] \text{if} \quad 180° < D_m < 360° \\[4pt] \qquad \psi_p = D_m - 360° \quad \text{or} \quad D_m - 180° \end{array}\right\} \quad (6.3)$$

It is clear from what has already been said (Figures 6.1, 6.2) that ΔI_m and ψ_p average close to zero for the past 20 m.y. Values for earlier periods for western Europe, North America, and Australia are plotted in Figure 6.18. In general, large values of ψ_p are sasociated with large values of ΔI_m, so that the departures from the present geocentric axial dipole field are systematic in time, and are not due to random causes.

The values ψ_p and ΔI_m may be combined into a single angle Φ, called the *divergence*, which is the angle between the mean direction for the rock unit (D_m, I_m) and that of the geocentric axial dipole field $(\mathfrak{D}_m, \mathcal{I}_m)$, and is calculated from this relationship (Figure 6.19):

$$\cos\Phi = \cos\psi_p \cos I_m \cos\mathcal{I}_m + \sin I_m \sin\mathcal{I}_m \quad (6.4)$$

Values of Φ increase with time (Figure 6.20), the rate of change being $0.20°/10^6$ years for Europe, $0.18°/10^6$ years for North America, and $0.09°/10^6$ years for the Australian results (based on Kulp's 1961 Time Scale). The rate of change for Australia is about one-half that for Europe and North America, and this is meaningful if it is assumed that the Earth's field has been that of a geocentric dipole, since in Australia the

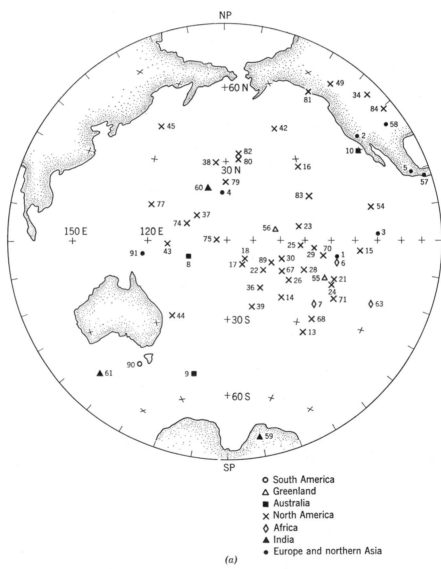

(a)

Figure 6.16. Paleomagnetic poles: Precambrian. Equatorial equal-area projection—(a) above, all results, (b) across, selected results. Poles numbered as in the Appendix.

change in directions is predominantly from high to intermediate inclinations, and those in Europe and North America from low to intermediate inclinations; the rate of change of inclination of a geocentric dipole field is greater by a factor two when the inclination is low than when it is high (equation 3.3). The increase of Φ with time does not in itself have any physical meaning, since such effects could arise from either systematic or random displacements, and it is necessary to examine the directions in which the displacements occur. This is done (Figure 6.19) by calculating the *deviation* α for each mean direction (D_m, I_m) in this way:

$$\sin \alpha = (\cos I_m \sin \psi_p)/\sin \Phi \quad (6.5)$$

If the divergences are random in direction, α will be distributed uniformly through 360°; if they are systematic, then α and Φ will be correlated. In Figure 6.21, α versus Φ is plotted on circular diagrams. The points are not random, their systematic grouping being particularly clear in the European data. The discontinuity in the Australian Paleo-

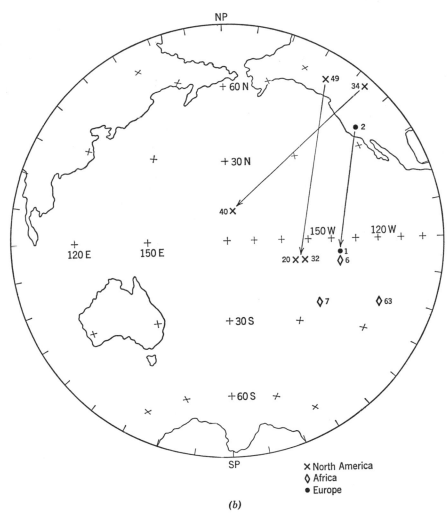

(b)

Figure 6.16 (*Continued*)

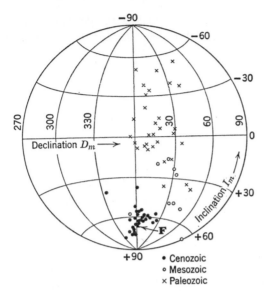

Figure 6.17. Variations with time of the directions (D_m, I_m) in western Europe (A group data). The directions are plotted on the lower hemisphere of an equatorial equal-area projection. The results are from France, West Germany, Spain, the U. K., and Norway. The axial dipole field (**F**) for a latitude 51° N is given as being representative for the region. Directions from Cenozoic, Mesozoic, and Paleozoic rock units are differentiated.

zoic results is due to the rapid change there during the Carboniferous.

The above analysis is useful for detecting broad trends but it suffers from the disadvantage, as Runcorn (1961) points out, that the divergence and deviation angles bear no simple relation to any parameter of worldwide significance, and so cannot be compared with independent geophysical or geological data. Furthermore, the divergence and deviation angles are divorced from the spherical environment of the paleomagnetic data and the method of plotting, on linear scales, parameters related to data distributed on a sphere exaggerates the scatter in these data.

§ **6.09   Relevant Hypotheses**   The paleomagnetic results may be considered as evidence for or against certain geological and geophysical hypotheses. These hypotheses

are interlinked to varying degrees. It is convenient to introduce them all here and then to give each separate consideration later. Geomagnetic hypotheses are considered in §§ 6.10, 6.11. Those related to paleogeography are set aside until Chapters Nine and Ten. The assumption required for these discussions is that the mean paleomagnetic directions of rock units represent the direction of the field averaged over a period of time long enough to average out the secular variation.

The hypotheses relevant to the interpretation of paleomagnetically determined field directions are set out in Figure 6.22 and Table 6.3. The first hypothesis is that of an *axially symmetrical geomagnetic field*, the simplest field of this type being that of a *geocentric dipole*. A further hypothesis, which may be regarded as an extension of the above, is that the axis of the axially symmetrical field coincides with the Earth's axis of rotation; the simplest case is that of a geocentric dipole whose axis coincides with the spin axis and this is the *axial geocentric dipole hypothesis*.

By taking a time sequence of paleomagnetic poles obtained from a given observing region the pole movements relative to this region may be traced. This is called *apparent polar-wandering* (§ 6.10) which may be alternatively expressed as changes in the latitude or rotation of sampling regions relative to a fixed pole. Apparent polar-wandering, estimated on the basis of the assumption of an axial geocentric dipole field (2*b*), may be further studied by comparing the changes in latitude and rotation with those inferred from independent paleogeographic evidence from the *same* region (Chapter Nine). Should this test give a positive correlation apparent polar-wandering may be taken to record movement of the Earth's rotational axis, and/or movement of the observing region relative to the Earth's body. The latter cannot be separately studied paleomagnetically, the observations provide evidence only of the motions of two or more regions relative to one another. For the present purposes, therefore, the hypothesis of *polar-wandering* is thought of as incremental movements of the coincident spin and magnetic axes relative to the Earth as a whole, and *relative continental displacement* or *continental drift* as horizontal movements of land masses relative to one another. The former is a general phenomenon and would be re-flected in the paleomagnetic results everywhere. The second involves special movements of each continent and may be expected to cause differences in the paleomagnetic results from different continents.

Mechanically, polar-wandering is thought of as movement of the whole Earth relative to the axis of rotation, which, aside from

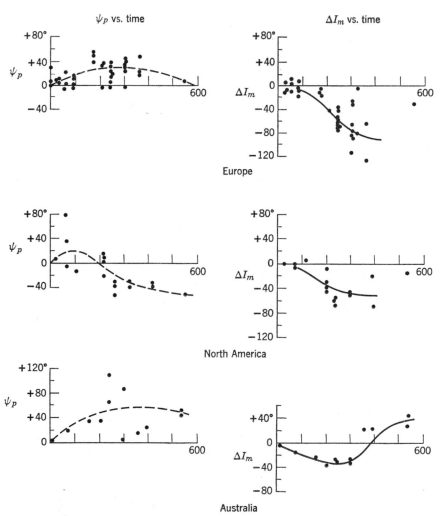

Figure 6.18. Variation of ψ_p and ΔI_m with time in millions of years. In the left-hand column ψ_p (or ΔD_m) versus time is given, and in the right-hand column ΔI_m versus time. The European, North American, and Australian results are given respectively from top to bottom. The wide scatter of ψ_p for Australia is because of the difficulty in determining declination when the inclination is high, as is commonly the case in the results from this continent. Redrawn from Blackett, Clegg, and Stubbs (1960) using Kulp's 1961 Time Scale; the values plotted are those that were available at the time of that review, but results published since that time do not change the general picture.

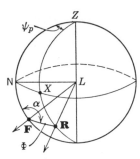

Figure 6.19. Derivation of the divergence Φ and the deviation α. **F** is the geocentric dipole field $\mathfrak{D}_m$, $\mathfrak{I}_m$, **R** the paleomagnetic direction D_m, I_m, and N true north. The angle N**F** is $\mathfrak{I}_m$, and X**R** is I_m.

Finally, it should be mentioned that the directions could be explained by assuming that the regions of observation have remained unchanged in position and that the ancient field was highly irregular and similar in form to the nondipole field nowadays (§ 3.2), but varying perhaps a million times more slowly. It would be easy to choose arbitrarily a time-variable distribution of magnetization within the Earth that would give the observed directions. This *nondipole hypothesis*, as it is sometimes called, is a hypothesis of desperation, useful at this stage only to those anxious to avoid the implications of paleomagnetism. No conceivable observation can refute it. In fact, it really is no hypothesis

precession and nutation, remains fixed relative to the Sun. It seems that this could arise from redistribution of mass due to geological processes in the crust or convection in the mantle (Gold, 1955). Continental drift has been regarded as mechanically implausible (Jeffreys, 1959), although this may not necessarily be the case (Scheidegger, 1957; Runcorn, 1962). Apart from the paleomagnetic evidence, the case for its occurrence rests on morphological, geological, and biological grounds. The ideas of polar-wandering and continental drift have been current in the geological literature for the past century, although with fluctuating popularity. The recent interest in them is due largely to the rapid developments in paleomagnetism from which numerical estimates of their effects can be made in a manner independent of previous geological and geophysical arguments.

A further relevant hypothesis is that of *changes in the Earth's radius*. There have been several suggestions that the Earth has expanded so that if a stable continental block retains its primitive dimensions it will come to cover a smaller surface area relative to the whole, so that the Earth's field, if dipolar, would change less rapidly as the continent's surface is traversed. These changes may be studied paleomagnetically (§ 10E.2).

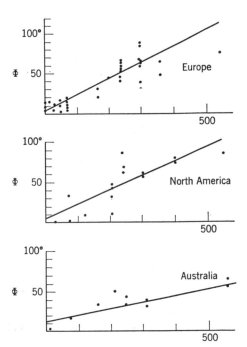

Figure 6.20. Variation of the divergence Φ with time (in millions of years) for Europe, North America, and Australia. A straight line is fitted to the results giving an average rate of change. Redrawn from Blackett, Clegg, and Stubbs (1960) using Kulp's 1961 Time Scale; the values plotted are those that were available at the time of that review, but results published since then do not affect the general picture.

at all,[2] since it does not predict any observable geological or geophysical effects, and so cannot be checked by independent observations, although the failure of all tests set out in Table 6.3 may, in a negative way, be considered as evidence in its favor. Nothing is gained by considering the nondipole hypothesis until the simple refutable hypotheses have been tested.

[2] If we apply Popper's criterion of demarcation (K. Popper, *Conjectures and Refutations,* Routledge and Kegan Paul, 1963, p. 37) by which he distinguishes scientific or refutable hypotheses from pseudoscientific or irrefutable hypotheses, then the "nondipole hypothesis" is nonscientific—since any paleomagnetic observation may be accommodated by introducing *ad hoc* a further variable in the time distribution of the Earth's magnetism.

§ **6.10 Apparent Polar-Wandering** From the results it is possible to trace the path of movement of the paleomagnetic pole relative to sampling regions. It is assumed in this context that the pole moves relative to fixed sampling localities, and that the different parts of a particular region have not undergone substantial relative movements since the times in question. It is important to note that such a path refers only to the region from which the observations were obtained. It may reflect polar-wandering or continental drift and the data from a single region are insufficient to allow one to decide which of these is responsible or, if both have operated, what their relative contributions have been.

Information about apparent polar-wandering is of geomagnetic interest and is also

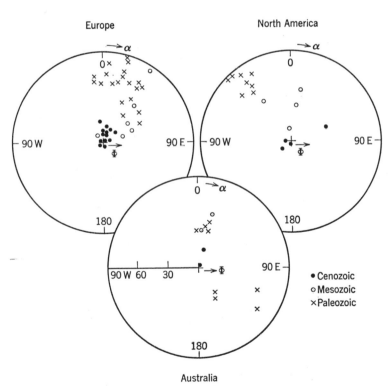

Figure 6.21. Divergence Φ versus the deviation α. The results from the Cenozoic, Mesozoic, and Paleozoic are distinguished. Redrawn from Blackett, Clegg, and Stubbs (1960), with the kind permission of the Royal Society and the authors.

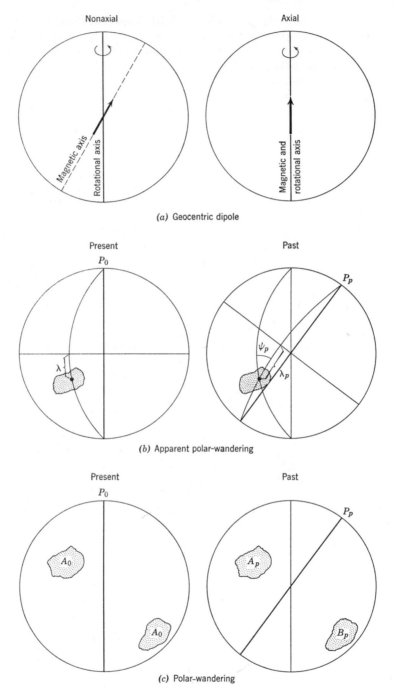

Figure 6.22. Schematic representation of some hypotheses relevant to the interpretation of paleomagnetic results. P_0 is the present geographic pole, P_p the paleogeographic pole. λ and λ_p are the present and ancient latitudes, and ψ_p the rotation. A and B are hypothetical continental regions. Crustal blocks are shaded, r_0 is the present radius and r_t the paleoradius.

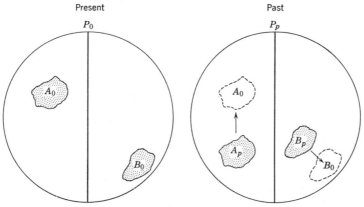

Present   Past

(d) Relative continental displacements or continental drift

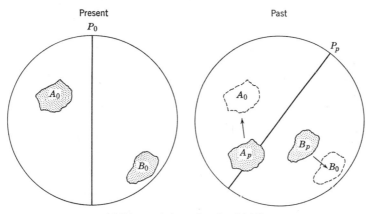

Present   Past

(e) Polar-wandering and continental drift

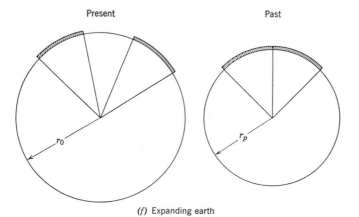

Present   Past

(f) Expanding earth

Figure 6.22 (*Continued*)

Table 6.3 Some Relevant Hypotheses and Tests

Hypothesis	Direction Tests	Intensity and Dispersion Tests	Paleogeographic Tests
1. Axially symmetrical field	Declination always zero and isoclines are concentric circles		
1a. Special case: geocentric dipole field	Declination always zero and isoclines concentric circles	Regular variation of intensity and between-site dispersion with paleolatitude	
2. Axially symmetrical field parallel to spin axis	Declination always zero and isoclines are concentric circles		Poles determined paleomagnetically coincide with poles of rotation determined paleogeographically
2a. Special case: axial geocentric dipole field	Paleomagnetic poles agree with one another	Regular variation of intensity and between-site dispersion with paleolatitude	Paleolatitudes and rotations determined paleomagnetically consistent with those inferred from paleogeographic evidence
3. Apparent polar-wandering	Paleomagnetic poles displaced progressively with time relative to the region of observation	2a assumed valid and same test applicable	Changes in paleolatitude and rotations determined paleomagnetically consistent with those inferred from paleogeographic evidence from the *same* region
4. Polar-wandering	Paleomagnetic pole paths determined from different continents in agreement	2a assumed valid and same test applicable	Pole displacements consistent with those inferred from the paleogeographic evidence
5. Continental drift	Paleomagnetic pole paths determined from different continents disagree	1a or 2a assumed valid and same test applicable	If 2a assumed correct, paleolatitudes and rotations determined paleomagnetically from *one* region inconsistent with the paleogeographic inferences from *another* region
6. Changes in the Earth's radius	Changes in inclination in a meridional direction are inconsistent with a geocentric dipole field	1a assumed valid and same test applicable	

applicable to certain geological problems. For instance it is of some interest for the study of ancient climates (Chapter Nine). Furthermore, the paths obtained from different regions should agree if these regions have not changed their relative positions, so that the results provide a test for the hy-

pothesis of continental drift. The possibility of carrying out such studies was suggested many years ago by Mercanton (§ 1.8) but the first estimates of apparent polar-wandering were not made until 1954 when the path relative to Great Britain for late Precambrian and later times was given (Creer,

---

General note for Figures 6.23 to 6.26. Apparent polar-wandering (*B* group data). The regions to which the results refer are stippled, with their coasts marked in full line. Other coastlines are dotted. The main sampling localities are indicated schematically by crosses; it is not possible to mark all the localities separately, particularly in such small regions as the U. K. where close sampling has been carried out. The poles are, in most cases, the mean poles calculated for geological periods (Table 6.2) and are labeled as follows: *Cm* Cambrian, *O* Ordovician, *S* Silurian, *D* Devonian, *C* Carboniferous, *P* Permian, *Tr* Triassic, *J* Jurassic, *K* Cretaceous, T_1 Lower Tertiary, T_2 Upper Tertiary. Equal area projections are used, 30° grid intersections being marked.

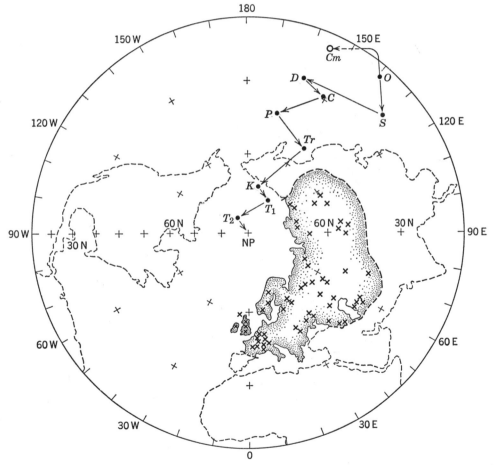

Figure 6.23. Polar movement relative to the Europe–north Asian region. The land area indicated is Europe and the U.S.S.R. west and north of the main Tertiary and Mesozoic orogenic belts of central and eastern Asia. Polar equal-area net.

Irving, and Runcorn, 1954). Since then pole estimates from certain other regions have been obtained, and although there are numerous and large gaps in the record, certain broad features are discernible. However, it will be many decades before an adequate coverage is available. The results are set out in Figures 6.23 to 6.30.

The pole paths from Europe-northern Asia (Creer, Irving, and Runcorn, 1957) and North America (Collinson and Runcorn, 1960) occupy a roughly similar position although there are differences. In the Precambrian there is a suggestion that the poles from North America are to the east of those from Europe, but in the Lower Paleozoic the mean poles are to the west. In the Permian and Triassic the North American determinations are again the more easterly whereas in Cretaceous and later time the paths are in broad agreement, except for one Eocene determination from North America [11.098]. These changes in relative longitude are rather curious. It is notable that it is in results from Permian and Triassic rocks which have been studied in the most detail that the longitude difference is most marked. There is little doubt that on the basis of the present evidence the longitude difference in the Permian poles from Europe-northern Asia and North America is significant (Figure 6.29, Table 6.2). In contrast the mean Lower Paleozoic poles (Table 6.2) have been obtained by averaging a few highly

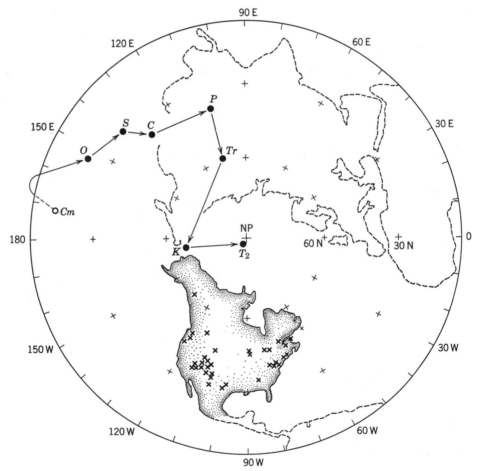

Figure 6.24.   Polar movement relative to North America.   Polar equal-area net.   See notes on p. 137.

scattered results only one of which [4.11] has been derived from detailed stability studies and this example is from the Appalachian region which has undergone subsequent tectonic deformation. On the basis of present evidence the broad agreement between the Lower Paleozoic results from North America and Europe-northern Asia may be regarded as significant but the differences between them may or may not be fortuitous; many more results are needed before this feature can be adequately discussed.

A further problem in connection with the results from North America and Europe-northern Asia is how to relate the Lower Paleozoic poles with those from late Precambrian rocks. Usually the paths are taken to swing east and then northerly toward North America and this would seem to be the most reasonable path for the North American data because of the broad agreement between poles from the Cambrian and Upper Keweenawan (Figure 6.27). Recent Russian pole determinations from beds of the Sinian System ([1.05, 57, 58] Figure 6.16a) fall to the Indian Ocean and suggest a westerly direction for the path from Europe-northern Asia prior to the Cambrian. These are problems which cannot possibly be answered until the time when more data become available.

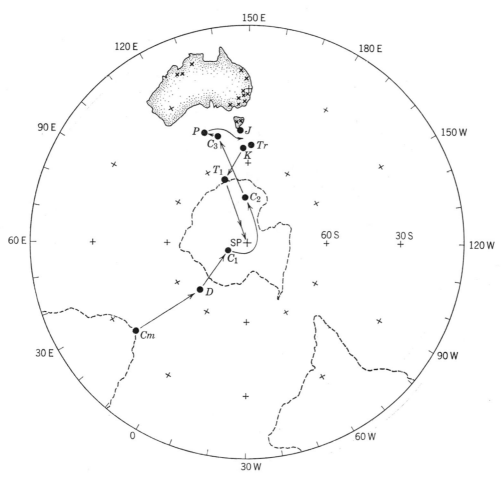

Figure 6.25. Polar movement relative to Australia. Results from within the Carboniferous are indicated separately, since they form a transition sequence C_1 the oldest and C_3 the youngest (C_1 [6.60]; C_2 [6.59]; C_3 [6.58]). Polar equal-area net. See notes on p. 137.

The Lower Paleozoic poles for Australia are based on preliminary results. The mean Devonian pole is about 80° away from Australia, but in the Carboniferous a comparatively rapid movement brings it just to the south of the continent, and it remains there, affected only by subsidiary movements, until the end of the Lower Cretaceous. In the Lower Tertiary it has moved away from Australia, and sometime in the Upper Tertiary [12.45] reached the present geographic pole (Figure 6.25).

Information on polar movement relative to India since the Paleozoic (Figure 6.26) is sketchy, being based on results from not more than three rock groups of presumed Jurassic and Upper Cretaceous to Tertiary age

(Clegg, Radakrishnamurty, and Sahasrabudhe, 1958; Deutsch, Radakrishnamurty, and Sahasrabudhe, 1957, 1958). The displacements are large, a rapid movement away from India being notable.

Results from other places are of a rather miscellaneous nature. The path for South America (Creer, 1962d) is only sketchily known and the Jurassic result from the Triassic-Jurassic Serra Geral Formation [9.53] is the only one underpinned by detailed stability studies (Figure 6.30). For Africa there are presently available only a few points in time although the detailed studies of the Karroo dolerites and extrusives [9.51] and the Precambrian intrusives [1.06, 07, 63] provide 3 firm points. An attempt (Bull and

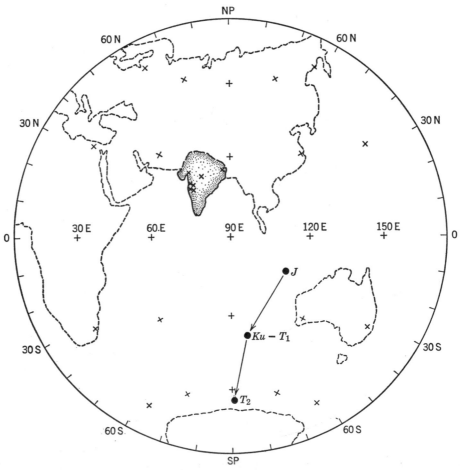

Figure 6.26. Polar movement relative to peninsular India. Equatorial equal-area net. See notes on p. 137.

Irving, 1960*a*) to construct a pole path for Antarctica has only a flimsy basis. A pole path has also been given for Japan (Nagata, Akimoto, Shimizu, Kobayashi, and Kuno, 1959) but this is a tectonically active area and strong inconsistencies within the region have recently been found and are attributed to bending of the Japanese arc (§ 10A.9). A pole path has been given for Greenland (Bidgood and Harland, 1961) but is based only on a reconnaissance of a few time levels [1.55, 56, 7.53, 8.45].

The pole paths obtained from Permian and younger beds in North America, Europe-northern Asia, India, and Australia are compared in Figure 6.28. The results from India and Australia diverge progressively in time from those of North America and Europe-northern Asia. The pole changes from Permian to Triassic are 18° of arc for Australia, 19° for North America, and 17° for Europe and although the magnitude of these changes are similar their directions differ. The consistency in results observed in Australia from Lower Triassic through to the end of the Lower Cretaceous is not found in Europe and North America where substantial changes occur within this time. In the Tertiary very rapid changes are evident in Australia and India, with changes of a lesser magnitude in Europe. One firm point is the strong and consistent differences between the Permian and Mesozoic results from Australia, and those from Europe-northern Asia and North America (Irving, Robertson, and Stott, 1963). This is shown in Figure 6.31, where all the individual determinations from these regions for this time

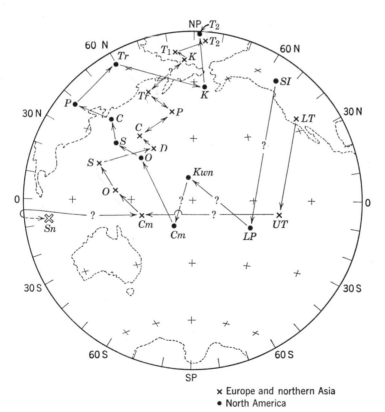

Figure 6.27. Pole paths of North America and Europe–north Asia compared. The poles are labeled as listed in the notes on p. 137, and the following additional Precambrian results are added: *SI*, Sudbury Irruptive, *LP*, Late Precambrian of the western U.S.A., *Kwn*, Upper Keweenawan, *LT*, Lower Torridonian, *UT*, Upper Torridonian. Equatorial equal-area net.

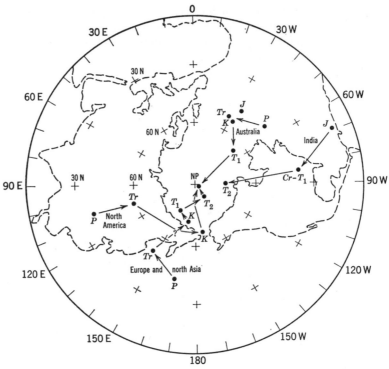

Figure 6.28. Pole paths for Permian and later time from North America, Europe–north Asia, Australia, and India compared. See notes on p. 137.

span are plotted. Numerous results are available from the northern continents, and the spread of points within the group is due, in part, to differences between the results from Europe and North America. The divergence of the two groups approaches 90°. Possible reasons for this, and other divergences that occur between results from rocks of Lower Tertiary or greater age from different regions, are now considered.

§ 6.11   Axially Symmetrical Fields

The westerly drift of the present field (§ 3.3) may be due to the acceleration of the mantle relative to the core, and since the bulk of the field probably originates within the core (§ 3.4) the field viewed from the surface over periods longer than the time taken for the mantle and core to undergo one relative rotation (that is, over 2000 years at present rates) would always appear axial in character. There are sev-

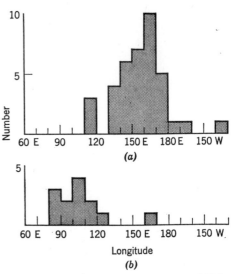

Figure 6.29. Longitudes of Permian and Triassic paleomagnetic poles from the Europe–north Asia region (*a*) and North America (*b*). Number of occurrences plotted vertically. *B* Group data.

eral variants of this hypothesis; for instance, the field could be that of a geocentric dipole, or of one or more geocentric multipoles, and the magnetic axis may, or may not, coincide with the Earth's rotational axis.

The hypothesis of an axially symmetrical field, in the general sense, has two conditions. The first is that the declination is everywhere zero, so that the paleomagnetic meridians plotted from different regions intersect in the symmetry axis. The second condition is that the paleomagnetic inclinations are equal at equal distances from the axis, the isoclines being concentric about the pole. For the special case of the geocentric dipole (1a; Table 6.3), it is necessary in addition that the paleomagnetic poles from different regions agree. For the special case of the axial geocentric dipole (2a) the paleomagnetic poles should agree with one an-other, and with the paleogeographic pole determined independently.

It is clear from Figures 6.1, 6.2, and 6.3, and Table 6.1 that the field for the entire Earth during the past few million years has been approximately that of a geocentric dipole parallel to the present axis of rotation. This is also roughly true for the Upper Tertiary (Figure 6.4g). But the hypothesis fails for earlier periods when the whole Earth is considered (Figures 6.5 to 6.11). An example of the failure, for Permian time, of axially symmetrical dipole hypotheses in general, and the geocentric dipole hypothesis in particular, is set out in Figure 6.32, using the Permian results from western Europe, North America, and Australia. The paleomeridians through the respective sampling regions intersect at three widely separated points showing that the first condition is not fulfilled. To test the second condition, P_1 is

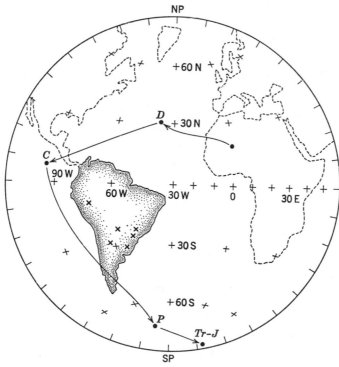

Figure 6.30. Pole path for South America. Equatorial equal-area projection. See notes on p. 137.

assumed the most probable pole for the symmetry axis, and the distances of P_1 from the European and North American sampling sites are similar, and the observed inclination values (means for rock units) are these:

North America, +20, +32, −1, +11,
  +31 (mean $\simeq$ +18)

Europe, −18, −16, −7, −9, +1, −10, −36,
  −9, −4, −5, −13, −6, +2 (mean
  $\simeq$ −10)

The sets are systematically different, so that the condition of concentric isoclines is not fulfilled.

Runcorn (1959) has considered the case of an axially symmetrical field due to an axial multipole. He first estimates the pole of possible symmetry axes from the intersection points of paleomagnetic meridians, and then shows that the observed paleo-

magnetic inclinations for various pre-Tertiary periods do not fit those expected from theory for an axial dipole, quadrupole, or octupole fields.

The high dispersion of poles from rocks of Permian to Lower Tertiary age from *different* regions is in marked contrast to the good agreement among results from the *same* region, the latter being indistinguishable from that found in the Upper Tertiary and Quaternary (compare (*a*) and (*b*) with say (*g*), Figure 6.6). This is consistent with the hypothesis that the paleogeomagnetic field, relative to individual regions, has been dipolar, and that the regions in question have moved relative to one another. If this hypothesis is correct and further that the paleomagnetically determined directions are true field directions, then continental drift has certainly occurred. The disagreement between poles, say from Australia and the

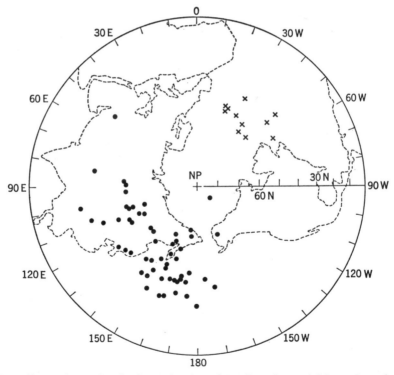

Figure 6.31. Comparison of pole determinations from Permian and Mesozoic rocks in North America, Europe–north Asia and in Australia. Polar equal-area projection. Dots are results from the northern continents, crosses are from Australia. Redrawn from Irving, Robertson, and Stott (1963), with the kind permission of the American Geophysical Union.

northern continents (Figure 6.31) is too large and systematic to be due to sampling inadequacies or to inaccuracies in geological dating. A further possibility (Hibberd, 1962), which might account for this disagreement, is that secondary magnetizations imposed long after formation, occur. But there are now results from both regions [e.g., 6.30, 58; 7.05, 13, 15, 42, 51] based on detailed studies which discount this (see discussion in Irving (1962)). A fine illustration of the discrepancy between contemporaneous poles from different continents is that between poles from the Tasmanian [9.30] and Ferrar Dolerites [9.38] (Figure 6.8); very careful radioisotope studies indicate that these intrusives are of the same age despite their

present geographical separation (McDougall, 1961, 1963).

This argument relating to continental drift depends on the assumption of a geocentric dipole field which is an extrapolation back into remote geological time of the known behavior of the field over the past few million years and its approximate behavior over the past 20 m.y. Enquiries into the validity of this hypothesis may follow one of two lines (Table 6.3). The paleomagnetic evidence may be tested internally by studying the variation of between-site dispersion and intensity as a function of latitude, or it may be compared with independent paleogeographic evidence. The former is now considered.

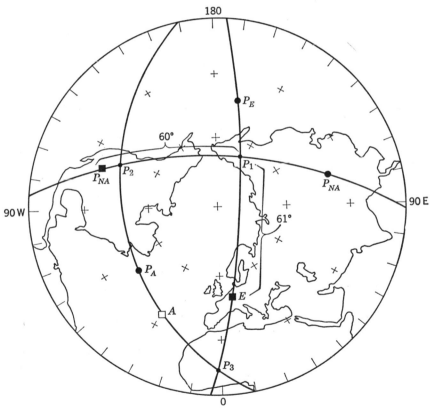

Figure 6.32. Test for axially symmetrical field using Permian data. P_E, P_{NA}, and P_A are the mean poles for western Europe, North America, and Australia. P_1, P_2, and P_3 are the intersection points of the paleomeridians. A is the antipole of the Australian sampling region. This figure is similar in essence to that given originally by Cox and Doell (1960) but is more detailed.

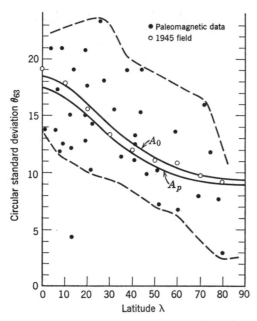

Figure 6.33. Comparison of site dispersions with dispersions of present field (Figure 3.8) and model A. Curves A_0 and A_p are the best fits to the present field and paleomagnetic dispersions, respectively. The dotted lines enclosed all results except [12.42]. Redrawn with additions from Irving and Ward (1964). Dispersion in degrees.

§ 6.12 Secular Variation: Evidence from Dispersion Estimates

The secular variation of the ancient field may be estimated from a statistical analysis of the dispersion of observations, or in a detailed step-by-step fashion by studying the variation of direction in successive rock beds in a known time sequence. The former is now considered and the latter in §§ 6.13 and 6.14.

In §§ 3.7 and 3.8 various statistical models of the Earth's field were described based on analogies with the present field. Their main features are that the intensity varies by a factor 2 between equator and pole, and that the dispersions vary with latitude, being greatest at the equator due to the lower dipole field strength there. The dispersions calculated from observations around a line of latitude for the 1945 field fit model A very well (Figure 6.33 and Table 6.4), model A

being that which assumes a steady dipolar field perturbed by randomly directed components of constant magnitude. Now it has been argued (§ 4.03) that site mean directions, particularly in igneous rocks, approximate to spot readings of the field so that the scatter in the site directions reflects the magnitude of the secular variation during the time in which the rock unit was laid down. Therefore conformity of observed dispersions to one or other of these models constitutes a test of applicability, in particular, for the hypothesis of a geocentric dipole field (Table 6.3).

In Figure 6.33 estimates of site dispersions are plotted against the paleolatitude calculated from the observed inclination (I_m) using equation 3.3. The results of an analysis based on model A (equation 3.9) are given in Table 6.4. The paleomagnetic

Table 6.4   Goodness of Fit of Paleomagnetic Dispersions and Dispersion Analysis of the 1945 Field (Creer, 1962a) to Model A for the Earth's Field (§3.8). Data of Irving and Ward (1964), reproduced by kind permission of Geofisica Pura e Applicata. N is the number of values used, and $\sigma_0 = F_d/F_0$. (1) values obtained from dispersion of site means; (2) obtained from between-site dispersion (§ 4.10). The values used are as follows: igneous (1) [1.06, 6.32, 7.11, 7.13, 7.14, 7.15, 7.42, 8.42, 9.27, 10.10, 11.005, 11.006, 11.012, 11.024, 11.091, 11.098, 12.01, 12.37, 12.62]; *igneous (2)* [5.36, 8.29, 8.44, 9.30, 9.38, 9.40, 10.09, 11.093, 12.42, 12.45]; *sedimentary (1)* [1.01, 1.02, 2.02, 7.51, 8.06]; *sedimentary (2)* [6.58]. *The standard deviation of the σ_0 values derived from the paleomagnetic observations is 0.12 and from the 1945 field 0.013.*

	N	σ_0
Igneous (1)	19	0.42
Igneous (2)	10	0.31
Sedimentary (1)	5	0.41
Sedimentary (2)	1	0.31
All paleomagnetic values	35	0.38
1945 field (unweighted)	9	0.396
1945 field (weighted)	9	0.395

data used has been selected for their high reliability. The small number (35) of the values used compared with those available is due largely to the fact that estimates of the relevant statistical parameters have not always been published in originals; for instance analyses based on samples or specimens as units cannot be used. Values from igneous and sedimentary rocks are taken separately according to whether the result was obtained by the direct application of equation 4.9 to the site means (dispersion of site means), or by the two-tier analysis (§ 4.10) in which the between-site dispersion is obtained freed of that within-sites. The choice of values is subjective, and will need revision as more data come to hand. The values have been obtained from rocks ranging in age from Precambrian to Recent. The circular standard deviations θ_{63} fall in the range 4° to 24°, with a maximum frequency at about 13° (Figure 6.34). The values are scattered, but there is a broad poleward decrease. The values for igneous and sedimentary rocks are similar, and this is consistent with the view that the site means in sediments approximate to spot readings as for igneous rocks (§ 4.03). As expected, the two-tier analysis gives the smaller values. The mean ratio σ_0 calculated from model A is comparable for all groups, and the over-all mean is similar to that derived from an analysis of the present field although the scatter is 10 times greater. The mean ratio σ_0 is equivalent to a standard deviation of 17.5° at the equator, compared to 18.5° for the present field. The curves fitted to the present field (A_0) and rock values (A_p) do not differ significantly.

Eventually it will be necessary to consider results period by period to study time variations, but there are insufficient data available at present to do this. These results are consistent with the hypothesis that the Earth's field has been predominantly that of a geocentric dipole since the Precambrian, but the data are not precise enough to provide an answer to this basic problem; they only point a possible way to its solution.

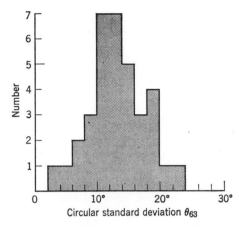

Figure 6.34. Histogram of site dispersion values. The circular standard deviation θ_{63} is plotted horizontally, and the frequency, vertically. The appendix numbers of individual values are listed in the legend to Table 6.4.

§ 6.13 Secular Variation: Evidence from TRM

It is not commonly possible to study the secular variation by the step-by-step survey of the directions in a successive time sequence since the scatter of directions at a single level is commonly as great as, or greater than, the scatter due to expected field changes. The results that have been obtained from igneous rocks and baked earths are given here, and those from sediments in the following section.

Mt. Etna Lavas. Chevallier (1925) studied 11 lava flows, the oldest dating from 394 B.C. Seven flows are dated at 1284, 1329, 1381, 1566, 1669 (Figure 1.1), and 1911. The directions in the 3 youngest flows agree well with the direct measurements of the field, except for the inclination in the 1566 flow (Figure 6.35). The declination follows a curved path with a period of 750 years and an amplitude of 18°. The variation in inclination is less regular. The mean of all 11 flows (4, +56; $a_{95} = 7°$) is not significantly different from the axial geocentric dipole field (0, +57). The circular standard deviation of flow means is 12°.

Baked Clays of Europe and North Africa. Clays or earth mixtures, which have been fired to make bricks or pottery, are useful paleomagnetically, since they acquire a TRM at the time of cooling in the direction of the ambient field. Studies of such material give the inclination but not the declination of the field, as the azimuth at the time of firing is unknown. More useful information may be obtained from the baked walls and floors of ancient kilns or fireplaces, since in favored localities the material is still *in situ* and the orientation may be completely specified. Paleomagnetic work of this type is sometimes referred to as *archeomagnetism,* since the study of such material comes within the province of archeology.

Detailed studies by Thellier and Thellier (1951, 1952) of a 4th century Roman kiln near Trêves in West Germany [12.04], of two Punic kilns contemporary with the sack of Carthage by the Romans (146 B.C.), and of a Roman kiln (about A.D. 300) also from

Tunisia [12.43] gave directions close to the axial geocentric dipole field.

Studies made in Cambridge, England (Figure 6.36a), of numerous kilns and hearths in England yielded reliable results at 14 sites [12.06]. The sites, which relate to the period of the Roman occupation and to the Middle Ages, are dated historically as follows: 1st to 4th century (10 sites), 12th century (1 site), 13th century (1 site), and 15th century (2 sites). For the first centuries A.D. the directions are west of north. In the 12th, 13th, and 15th centuries they are east only. The youngest values are not inconsistent with an extrapolation from the curve obtained from direct observations of the field. The dotted line in Figure 6.36 only denotes the rough time sequence of points. It is not intended as an actual path of secular change. The mean of the values is 0, +66, very close to the geocentric axial dipole field.

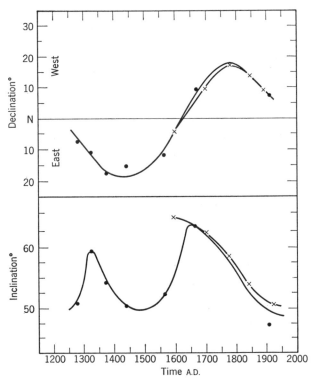

Figure 6.35. Secular variation in Sicily. The dots are obtained from lavas and the crosses are from direct observations of the field. Redrawn from Chevallier (1925), with the kind permission of Masson et Cie and Professeur R. Chevallier.

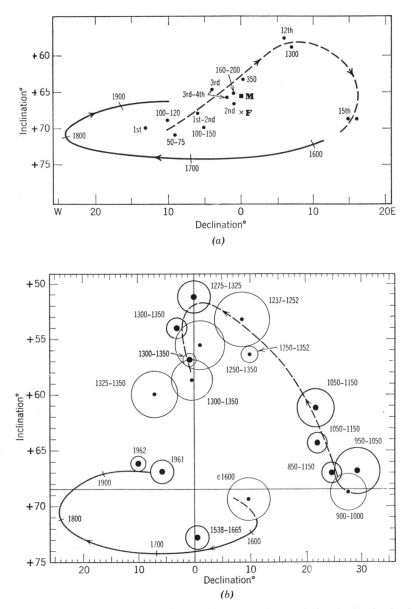

Figure 6.36. Paleomagnetic and direct observation of secular variation in England; (*a*) Cambridge work, (*b*) Oxford work. The full line gives the mean annual directions of the field observed since 1578 at London. In (*a*) the dots are the archeomagnetic values, **M** their mean direction, and **F** the geocentric axial dipole field. Labels (e.g., 1st, or 100–120) indicate the century or date A.D. (*a*) redrawn from Cook and Belshé (1958), and (*b*) redrawn from Aitken and Weaver (1962), with the kind permission of the authors. In (*b*) the circles of confidence are calculated at $\wp = 0.20$, and the bold dots are points of high physical reliability and the small dots are points of less reliability—categories A and $B + C$, respectively, as designated by Aitken and Weaving.

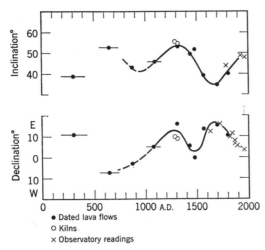

Figure 6.37. Secular variation in Japan inferred from direct and indirect observations. Redrawn from Yukutake (1961) with the author's kind permission.

Studies made in Oxford, England (Figure 6.36b), seem not to confirm the Cambridge data, discrepancies among results from 13th century material being notable. The Oxford workers suggest that the trend of secular change from the 9th to 14th centuries was counterclockwise not clockwise as at present and as the Cambridge data indicate.

Japan. There has been much study of Recent lavas in Japan [12.40], and the results suggest a variation of inclination with a period of 600–700 years and the declination with a period of 400–500 years (Figure 6.37). Extensive archeomagnetic work has been carried out [12.41] but in all but two cases the results are not related to an accurate time basis.

Tasmanian Dolerite (Jaeger and Green, 1956). As an igneous sheet cools, the Curie point isotherm moves inward from the margins to the center, freezing-in the field direction as it goes. The direction variations should be symmetrical about the center and this appears to be true in the inclinations observed in a bore core of Tasmanian Dolerite (Figure 6.38). In this example the directions are nearly vertical so that the absence of declination values is not important. The inclination plotted against a time scale ob-

tained from the calculated cooling rates suggests an oscillation of about 3°, and a periodicity of 400 years, but the effect, although apparently systematic, may not be significant in view of the scatter of observations. The high precision, correlated with higher inclinations, indicates that the secular variation in high paleolatitudes was small.

A further example of the study of secular variation using the TRM of igneous rocks is given in § 10D.2.

§ 6.14 Secular Variation: Evidence from Sediments

The rate of deposition of sediments may be slow, and so the secular variation may be present in a fist-size sample. If this occurs, then successive disks cut with their planes in the bedding plane should show systematic directional changes, and these should be the same in a parallel sequence taken from the same sample. Moreover, if such a variation is found, it would be good evidence for the reliability of the observations as field indicators. Not many samples have been studied in this way, but those that have show no evidence of such a systematic pattern. An example from a dark red arkose of very fine sandstone grade from the Torridonian Sandstone Series is given in Figure 6.39. There are no systematic trends in the same disk sequence,

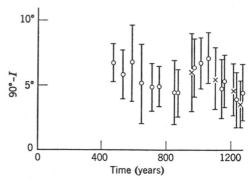

Figure 6.38. Inclination versus cooling time for Jurassic dolerite sill in Tasmania. Crosses are values from depths below the middle of the sheet plotted with the upper half. Redrawn from Jaeger and Green (1956), with the kind permission of *Geofisica Pura e Applicata* and the authors.

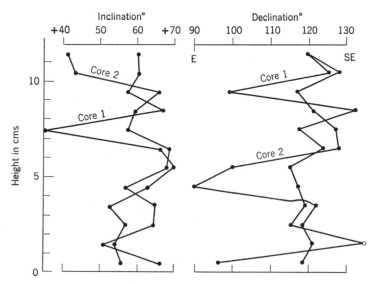

Figure 6.39. NRM direction in successive disks cut from parallel cores 12 cm long in very fine sandstone from the Applecross Group of the Torridonian Sandstone Series. Redrawn from Irving (1954).

and the agreement between disks from the same bedding level is variable—sometimes very good, and sometimes differences of 20° occur in one or other component. It is clear that, in this example, there is no record of the secular change in rock thickness on this scale.

Much work has been carried out on varved siltstones. The field can be assumed to have varied little during the deposition of an annual layer, so that a time sequence should provide good material for detailed studies of field variations. Laboratory experiments using dispersed varve material show an inclination error (§ 2.12), and there is evidence from certain Icelandic varves, deposited in the 18th century, that a similar effect occurs in nature in these deposits (Figure 6.40). Samples from two sections about 300 m apart show inclinations up to 20° less than that of the Earth's field inferred by extrapolation from observatory records. Different colored beds are found at both sites, and coarser grey layers have shallower inclinations than ochre colored beds.

Detailed studies have been carried out in the sediments of the Angerman River in Sweden [12.13]. Samples covering the pe-

riod 1100 B.C. to A.D. 750 were obtained from two localities from overlapping sequences (Figure 6.41). The over-all mean direction $(2, +75; a_{95} = 4°)$ agrees well with the axial geocentric dipole field $(0, +76)$. Results from many Recent igneous rocks also show this feature and this suggests that a large natural inclination error is not present in the Angerman varves. The beds dip at different angles at the two sites, and after correction the directions are in better agreement, particularly in the time range A.D.

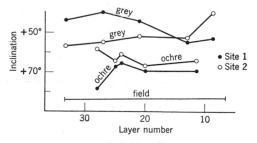

Figure 6.40. Inclination in the varves of Hagavatn, Iceland. Redrawn from Griffiths, King, Rees, and Wright (1960), with the kind permission of the Royal Society of London and the authors.

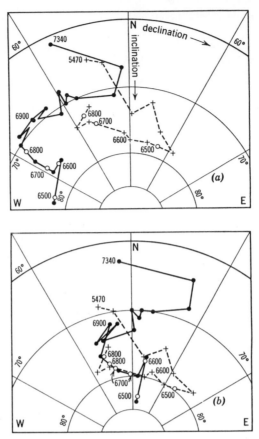

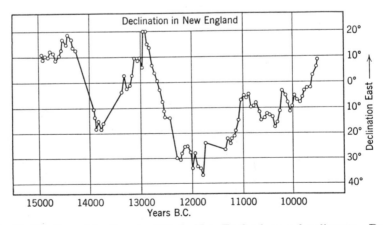

Figure 6.41. NRM direction in Swedish varved clays from the Angerman River; (a) uncorrected, (b) corrected for geological dip. Dates are in years on Liden's Time Scale (7602 = A.D. 1000). Dots are results from the locality of Prästmon and crosses from Undrom. Circles are interpolated points. Redrawn from Griffiths (1953), with the kind permission of the editors of *Nature* and D. H. Griffiths.

Figure 6.42. Declination of fossil magnetism in New England varved sediments. Redrawn from Johnson, Murphy, and Torreson (1948), with the kind permission of the American Geophysical Union and A. E. Johnson.

0–300. The circular standard deviation of the group directions is 14°, similar to that in the Mt. Etna lavas which cover roughly the same time period (§ 6.13).

Extensive work has been carried out on the varves of New England [12.47], covering a period of about 5000 years over 10,000 years ago, much older than the sequences studied in Sweden. They yield declination values which show a more or less consistent variation with an amplitude of up to 50° and a period of the order a thousand years, with possible smaller oscillations of shorter duration (Figure 6.42). The inclinations were systematically lower than the present field and were considered affected by depositional errors; moreover the inclinations were generally higher in younger varves suggesting that compaction (§ 2.15) may have diminished the inclination in the older beds.

Reversals of magnetization

§ 7.1 **Introduction** In many paleomagnetic studies the directions of natural remanent magnetization (NRM) fall into two distinct groups opposed in direction to one another. In those cases where care has been taken to correct for unstable components the mean direction of the groups are, within the experimental errors, found to be 180° apart. Of all rock specimens studied, whether igneous or sedimentary, about one-half have negative (or normal) polarity and one-half have positive (or reversed) polarity (§ 4.13). A *reversal of magnetization* is defined as the actual change from one polarity to another. The phenomenon of reversals may be interpreted in one of two ways: that the geomagnetic field may have periodically reversed itself, or, alternatively, that some rocks acquire a spontaneous magnetization in a direction opposite to that of the applied field. The former is referred to as the hypothesis of *reversals of the geomagnetic field,* and the latter as the hypothesis of *self-reversed magnetization.* The field reversal may have been brought about either by 180° rotation of the main dipole axis or by decay of the dipole field followed by its build-up in the opposite sense.

Several possible mechanisms of self-reversal have been suggested. At first sight it may be thought possible to test for oc-

currence of these in igneous rocks simply by observing whether the total thermoremanence (TRM) acquired in the laboratory is parallel or antiparallel to the applied field. But there are many uncertainties in the interpretation of such experiments; there is always the possibility that laboratory heat treatment causes mineralogical changes which actually obliterate the self-reversal mechanism, nor do these experiments provide information about possible slow changes occurring on the geological time scale. Furthermore, it is not possible to simulate self-reversal mechanisms in sediments. Consequently, so far as work has proceeded at present, the most important tests of these rival hypotheses are field experiments (§ 1.5), especially the study of the relation of reversals of polarity to stratigraphy and rock types, and the study of heating experiments carried out by nature at igneous contacts.

If the observed reversals of magnetization arose, for the most part, from field reversals, then certain effects should be recognized, and the presence or absence of these may be taken as evidence for or against the hypothesis of field reversals. These predictions may be summarized in 5 points.

1. The same polarity should occur in rocks of the same age, irrespective of rock type,

in all regions, provided the field has maintained the same polarity for a sufficiently long period of time to establish, by geological methods, the contemporaneity of beds. The time variations of polarity should be the same, period for period, in the standard sections of all regions. Positive and negative zones should be identifiable, and these should occur in stratigraphic succession, so that the boundaries between zones of opposite polarity are parallel to the time planes and do not cut across them.

2. At the boundaries between positive and negative levels there should occur, in some instances, beds with transitional directions of magnetization. Because of the fragmentary nature of the record (§ 4.03) it is not to be expected that transitional levels will occur in all cases. In favorable circumstances, traverses through the *same* stratigraphic levels at *different* localities should reveal comparable direction changes.

3. There should be no systematic differences of chemical, mineralogical, or physical properties of the magnetic minerals in positive and negatively polarized rocks.

4. The polarities in igneous bodies should be the same as those in their respective baked contact rocks.

5. The laboratory tests for self-reversal mechanisms should prove negative when due account is taken of the uncertainty of such tests.

In §§ 6.02 to 6.07, where the paleomagnetic directions were reviewed period by period, mention was made of the variation in polarities observed, and certain examples of reversals have already been figured (Figure 4.2*c* and *d*). This chapter begins with a description of certain examples of reversals. This is followed by an account of hypothetical self-reversing mechanisms, of self-reversal properties found in the laboratory, and of the field evidence.

§ 7.2 Examples of Reversals Dated Stratigraphically

Time sequences of alternating polarities were first established stratigraphically, mainly on the evidence of super-

Table 7.1 Tentative Sequence of Alternating Polarities in the Massif Central. *Compiled from Roche (1950a and b, 1951, 1956, 1958, 1960) and adopting the Tertiary time divisions given by Fourmarier (1950, p. 402). Negative (normal), positive (reversed).*

Age	Polarity
Upper Pleistocene	−
Lower Pleistocene	+ { reversal "au cour du Pleistocene inferieur"
PLIOCENE	
Villafranchian	+
Astian	?
Plaisancian (lower)	+
MIOCENE	
Pontian	+ and −
Vindobonian	?
Burdigalian	−
OLIGOCENE	
Aquitanian	+
Stampian	+
Sannoisian	?

imposition of beds; examples of these are given in this section. More recently, there have been attempts to establish sequences on the basis of radiometrically determined rock ages, and these are described in § 7.3.

Massif Central (Table 7.1). Following earlier work (§ 1.6), Roche has studied numerous igneous bodies in the Massif Central of France. Peperites of Stampian age in the Limagne give negative anomalies in the geomagnetic field and presumably have positive directions. Samples from a basalt, intrusive into the peperites have positive directions [11.002]; this basalt is considered to be of Aquitanian age. Oligocene intrusives [11.001] from Gergovie are positive, and some lava flows in the same region of probable Burdigalian age are negative. Five upper Miocene flows showed both positive and negative directions [11.003–005]. Positive polarities are found in Mio-Pliocene

Table 7.2   Generalized Stratigraphic Column of Iceland and Magnetic Polarities, from Hospers (1953–54). *Negative (normal), positive (reversed). Reproduced by kind permisson of the Royal Netherlands Academy and J. Hospers.*

Historic lava flows A.D. 1729 to
  1947–48   —
Postglacial lava flows: from 2000 to 7000
  years old   —
Interglacial lava flows and sediments,
  approximately 150,000 years old   —
Palagonite Formation: sampled portion
  0.5 m.y. or less   —
Early Quaternary lava flows and sedi-
  ments: 0.5 to 1 m.y.   +
— *break* —
Pliocene sediments and lava flows: 2–12   {—
  m.y. old   {+
— *break* —
Tertiary lava flows (and some sedi-   ⌈+
  ments): those sampled are probably |—
  Miocene: 12–26 m.y. old   {+
                                                        ⌊—

[11.006] and Plio-Pleistocene [12.01] lava flows. Certain lower Pleistocene lavas are positive, whereas lavas in the later Pleistocene all have negative directions [12.02]. Roche places the time of the last reversal as the middle of the lower Pleistocene. The levels of reversal prior to this are only roughly established, although there have been several since the Oligocene.

Iceland. The reversal sequence compiled by Hospers from his work in Iceland is given in Table 7.2. This work has been extended by Einnarson (1957*a*) and by Rutten and Wesink (1960). Recent and glacial lavas and sediments are magnetized in the same sense as the present field [12.52–54]. Early Quaternary beds are positive [12.51]. Levels with both polarities occur in Pliocene and earlier Tertiary flows and sediments [11.108, 12.49, 12.50], but it is unlikely that all the zones present have yet been recognized. As in the Massif Central, the last

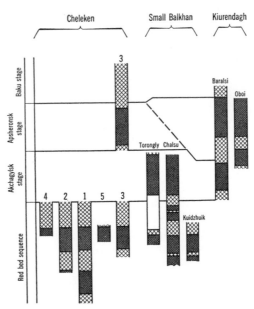

Figure 7.1. Alternating polarity in the Pliocene and Quaternary sections of western Turkmenia. Each column gives results from separate sections. Beds with positive polarity (reversal) black, those with negative (normal) polarity cross-hatched. The sections on the Cheleken peninsula are numbered 1 to 5. The section from the Small Balkhan and the Kiurendagh have their appropriate geographical names. Redrawn from Khramov (1958).

reversal occurs towards the base of the Quaternary.

Western Turkmenia (Khramov, 1958). In western Turkmenia, in the region east of the Cheleken peninsula toward the Great and Small Balkhan and the Kiurendagh, a thick succession of Neogene and Quaternary sediments are exposed. Khramov has found a sequence of alternating polarities which are given schematically in Figure 7.1. The order in each section is established by superimposition. The Red Bed sequence is Pliocene [11.043]. The Akchagylsk and Apsheronsk stages are either Pliocene or lower Pleistocene [12.30]. The Baku stage is Quaternary [12.29]. The last reversal occurs about the boundary of the Apsheronsk and Baku stages. Numerous reversals have been identified in Tertiary sections. In Figure 7.2 the reversal sequence is applied to correlation problems discussed later (§ 10C.4).

Reversals in the Late Paleozoic (Table 7.3). All beds of uppermost Carboniferous age so far studied have positive polarization,

their directions being indistinguishable (within the errors) from those observed in overlying Permian beds. The mean directions of all Permian beds so far studied, except those from the Upper Tartarian of Russian, are positive. The Upper Tartarian, which is often classified with the Triassic, has both polarities. Negative or mixed polarities characterize Lower Triassic beds elsewhere in the world. Beds laid down in the time range of uppermost Carboniferous to uppermost Permian are characterized by mean directions with positive polarity. The formations studied give a fair coverage of this span of time, so that although further sampling may reveal negative directions the chance of them being of more than subsidiary importance is considered small. This span of time does not coincide with the geological Permian Period, and there is, of course, no reason why it should do so. In western Europe the change from negative to positive appears to occur within the Westphalian, or between the Westphalian and Stephanian, although

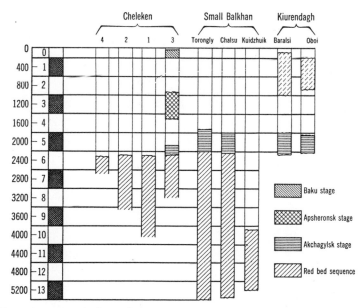

Figure 7.2. Tentative age relations of the Pliocene and Quaternary beds of western Turkmenia as indicated by their paleomagnetic results. Based on data of Figure 7.1. Columns labeled as in Figure 7.1. Periods of years × 10³ are given on the left together with the magnetic zones proposed by Khramov. The polarity groups are numbered backwards in time from 0 to 13, 0 being the contemporary polarity. Redrawn after Khramov (1958).

Table 7.3 Magnetic Polarities: Carboniferous, Permian and older Triassic Rocks. *Brought up-to-date from Irving and Parry (1963).* M denotes beds with mixed polarity.

	U.S.S.R.			Western Europe			North and South America			Australia	
Triassic	Tr	Siberian Traps [8.20]	M								
	Tr	Intrusives Siberia [8.25]	M								
	Tr	Sediments Taimyr [8.21]	–								
	Trl	Sediments [8.14]	M	Trl	Bunter [8.04]		Trl-m	Moenkopi Fm [8.31]	M	Trl	Narrabeen Sediments [8.28]	–
				Trl	Vosge Ss. [8.03]		P-Tr	Chugwater Fm. [8.30]	M			
Permian	Pu	Up. Tartarian [7.25]	M								(Illawarra Reversal 100 m)	
	Pu	Lr. Tartarian [7.29]	+				Pu	Corumbatai Fm. [7.60]	+			
	Pu	Kazanian [7.34]	+	Pm	Montenis Ss. [7.06]	+				P(m-u)	Upper Marine Latites [7.42]	+
	Pu	Ufimian [7.37]	+	P(m?)	Nideck Porphyry [7.07, 7.54]	+	P(l-m)	Yeso Fm. [7.50]	+			
	Pm-u	Maymecha-Kotuy Ultrabasics [7.39]	+	P	Nahe Igneous Rocks [7.12]	+						
				P	Mauchline Beds [7.16, 7.17]	+						
				P	Ayrshire Kylites [7.18]	+	P	Culter Fm. [7.46]	+			
				P	Esterel Suite [7.04, 7.05]	+						
				Pl	Exeter Traps [7.14]	+	Pl	Abo Fm. [7.48]	+	Pl	Lower Marine Basalt [7.43]	+
				Pl	Oslo Igneous Complex [7.13]	+	Cu-Pl	Red beds Prince Edward Island (Roy, 1963)	+			
	Pl	Beloyarsk Suite [7.57]	+	Pl	St. Wendel Ss. [7.08]	+	Cu-Pl	Supai Fm. [7.51]	+			
	Pl	Donbas Sediments [7.38]	+	Pl	Rotliegende [7.09]	+	Cu-Pl	Sangre de Cristo Fm. [7.52]	+			
				Cu-Pl	Whin Sill [7.15]	+						
Carboniferous	Cu	Araucarite Stage [6.40]	+	Cu	Stephanian [6.04]	+	Cu	Naco Fm. [6.66]	+	Cu	Upper Kuttung Glacials [6.58]	+
				Cu	Midland Sills [6.32]	+					(Paterson Reversal 2 m)	
	Cu	Avilov Stage [6.41]	+	Cu	Pennant Ss. [6.37]	–				Cu	Paterson Toscanite [6.59]	–
				C	Sediments U.K. [6.38, 6.39]	M						
				C	Southdean Basanite [6.13]	+	Cl-u	Sediments, Canada [6.68]	+	Cl	Lower Kuttung Lavas [6.60]	+
				Cm	Tideswelldale Rocks [6.26]	+						
	Cl	Tula Horizon [6.44]	M	Cl	Derbyshire Lavas [6.29]	M	Cl	Barnett Fm. [6.63]	M			
	Cl	Tournai Stage [6.45]	M	Cl	Carboniferous Lst. [6.14]	M	Cl	Codroy Beds [6.67]	+			
	Cl	Siberian Platform Beds [6.55]	–	Cl	Kinghorn Lavas [6.11]	M						
				Cl	Wenlock Lava [6.35]	–						

Kiaman (bracket spanning the Permian interval)

the actual level has not yet been identified on the ground. A level of reversal, which may correspond to this, occurs between the Paterson Toscanite [6.59] and the overlying glacial sediments [6.58]: this is referred to as the *Paterson Reversal*. The upper reversal in the Russian sections occurs either between the Lower and Upper Tartarian or within the latter, and may be represented in Australia by the *Illawarra Reversal* which occurs between the latites of the Upper Marine Series [7.42] and the Lower Triassic Narrabeen sediments [8.28].

§ 7.3 Examples of Reversals Dated Radiometrically

Results covering the past few million years have been obtained by two independent groups of workers. The dating is based entirely on radiometric determination (K-Ar on whole rock samples) and there is little stratigraphic control of the results, which have, in many cases, been obtained from widely separated outcrops. There are many difficult problems associated with the radiometric dating of such young material so that much uncertainty must be ascribed to the present results and it is entirely possible that some determinations will be revised in the near future.

McDougall and Tarling obtained their results from samples from the Hawaiian Islands (Figure 7.3). Their data suggest that the most recent reversal occurred 1 m.y. ago, and the penultimate reversal about 2.5 m.y. ago. A pattern of alternating polarities appears in older rocks but the sampling detail is insufficient for the accurate dating of earlier reversals, although it appears that the periodicity is not constant but varies from 0.2 to 1.5 m.y.

Cox, Doell, and Dalrymple base their polarity sequence on results from the western U.S.A., Africa, and Europe (Figure 7.4). They place the last reversal as 1 m.y. ago which is in very good agreement with the Hawaiian work. With the exception of the African point from the Olduvai Gorge, Tanganyika (Grommé and Hay, 1963), the results indicate that the penultimate reversal was about 2.4 m.y. ago, also in good agree-

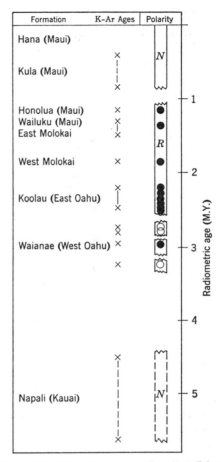

Figure 7.3. Polarity epochs, Hawaiian Islands. The levels studied paleomagnetically and radiometrically are marked by dots (positive) and circles (negative) in the third column, and crosses in the second column. Redrawn from McDougall and Tarling (1963), with the kind permission of the editors of *Nature* and the authors.

ment with the Hawaiian work (McDougall and Tarling, 1964). It might be noted that Cox, Doell, and Dalrymple label their "geomagnetic epochs" N1, R1, and N2; comments on this scheme are made in § 10C.5.

§ 7.4 Self-Reversal Mechanisms: Theoretical Aspects

Néel (1951, 1955) showed on theoretical grounds that under conditions which might commonly arise in the histories of natural minerals, there were several possible mechanisms by which a remanence di-

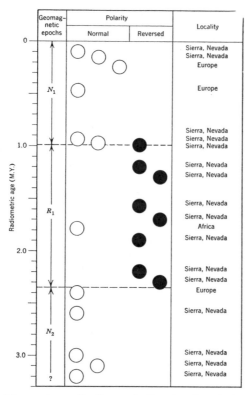

Figure 7.4. Radiometrically dated polarity epochs—California and elsewhere. Compiled from Cox, Doell, and Dalrymple (1963a, b, c, 1964).

models involving a mixture of two constituents, A and B, in which the magnetization of one is antiparallel to that of the other, and the sign of the remanence depends on the balance between the magnitudes of the A and B moments; the constituents A and B are hypothetical minerals, and may refer to different species in different cases. Secondly, there are single constituent models involving ferrimagnetic antiparallel coupling of sublattices within a single crystal. Finally, there are models involving cation migration.

Two Constituent Models. Three broad types of two constituent models may be envisaged: (a) self-reversal through magnetostatic interaction between A and B; (b) self-reversal through exchange energy interaction across the boundaries between A and B grains; (c) self-reversal of a magnetization initially parallel to the applied field, by the occurrence of secondary changes which preferentially affect one constituent, so that the balance between A and B is altered.

Interaction between two intimately mixed constituents, A and B, may produce self-reversal of the total TRM, if A has the higher Curie point. During cooling A becomes magnetized parallel to the applied field. As cooling continues through the Curie point of B, the TRM of A may act, by one of several mechanisms, so as to order the magnetization of B in a direction opposed to that of A and to the applied field. A self-reversal occurs if, on cooling to normal temperatures, the magnetization of B exceeds that of A. If, after cooling, the magnetization of B is less than that of A so that the total TRM is initially parallel to the field, a self-reversal can be produced if the magnetization of A decays more rapidly in time than that of B; for example, if the half-life for viscous decay of A were, say, a thousand years and that of B a million years, and if initially $A = 2B$, then after a little more than a thousand years a reversal would occur spontaneously. Self-reversal may also occur if A is selectively removed or replaced chemically without affecting B.

The interactions in two constituent models may arise from magnetostatic or exchange

rection could become reversed from that of the field in which it was initially acquired. At much the same time, Nagata (1952) published the first results of a long series of detailed studies, by himself and his colleagues, of the *Haruna dacite*, showing that the total TRM of this rock is directed antiparallel to the applied field, so proving that self-reversals can in fact occur. Since then, further mechanisms have been suggested (see Uyeda, 1958) and self-reversal properties have been shown to occur in certain synthetic material, and in natural material subjected to special laboratory treatment. But it is only in the Haruna dacite that spontaneous self-reversal of the *total* TRM is known to occur in a *natural* rock. Model processes which could potentially give rise to spontaneous self-reversal are of two main types. There are forces. Magnetostatic interactions occur during cooling if the field applied to constituent B is controlled by the magnetization of A. The total field in the region of B is the sum of the external field h_{ex}, and the demagnetizing field h_d due to free poles and opposed to h_{ex}, and to certain other fields such as those produced by the moments of surrounding particles; for the total field to be negative (negative interaction) there are stringent requirements of grain size and the relative magnitudes of spontaneous magnetization. Many different geometrical situations have been studied theoretically, and in some the interaction is found to be positive, and in others it is negative. In cases where A and B occur as small spherical grains uniformly mixed together, the interaction is positive, and both are magnetized parallel to the field. Similarly, when A is embedded as spherical inclusions in B, no significant interaction occurs. Self-reversal can occur, however, under certain conditions where ellipsoidal grains of B are embedded in A (Figure 7.5a). A further case, which has been studied experimentally, is that of alternating parallel sheets of A and B comparable to the intergrowths common in the iron ore minerals (Figure 7.5b). In the experiment a synthetic specimen of alternating laminae of magnetite and pyrrhotite was heated and cooled in the Earth's field aligned along the laminae. In this case magnetite,

having the higher Curie temperature, is the A constituent, and pyrrhotite the B constituent (Figure 7.6). Subsequent measurements made on individual plates after the model was dismantled showed the pyrrhotite to be reversed with respect to the field, the magnetite being magnetized parallel to the field. The latter was the greater, so that the total TRM of the specimen was not reversed but was parallel to the applied field. Negative interactions are most likely to occur in fields much weaker than that of the Earth's, and no example has yet been found in nature.

A further possible interaction between A and B constituents of differing Curie points involves exchange interaction across their common boundaries (Néel, 1955). If the crystal lattices of the two constituents are in good register, antiparallel (or parallel) alignment of spontaneous magnetization on either side of the boundary may occur. Self-reversal, in which B exceeds A at normal temperatures, is most likely in rocks when A and B are both ferrimagnetic, or, if A is parasitically ferromagnetic and B is ferrimagnetic. The latter is the more effective because of the feebleness of parasitic ferromagnetism, and this appears to be the explanation of the self-reversal in the ilmenite-hematite series.

Self-reversal could arise in sedimentary rocks if their magnetic minerals, deposited

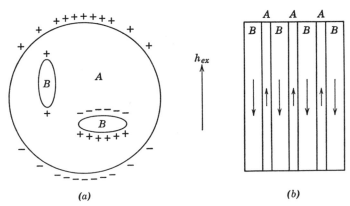

(a)   *(b)*

Figure 7.5. Magnetostatic self-reversal mechanisms. (*a*) Néel's model. (*b*) Alternating laminae of A and B, the magnetization of B outweighing that of A. Compiled from Uyeda (1958).

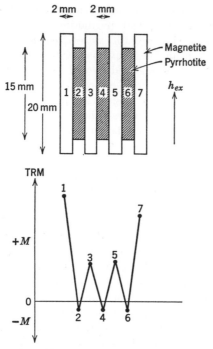

Figure 7.6. Negative magnetostatic interaction in a model experiment. Above is a diagram of the laminated model, and below the magnetization of the individual plates is given, $+M$ being the magnitude in the direction of the applied field, h_{ex}, and $-M$ that in the reverse direction. The dimensions are in millimeters. Redrawn from Uyeda (1958), with the kind permission of the Science Council of Japan and S. Uyeda. See also Grabovosky and Pushkov (1954).

detritally or chemically, are of the two-constituent type. Subsequent demagnetization or removal of the initially dominant component could lead to self-reversal.

Ionic Ordering (Néel, 1955; Verhoogen, 1956). A mineral may undergo self-reversal when cations migrate to preferred sites in the crystal lattice. This may be thought of as a change from a disordered to an equilibrium-ordered state. Rapid cooling may freeze the cations in a disordered state, and then, over long periods of time, they will migrate to ordered positions possibly resulting in a self-reversal. Verhoogen shows that this mechanism is feasible, in theory, for natural impure magnetites, and estimates the time required for ordering to produce self-reversal to be 10^5 to 10^6 years.

One Constituent Model. Spontaneous magnetization of ferrimagnetic minerals is acquired by both sublattices at the same Curie point, but the magnetization of each varies with temperature, so that the net magnetization may reverse upon cooling (Figure 7.7). This type of behavior has been shown to occur in synthetic lithium chromium spinels (Gorter and Schulkes, 1953), but has not yet been found in rocks.

§7.5   Observed Self-Reversal Properties in Rocks

Mt. Haruna Dacite (Nagata, 1952; Nagata, Uyeda, and Akimoto, 1952; Nagata, Uyeda, Akimoto, and Kawai, 1952;

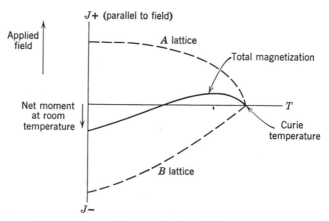

Figure 7.7. Self-reversal in ferrimagnetic material in which the variation of spontaneous magnetization with temperature is different for the two sublattices.

Uyeda, 1955, 1958; Nagata and Uyeda, 1961). The Haruna rock is a hypersthene dacite pumice occurring on the flanks of an extinct volcano (age not specified in originals) in the Kwanto district of Japan. Its NRM has a specific intensity of 4.3×10^{-3} and a mean direction 215, -14. The direction is not reversed from the present field as would be expected if the NRM were due entirely to a self-reversal, but is inclined at 135° to it. The absence of exact antiparallel alignment may be due to secondary components, but no experiments to test this have yet been reported.

The dacite contains 2 per cent by volume of magnetic minerals, made up of Fe_2O_3, FeO, and TiO_2 in the ratio 57.9:34.7:7.4, with traces of MnO and V_2O_3. The most striking magnetic effect is that which occurs if the rock (or separated magnetic mineral) is heated to temperatures of more than 210°C and cooled in a weak magnetic field, a total

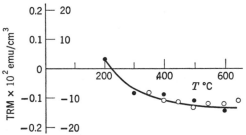

Figure 7.8. The total TRM acquired by the Mt. Haruna dacite (dots referring to the left-hand intensity scale) and magnetic mineral extract (circles referring to the right-hand intensity scale) taken from the dacite, on cooling from temperature T to room temperatures in a field of 0.5 oe. Compiled from Nagata, Uyeda, and Akimoto (1952).

TRM is developed in a sense opposite to that of the applied field (Figure 7.8). The curves for saturation magnetization, J_s, and susceptibility, χ, versus temperature, are given in

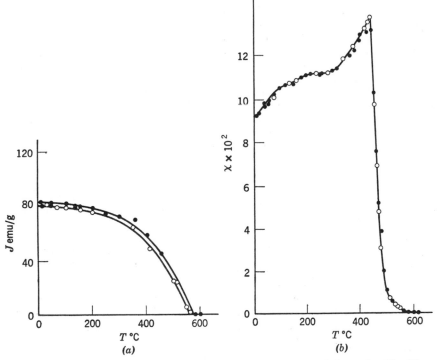

Figure 7.9. Thermomagnetic curves for magnetic minerals extracted from the Mt. Haruna dacite. (a) Magnetization J in 2000 oe versus T; (b) susceptibility measured in 1.35 oe versus temperature T. Heating and cooling results are distinguished by dots and circles and are almost identical. Redrawn from Nagata, Uyeda, and Akimoto (1952), with the kind permission of the Society of Terrestrial Magnetism and Electricity of Japan.

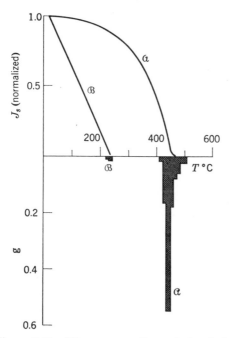

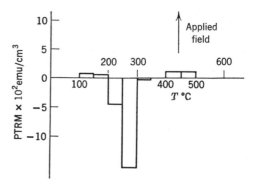

Figure 7.11. Partial TRM (PTRM) of the magnetic mineral extract from the Haruna dacite. The PTRM (measured at room temperatures) acquired in an applied field of 0.5 oe is reckoned positive when along the field, and negative when opposed to it. Redrawn from Nagata, Uyeda, and Akimoto (1952), with the kind permission of the Society of Terrestrial Magnetism and Electricity of Japan.

Figure 7.10. Thermomagnetic analysis of the magnetic mineral extract from the Haruna dacite. The separation spectrum given in the lower half is the weight extracted electromagnetically from a given sample of magnetic minerals between the temperature intervals indicated. The total weight of the sample is 1.015 g. Typical J_s/T curves for the α and $\mathfrak{B}$ fractions are given above, J_s being the magnetization in 2400 oe which is near saturation. The J_s values are normalized to unity at room temperatures. Simplified from Nagata, Akimoto, and Uyeda (1953*a*).

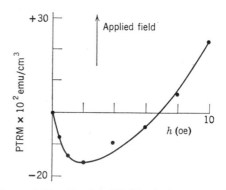

Figure 7.12. Partial TRM of the magnetic mineral extract from the Haruna dacite acquired between temperatures of 250°–350°C in a field h. Negative magnitudes indicate a remanence opposed to h. Redrawn from Nagata, Uyeda, and Akimoto (1952), with the kind permission of the Society of Terrestrial Magnetism and Electricity of Japan.

Figure 7.9; the latter shows two steps corresponding to Curie points at about 450° and 280°C, whereas the J_s/T curve is characteristic of titanomagnetites showing a single Curie temperature at 450°C. The thermomagnetic curves are reversible, the heating and cooling results being indistinguishable. Thermomagnetic separation of the magnetic minerals yields two constituents, α corresponding to the peak at 450°C, and $\mathfrak{B}$ to that at 230°C; the abundance ratio, $\mathfrak{B}/\alpha$, being about 0.02 (Figure 7.10). The relative abundance of $\mathfrak{B}$ accounts for its dominating effect on the J_s/T curves. The α constituent separately has a J_s/T curve typical for titanomagnetites, and a specific intensity at room temperature of

about 80 emu. $\mathfrak{B}$ has an unusual linear J_s/T relationship and a specific intensity at room temperature of about 20 emu. Typical J_s/T curves from α and $\mathfrak{B}$ grains are given in Figure 7.10. The partial TRM has small components parallel to the field above 400°C and below 200°C, but the dominant components are built up between 250° and 350°C (Figure 7.11). The partial TRM in the range 250° to 350°C

is self-reversed in fields up to 7 oe, but on cooling in stronger fields the self-reversal is suppressed, the partial TRM being parallel to the
applied field (Figure 7.12). It seems therefore
that the reversed TRM induced in the laboratory, and probably also the NRM, is due to
the $\mathcal{B}$ constituent, even though this is present
in very much smaller quantities than α.
Chemical analyses showed α to be a titanomagnetite, and $\mathcal{B}$ to be an ilmenohematite
(Figure 7.13). Composite $\alpha\mathcal{B}$ grains also
occurred.

At first, the reversed TRM was thought to
be due to a magnetostatic interaction between
the α and $\mathcal{B}$ constituents. Later, however,
Uyeda (1955) found that the reversed TRM
was intensified by purification of the $\mathcal{B}$ constituent, which is the opposite of what would
be expected if an α-$\mathcal{B}$ interaction occurred; $\mathcal{B}$
alone appears to be responsible for the self-
reversal, and the α constituent seems to have
nothing to do with the phenomenon. For
comparison with this result Uyeda (1957, 1958)
examined the TRM characteristics of the
ilmenite-hematite series and found that synthetic specimens showed self-reversal properties in the compositional range 45 to 60 per
cent ilmenite; a specimen with 48 per cent
ilmenite was self-reversing even in an applied
field of 10^4 oe (Figure 7.14). This property is
thought to be an order-disorder phenomenon
arising out of negative exchange interaction

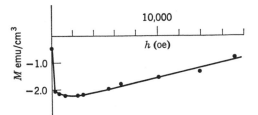

Figure 7.14. Self-reversal of ilmenohematite.
Total TRM as a function of applied field h
of synthetic ilmenohematite $0.48FeTiO_3 \cdot 0.52$-
Fe_2O_3. Redrawn from Uyeda (1958), with the
kind permission of the Science Council of
Japan and S. Uyeda.

across grain boundaries (§ 7.4) and this is
held also to be the explanation for the self-
reversal of the $\mathcal{B}$ constituent in the Haruna
dacite. However it is not clear why the field
required to suppress the reversed TRM in the
$\mathcal{B}$ constituent is only about 7 oe (Figure 7.12),
which is small compared to that in synthetic
minerals, and to the exchange forces involved.

One of the surprising features of this work
is that although the α titanomagnetite makes
up 98 per cent of the magnetic minerals and
dominates the J_s/T curves (Figure 7.9a) it
does not contribute appreciably to the TRM,
nor, apparently, to the fossil magnetism. It
seems that the titanomagnetite must be magnetically so unstable that it is incapable of
holding an appreciable remanence. The situation may be qualitatively comparable to that
found from studies of TRM in single crystals
of magnetite and hematite in which the latter
develop a much larger remanence than the
former in fields of strength comparable to that
of the Earth (Figure 2.17c).

Partial Self-Reversals. Two cases have been
found of self-reversal of partial TRM without
reversal of the total TRM; the Mt. Asio
dacitic pitchstone (Nagata, Akimoto, and
Uyeda, 1953a), and the iron sand from Sokoto
Mines (work of Saito, see Uyeda, 1958). In
both, the TRM acquired between 200° and
300°C in fields of 1 or 2 oe, is reversed from
the applied field, but is small in magnitude
compared with that acquired parallel to the
field in other temperature intervals, so that
the total TRM is directed along the field. In

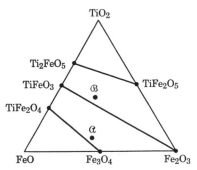

Figure 7.13. Chemical composition of the α
and $\mathcal{B}$ constituents of magnetic mineral extracts from the Haruna dacite represented in
per cent mol. on a ternary diagram. Redrawn
from Nagata, Akimoto, and Uyeda (1953a),
with the kind permission of the Society of Terrestrial Magnetism and Electricity of Japan.

Feet below
surface

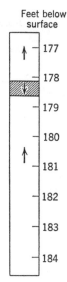

Figure 7.15. Reversal of NRM in continuous bore core of Triassic sediments, Tasmania. The arrows indicate the directions which are almost vertical.

both cases the partial self-reversal is associated with ℬ minerals of the type just described.

Pyrrhotite-Bearing Rocks. Self-reversal properties have been found, under laboratory conditions, in specimens from a shale band a few inches thick, which occurs at a distance of about 80 ft above the upper contact of a 400 ft sill (Everitt, 1962c). The shale is of Carboniferous age, and the locality Rashiehill near Stirling, Scotland. The specimens were bore core, and so declinations were indeterminate. The directions were highly scattered but it appears that the NRM has a "net reverse magnetization relative to other parts of the core." The original magnetic material α' is transformed irreversibly to a second mineral $\mathcal{B}'$ at between 310° and 340°C, and within this range a mixture of α' and $\mathcal{B}'$ occurred. Mineral $\mathcal{B}'$ appears to be pyrrhotite $Fe_{1-x}S$ with $x = 0.125$. Mineral α' is related to $\mathcal{B}'$ but is not one of the "ordinary forms" of pyrrhotite. In the experiments, the shale was first given a maximum isothermal remanent magnetization (M_{max}), heated to various temperatures in the vicinity of the transition range, and then cooled in zero field, measurements being carried out during cooling. If the

temperature either did not exceed 310°, or exceeded 340°C making the transformation complete, the magnetization remained in the same direction. If the specimen was heated to between 313° and 330°C, the magnetization reversed on cooling, taking up a direction opposed to the IRM. The reversal in the transition range is attributed by Everitt to magnetostatic interaction between the mixed $\alpha'\mathcal{B}'$ phases, the material $\mathcal{B}'$ being magnetized in the reverse field of the parent α'.

There are results from two other pyrrhotite-bearing "reversed" rocks. The first case (Figure 7.15) is from some horizontally bedded tuffaceous sediments of Triassic age from Tasmania (Almond, Clegg, and Jaeger, 1956). The sediments are intruded by dolerite, and the samples were obtained from a vertical bore core which had previously passed through a sill whose lower contact was at a depth of 150 ft. A *continuous* core at a depth 177.5 to 184.6 ft was sliced into 38 evenly spaced disks. The directions were within a few degrees of the vertical directed upwards; but in a piece 5 in. long, at a mean depth of 178.4 ft, and about 30 ft below the contact, the directions were downward. The change was studied in detail, and the reversals occurred within the thickness of a sawcut. This downwardly directed magnetization is of restricted occurrence, being in contrast to the negative inclinations found elsewhere in the Tasmanian dolerites and associated sediments. The magnetic mineral in the tuff is pyrrhotite. On heating above the Curie point and cooling in a field the remanence is directed along the field. It is conceivable that the observed reversal arose as a result of a mineralogical transformation, comparable to that observed by Everitt, and due to heating by the dolerite. If this is so then it indicates that the maximum temperature reached at a distance of 30 ft from the contact was roughly 325°C.

The second case is of an igneous rock (Robertson, 1963). An extensive survey of the Cretaceous Mt. Dromedary Igneous Complex in eastern Australia showed that with the exception of one rock type, the fossil magnetism, is directed steeply upwards [10.10]. The exception is a fine-grained monzonite which has tightly grouped directions pointing steeply downward. Thermal demagnetization of the NRM showed two steps, one large drop in intensity at somewhat less than 340°C, and another, much smaller, at 565°C. The dominant magnetic mineral was identified as pyrrhotite of grain size 0.5 mm, with subordinate magnetite of about one-tenth this diameter; these correspond neatly to the observed Curie temperatures. After partial demagnetization at temperatures between 340° and 550°C, the directions were reversed from the NRM, although widely scattered, and this is consistent with the view that the high temperature component due to magnetite was acquired parallel to the applied field but that the pyrrhotite became self-reversed.

These last two examples have been mentioned since they both occur in rocks in which the dominant magnetic mineral is pyrrhotite, and their positive downward inclinations are exceptional to those in associated rocks. The ratio of the observed positive to negative inclinations, in terms of specimens measured, is of the order one-tenth or less, whereas it is generally characteristic of paleomagnetic surveys that the directions are either all of one sign or, if reversals are present, the ratio

is roughly unity. The special nature of these occurrences suggests that they may best be explained according to the hypothesis of self-reversal rather than of field reversals. The fact that self-reversal does not occur in the laboratory may only reflect the level of testing; the magnetic properties are sensitive to heat, and self-reversal mechanisms may have been destroyed by the testing itself.

Allard Lake Ilmenohematite. The Allard Lake rocks have been studied magnetically by Hargraves (1959) and Carmichael (1959, 1961); in this context we are concerned only with the self-reversal properties found by the latter author. The NRM of these deposits is positive. The total TRM of natural crystals is parallel to the applied field, although it shows an unusual decrease in the range below 200°C (Figure 7.16). Heating enhances this effect, and after being treated at 900°C for 100 days and cooling in a field of 0.5 oe the remanence is reversed at a temperature just below 100°C. The compositional range showing this property is 25 to 15 per cent ilmenite, which is different from the self-reversing range found in synthetic minerals by Uyeda (Figure 7.14).

Adirondack Rock. Finally, mention is made of a single specimen from the hematite-

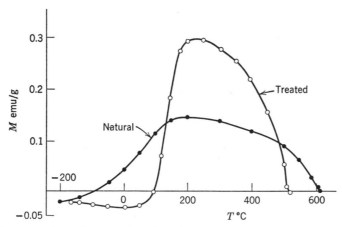

Figure 7.16. Remanent intensity as a function of temperature in natural and in treated (900°C for 100 days) crystals of ilmenohematite from Allard Lake. Scale for treated crystal × ⅓. Redrawn from Carmichael (1961), with the kind permission of the Royal Society of London and C. Carmichael.

ilmenite-bearing Precambian metamorphic rocks of the Adirondack Mountains in New York, which is said to have developed a total TRM antiparallel in direction to the applied field (Balsley and Buddington, 1954).

Summary. In the Haruna rock, the spontaneous self-reversal of total TRM occurs by cooling the natural rock. In the Asio and Sokoto rocks, a partial TRM component is self-reversed, but the total TRM is parallel to the field. In the Allard Lake specimens and the Carboniferous pyrrhotite shale, specific heat treatments are necessary to induce self-reversal. Out of the many thousands of total TRM experiments on natural rock, the Haruna dacite is the only established case of spontaneous self-reversal. The demonstrated cases of self-reversal properties in rocks occur in minerals of the ilmenite-

hematite series and in pyrrhotite. No self-reversals have ever been found in magnetite, titanomagnetite, or hematite, which are the minerals responsible for the fossil magnetism of most igneous rocks and sediments.

§ 7.6   Transition Zones   Where an initial discovery of opposed polarities has been followed up by more detailed field sampling, scattered directions are often found to occur in the transition beds. They occur in the Torridonian Sandstone Series [1.01] in the Iceland lavas, in the Pliocene lavas of Japan [11.070], in the Neogene sediments of Turkmenia [11.043, 12.30], in the Okler Series of Siberia [5.40], and in the Stormberg lavas of South Africa [9.25, 9.46–9.50]. No general picture of the actual way in which the reversal of directions occurs has yet emerged,

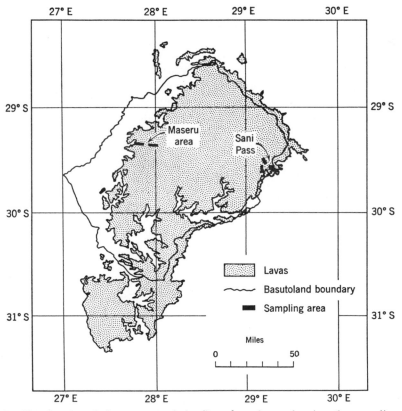

Figure 7.17. Sketch map of the outcrop of the Stormberg lavas showing the sampling localities. Redrawn from Van Zijl, K. W. T. Graham, and A. L. Hales (1962*a*), with the kind permission of the Royal Astronomical Society, London, and the authors.

and it is probable that pattern of change is different in each case. One difficulty in mapping these changes is the incompleteness of the rock record and of its exposure in any particular section. It is only in those places where deposition has been comparatively rapid and continuous, and where good exposures of stable rock types occur, that suitable observing conditions are found. There is also the possibility (Hibberd, 1961) that transition effects could be produced by variable partial instability, so that an apparent transition may, in reality, be a smeared distribution [11.070].

Stormberg Lavas (Van Zijl, K. W. T. Graham, and Hales, 1962a and b). These

lavas are of late Triassic or Lower Jurassic age. Sampling was carried out up steep escarpments in the Sani Pass and Maseru areas about 80 miles apart (Figure 7.17). The lavas are flat-lying so that results obtained at the same elevation in each traverse may be compared. The directions are plotted in Figure 7.18 as a function of altitude. The results from both traverses show good agreement. The lower 800 ft of lavas have directions to the southeast with intermediate positive inclinations, the upper 2400 ft have northwest directions with negative inclinations. In both traverses there is a transition sequence of about 600 ft in which the directions change systematically. The transition

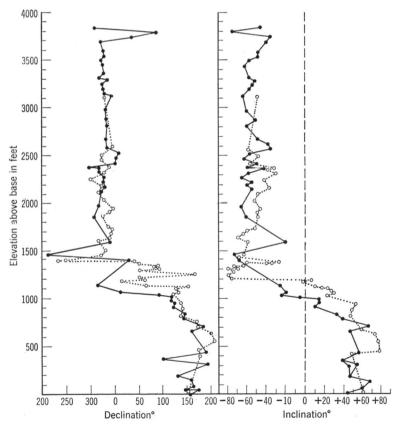

Figure 7.18. Stormberg lavas transition sequence: declination and inclination versus elevation above the base of the lavas. All specimens have been magnetically cleaned in 219 oe. Circles give results from the Maseru area and dots from the Sani Pass area. Certain results from sites with scattered directions are not included. Redrawn from van Zijl, K. W. T. Graham, and A. L. Hales (1962), with the kind permission of the Royal Astronomical Society of London and the authors.

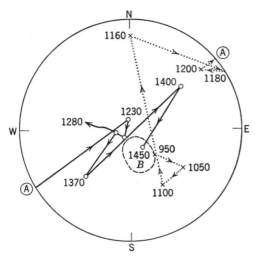

Figure 7.19. Stormberg lavas transition sequence: direction changes in the transition zone in the Maseru area. Directions labeled with the sample altitudes are plotted on lower hemisphere of a stereographic net; circles are south poles down, crosses are north poles down. Ⓐ follows Ⓐ as the inclinations become negative. The dotted area *B* is that typically occupied by directions outside the transition zones. Redrawn from van Zijl, K. W. T. Graham, and A. L. Hales (1962a), with the kind permission of the Royal Astronomical Society of London and the authors.

directions in the Maseru area are plotted in Figure 7.19; although the changes are not smooth, there is a roughly discernible trend of the north-seeking directions from southeast positive, to northeast with low inclinations, over to northwest negative. The magnetic mineral has been identified as magnetite, and there is no observed difference between the mineral in lavas with negative, transitional, or positive directions.

Iceland Lavas (Figure 7.20). From magnetogeological mapping (§ 10C.4) of the basalt lavas of Iceland, Einarsson (1957a) recognized a series of polarity zones which he called (working back from the present), N_1, R_1, N_2, R_2, and so on to N_8. Sigurgeirsson (1957) has studied the transition from N_4 to R_3, R_3 to N_3, R_2 to N_2, and N_2 to R_1, the second of these being investigated in most detail. Sigurgeirsson contends that

the poles from each transition zone "are distributed rather regularly, indicating a definite path followed by the magnetic pole during reversal of the magnetic field." The paths, however, are different in each zone.

Okler Series [5.40]. Vlassov and Kovalenko (1963) have recently described transition sequences from these Devonian sediments of Siberia. Numerous samples from a section 30 m in thickness revealed five polarity zones (3 negative and 2 positive) of approximately equal thickness. The boundaries between zones in two cases are marked by sudden reversals, but in two instances more or less smooth transitions occur which are remarkably similar in both cases.

§ 7.7   **Consistency Evidence**   If self-reversal mechanisms are commonly present in rocks, it is reasonable to expect that they are randomly distributed in time and space, whereas if rock reversals are to be explained by periodic reversals of the field, then the polarities should be constant in a rock unit of given age, and it ought to be possible to match the reversal sequences in the standard sections of different regions. The test is not conclusive, since, if stratigraphic conformity were demonstrated, it could still be argued that the distribution of self-reversing mechanisms are time-dependent, so that mineralogically more suitable rocks were deposited at one time than another. But in view of the great variety of igneous and sedimentary processes operating in any one geological period, this argument depends on very great coincidences of circumstances beyond what may be reasonably assumed.

Examples of Consistent Polarities. Recent lavas are always found to have the same polarity as the present Earth's field. This was noticed over 60 years ago (§ 1.8) in the mid-Italian Volcanics, and has since been found in Japan [12.40], Sicily [12.09], Iceland [12.54], Samoa [12.63], and Hawaii [12.56]. There are, however, two archeomagnetic curiosities. First, Folgheraiter described Etruscan vases with negative inclinations (§ 1.8). Second, Mercanton (1918) studied certain bronze-age anchors made by Swiss lake-dwellers; these were made of baked clay and shaped like bells or truncated pyramids. Mercanton found directions parallel to their bases, which indicated that the field had a shallow negative inclination in Switzerland during the Bronze Age (the present inclination is about $+62°$). These observations on vases and anchors have never been repeated, and it is possible that the position of their bases at the time of firing has been incorrectly assumed, or that the material is magnetically unstable.

Studies of Icelandic lava flows show that specimens with positive and negative polarizations were not randomly spread, but occurred in zones of constant polarity, each zone containing an average of 25 flows [11.108, 12.49, 12.50]. The Tertiary lavas and intrusions of Skye are all positively polarized [11.012]. Lavas, intrusives, and baked sediments of the Antrim Igneous Suite are also all positive [11.018–024]. The negative magnetic anomaly associated with the Pilansberg dike system of South Africa sug-

gests that its remanent magnetization is of constant polarity (Gelletich, 1937), a suggestion which Gough (1956) has confirmed by direct study of the remanence [1.06]. The most impressive example of consistency is the occurrence of positive polarization in rocks of uppermost Carboniferous and Permian ages (Table 7.3) in Europe, Asia, North and South America, and Australia. It is observed in red beds, lavas varying in composition from basalts to rhyolites, and in intrusive rocks.

Close Positional Intermixing of Polarities. Exceptions to this pattern of consistency occur. These usually take the form of close positional intermixing of positive and negative polarities within the same rock body, the whole of which is considered to have been formed at approximately the same time. Such occurrences are difficult to explain on the hypothesis of field reversal, and may be considered evidence for the occurrence of self-reversal mechanisms. An occurrence in pyrrhotite-bearing sediment has already been mentioned (Figure 7.15). The remaining examples (below) probably

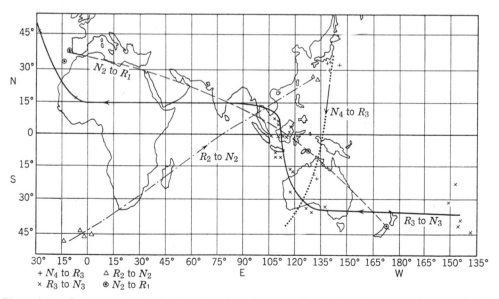

Figure **7.20**. Paleomagnetic poles (south poles) corresponding to the directions of magnetization observed in four transition zones between polarity zones in Iceland. Redrawn from Sigurgeirsson (1957), with the kind permission of Taylor and Francis, London, and the author.

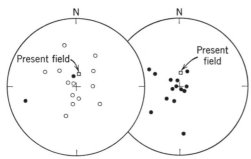

Figure 7.21. Close positional mixing of polarities in a single lava flow of the Older Volcanics of Victoria, Australia. A stereographic projection is used. (*a*) Directions of NRM, (*b*) directions after magnetic cleaning in 150 oe ($\widetilde{H}p$). Dots (open symbols) are positive (negative) inclinations. Redrawn from Mumme (1962*a*), by kind permission of the Royal Astronomical Society of London and the author.

have explanations other than self-reversal mechanisms.

Intermixing of positive and negative polarities in the same lava flow occurs in some exposures of the Older Volcanics of Victoria. It has been shown, by demagnetization studies, that this is due to partial instability, the stable component giving the positive directions approximately antiparallel to the Earth's field, the negative directions being due to secondary viscous components, which

are removed by magnetic cleaning (Figure 7.21).

Previous to the work just described, mixed polarities had been found in the Pleistocene basalts of Yamaguchi prefecture, Japan (Asami, 1954–57). These occur in an outcrop of about 1 m square. Most directions are well grouped, and are roughly opposed to the present field. The remainder are highly dispersed with positive inclinations, but are not accurately reversed from the other set. In a general study of these basalts Domen (1960) showed that specimens with negative polarity are found to be less resistant to demagnetization than those with positive polarity, although no general magnetic cleaning of the type just described has been carried out. This result suggests that partial instability might be responsible for the mixed polarities.

Finally, Jaeger and Joplin (1955) found that part of a dolerite sill in Tasmania had positive directions (downward and vertical), whereas the remainder of the sill was negative, as for all other Tasmanian dolerites [9.30]. The measurements were obtained on bore core oriented by drillers. A repeat bore in the same sill, 500 ft from the previous site with carefully controlled orientation, showed uniform negative polarization (Jaeger and Thyer, 1960); it is fairly cer-

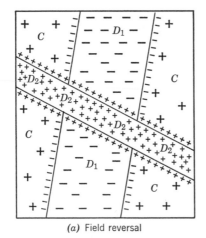
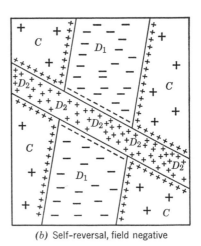

(*a*) Field reversal   (*b*) Self-reversal, field negative

Figure 7.22. Contact test for hypothesis of (*a*) field reversal and (*b*) self-reversal. *C* is the country rock, D_1 an intrusive cutting *C*, and D_2 an intrusive cutting both *C* and D_1. The polarities are marked.

tain, therefore, that the reported reversal was due to misorientation of the bore core originally studied.

§ 7.8   **Igneous Contact Studies**   Rock in the immediate neighborhood of an igneous body is heated, and on cooling may acquire a remanence in the same field as the body (§ 5.05). Since the country rock and igneous body are generally very different materials, a comparison of their polarities constitutes a useful test. On the hypothesis of field reversals it is to be expected that the body and contact will have the same polarity, whereas if self-reversals are to account for the observations, then in roughly half of the cases studied the polarities should be the same and in the other half opposed. The test is set out in Figure 7.22, with special reference to intrusions. The country rock C is cut by an intrusive D_1, and

a second intrusion D_2 cuts both C and D_1. C is observed to have positive polarity, D_1 is negative, and D_2 positive. If these polarities are due to a change in sign of the field, so that at the time of formation of C the field was positive and of D_1 negative and of D_2 positive again, then it is to be expected that the contacts will always be magnetized in the same sense as the intrusive. Whereas, on the hypothesis of self-reversal, in which it is assumed that the polarity of the field was constant throughout, then the observed pattern of opposed directions is due to self-reversals in C and D_2 but not in D_1. The contact D_2:C should have the same polarity as D_2 and C. The contact D_1:C and D_2:D_1 should have polarities opposed to the intrusives D_1 and D_2 respectively. The contacts D_2:C and D_2:D_1 should be of opposite signs although they were baked by the same intrusion.

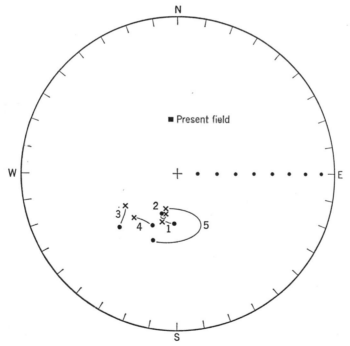

Figure 7.23. Directions of magnetization in igneous rocks and baked sediments of the Massif Central. All remanence polarities are positive (up). The present field is negative (down). Dots are mean results from igneous bodies and cross results from associated baked sediment. (1) to (4) are lava flows (respectively, Mount Coupet, Pontfarein, La Roche Noire, and Dolaizon) and their underlying sediments; (5) Gergovie intrusive dike and baked calcareous marls. Equal-area projection. Compiled from Roche (1953).

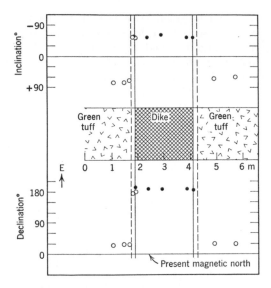

Figure 7.24. Magnetization directions in a dike, country rock, and contacts near Sendai, Japan. Dots are directions in the dike. Circles directions in tuff. The limit of the baked contact zone is marked by a dotted line. Redrawn from Kato, Takagi, and Kato (1954), with the kind permission of Society for Terrestrial Magnetism and Electricity of Japan.

The test, although powerful, is not conclusive, since contact reheating and cooling may not reproduce the original conditions. For example, the rock may have been subjected to physicochemical changes during the period between initial cooling and reheating, and the reheating itself may also have caused changes. Nevertheless, it is reasonable to expect that if self-reversals produced all the observed cases of reversals then there should be many contacts in which the polarities are opposite to those in the body which baked them. In view of the excellent reversibility on thermal cycling of the magnetic properties of the Haruna dacite (Figure 7.9) it would be unreasonable to argue that self-reversal mechanisms have all been uniformly suppressed. Four examples are now described.

In the first study of baked contact rocks Bruhnes and David found concordance in directions and sign between several lava flows and underlying baked clays in the Massif Central (§1.8). More recent results are given in Figure 7.23. The directions in flows and underlying baked sediments are

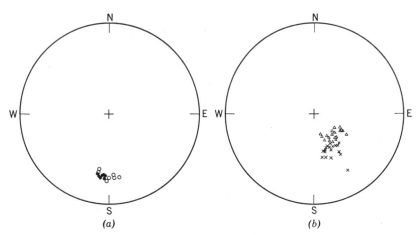

Figure 7.25. Directions of magnetization in igneous and baked sediments of the Stormberg Series. (a) Directions in a sandstone lens (dots) and adjacent lava (circles) in transition zone; south poles down. (b) Directions in lavas (crosses) and underlying Cave Sandstone (triangles) at Sani Pass; north poles down. Stereographic projection. Redrawn from van Zijl, K. W. T. Graham, and Hales (1962a), with the kind permission of the Royal Astronomical Society of London and the authors.

in good agreement; in two flows (Mount Coupet, Dolaizon) the material of the sediment is derived from the adjacent Archean basement and is not of volcanic origin. The directions in a dike of Aquitanian age, and in calcareous marls of Stampian age baked by this dike, are in good agreement. The igneous and baked materials are very different mineralogically, yet they have the same magnetic polarity.

The second example is from Japan. Certain green tuffs of Miocene age occurring near Sendai are intruded by several dikes which are thought to be late Miocene or Pliocene. The dikes are of basaltic andesite and have a mean direction 183, −58. The tuffs are magnetized close to the present field with a mean direction 31, +68 except that within 20 cm of contacts the directions swing round and become parallel to those in the dike. Results from one dike are given in Figure 7.24.

The third example is from the Stormberg Lavas. The directions in lavas and baked sediments from the transition zone (§ 7.6) are in excellent agreement (Figure 7.25a). The occurrence of transition zones is consistent with the field reversal hypothesis, and the concordance between contacts and lavas provides additional support. The baked sandstone at the base of the Series is in rough agreement with the lava immediately overlying and has the same polarity, but there is a systematic difference of the order 10° (Figure 7.25b). Experiments show that this is not caused by sample orientation errors or variable instability. It is possible that, due to differences in the Curie points, the lavas and baked sediments acquired their magnetization at slightly different times, between which the field direction changed. A further possibility is that the field in which the sediment became magnetized was somewhat disturbed due to nearby previously magnetized lava.

In the foregoing examples the igneous bodies have been small and the reheating local. Effects encountered in the vicinity of an extensive intrusive complex are now

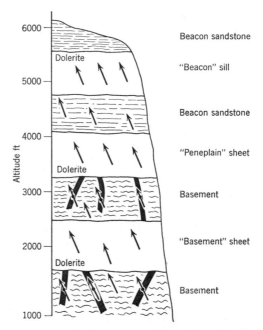

Figure 7.26. Schematic geological section in South Victoria Land. Basement dikes black, Admiralty Granites wavy lines. Vertical section through horizontal component of magnetization which is approximately N 250° E. The arrows give, in a schematic fashion, the directions observed in each unit. The result is based on collections from over a hundred collecting sites [9.37–42]. Compiled from Bull, Irving, and Willis (1962).

described. A section over 5000 ft thick, exposed in the Wright, Victoria, and Taylor, dry valleys of South Victoria Land (Figure 7.26), consists of a Basement Complex of Admiralty Granites ([9.41] Precambrian or Lower Paleozoic) intruded by dikes [9.40]. This is overlain by Beacon Sandstones [9.39]. The whole sequence is intruded by the Jurassic Ferrar Dolerites [9.37, 38], which occur as three thick sheets, the middle one commonly occurring at or about the peneplain between basement and sandstone. The dolerites make up almost one half the total thickness. The remanence directions after magnetic cleaning are uniform throughout, and it seems probable that the sandstones and basement rocks were heated and

Table 7.4   Comparison of Polarities in Igneous and Baked Contact Rocks. Analysis of Wilson (1962b) brought up-to-date to include the B group data.

Igneous	Baked Contact	N
−	−	34
+	+	49
Oblique	Oblique	2
−	+	2
+	−	0

remagnetized in the Jurassic when the dolerite was intruded. It has been estimated from petrological studies that the temperature of the sediments may have exceeded 160°C (Elliot and Evans, 1963). It seems possible that the fossil remanence of the basement and sediments is a medium-temperature VRM (§ 2.13). It is notable that the basement rocks give K-Ar ages of Jurassic or a little older [9.41] which is much too young from the stratigraphic evidence and it seems that heating by the dolerite intrusions was sufficient to remove radiogenic argon.

In Table 7.4 a general comparison of the polarities observed in igneous rocks and their baked contacts is made. There are results from all continents, and all geological periods except the three lower divisions of the Paleozoic. There are 85 examples in which the polarities of the igneous body and contact agree and two cases of disagreement. The latter are from the Karroo Dolerite, sampled in mines at Estcourt, South Africa [9.27]; sediments were studied at 8 contacts, and in 6, the polarities agree and in 2 are different. This could be due to self-reversal or to instability in the dolerites.

§ **7.9   Discussion**   The results are now to be summarized. (1) Recent and late Pleistocene rocks, so far studied, are negatively magnetized in the same sense as the present field. (2) All late Carboniferous and Permian rocks (except the Upper Tartarian) are positively polarized. (3) In early Pleistocene and older rocks frequent reversals of

polarity occur in a manner unrelated to the rock type; instances of both positive and negative polarities occur in acid and basic igneous rocks, in plutonic and hypabyssal intrusives, in lavas, and in sediments. (4) Although few transition zones have yet been located the fact that transitions do occur is inconsistent with the hypothesis of self-reversals. (5) Out of the thousands of experiments of total TRM induced in the laboratory, self-reversal has been demonstrated beyond doubt to occur in only one natural rock type. At the present level of laboratory testing self-reversed magnetization is an exceedingly rare phenomenon. (6) Contacts baked by igneous bodies usually have the same polarity as that of the igneous body. The baked material includes a wide variety of rocks, ranging from several types of sandstone, green tuffs, and calcareous marls, to granites, basalt, dolerite, felsite, and laterite. In 97 per cent of contacts studied the polarity of the igneous body is reproduced. (7) In this observational picture there is, however, an important deficiency—few really detailed studies have yet been reported of the magnetic properties side-by-side with chemical and mineralogical analyses of rocks with positive and negative polarization in the same rock sequence. Although some accounts of such work have been given (for example, Domen, 1960; van Zijl, K. W. T. Graham, and Hales, 1962a; Ade-Hall and Wilson, 1963; Cox, Doell, and Dalrymple, 1963b and c) it is clear that more studies are desirable.

These results are consistent with the hypothesis that by and large the observed rock polarities reflect the polarity of the paleogeomagnetic field which has, in consequence, frequently reversed in polarity in the past. The alternative hypothesis of self-reversed magnetization, although possibly true in certain cases (§ 7.5), finds no support in the majority of field or laboratory observations. The studies of igneous contacts and transition zones which could, potentially, disprove the hypothesis of field reversal have so far failed to do so, and the agreement of the field evidence (§§ 7.6, 7.7, 7.8) with the predictions of the hypothesis provides a substantial case for it.

In a rock formation in which both polarities have been observed, the proportion of samples showing intermediate directions is only a few per cent, and so it is likely that the transition period is short compared to the time for which constant polarity is maintained. Hospers, from his work in Iceland, estimated that the reversals took about 2000 to 20,000 years and had occurred approximately every 250,000 to 500,000 years since the middle of the Tertiary. Recent radiometric dating of reversals (§ 7.3) suggest

that the periodicity was somewhat longer. Eventually it will be of much interest to investigate the variation with time of the frequency of occurrence of positive and negative magnetizations and to correlate the various reversal levels from continent to continent. The results available at present are too few to attempt to do this in any general fashion, although it is clear that the frequency with time is not constant; the periodicity in the Neogene appears to have been on a time scale of a million years whereas in the late Paleozoic the field appears to have maintained a constant positive polarity for about 50 m.y.

Intensity of the earth's field in the past

§ 8.1 Introduction The intensity of fossil magnetism is related to the intensity of the magnetic field in which it was acquired, so that, in principle, determinations of this field intensity can be made. But there are many other variable factors which affect the remanent intensity and it is difficult to correct for all of them. These variables are: (1) the amount and type of magnetic material present, (2) its magnetic stability, (3) the process by which the remanence was acquired in the first place, and (4) the later history of the rock.

Estimates of two types may be made: determinations of *relative field intensity* based on comparisons between values of the intensity of fossil magnetism, and estimates of *absolute field intensity* which depend on comparisons of the intensities of fossil magnetism with the remanence induced in the same rock material under controlled laboratory conditions. The latter depend on the fact that for certain magnetization processes the intensity of synthetic remanence is found to vary linearly with the intensity of the applied field in low fields of about 1 oe, so that if F_p is the strength of the field in which a fossil remanence of intensity M_n was acquired, and M' is the strength of the synthetic magnetization acquired in a known field F then

$$F_p = FM_n/M' \qquad (8.1)$$

There are many uncertainties. The fossil remanence may have undergone viscous demagnetization in time, or it may have been modified by the addition of secondary components. The synthetic magnetization may not have been acquired under conditions comparable to those under which the primary magnetization formed. Slow chemical changes may have occurred since the time of formation. Finally, the process of remagnetization in the laboratory may have altered the magnetic minerals, so that the material which acquires the synthetic remanence may differ from that in which the primary remanence originated.

§ 8.2 Methods One method of studying relative field intensities is to compare the intensities of fossil magnetism; if numerous results are available from rock units supposedly magnetized in a comparable fashion, statistical treatment may be expected to yield information about broad changes in the strength of the ancient field. A second possibility is to use the ratio $Q_n' = M_n/\chi$ (§ 2.02). Values of Q_n' depend more strongly on the intensity of the initial magnetizing field than do the fossil intensities alone, since the use of the susceptibility χ

will correct approximately for variations in the amount and type of magnetic material. Good alignment and therefore high Q_n' values may be expected to occur when the magnetization process is efficient, or the applied field strong, so that for the same process (say thermoremanent magnetization (TRM)) the ratio should be a relative measure of field strength provided there has been negligible viscous decay. Frequently, however, Q_n' values relate to magnetic stability, low values being typical of unstable material (Table 5.6 and also Powell (1963)), and in these cases the remanence has probably decayed extensively in geological time. Furthermore, in certain rocks Q_n' appears to depend on the cooling rate, and variations by a factor 10 can occur in the same rock body (Figure 10.25), so that even for the same magnetization process considerable fluctuations can occur. The method, like the straight comparison of fossil intensities, seems dependent on so many intangibles that its potential usefulness cannot be assessed at present.

Two methods have been used to estimate absolute field intensities. One employs detrital remanent magnetization (DRM), and the other TRM. DRM has been used to estimate field intensities in the Pleistocene (Johnson, Murphy, and Torreson, 1948). Glacial varves from New England dispersed in water and redeposited, acquired a DRM whose intensity varies linearly with the strength of the applied field F when $F < 3$ oe. Comparison with the magnitude of fossil remanence (equation 8.1) yields a value of 1 to 2 oe for the Earth's field in New England some 10,000 years ago. Much uncertainty is attached to this estimate, for the laboratory conditions may be very different from those in nature, and the fossil remanence may contain substantial viscous components.

The use of TRM for determining the strength of the paleogeomagnetic field began

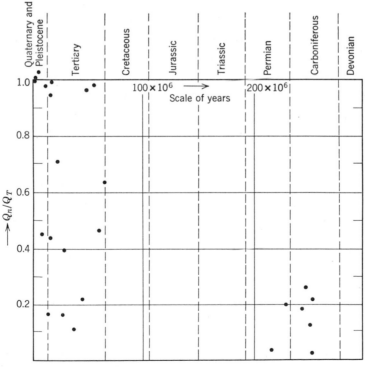

Figure 8.1. The variation of $Q_{n/T}$ with geological age. Redrawn from Koenigsberger (1938), with the kind permission of the American Geophysical Union.

Table 8.1 Comparison of Estimates of the Intensity (in oe) of the Earth's Field for Different Temperature Ranges (using equation 8.2) and for Different Specimens from the Same Collecting Locality. Calculated from the data of Thellier and Thellier (1959a).

Specimen No.	100° to 300°C	300° to 670°C	100° to 670°C
5	0.68	0.72	0.71
13	0.76	0.73	0.74
15	0.66	0.71	0.69
18	0.80	0.84	0.83
21	0.67	0.68	0.68

with studies by Koenigsberger (1938) of the ratio $Q_{n/T} = Q_n/Q_T$ (§ 2.02). The value $Q_T = M_T/\chi F$ is obtained by giving a rock a TRM in a field F, and afterward measuring the intensity M_T and susceptibility χ in F. If, during heating, mineralogical changes have been negligible, and if the primary fossil remanence was a TRM which has decayed little in time, then $Q_{n/T} = M_n/M_T = F_p/F$. Koenigsberger found that $Q_{n/T}$ values, measured for many different igneous rock types, increased with geological time (Figure 8.1). This indicates either that the Earth's field during the Paleozoic was roughly 10 times weaker than at present, or that there has been a general viscous decay with time in the material studied.

The Thelliers' Method. Of much importance are the investigations of Thellier (1937b and c) and Thellier and Thellier (1959a and b), who studied baked material (bricks, tiles, and hearths) collected from archeological sites. Their method employs relationship 8.1 where M' is a synthetic TRM, and the fossil magnetism is thermoremanent in origin. The method exploits the additive property of partial TRM in order to investigate the many uncertainties in intensity determinations. This property (§ 2.10) allows determinations to be made using the TRM components appropriate to different temperature ranges. Since field

variations may be expected to be negligible during the period of initial cooling of a single specimen, and of different specimens from the same collecting site, then values obtained for different temperature intervals in the same specimen, and from different specimens at the same locality, should agree. This criterion may be stated

$$F_p = FM_{n(T_1-T_2)}/M'_{(T_1-T_2)}$$
$$= FM_{n(T_2-T_3)}/M'_{(T_2-T_3)} \text{ etc.} \quad (8.2)$$

where $M_{n(T_1-T_2)}$ and $M'_{(T_1-T_2)}$ etc., are the partial TRM components of the fossil and synthetic remanences in the temperature ranges $(T_1 - T_2)$, $(T_2 - T_3)$, T always being less than the Curie temperature. The second criterion is that viscous components should be negligible, and in order to ensure this, the partial TRM components used are always in temperature ranges greater than 100°C, so that the specimen is thermally cleaned (§ 5.09). The Thelliers' third criterion is that the magnetic properties of the material should be reversible on thermal cycling so that effects of chemical change during the experiment may be discounted. This is investigated by repeating the process of synthetic magnetization but employing longer periods of heating; if the partial TRM values are unchanged the material is accepted as suitable, for if chemical changes did occur they may be expected to increase with heating period, and the absence of differences implies that such changes are negligible.

The procedure used by the Thelliers is as follows: tests are first made for the presence of viscous components imposed since the time of firing, and if these constitute more than a few per cent of the fossil magnetism the material is rejected; next the material is thermally cleaned at 100°C; then the partial TRM components, both of natural and synthetic remanences, are obtained and the consistency criterion (equation 8.2) applied. An example of a successful test is set out in Table 8.1. Five tiles taken from a Roman building in Switzerland constructed between A.D. 150 and 200 were studied. The synthetic TRM was acquired in 0.464 oe. The mean standard deviation for results from the same sample for different temperature ranges (rows) is 0.02 or 3 per cent, and that between samples for the same temperature range (columns) is 0.06 or 8 per cent. In view of the intricate nature of the experiments this agreement is very good indeed, and indicates the reliability of the mean value of 0.73 oe as an estimate of the strength of the field in Switzerland about 1800 years ago.

§ 8.3   Determinations for Historic Time, Western Europe, and Northern Africa.

The Thelliers obtained seven determinations from localities in France, Switzerland, and Tunisia, the dates of which range from 600 B.C. to A.D. 1750. The results are given in Table 8.2, where they are compared with direct measurements carried out in Paris over the past century. The older values indicate higher intensities than at present. The high values obtained from the more southerly localities discount the possibility that the effect is due to the latitude spread, which is about 14°. Therefore possible explanations for these results are (1) that they represent secular fluctuations in the field intensity, (2) that they are due to changes in geomagnetic latitude of the collecting sites, and (3) that they reflect a decrease in the aggregate magnetic moment of the Earth.

As a measure, for comparative purposes, of the fluctuations due to the nondipole field, the Thelliers suggest that the present intensity variation along the +65° isocline may be used, this inclination being characteristic for the sampling region; the range of values between 0.46 and 0.5 oe is much less than the high intensities indicated by the archeomagnetic data. Furthermore, the secular variations in intensity may be expected to have periodicities comparable with the secular fluctuations in direction, and therefore they may be expected to reveal themselves as a random scatter, not as a consistent trend, as is observed. The second possibility—that the results reflect changes in

Table 8.2   Estimated Intensity of the Geomagnetic Field in Historic Time in Western Europe and North Africa. I_m is the mean paleomagnetic inclination. F_p is the field intensity, and F_{65} is the intensity corrected to the +65° isocline (equation 8.3). Data of Thellier and Thellier (1959a), reproduced by kind permission of the authors; the last entry in column five was kindly supplied as a private communication by Professor E. Thellier.

Locality	Date	$I_m°$	F_p(oe)	F_{65}(oe)	Type of Measurement
Paris	1955	64.6	0.464	0.466	magnetic observatory
Paris	1930	64.6	0.459	0.461	magnetic observatory
Paris	1885	65.3	0.463	0.462	magnetic observatory
Paris	1848	66.8	0.471	0.460	direct measurement
Versailles	1750	74.0	>0.48	>0.43	archeomagnetic
Lille	1460	63.0	0.56	0.57	archeomagnetic
Paris	200	62.2	0.70	0.73	archeomagnetic
Basle	175	63.5	0.73	0.74	archeomagnetic
Fréjus	0	60.5	0.65	0.69	archeomagnetic
Carthage	−146	58.0	0.71	0.78	archeomagnetic
Carthage	−600	—	0.76	0.92	archeomagnetic

latitude—is discounted by the fact that the paleomagnetic direction results reveal no changes in latitude during the past few thousand years (§ 6.02).

Therefore it seems possible that the results indicate a decrease in the Earth's dipole moment, and in order to study this in more detail it is necessary to correct for the differences in geographical position of the collecting sites. The Thelliers achieved this by assuming that the field was dipolar and that the paleomagnetic inclination (I_m) defines the latitude of the collecting site (equation 3.3). The field intensities F_p are reduced to the values F_{65} which they would have at a latitude appropriate to an inclination of +65°, using this relationship derived from equation 3.1

$$F_{65} = \frac{F_p(1 + 3 \cos^2 I_m)^{\frac{1}{2}}}{(1 + 3 \cos^2 65°)^{\frac{1}{2}}} \qquad (8.3)$$

The reduced values are given in Table 8.2 and Figure 8.2. The broken line is fitted by eye and indicates an intensity decrease of about 50

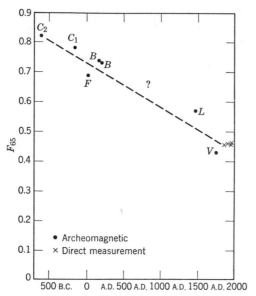

Figure 8.2. Reduced field intensity F_{65} for historical times for western Europe and northern Africa. The archeomagnetic determinations, listed in Table 8.2, are as follows: V Versailles, L Lille, B Basle (Table 8.1), P Paris, F Frejus, C_1 and C_2 Carthage 146 B.C. and 600 B.C.

per cent in the past 2500 years, the slope being 15 γ per year. A further method (Doell and Cox, 1961a) is to reduce the values to a single reference location again assuming a dipole field. The reduced field F_0 is given by

$$F_0 = \frac{F_p(1 + 3 \cos^2 p_0)^{1/4}}{(1 + 3 \cos^2 p)^{1/4}} \quad (8.4)$$

where p and p_0 are the geomagnetic colatitude of the collecting and reference locations respectively. The reference location is 50° N, 5° E.

The second method allows a comparison to be made between the rate of decrease of the Earth's dipole moment inferred archeomagnetically with that determined from spherical harmonic analysis. The latter shows that during the past century the geomagnetic pole has not changed its position substantially but that during this time the average field intensity has fallen (§ 3.3, Figure 8.3). This decrease may be expressed as the rate of change of the theoretical equatorial dipole field H_0, which is 15 γ per year (Figure 8.3), or 25 γ per year at the

chosen reference locality. The intensity of the theoretical equatorial dipole field for earlier times may be calculated from the reduced intensity F_0 using the relationship $H_0 = F_0(1 + 3 \cos^2 p_0)^{-1/2}$. The rate of change of F_0 over the past 2000 years for the reference location 50° N, 5° E is 12 γ per year, or 7 γ per year at the equator (Doell and Cox, 1961a), which is about one-half that inferred from analyses of the field for the past century.

Japan (Nagata, Arai, and Momose, 1963). Results covering the period 3000 B.C. to A.D. 1778 are given in Table 8.3. The material used is tile, unglazed pottery, and basalt, for which heating experiments show that equation 8.2 is satisfied. Estimates for 2000 years ago are 1.5 times the present field. The subsequent decrease to the present intensity is not regular, the period A.D. 735 to 1300 (which is not represented in Europe) being characterized by intensities similar to that at present. Estimates for 3100 to 1000 B.C. are 0.8 to 1.0 times the present field.

Armenia (Burlatskaya, 1962). Determinations from baked earths yield intensities 1.5 times that at present from material 2000 years old; from material 4600 years old the ratio is 1.1.

Summary. The results from these three regions indicate that the equatorial field of the geomagnetic dipole 2000 years ago was about 0.15 oe less than at present. The field

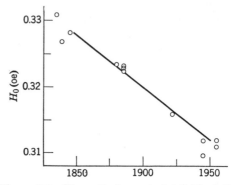

Figure 8.3. Theoretical equatorial field of the inclined geocentric dipole for the last century. Redrawn from Doell and Cox (1961a), with the kind permission of Academic Press, New York, and the authors.

intensities 5000 years ago were comparable to those at present indicating that the decrease over the past 2000 years is a short-term effect when viewed on the geological time scale.

§ 8.4 Determinations for the Geological Past

The determinations just described were made on archeological remains which were fired and cooled over a short time period, so that the partial TRM components obtained by demagnetization in the laboratory of the fossil magnetism may well correspond to those acquired in the first instance. But in geological material the cooling may have extended over hundreds of years or more, so that if the blocking temperature spectrum is wide the partial TRM components obtained in the laboratory, and those acquired initially, may not correspond (§§ 2.10, 2.13). The magnitude of such effects and those of viscous decay, are entirely unknown, so that all determinations of field intensity for the geological past have to be regarded as tentative guesses

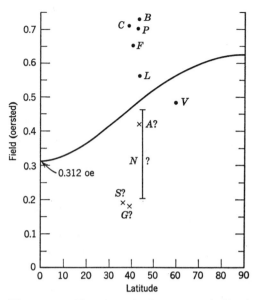

Figure 8.4. The curve is the present inclined geomagnetic dipole field. Dots give the archeomagnetic results listed in the legend to Figure 8.2. Crosses are the results from the geological past plotted with respect to paleolatitude.

Table 8.3 Estimated Intensity of the Geomagnetic Field in Japan. *N is the number of samples studied and F_p is the intensity in oersted. Calculated from the data of Nagata, Arai, and Momose (1963).*

Material	N	F_p
Basalt, 1778	5	0.55
Basalt, 1552	4	0.55
Basalt, 1421	6	0.61
Basalt, 1300 ± 30	4	0.50
Basalt, 1070 ± 70	4	0.47
Tile, 765 ± 15	4	0.50
Tile, 735 ± 15	3	0.49
Pottery, 565 ± 15	3	0.53
Pottery, 525 ± 10	8	0.63
Basalt, 300 ± 100	5	0.71
Basalt, −150 ± 150	2	0.71
Pottery, −300 ± 250	4	0.56
Pottery, −1000 ± 400	1	0.46
Pottery, −2000 ± 500	1	0.43
Pottery, −2500 ± 300	3	0.39
Pottery, −3100 ± 300	1	0.36
Present field, Japan	—	0.461

only. The determinations that have been made are mentioned here not because they constitute a large or reliable body of data but because of their great potential usefulness. Such determinations are of much interest for theories of origin of the field, and also, as Wilson (1961) points out, for testing the validity of the hypothesis of a geocentric dipole field (§ 6.10). If this hypothesis is correct, then the field strength for any geological period should vary as a function of paleolatitude (§ 3.5). Such a test requires the study of average values combined so as to mean out not only the intensity fluctuations resulting from the nondipole field, but also fluctuations due to short period (short on the geological time scale) variations of the Earth's dipole moment (§ 8.3). The theoretical geomagnetic dipole field for 1945 is plotted as a function of latitude in Figure 8.4 together with the archeomagnetic results. Field intensity determinations for the geological past are added with question marks to emphasize their uncertainty. The values are for Upper Quaternary andesite from the Nugere Volcano, France (N), for the Middle Quaternary clays baked by lavas of the Gravenoire Plateau, France (G) (Thellier and Thellier, 1959a), for Lower Tertiary laterite baked by lava in the Antrim Igneous Suite (A) (Wilson, 1961) and the late Triassic to Lower Jurassic Stormberg lavas of South Africa (S) (van Zijl, K. W. T. Graham, and Hales, 1962b). The geological values fall below the curve, and this could mean that the field in the past was weaker than at present or it could be due to viscous decay or chemical changes in the rock material. The results nevertheless indicate that since the Triassic there has been a field of not less than about one-tenth the present strength. The data are, of course, quite insufficient to make tests of the dipole hypothesis.

One further point relates to the intensity during a field reversal. If reversal of the field occurs by diminution of the axial geocentric dipole followed by its build-up in the opposite sense then the intensity will not fall to zero since the nondipole fields remain. Estimates of the ratio of intensity of the reversing field to that of the steady field have been made for the Cenozoic of Iceland (Sigurgeirsson, 1957) and the late Triassic to early Jurassic of Basutoland (van Zijl, K. W. T. Graham, and Hales, 1962b), the values being ½ and from ¼ to ⅕ respectively. The ratio for the minimum field from Model A (§ 3.8) putting $\sigma_0 = 0.4$ are for the appropriate paleolatitudes ⅙ and ¼. In view of the uncertainty in the intensity estimates this agreement between Model A and observation is reasonably good.

CHAPTER NINE

Paleolatitudes and paleomeridians

§ 9.01 **Introduction** In this chapter comparisons are made between the paleomagnetic results and the geological evidence of past conditions. These comparisons follow directly from the hypothesis that the Earth's field has been an axial geocentric dipole, and they were initially set out (Irving, 1956b) as a test for that hypothesis. The essence of the method is to use the paleomagnetic data to obtain numerical estimates of the past position on the Earth's surface of particular geological features in order to institute a comparison between their past distribution and the present distribution of their modern equivalents. In this context a *geological feature* or *occurrence* is thought of as a rock occurrence containing evidence of past conditions, and its *past position* is its position relative to the paleogeographic axis at the time it originated. The field of application of this idea is very broad, touching on many aspects of historical geology, and it will be necessary in the course of this chapter to restate the idea in a variety of ways to meet different situations as they arise.

The paleomagnetically determined field directions show that during the past few million years the Earth's field has been that of an axial geocentric dipole, but directions for periods prior to the Upper Tertiary diverge sharply from this field direction (§ 6.08). The only reasonable explanation is that during and prior to Lower Tertiary time either the Earth's field has been nondipolar or, if the field has been dipolar, then the magnetic axis has changed its attitude relative to certain regions which have also moved relative to one another. Now if the Earth's dipole has also been axial, then the paleomagnetic pole also gives the position of the paleogeographic pole relative to the region from which the paleomagnetic results were obtained. The question of prime concern in this chapter is to ask to what extent these postulated changes are consistent with the geological evidence of changes in paleoclimate from these *same* regions: inconsistency would imply that the Earth's field has not been axial; consistency implies that the field has been axial and further that continental drift has occurred.

The comparisons between paleomagnetic and paleoclimatic results are comparisons between the results of independent investigations of the time variation of different phenomena, which, it may be suspected, are related to one another at bottom. The axial form of the present field has led workers to suggest that the core motions which generate the field are controlled by rotational forces (§ 3.4). The surface temperature gradient between equator and poles arises from the fact that, discounting seasonal changes, the spin axis is at a right angle to the Sun's rays. This gradient governs the present-day climatic zonation, so that a connection, between the form of the paleogeomagnetic field and the distribution of different paleoclimatic types, may be expected.

In order to clarify the arguments the comparisons are grouped formally into two categories, the first being relevant to hypotheses of an axial geocentric dipole field and of apparent polar-wandering, and the second to the hypothesis of continental drift (§ 6.09).

Type (1) Comparisons: Internal Consistency. If the Earth's field has always been that of an axial geocentric dipole, then the evidences of past climate in a particular region should be broadly consistent with the movements calculated from the paleomagnetic observations on rocks in the *same* general region. If consistency is found, then it suggests that the paleogeographic pole has moved relative to the region of observation in the manner set out in Figures 6.23 to 6.30. Inconsistency indicates either that the field has not been an axial geocentric dipole, or that the geological evidences of past climates are independent of paleolatitude.

Type (2) Comparisons: External Consistency. If type (1) comparisons yield consistent results, and if the land masses have remained fixed relative to each other, then the paleoclimatic evidence at *all* places on the Earth should be consistent with the paleolatitude changes deduced from the paleomagnetic results from rocks from any one region. Conversely, consistency is not to be expected if substantial relative movements have occurred. Such comparisons therefore constitute a test for the hypothesis that different land masses have not moved relative to each other since the interval of time in question.

In this chapter comparisons of type (1) only are made. The arguments used are independent of the question of continental drift to which type (2) comparisons prop-

erly refer. Comparisons of type (2) are delayed until Chapter Ten (§ 10B.2). It is necessary to make comparisons of type (1) before those of type (2) since any investigation of external consistency is meaningless unless internal consistency can first be demonstrated. Before embarking on particular details, it may be helpful to make clear the nature of the arguments in relation to one point, which is, that they do not depend for their validity on *a priori* assumptions about the nature of the paleogeomagnetic field and of past climate, but on whether or not there is consistency between the paleomagnetic and geologic data collected independently and usually, in the first place, for entirely different purposes.

§ **9.02 Estimates of Past Position** The current geographical position is defined by latitude (λ) and longitude (ϕ) relative to the rotation axis and the Greenwich meridian. The historical problem is to describe the paleogeographic position of a *reference locality* S_r (λ_r, ϕ_r) relative to the paleogeographic axis defined by the pole P_p (λ', ϕ') and its antipole, and which is estimated from the paleomagnetic results (§ 3.6). The reference locality S_r may be a town central to a region of particular interest, or a locality at which a geological feature occurs. The position of S_r may be defined by calculating the paleolatitude λ_p and rotation ψ_p relative to the ancient axis (Figure 9.1). When S_r coincides with the sampling locality for which the mean paleomagnetic direction (D_m, I_m) is known, then λ_p is obtained from the relationship $\lambda_p = \tan^{-1}$ ($\frac{1}{2}$ tan I_m) and ψ_p from equation (6.3). When S and S_r differ in position, λ_p and ψ_p may be calculated from these relationships:

$$\sin \lambda_p = \sin \lambda_r \sin \lambda'$$
$$+ \cos \lambda_r \cos \lambda' \cos (\phi' - \phi_r) \quad (9.1)$$

and $\sin \psi_p = \sin (\phi' - \phi_r) \cos \lambda'/\cos \lambda_p \quad (9.2)$

If, at the reference locality, there is a directional feature (say a tectonic trend or paleowind direction) making an angle ∂ with the present meridian, its direction relative to the paleomeridian is specified by the angle $\partial_p = \partial - \psi_p$ (Figure 9.2).

In these procedures relative movement between S and S_r is assumed unimportant. The effect of relative translation would only be felt if it were of comparable magnitude to the error in determining the pole position ($\simeq 10°$), that is, relative movement within the same continental framework of the order of 1000 km. Relative rotations cannot produce an error greater than twice the distance between the two areas, which rarely exceeds the statistical error. It must also be assumed that the directions of the field did not change between the time the occurrence in question was deposited, and the time of magnetization of the formations studied paleomagnetically. Polar shifts with-

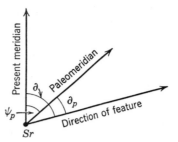

Figure 9.2. The angle ∂_p.

in geological periods are often small, and in such cases as the Permian and Triassic of Europe; the Triassic of North America or the period of late Carboniferous to Lower Cretaceous in Australia, many time levels have been studied so that errors from this source will be small.

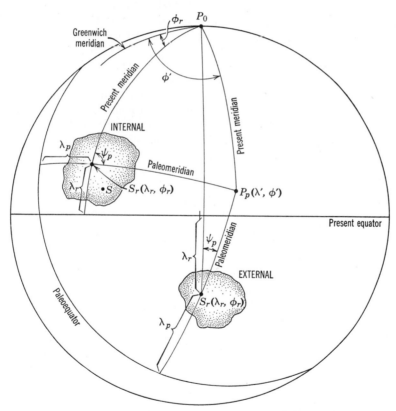

Figure 9.1. Calculation of paleolatitudes and paleomeridians. S is the sampling locality from which the pole P_p is defined. S_r is the reference locality. The estimates of λ_p and ψ_p relate to type (1) tests when S and S_r are on the same land mass, and type (2) tests when on different land masses; hence the designations INTERNAL and EXTERNAL.

§ **9.03   Presentation of Estimates** In the method just described it is assumed that the reference locality S_r is fixed and the pole P_p is displaced relative to the present pole. This is a matter of convenience and has no physical significance in this context; values of ψ_p and λ_p could also be calculated if P_p were assumed fixed at the present pole and S and S_r moved accordingly. But an assumption of much potential physical importance is that no relative movement between S and S_r has occurred since the time in question. This assumption is most likely to be satisfied where S and S_r are in flat-lying beds resting on the same stable block such as, let us say, the Russian Platform, but there is less reason to suppose it satisfied when the localities are situated in different continents or in tectonically active belts. It is useful therefore to define two types of estimates corresponding to the two types of comparisons already defined (§ 9.01): (1) *internal estimates,* when S and S_r are from the *same* general region, and (2) *external estimates,* when S and S_r are in *different* regions usually in different continents (Figure 9.1).

The estimates may be compiled in various ways depending on the task in hand. The following list applies to internal or external estimates and to paleolatitudes or rotation angles. It has been drawn up with internal estimates of paleolatitude primarily in mind, but the procedures apply generally, for example, to space or time variations in structural trends, although this aspect has not yet been exploited.

(1) *Paleolatitude Time Variations for Reference Localities* (§ 9.06). The time variations of paleolatitude for a reference locality central to a particular region may be calculated and compared with the paleoclimatic evidence for that region.

(2) *Regional Variations of Paleolatitude and Paleomeridian Directions* (§ 9.07). The space variations over a given region for a given time may be represented as maps on which the parallels of paleolatitude and ancient meridians for that time are drawn, and

to which geological features are added for comparison.

(3) *Paleolatitude Spectra* (§ 9.08). The paleolatitude values for a particular geological feature may be compiled as a histogram to give the spectrum of that particular occurrence; variation in time may then be studied by comparing results from successive geological periods.

(4) A fourth procedure is to plot each occurrence of a particular indicator on a graph of paleolatitude versus time; this method will be of much use when more refined data are at hand, but at the present stage time variations can be adequately studied by considering a time sequence of histograms. And now a few remarks are made about the study of paleoclimates.

§ **9.04   Paleoclimatic Indicators** There are two steps in the study of paleoclimates: first, the recognition of some feature, called a *paleoclimatic indicator,* which may be taken as evidence for the occurrence of a particular climatic condition at the time it was formed; and second, the use of a model of past climate zonation of the Earth so that the indicator can be placed in its correct paleoclimatic zone. In practice, the arguments fall back on analogies with present conditions; indicators showing features comparable to modern deposits may be considered to have been formed under similar conditions to the modern deposit. Moreover, the models of paleoclimatic zones used are based, perhaps with modifications as to details, on the Earth's present climate, in particular on the latitude dependence of mean temperatures. In the interpretation of specific instances one of the most intractable problems facing the geologist is the qualitative nature of the evidence. Possible variations, difficult or impossible to assess, may occur in the tolerance of the chosen indicator to the paleoclimate, or in the model used for assigning the indicator to its paleoclimatic zone. For example, at the present time, corals in bioherms will not tolerate continued minimum temperatures of less than 18°C, but, because of biological changes, it may not be safe to assume that this same isotherm has delimited the region of growth of bio-hermic corals since their beginnings in the Ordovician; further, the position of the 18°C isotherm may have been well to the north or south of its present position, so that the allocation of a coral occurrence to a particular paleolatitude is a qualitative procedure open to easy criticism. For example, on the basis of assumed fluctuations in the model, some authors contend that biohermic coral growth at some periods extended almost to the North Pole. The first of these aspects is now considered. Climatic zones are discussed in § 9.05 and returned to in § 9.22.

The geological features considered are those which have been formed either on land or in shallow seas, because it is in such settings that paleoclimate is most likely to have been a factor in the environment of formation. The question of their usefulness as indicators of paleoclimate is one on which geological opinion is divided. The following brief and selective remarks are not intended to argue a point, but only to introduce the studies described later in the chapter.

Certain types of unsorted sediments which contain scratched erratics are thought to have originated from melting glaciers because of their likeness to the deposits of modern glaciers. They are called *tillites*. This interpretation is strengthened when the tillite is found to rest on striated pavements, and when they occur interbedded with banded sediments (usefully called varvoids) comparable in structure to recent glacial varves. Local occurrences may arise from mountain glaciation and indicate the presence of extensive high land. Widespread occurrences spaced through thick sequences, especially when interbedded with marine sediments, suggest a wide area of low-level glaciation, and indicate low mean temperatures, and, in particular, low summer temperatures.

The deposition of *evaporites* (beds of chloride, and sulfates such as halite, gypsum, and anhydrite) are thought to require high temperatures for at least some part of the year. The relative absence of terrigenous material, and low precipitation favors their accumulation. The most notable modern deposits are in the tropical and temperate deserts or semi-deserts, associated with the dry trade wind belts and with the arid centers of large continents.

"Although calcareous oozes extend beyond the Arctic Circle in the North Atlantic, nevertheless carbonate deposits are most widespread in that half of the Earth's surface between the 30th parallels" (Rodgers, 1957). This is presumably related in a general way to the fact that the surface waters in the warm oceans are more nearly saturated with calcium carbonate than those of the cold oceans. The occurrence of thick and extensive fossil carbonate deposits, particularly those with associated reefs, may therefore be supposed to indicate warm conditions at the time of formation.

The widespread occurrence of thick dune-bedded sandstones (the so-called *desert sandstones*) associated with red marls and clays exhibiting such features as sun-cracked surfaces, indicate deposition in regions of low seasonal rainfall bare of vegetation for much of the year.

The color of sediments may be useful as a guide to paleoclimate. Warm climate with seasonal rainfall favors the oxidation, hydrolysis, and fine division of iron compounds to produce red earths and laterite. Excessive leaching of laterite yields bauxite. In cold and wet conditions iron remains in a state of low oxidation, producing yellow or grey soils. The presence of ancient laterites indicates a warm climate at the time of formation. Erosion of red and grey soils will tend to produce red and grey sediments respectively, but the red color may be lost in the former case if abundant carbon (plant fossils, for instance) is present. Red soils may have inherited their color from pre-existing red beds, but because of the variability of rock types present as source rocks for a sedimentary basin, this is likely to be only a local effect. It seems therefore, that the presence of drab colored continental or shallow marine sediments, although consistent with the view that the climate at the time was cool, is not positive evidence for this. Furthermore, thin red strata of limited extent do not necessarily indicate a warm climate. But the repeated accumulation through long time periods of red beds totaling many thousands of meters, and spreading over regions of continental extent, is sometimes taken as indicative of warm conditions.

Fossils have been used often as indicators of past conditions, as in the two cases mentioned below. *Coral reefs* are currently most abundant in warm shallow seas, particularly within the tropics (Figure 9.54), and on account of this, fossil limestones, richly coralliferous, whether biohermal or biostromal, are often regarded as indicative of clear warm water at the time of deposition. However, many corals occur at depths as great as 6000 m at temperatures below 0°C, and at latitudes of 70°, and are often sufficiently concentrated to form banks (Teichert, 1958). Such corals (ahermatypic) have no symbiotic algae. Hermatypic corals, which have symbiotic algae, are essentially tropical forms and form the large modern reefs; it is possible that their restriction is due indirectly to the algae and not to temperature. A distinction between these types cannot be made in fossil forms, and there may be some doubt as to whether a fossil coral deposit is to be compared to modern tropical reefs or to deep water coral banks. But the coral banks to which Tiechert refers are associated with argillaceous sediments whereas fossil reefs occur most commonly in calcareous formations.

Plant remains may suggest past climatic conditions. The presence of trees indicates mean summer temperatures above freezing. Most trees in equatorial rain forests have no annular rings, growth being constant throughout the year. Elsewhere, and particularly in temperate trees, rings are usual because of the seasonal growth induced by alternating cold and warm, or wet and dry seasons. The presence or absence of rings in fossil trees may therefore be taken to indicate the presence or absence of seasonal changes. *Coal* deposits indicate the existence of moist conditions, which could arise from heavy

precipitation in warm environments or modest rainfall in cool climates.

The above features, if taken to indicate paleoclimate, do so only in a qualitative fashion, and mention may be made here of the measurements of oxygen isotopes from which attempts to estimate absolute paleotemperatures may be made. This matter is described later (§ 9.19).

The usefulness of these indicators rests not so much in the power of any one feature as in the collective agreement which is sometimes observed. Thick evaporite deposits, red beds, dune-bedded sandstones, and carbonate deposits with organic reefs may occur in the same geological system in the same general region, interbedded or merging laterally; such is the case in the Permian of Europe and North America. But the many indications of glacial activity in the lower levels (late Carboniferous and early to middle Permian) of the Gondwana beds, e.g., in India or Australia, are unaccompanied by any of these characteristics.

§ **9.05   Climatic Zones**   Most surface heat is derived from the sun, so that mean temperature is determined by a general latitude control, on which are superposed variations caused by ocean currents, topography, size of land masses, and so on. These variations differ with longitude, but the mean summer, winter, and annual temperatures around the parallels is a function of latitude (Figure 9.3). Four zones are recognized (Table 9.1). The equatorward limit of the polar cold dry zones is taken as 70°, which is the latitude at which mean summer temperature is roughly zero; this also corresponds with the poleward limit of tree growth. Following Blackett (1961), the other limits are set by the use of a *coefficient of aridity*, which is the ratio, expressed as a percentage, of the total length along each parallel of the present arid regions to the total length of land. From the form of the "aridity" curve the limits of the arid zones are set, and define the equatorial and temperate zones. About half the surface is in the warm arid zone, and most of the remainder is divided equally between the warm wet zone centered on the equator, and the cool wet zones in temperate latitudes.

There are many factors which may have operated in the past to produce changes in these zones, and one of the purposes of calculating paleolatitude spectra of indicators is to form some idea of these changes. Such factors are: fluctuations in solar heat, possible variations in inclination of the Earth's axis or in the ellipticity of its orbit, variations in the distribution of land and sea, variations in the altitude of land and oceanic circulation, in cloudiness, or in the composition of the atmosphere arising, say, from episodic vulcanism. Brooks (1949) main-

Table 9.1   Present Climatic Zones. Mainly from Blackett (1961), who uses data from Brooks (1949).

Zone	Latitude Limits	Percentage of Earth's Surface
Warm wet	15° S to 15° N	26
Warm arid (N and S)	15 to 45°	45
Cool wet (N and S)	45 to 70°	23
Cold dry (N and S)	70 to 90°	6

tains that the present meteorological situation is not typical. At present the climate is dominated by the presence of polar ice caps, which increase the temperature difference between the equator and poles above that which would otherwise exist in their absence. Under the "normal" regime the mean annual temperature difference between pole and equator is of the order of 25°C compared with about twice this at present. These two situations Brooks calls *glacial* and *nonglacial*. The nonglacial periods are characterized by warmth and dryness, and are thought to have been times of low relief and widespread shallow seas. Nonglacial climate was typically developed in the Mesozoic and early Tertiary. In view of these possible variations it may be misleading to be guided too rigidly by the modern analogy and to attempt to place paleoclimatic indicators within the framework of the present zones. However, as Brooks emphasizes, there will always be an average latitude effect even though less pronounced at some periods than at present.

§ **9.06   Paleolatitude Time Variations for Reference Localities**   Paleomagnetic results from a single region may be explained by supposing apparent polar-wandering relative to the region, so that during any geological period the climate in that *same* region should be broadly consistent with the paleolatitude calculated from paleomagnetic observations. In the present connection it is desired to consider only the effect of latitude, and so large variations may be expected; the most that can be hoped for in these comparisons is either a general agree-

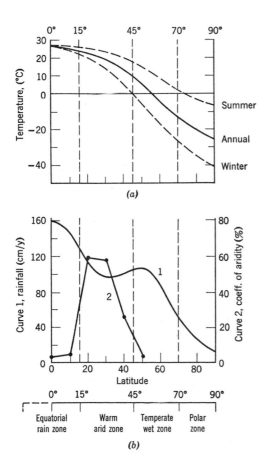

Figure 9.3. Present climatic zones. Redrawn from Blackett (1961), with the kind permission of the Royal Society of London and P. M. S. Blackett.

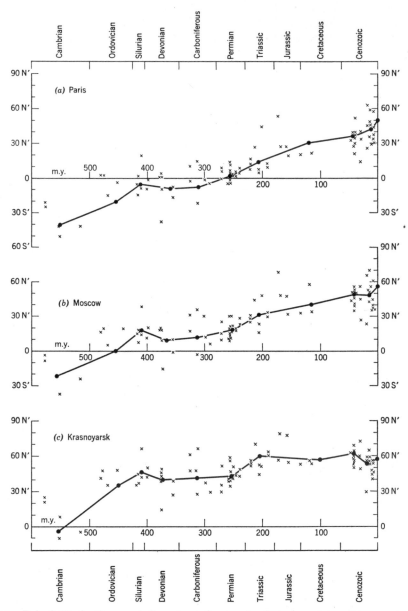

Figure 9.4. Paleolatitude time variations for reference localities: an internal comparison. Estimated paleolatitudes are plotted against Kulp's 1961 Time Scale. Small crosses give values obtained from individual paleomagnetic results given in the appendix; dots are from means for periods (see Table 6.2) and lines are drawn joining these means to indicate broad trends. The reference localities are as follows: (a) Paris (48°52′ N, 2°18′ E); (b) Moscow (55°50′ N, 37°40′ E); (c) Krasnoyarsk (56°10′ N, 92°15′ E); (d) Salt Lake City (40°55′ N, 111°50′ W); (e) Cincinatti (39°17′ N, 84°25′ W); (f) Nagpur (21°5′ N, 79°5′ E); (g) Canberra (35°15′ S, 149°10′ E).

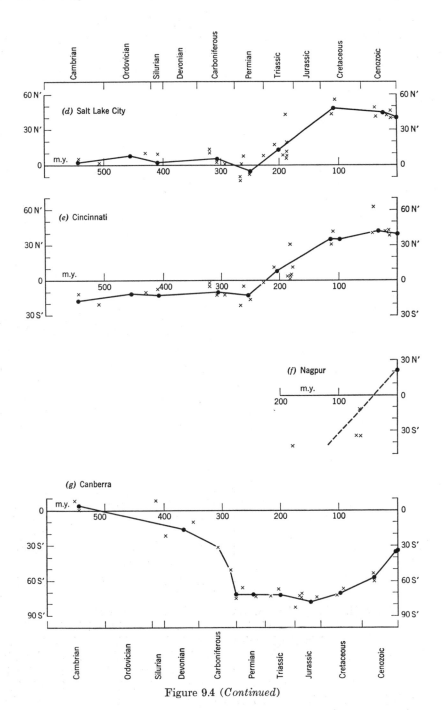

Figure 9.4 (*Continued*)

ment or a gross inconsistency. At this point, all that is needed is an indication of general trends to preface the application of the more exact method of spectral analysis (§ 9.08). For this purpose the time variations of paleolatitude are calculated for a reference locality central to a given region, and at this rather crude level of comparison it is legitimate to compare the paleoclimatic evidence from the region as a whole with the variations calculated for the reference locality. In these calculations, individual poles or averages for periods may be used. The results for Europe and northern Asia, North America, India, and Australia are given in Figure 9.4. The lines, indicating the mean variation, join values obtained from mean poles for periods. The values for individual poles indicate the scatter about this mean, and also give some idea of the density of observations but not, it should be noted, of their quality.

Europe and Northern Asia. Paris, Moscow, and Krasnoyarsk have been chosen as reference localities since they illustrate the remarkable east-west paleolatitude gradient in this region for the Paleozoic and Mesozoic. The estimated paleolatitude for Paris, which may be taken as representative of western Europe, is comparable to that which might be expected from the stratigraphic record. Carbonate deposits, with reefs, occur in the Lower Paleozoic, particularly in the Silurian (Hill, 1958a). The sequence of Devonian red sandstones, limestones, and coral reefs, Carboniferous limestones and coral reefs, Permian and Triassic dune-bedded sandstones, red beds, evaporites, limestones, and coral reefs suggest a warm climate. Schwarzbach (1961b) speaks of warm climates throughout the Paleozoic and Triassic for western Europe, and in the Permian he says that the evidence "combines to form a picture of warm and at times—extremely dry climate." This is consistent with the estimated paleolatitudes of between 20° N′ and 20° S′, but the correlation of aridity in the Permian with values within a few degrees of the paleoequator is notable. The chalk and large reptiles of the Cretaceous, and the

"tropical" flora and bauxites of the Lower Tertiary of western Europe, are to be compared with paleolatitudes 10° to 20° less than present values. Paleotemperatures recorded for the Jurassic and Cretaceous indicate higher values than at present (see § 9.19).

The paleolatitude variations for Moscow are representative for the Russian platform. Limestones and dolomites occur in the Lower Paleozoic, and in the Devonian, red beds, lagoonal evaporites, and limestone; in the Carboniferous, limestones and bauxites were formed, and in the Permian and Triassic, red beds, limestones, and evaporites (Nalivkin, 1960). The stratigraphic record is suggestive of a climate warmer than the present, and is consistent, in the broad, with the estimated paleolatitudes.

Further east on the Siberian platform, for which Krasnoyarsk is taken as a representative location, the geological sequence is different. Red beds, dolomites, limestones, and evaporites occur in the Lower Paleozoic, and limestones and red beds in the Carboniferous. But in the Permian, Jurassic, and Cretaceous (the Triassic is represented chiefly by igneous rocks), the beds are predominantly grey-colored, and the red beds, evaporites, and limestones, which occur in western Europe and in the Russian platform at this time, are absent. Extensive continental and marine Jurassic beds occur, which suggest that this absence is not due to the absence of suitable depositional environments. These features are broadly consistent with the east-west paleolatitude gradient calculated from the paleomagnetic data.

North America. Reference localities have been chosen representative of the eastern (Cincinnati) and western (Salt Lake City) regions. Extensive dolomites, limestones with Archeocyathinae, and coral reefs, occur in the Lower Paleozoic. Coral reefs and evaporites are particularly extensive in the Upper Silurian. Widespread red beds, evaporites, limestones with coral reefs, and desert sandstones occur in the Upper Paleozoic, and red beds and evaporites in the Triassic. This evidence is consistent with paleolatitudes of less than 30° for most of the continent for these times. In the Cretaceous, limestones and evaporites occur, but are confined to the south.

Australia. The reference locality used is Canberra, which, although in the southeast of the continent, is central to the region which has been studied in the most detail geologically and paleomagnetically. Low paleolatitudes are estimated for the Lower Paleozoic and Devonian and Lower Carboniferous, and this correlates with the occurrence of red beds, limestones, and dolomites. Archeocyathid reefs occur in the Cambrian (§ 9.14), well-developed coral faunas in the Ordovician (Hill, 1950), and coral reefs in the Silurian, Devonian, and Lower Carboniferous (Hill, 1957, 1958a; Teichert, 1952). Evaporites are found in the Cambrian. In the Upper Carboniferous and Permian, beds of glacial origin occur, and these correlate with high paleolatitude (§ 9.18). A paleolatitude transition occurs within the Carboniferous, possibly within the interval Viséan to Westphalian. Red beds and coral reef limestones are widespread in the Lower Carboniferous, suggesting warm climate, in sharp contrast to the evidence of glaciation in the Upper Carboniferous. The paleolatitude change within the Carboniferous is consistent with this evidence.

The Mesozoic climate has been described by David (1950). "The Triassic climate was probably in general mild and at times it was pluvial, while the pronounced growth-rings of the conifers tell a story of well-marked seasonal change." "Of the Jurassic climate we can say but little. Some of the boulders in the Victorian sandstones have been interpreted as indicating transport by local alpine glaciers, but this is very doubtful. . . . The vegetation of the coal-swamps probably grew in a cool, moist climate, but the common occurrence of ironstones among the sediments suggests occasional reversal to somewhat arid conditions." Regarding the Cretaceous, this is said: "The balance of evidence, however, favours the view that the land temperatures as well as those of the epicontinental sea were cold. The rich foraminiferal fauna . . . indicates moder-

ately warm and deep water in the Australian geosyncline. This had direct communication with the Tethyan Sea, though the entire absence of coral-reefs and rudistid lamellibranchs would imply that the climate was not of tropical warmth." The evidence of somewhat warmer (but not tropical) conditions in Western Australia is of interest because this region gives the lowest paleolatitudes in the Cretaceous (about 50° S', Figure 9.16). The main point of interest is the complete absence of coral reefs (Teichert, 1952), and the absence of thick red beds, limestones, and evaporites, such as are so commonly encountered in beds of this age in the Mesozoic of Europe and North America (§ 9.21). The paleolatitudes in the Mesozoic are high, and these are consistent with the evidence of cool climate and the absence of evidence for hot conditions.

Finally, paleotemperature studies (Dorman and Gill, 1959a, b) indicate an increase in temperature for Victoria from little over 10° in the Paleocene to between 15° to 20°C in the Upper Tertiary. This is consistent with the decrease in paleolatitude.

India. The results from peninsular India relate only to a few levels. The oldest value is assigned with some uncertainty to the Jurassic [9.23]. Although limestones occur there is little paleoclimatic evidence in peninsular India for this and later periods. There are no paleomagnetic results from the climatically interesting glacial beds at the base of the Gondwana System.

Africa and South America. Paleomagnetic results are available only from a few time intervals so that time variations cannot be studied, but it is worth noting that Jurassic coral reefs in east and north Africa, and evaporites in east and west Africa and Argentina are to be compared with low paleolatitudes. Furthermore, the extensive desert sandstones at the top of the Gondwana beds are in paleolatitudes of less than 35° (Figures 9.47 and 9.72).

Discussion. These comparisons yield a *prima facie* case for the view that the paleomagnetic and paleoclimatic results obtained from the *same* general region show broad internal consistency, and this favors the hypothesis that the Earth's field has been an axial geocentric dipole since the Lower Paleozoic and the hypothesis of apparent polar-wandering relative to the above regions. The next step is to study the paleolatitude spectra of individual climatic indicators to see if this first impression is justified in detail, but before this is done it is convenient to set out the variation in regional fashion.

§ 9.07   **Regional Variations**   An atlas of paleolatitude and paleomeridian maps for Europe and northern Asia, North America, and Australia, for Cambrian and later time, is given in Figures 9.5 to 9.32. These are the regions, defined in § 6.03, for which the paleomagnetic data are most complete. Maps for

two periods of time for peninsular India are given in Figures 9.33 and 9.34, and for single periods for South America (Figure 9.72), Africa (Figure 9.47), and Antarctica (Figure 9.35). These maps are subject to uncertainties due to inadequacies in the sampling coverage in time, or by area. The observational basis for each map is given in the appendix and may be traced by means of the footnotes in Table 6.2.

Inadequacies in the time record arise since the rock record is incomplete, and since the proportion of rocks that have received paleomagnetic study is small. In certain cases (for example the Permian of Europe and north Asia, or the Mesozoic of Australia), many time levels have been studied, and the internal agreement observed suggests that the mean result is characteristic for the span

General note for Figures 9.5 to 9.14. Regional variations of paleolatitude and paleomeridians; Europe and northern Asia based on *A* group data. The paleomeridians are labeled with arbitrary numbers, the zero meridian being taken through Greenwich. In the bottom right-hand corner of each figure a letter is given denoting the relative reliability of each map as follows: A high, B moderate, C low. These reliability indices are assigned on the basis of authors' assessment of the adequacy of the paleomagnetic coverage bearing in mind the extent to which the *A* group data has been confirmed by the *B* group data.

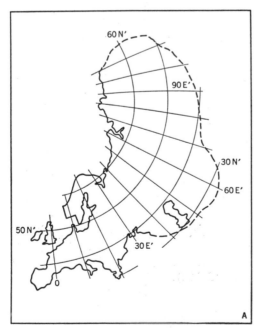

Figure 9.5. Upper Tertiary.

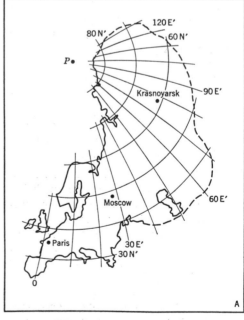

Figure 9.6. Lower Tertiary.

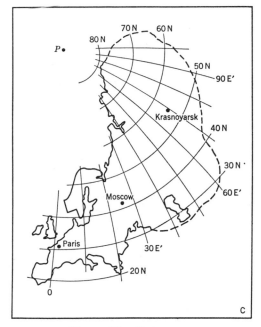

Figure 9.7. Cretaceous.

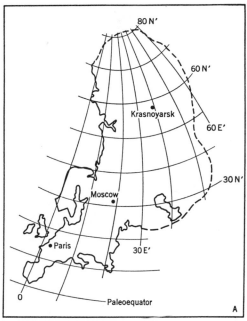

Figure 9.8. Triassic.

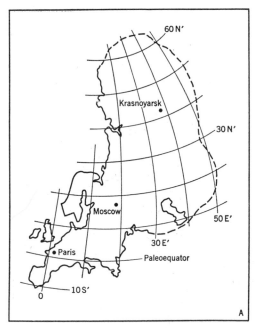

Figure 9.9. Permian.

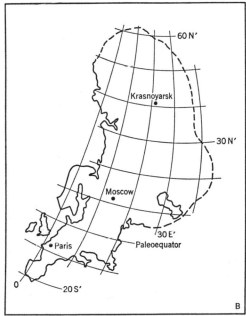

Figure 9.10. Carboniferous.

Figure 9.11. Devonian.

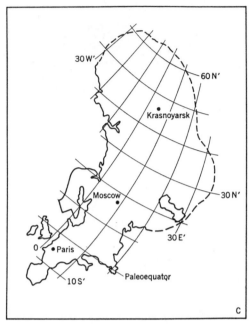

Figure 9.12. Silurian.

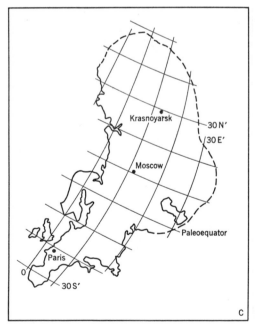

Figure 9.13. Ordovician.

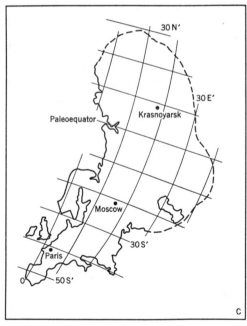

Figure 9.14. Cambrian.

General note for Figures 9.15 to 9.24. Regional variations of paleolatitude and paleomeridians in Australia based on *A* group data. The paleomeridians are numbered arbitrarily, zero being taken through Canberra. Reliability indices are described on p. 196.

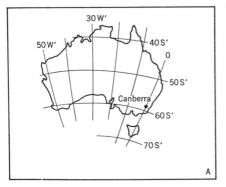

Figure 9.15. Lower Tertiary.

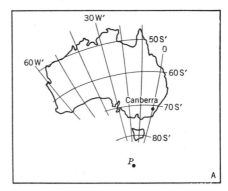

Figure 9.16. Cretaceous.

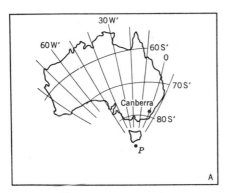

Figure 9.17. Jurassic.

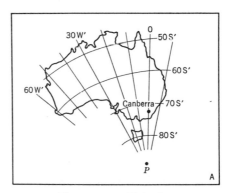

Figure 9.18. Triassic.

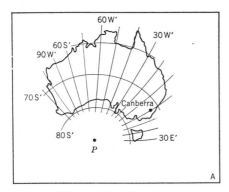

Figure 9.19. Permian.

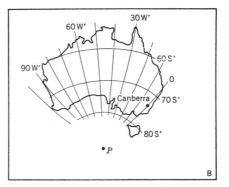

Figure 9.20. Late Carboniferous (glacial levels).

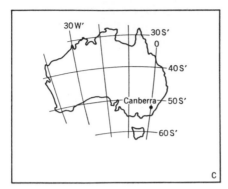

Figure 9.21. Carboniferous (Paterson Toscanite).

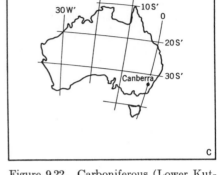

Figure 9.22. Carboniferous (Lower Kuttung).

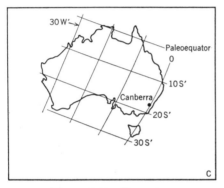

Figure 9.23. Devonian.

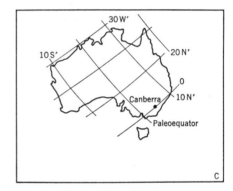

Figure 9.24. Cambrian.

of time involved. But in other cases measurements are available only from a part of a geological period. For example, the Silurian of North America is represented by results from beds of Upper Silurian age only (§ 6.06), but the Ordovician and Carboniferous paleolatitudes are very similar to those of the Upper Silurian, suggesting that changes at that time occurred slowly. It is therefore reasonable to assume that the map for the Upper Silurian is approximately correct for, say, the Middle Silurian.

There are also inadequacies in the regional coverage. In constructing these maps, relative movement between any part of the region and the paleomagnetic sampling area is assumed small. In such cases as the Devonian, Permian, and Triassic of Europe and northern Asia, and the Triassic of North America, the sampling localities are widespread, and this assumption is reasonable. In Australia the regional coverage is less, but the continent is one that has not been extensively disturbed tectonically since the middle Carboniferous, and little disturbed since the Paleozoic, so that from this viewpoint the Mesozoic and, with less certainty, the Upper Carboniferous and Permian maps are likely to be realistic. In certain areas extensive tectonic activity has occurred since the time covered by some of these paleogeographic maps. For example, in North America the orogenies leading to the formation of the western cordillera may have caused movement of points relative to the Mesozoic and Paleozoic maps, but the agreement between results from Carboniferous beds in the Colorado plateau [6.66] within this orogenic belt, and those in the Appalachian province [6.67, 68] which were disturbed by orogeny in the early Permian, suggests that no large relative displacement occurred. A further example is in the Europe and northern Asia region where results from Devonian beds of the Russian Platform west of the Urals [5.10, 16] and from the Siberian Platform [5.31, 46] to the east, are concordant, suggesting that the later deformation of the Ural geosyncline has lead to relatively little movement between these components of the Europe-northern Asia region.

These views may be too optimistic, but

General note for Figures 9.25 to 9.32. Regional variations of paleolatitude and paleomeridians in North America based on *A* group data. The paleomeridians are numbered arbitrarily, zero being through New York. The reliability indices are explained on p. 196.

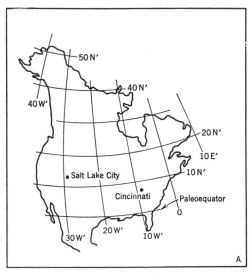

Figure 9.25. Upper Tertiary.

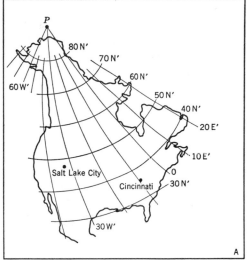

Figure 9.26. Cretaceous.

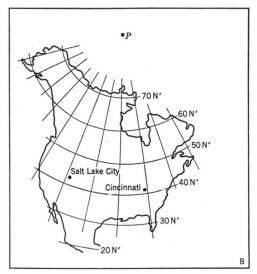

Figure 9.27. Triassic.

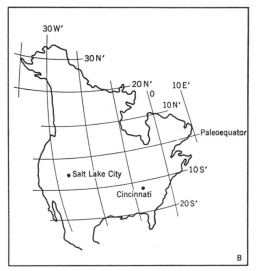

Figure 9.28. Permian.

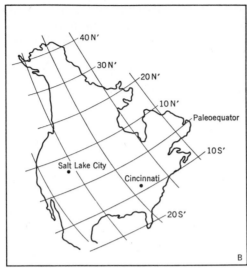

Figure 9.29. Carboniferous.

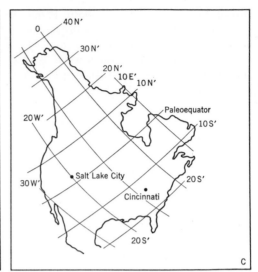

Figure 9.30. Silurian.

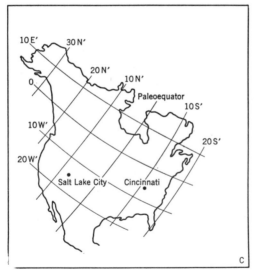

Figure 9.31. Ordovician.

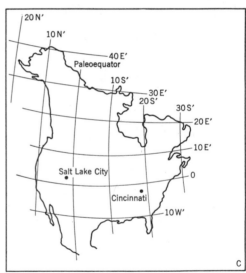

Figure 9.32. Cambrian.

the validity of any particular map may be tested by taking further observations. The areal and time coverage provided by the existing paleomagnetic data is wide, bearing in mind that it is only in the past 15 years that concerted efforts have been made, but it is exiguous compared with the data which could potentially be collected. These maps are therefore presented only as a statement of present results. The possible errors mentioned above are not permanent uncertainties; they can be remedied simply by further work using existing techniques.

§ **9.08 Paleolatitude Spectra** The procedure here is to calculate the paleolatitudes of the occurrences of a particular feature, and then to compile the values in *equal-angle* or *equal-area histograms*. In the former an equal latitude interval is used, and the procedure gives a clear presentation when the values fall within a certain range. When the values are widely spread it is preferable to use equal-angle histograms in which frequency is plotted against equal intervals of the sine of latitude (intervals of 0.1 being used) so that each has equal area. Histograms may be compiled either using the full scale between the north and south poles, or irrespective of sign, so that values for the same interval from both hemispheres are combined. Values can, of course, be obtained only for those regions and times for which paleomagnetic results are available, so that revisions will be needed as more data come to light.

Problems of weighting of the geological information arise, because of the irregulari-

General note for Figures 9.33 and 9.34. Regional variations of paleolatitude and paleomeridians in India. The reliabilities indices are explained on p. 196.

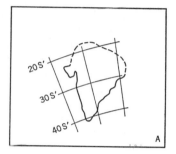

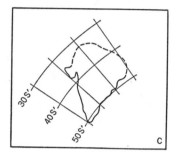

Figure 9.33. Late Cretaceous-Lower Tertiary.

Figure 9.34. Jurassic.

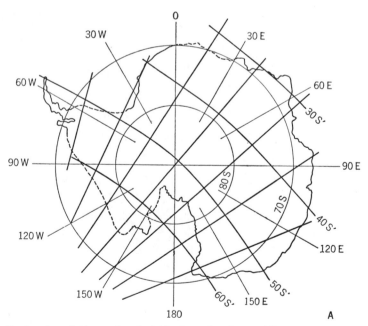

Figure 9.35. Regional variations of paleolatitude and paleomeridians in Antarctica in the Jurassic. The reliability index is explained on p. 196. The present network is added in thin line.

ties in the geological source data, and because of the variation of thickness and extent of deposits. There are irregularities in source data because of variability in geological study in different regions, and results from regions which have received the most detailed study (in particular, North America, Europe, and the U.S.S.R.) will tend to outnumber those from other regions. No weighting for this effect is made. The geological sources used for compiling the spectra are given in the originals cited, or in this text for those spectra not published before. Weighting for areal extent is considered to be more important than weighting for thickness, since the latter may be governed more by local than by regional factors. In gen-

eral, each named formation or occurrence has been given unit weight, with the proviso that no more than one entry is permitted for any one place for a single geological period. This weighting is subjective and no doubt different workers would adopt different procedures; however, it is felt that the salient features would not be altered.

§ **9.09** **Evaporites** Nowadays evaporite deposition occurs predominantly in tropical and temperate arid regions between latitudes of 10° and 50° (Figure 9.48). The distribution has two peaks each corresponding to the northern and southern arid belts. The size of the regions and their latitude spread is greater in the northern than in the south-

General note for Figures 9.36 to 9.46. Generalized distribution maps of paleoclimatic indicators. **E** evaporites, **C** coal, **R** red beds, **D** desert sandstones. Diagonal shading gives the carbonate occurrences, and crosshatching the dolomite deposits. For further descriptions see text, § 9.09. Redrawn from Briden and Irving (1964).

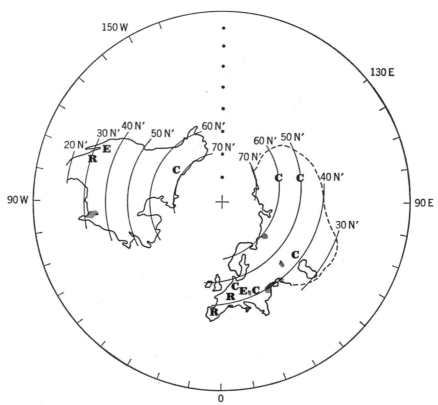

Figure 9.36. Upper Tertiary.

ern hemisphere, and this is related to the land areas present. No occurrences are recorded north of 53° N or south of 43° S, and there are only two regions, one in east Africa and the other in coastal Peru, in which evaporite deposition occurs within 10° of the equator.

The oldest evaporites are of Cambrian age, and subsequently deposits were laid down in all the later geological periods. The distributions for various periods have been given by Lotze (1957) and Green (1961), and the following analyses depend primarily on these sources. The distribution of evaporites for those periods and regions for which estimates of paleolatitude can be made are plotted in a general fashion in Figures 9.36 to 9.47 and 9.73. In the interests of clarity, it is not possible to enter all the occurrences which have been used in the analyses in this

and later sections. In Figures 9.40 to 9.42 Mercator's projection is used for the Triassic, Permian, and Carboniferous, which are critical periods for this study, the paleolatitude lines being extended over the regions to which they are considered to apply. A different presentation is used in Figures 9.36 to 9.39 and 9.43 to 9.46; in order to condense the information each region is placed in its correct latitudinal position (that is, present latitude) on equal-area projections but with Australia in an arbitrary longitude. This is done in order to avoid drawing separate diagrams for each land mass.

The present latitude distribution of Mesozoic evaporites is broadly comparable to that of modern deposits. In the Paleozoic there are numerous occurrences further to the north. Mesozoic and Paleozoic evaporites viewed together are seen to occur mostly in

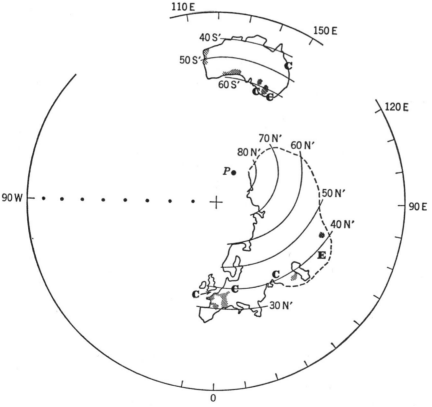

Figure 9.37. Lower Tertiary. See p. 204 and above for explanations of the position of Australia and the symbols used.

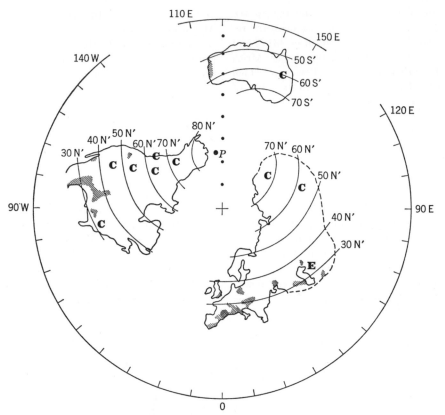

Figure 9.38. Cretaceous. See pp. 204 and 205 for explanations of the position of Australia and the symbols used.

intermediate or high and predominantly northerly latitudes; the full range is wide, from 31° S to 83° N, but over 70 per cent fall between 30° and 60° N (Figure 9.49). This distribution can be represented in a general way as a steady northward shift going back through geological time, the total shift of the average trend being about 30°, from approximately 30° N today to about 60° N in the Cambrian (Figure 9.50). The scatter of values about the average trend is large, departures of up to 20° and more on either side being common, but it appears to be statistically significant (Green, 1961). The rates of change estimated for the northern continents are 0.05°/m.y. (Green, 1961), and 0.07°/m.y. for America and 0.11°/m.y. for Europe and Africa (Blackett, 1961).

The paleolatitudes are generally low and although the full range is from 59° S' to 40° N' over 75 per cent are within 30° of the paleoequator (Figure 9.48c). The time variation shows an interesting trend. In the Lower and Upper Paleozoic the distribution has a single peak and centers neatly on the paleoequator (Figure 9.49), contrasting with the bimodal modern evaporite distribution (Figure 9.48a). The Mesozoic values are

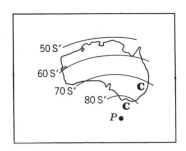

Figure 9.39. Jurassic.

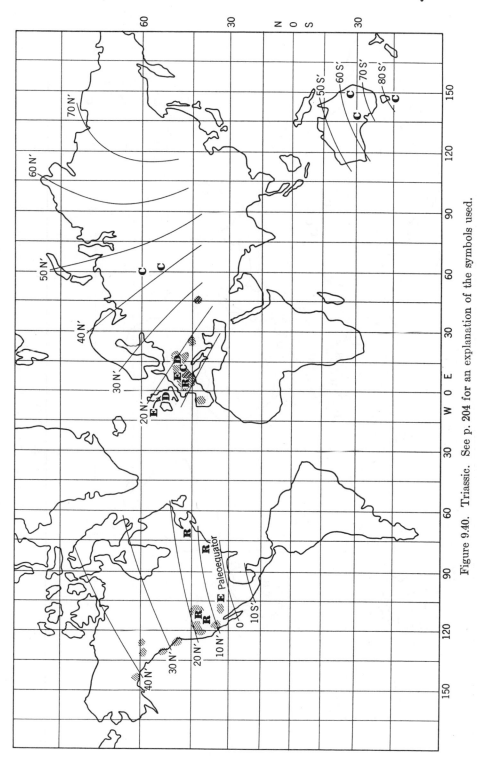

Figure 9.40. Triassic. See p. 204 for an explanation of the symbols used.

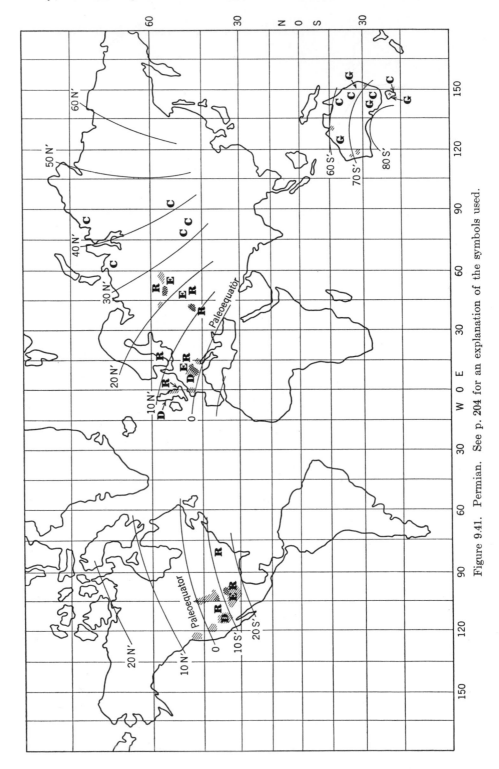

Figure 9.41. Permian. See p. 204 for an explanation of the symbols used.

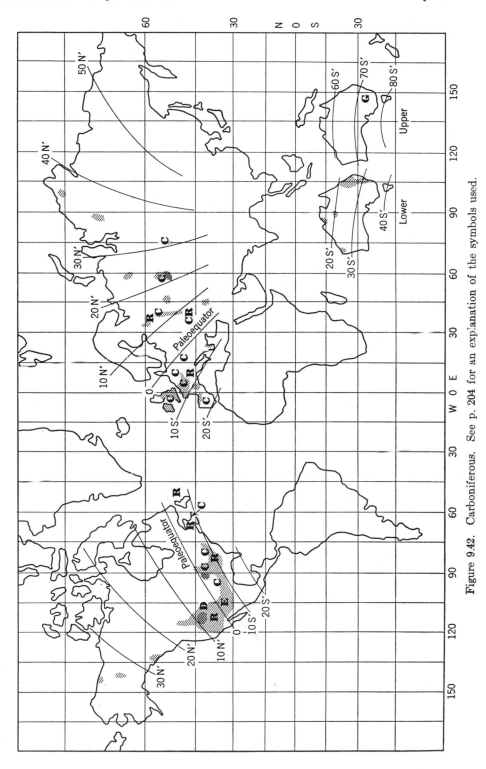

Figure 9.42. Carboniferous. See p. 204 for an explanation of the symbols used.

predominantly within the range 10° to 30° N', which is more consistent with the modern distribution, although closer to the paleo-equator on average. The Tertiary values commonly range from 30° to 45° N', not dissimilar to the Mesozoic range and the northern hemisphere range of modern deposits. It is the Mesozoic and Tertiary values that impart a northerly bias to the total histogram (Figure 9.48c).

§ **9.10 Carbonates: General** In §§ 9.11 to 9.14, special types of carbonates will be singled out for individual treatment, but here carbonates in general will be considered. The results are based primarily on the data from North America, Europe, the U.S.S.R., and Australia. The broad features of the distribution are given in the maps (Figures 9.36 to 9.46).

In North America carbonates occur in all

systems but are particularly abundant in the Paleozoic up to and including the Carboniferous. They occur over the whole continent except for the Precambrian shield, but the frequency is greatest in the U.S.A. in latitudes around 40°. The paleolatitudes of Paleozoic carbonates fall predominantly within 30° of the paleoequator. No values are given for the Devonian since no reliable paleomagnetic data are available from rocks of that period, but since Upper Silurian and Lower Carboniferous paleomagnetic results give low latitudes for this continent, interpolation would suggest low paleolatitudes for the extensive Devonian limestones of the U.S.A. and western Canada. Triassic and Cretaceous values are all low to intermediate, and the few Upper Tertiary deposits to which paleolatitudes can be assigned fall around 30° N'.

Carbonates are abundant in Europe in

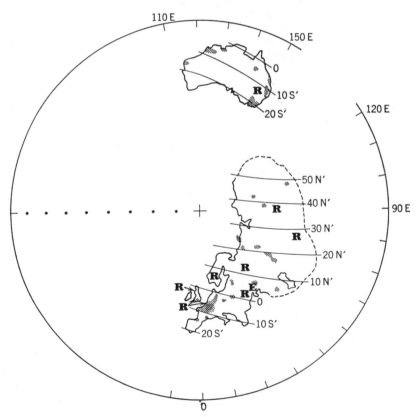

Figure 9.43. Devonian. See pp. **204** and **205** for explanations of the position of Australia and the symbols used.

most geological periods. Their present latitude distribution shows a peak at about 48° N. The paleolatitudes of Paleozoic deposits are again predominantly within 30° of the paleoequator, while Mesozoic and Tertiary carbonates extend into slightly higher northerly paleolatitudes, roughly 10° lower than their present values (Figures 9.37 and 9.38). The group as a whole is predominantly in paleolatitudes lower than 35°.

In the U.S.S.R., carbonates are widespread in the Paleozoic up to and including the Carboniferous, whereas in the Permian and Mesozoic they are mostly confined west of the Urals. This is correlated with the east to west paleolatitude gradient. In the Paleozoic the paleolatitudes are predominantly low, and in the Mesozoic and Tertiary they extend into the intermediate range. Cumulatively, the values are predominantly northerly, with a maximum at 25° N′.

Australia is not rich in carbonates compared to Europe and North America. There are many occurrences in the Lower Paleozoic and Devonian, but few in the later Paleozoic. Only thin limestones of small areal extent occur in the Mesozoic, with rather more extensive developments in the Lower Tertiary. The Lower Paleozoic to Lower Carboniferous group falls predominantly within 30° of the paleoequator. Permian and Mesozoic carbonates occur in intermediate southerly paleolatitudes. Lower Tertiary limestones occur in intermediate southerly paleolatitudes at a time when the paleomagnetic evidence indicates that the paleolatitude was decreasing.

In other continents paleomagnetic information (*A* group data) is limited to a few geological periods: for South America in the Jurassic, for Africa in the Triassic and Jurassic, and for India in the Jurassic and

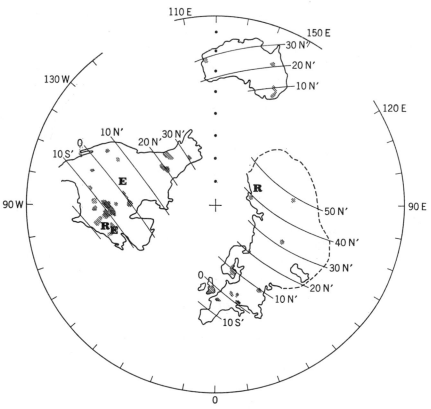

Figure 9.44. Silurian. See pp. 204 and 205 for explanations of the position of Australia and the symbols used.

Lower Tertiary. Records of limestone occurrences for these periods and places are few, but all have paleolatitudes of less than 40°.

In Figure 9.51 all estimates (over 600) for carbonates are lumped together. This procedure gives too much weight to the North American occurrences, but it illustrates a rather striking general point, that is, that 90 per cent of them fall within 40° of the paleoequator and 73 per cent within 30°. This is similar to the distribution of modern shallow water carbonate deposition.

§ **9.11 Dolomite** (Figures 9.36 to 9.46 and 9.52). Dolomite occurs most frequently in the late Precambrian and Lower Paleozoic but rarely in the Mesozoic and Tertiary. Precambrian occurrences are not considered here. Of the 79 localities listed 56 are in the Lower Paleozoic, 12 in the Upper Paleozoic, 10 in the Mesozoic, and 1 in the Tertiary. The present latitude distribution is asymmetrical with respect to the equator, the major group having a peak at 60° N, with a subsidiary southerly group from the Australian Cambrian. The paleolatitudes are roughly centered about the paleoequator, with 95 per cent of values less than 30°. Since dolomite is a replacement deposit, after limestone, it is to be expected that the paleolatitudes should follow those found for carbonates generally. The usefulness of dolomite as a climatic indicator is rendered uncertain because of the possibility of a long time gap between the deposition of the initial limestone and its subsequent dolomitization, but studies of recent sediments in the Persian Gulf indicate that the change occurs soon after deposition (Wells, 1962; Curtis, Evans, Kinsman, and Shearman, 1963).

§ **9.12   Corals** Considering the American, European, and African land masses there is

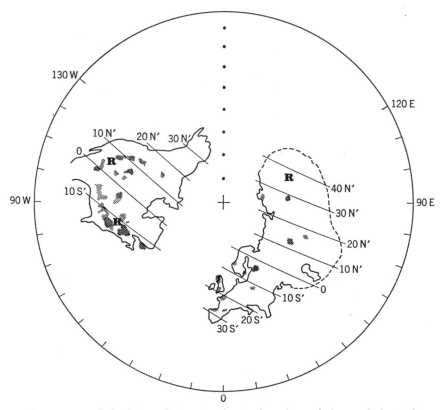

Figure 9.45. Ordovician. See p. 204 for explanations of the symbols used.

a broad northerly trend in the distribution of corals working backward in time. The trends for the Americas and Europe-Africa are similar; the mean is roughly 0.13°/m.y., similar to the change in the position of the paleoequator deduced from the paleomagnetic results from these regions (Figure 9.50).

Spectral analysis has been carried out for one group of corals only—the Ordovician fauna, using the compilation of Hill (1950). The fauna are divided into four groups, named after characteristic types. They occur predominantly in northern Europe, and in the north and east of North America. Out of a total of 54 localities there are only 9 for which paleolatitudes cannot be estimated because of the absence of paleomagnetic data: one locality in Tasmania, one in Bear Island, and 7 in Greenland and the Arctic archipelago of Canada. The present

latitudes of the remainder, making up 85 per cent of Hill's localities, lie between 30° and 70° N. In marked contrast over 90 per cent of the paleolatitudes are within 20° of the paleoequator, southerly values predominating (Figure 9.53).

§ 9.13 **Organic Reefs** The latitude distribution of modern coral reefs is roughly symmetrical about the equator (Figure 9.54). Most occurrences are in latitudes of less than 30°, and there are about 75 per cent in latitudes of less than 20°. The maximum frequency is between 10° and 20°, and there is a noticeable decrease within 10° of the equator. This may be due to the muddiness of equatorial coastal waters derived from the large rivers of this zone.

Considering the land sector between 160° W and 70° E (that is, Europe, Africa, and the Americas), a feature of the distribu-

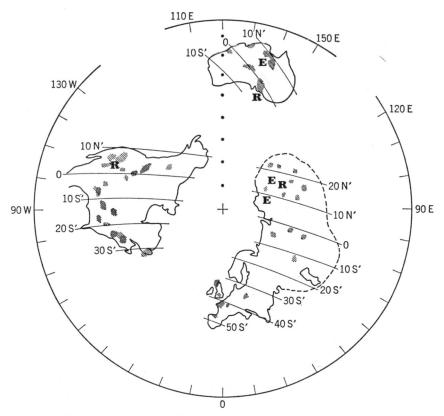

Figure 9.46. Cambrian. See pp. 204 and 205 for explanations of the position of Australia and the symbols used.

tion of fossil reefs is that, working backward in time, they occur progressively further northward. This trend for longitude 40° E is shown schematically in Figure 9.55. In the Asian-Australasian sector (longitudes 70° to 160° E) the distribution with time does not show a comparable trend. For example, in Australia in the Silurian, Devonian, and *Lower* Carboniferous, extensive reef development occurred between the present latitudes of 15° to 40° S; furthermore reefs are absent in the *Upper* Carboniferous and do not reappear until the Tertiary (Hill, 1957; Teichert, 1952). There is a sharp contrast with the northerly trend for longitude 40° E.

For the spectral analysis three examples are given followed by a more general treatment. The distribution of Niagaran (Middle Silurian) reef areas in North America

is given in Figure 9.56. Numerous reefs have been identified in the Great Lakes region, and in northern and eastern Canada there are many areas in which reefs occur. The present latitudes range from 37° to 57° N with localities still farther north in Cornwallis Island (75° N). In contrast the paleolatitudes are between 2° N′ and 13° S′.

In the second example, Devonian reefs are plotted in Figure 9.57, together with their present and paleolatitude distribution. Extensive reefs occur in North America but no Devonian paleomagnetic results fulfill the minimum reliability criteria and comparisons cannot yet be made. The present latitude distributions in Australia and Eurasia are very different. In Australia the range is broadly similar to that of present-day corals, although the most southerly locality in Victoria is over 10° farther south

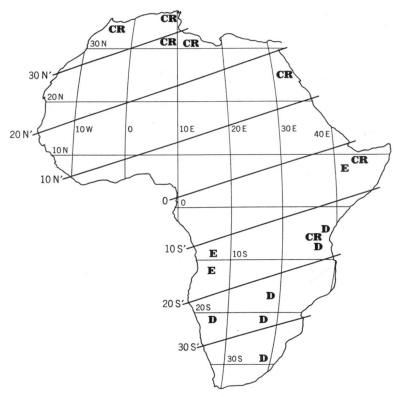

Figure 9.47. Paleolatitude of Africa in the late Triassic to Lower Jurassic. Present latitudes and longitudes are in faint line, paleolatitudes in heavy line. **D** desert sandstones (Du Toit, 1937), **CR** Jurassic and Triassic coral reefs (Hill, 1957), **E** evaporites (Lotze, 1957).

than the southern tip of the Great Barrier Reef; but there is no gross contrast. In Europe and Russia, however, the range is from about 40° N to over 72° N in Novaya Zemblya. The paleolatitudes are lower in all localities, markedly so in the European cases, less so in the Australian. Only one occurrence, from Central Siberia, has a paleolatitude in excess of 30°, and this value is only 32° N'.

In the third example the time variations of reef occurrence in eastern Australia are plotted side-by-side with paleolatitude (Figure 9.58). In the Silurian, Devonian, and Lower Carboniferous there are many coral reefs, but none has been found in the Upper Carboniferous, Permian, Mesozoic, or Lower Tertiary, and they do not reappear until the commencement of the Great Barrier Reef in late Tertiary time. The comparison with paleolatitude inferred from the paleomagnetic data is good, the periods of low latitude corresponding to periods of reef development, and the periods of high latitude to periods in which coral reefs are absent. Particularly striking is the correlation of the paleolatitude transition with the cutoff of reefs in the middle Carboniferous.

The general latitude distributions of Silurian, Upper Paleozoic, and Mesozoic coral reefs are compiled in Figure 9.54. The present latitudes range from 40° S to 80° N. There is a high concentration between 30° and 60° N, with a comparatively low frequency (25 per cent) in the latitudes in which modern corals occur; in contrast over 90 per cent of the paleolatitudes fall within this range. This is a more general statement of the effects noted in the foregoing examples; namely, that at the time of organic reef formation in Europe, North America, and Australia, these regions were situated in low paleolatitudes.

§ **9.14   Archeocyathinae**   These fossils played the role of reef builders in the Lower Cambrian. They occur in Siberia, North America and Australia, and, less commonly, in Europe. Their present latitudes range from 70° N to 40° S (Figures 9.59 and 9.60).

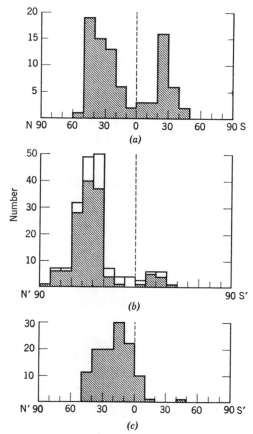

Figure 9.48. Equal-angle latitude histograms for evaporites. (*a*) Latitude distribution of areas of modern evaporite deposition. Compiled from Lotze (1957, Figure 32) using this weighting procedure: unit weight has been given to each isolated area, and for the larger areas, such as say the Gobi Desert, unit weight has been given to each intersection on a 2 mm grid placed over Lotze's map. (*b*) Present latitude of all listed fossil evaporites, shaded portions are those for which paleomagnetic control is available. (*c*) Paleolatitude. Based mainly on Irving and Briden (1962).

The paleolatitudes of the Siberian, North American, and Australian occurrences form a single group with over 80 per cent lying within 20° of the paleoequator. This is in marked contrast to their present latitude distribution in which only one value (from northern Australia) lies within the latitude range of modern coral reefs. The occur-

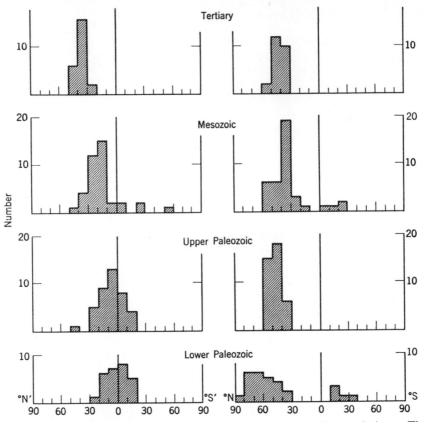

Figure 9.49. Equal-angle latitude histograms of evaporites showing time variations. The right-hand histograms give present latitude, the left-hand ones give paleolatitudes.

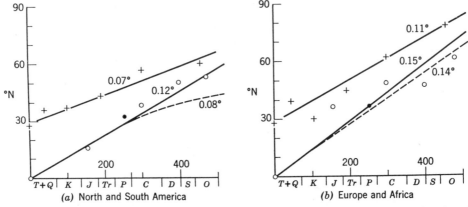

Figure 9.50. The mean latitude of evaporites (crosses) and corals (circles) for the Americas and Europe and Africa. Straight lines are drawn through the coral and evaporite values; the dotted line gives the position of the paleoequator with respect to the present frame. The coral results have been obtained by averaging, for certain groups of periods, the present latitude of the fossil occurrences recorded on the maps given by Hill (1948, 1950, 1957, 1958a). The evaporite results have been obtained similarly, using the distribution maps of Lotze (1957). Each line is labeled with the appropriate mean slope in degrees per m.y. The horizontal scale is the Holmes B Time Scale (Holmes, 1960). Redrawn from Blackett (1961), with the kind permission of the Royal Society and P. M. S. Blackett.

rences in Spain, Poland, and France (and also, it would appear, in Sardinia) lie in intermediate southerly latitudes isolated from the main group.

§ **9.15   Permian Fusulinids** Eventually it should be possible to study the paleo-latitude spectra of individual fossil genera, families, or larger groups. Some results on the distribution of the Archeocyathinae have just been given, and study of the latitude distribution of certain Permian fusulinids is now described as an example of what could, in principle, be done for many groups. This group is chosen because its distribution is thought to be temperature controlled (Stehli, 1957); they are regarded as typically warm water forms. Stehli (1957) has given compilations of the distribution of

fusulinid groups which provide an excellent basis for this study, since they give not only the locations which have yielded fossils, but also the location of Permian marine beds in which they are not known to occur; this latter information is important for testing whether or not observed effects arise from inadequacies in the geological or paleomagnetic record.

The localities for which there is paleomagnetic control are marked in Figure 9.61. Localities in other regions are marked in Figure 10.12. Considering present latitudes, there is a northward termination to the occurrences between 50° and 60°, and Stehli argues that this is probably the boundary between subtropical and temperate marine temperature zones "roughly coincident with the 15°C winter isotherm of the Permian."

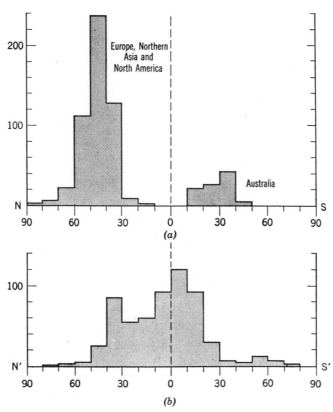

Figure 9.51. Equal-angle latitude histograms of carbonate deposits of North America, Europe, U.S.S.R., and Australia combined. (*a*) Present latitude; (*b*) paleolatitude. Compiled from Briden and Irving (1964), who list the sources from which the occurrences have been compiled.

He points out that this boundary is parallel to the present equator, and concludes that this is consistent with the assumption that the geographical pole in the Permian was approximately in its present position, and is "not in accord with the data derived from the remanent magnetism of rocks" since the Permian pole derived from paleomagnetic results from North America lay in what is *now* eastern Asia, close to the abundant fusulinid faunas of China and Japan. Bain (1958) disagrees with Stehli's conclusions, arguing that the fusulinid distribution could equally well be contained within a wide belt of sinusoidal form, whose zero is displaced northwards from the present equator. He obtains a pole position displaced from the present pole but different from that given by the paleomagnetic evidence, from Europe and North America.

The paleolatitudes are plotted in Figure 9.62. The estimated paleolatitudes of Permian marine beds range from 20° S′ to 25° N′ for North America, 0° to 50° N′ for Europe and northern Asia, and from 60° to 80° S′ for Australia; considered irrespective of whether north or south, and apart from a hiatus between 50° and 60°, the range of paleolatitudes is from 0° to 80°—so that it is not unlikely that a reasonably representative sample of Permian localities has been obtained. The present latitude distribution lies roughly between 30° and 60° N. The paleolatitudes of the North American occurrences are chiefly between 20° S′ and 10° N′, and there are 4 marine localities with

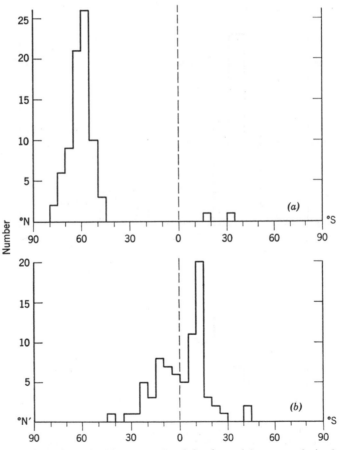

Figure 9.52. Equal-angle latitude histogram for dolomites; (*a*) present latitude, (*b*) paleolatitude. From Briden and Irving (1964).

no fusulinids. In Europe the paleolatitudes range from 0° to 30° N′, with several barren localities. In northern Siberia, barren localities occur between 30° and 50° N′. In Australia, where numerous marine Permian localities occur, no representatives of these groups were recorded by Stehli. The cumulative picture shows a close grouping of paleolatitudes around the paleoequator with only one occurrence more than 30° away. The paleolatitudes of the barren marine localities have a much wider range, suggesting that the restriction of the paleolatitudes to low values is a real effect not due to inadequacies of

the record. These results are consistent with the view that the fusulinids were tropical forms. There is no inconsistency between the available paleomagnetic results and the fusulinid distribution when observations from the *same* region are considered. As already noted, there is an apparent inconsistency between the abundant occurrences in China and Japan and the paleomagnetic poles from North America, but this arises between observations from *different* regions. Paleomagnetic data, and the pole positions and paleolatitudes derived from them, refer *only* to the regions from which the rocks

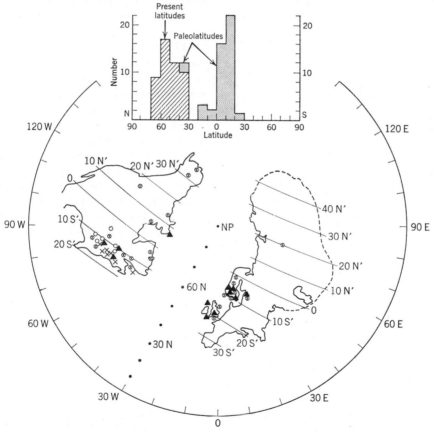

Figure 9.53. Present and paleolatitudes of Ordovician corals. Distributions from Hill (1950). Crosses indicate occurrences of *Lichenaria* fauna (Middle Ordovician); circles the *Lambeophyllum-Tetradium* fauna (Middle Ordovician); triangles the Trenton *Streptelasma* fauna (Middle Ordovician); circles with crosses indicate occurrences of the Richmond *Meliolitid* fauna (Upper Ordovician). North America and Europe and Siberia are given in their present relative positions on a polar equal-area projection. In the histogram present latitude distribution is shaded and paleolatitude stippled.

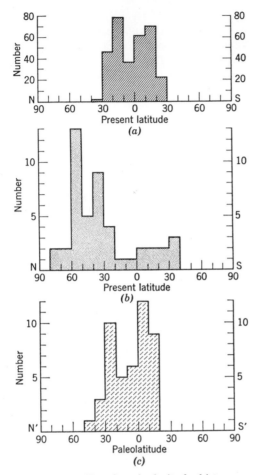

Figure 9.54. Equal-angle latitude histograms for organic reefs. (*a*) Present latitude of modern coral reefs, compiled from map of Termier and Termier (1952), (*b*) present latitude of fossil reefs, (*c*) paleolatitude of fossil reefs. Fossil reef occurrences compiled mainly from Hill (1957, 1958*b*).

were collected for magnetic study. The paleolatitudes of the fusulinids of east Asia will remain unknown until reliable paleomagnetic results from Permian rocks of this region are described. It might be noted that recent results from China [7.58, 59] indicate a low paleolatitude for the Chinese fusulinid occurrences which is entirely consistent with the results in Figure 9.62; however the data do not fulfill the minimum reliability criteria and require confirmation by more detailed studies.

§ **9.16   Red Beds** Red beds are marked in a general fashion on Figures 9.36 to 9.46. The latitude histograms in Figure 9.63 have been compiled from a list of 64 occurrences which, although far from complete, is considered representative, since the major ones are included. Some late Precambrian red beds (6 occurrences) are included, the paleolatitude estimates being made directly from the observed mean inclination. In addition there are 17 Lower and 26 Upper Paleozoic values, 12 Mesozoic and 4 Tertiary. The present latitude distribution is wide, midnortherly latitude entries being the most numerous. The paleolatitudes are low 88 per cent of values being less than 30°.

§ **9.17   Coal** The major occurrences, including brown coals and lignites, are marked on Figures 9.36 to 9.46. To show latitude distributions equal-area histograms have been used, there being some advantages in this procedure when, as with coals, values occur in all latitudes. The histogram of present latitudes of those occurrences (134 in all) for which paleolatitudes may be estimated shows a marked peak at 48° N (Figure 9.64*b*). The latitude histogram of deposits from all continents (as shown in Figure 9.64*a*) has the same general form, which is

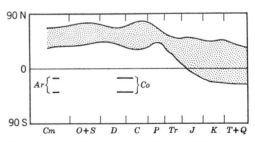

Figure 9.55. The present latitude distribution of fossil reefs in longitude 40° E (Schwarzbach, 1961*a*). The latitude ranges of the Cambrian Archeocyathid reefs (*Ar*) and the Devonian and Lower Carboniferous coral reefs (*Co*) of Australia, for the approximate longitude 140° E, are added for comparison. The normal symbols are used for the geological periods—the Ordovician and Silurian being lumped together.

similar to, but rather more marked than, the present latitude frequency of land distribution. The occurrence of coal appears to be related to land distribution and there is no relationship between present latitude and geological age, such as there is in many other indicators, for instance, in organic reefs (Figure 9.55) and evaporites (Figures 9.49 and 9.50). Thus Carboniferous coals occur extensively in Europe and the U.S.A. at present latitudes of about 45° to 50° N, whereas Mesozoic and Tertiary coals and lignites in the Cretaceous of Canada and the Jurassic of Siberia occur in similar or higher latitudes.

The paleolatitudes fall into two broad groups: the Carboniferous coals, of which the majority fall in paleolatitudes of less than 30°, and the Permian and later coals which mainly fall in latitudes higher than this. This is a statistical effect, so that a few Permian and later occurrences (for example, the lower Permian coals of Autun, France) are in low paleolatitude, but by and large the grouping is clear. The two groups

are tentatively delineated in Figure 9.65. The Permian *Glossopteris* flora coals of Australia and the Permian Angara flora of southern Siberia are both in intermediate or high paleolatitudes; these floras have some elements (notably *Gangamopteris*) in common. There are as yet no paleomagnetic results from the Permian coal measures of Africa and India to check whether or not the *Glossopteris* flora of these regions is also associated with high paleolatitudes. Mesozoic and Lower Tertiary coals give predominantly intermediate or high paleolatitudes, for example, the extensive Cretaceous coals of Canada, the Triassic of Australia, the vast Lower Tertiary deposits of Australia, and the Jurassic coals of Siberia.

Coal forms where the accumulation of vegetation exceeds its removal or decay. These regions are the hot rain forests where, although decay is rapid, growth rates are high, and in cool places where, although growth may be less rapid, decay is inhibited by cold winters. The change from low paleolatitude

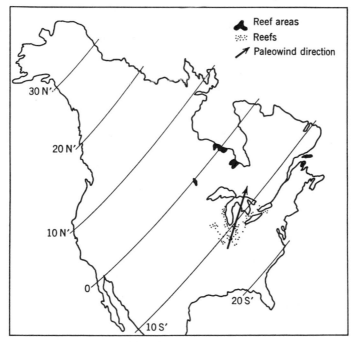

Figure 9.56. The distribution of Niagaran reefs in North America. Distribution is redrawn from Lowenstam (1957). The approximate paleowind direction is also from Lowenstam. The paleolatitudes are estimated from Upper Silurian paleomagnetic results.

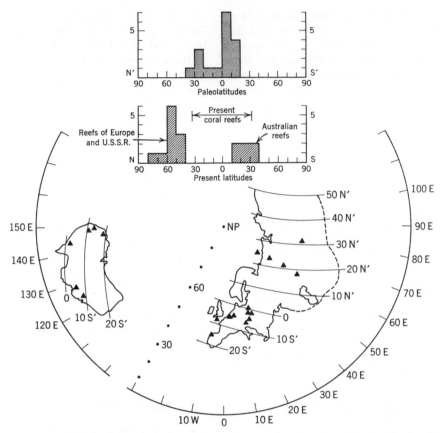

Figure 9.57. Present and paleolatitudes of Devonian coral reefs. Localities marked as triangles are from Hill (1957). Arbitrary longitudes. The projection is polar equal-area, the latitude scale to be reckoned south for Australia, and north for Europe. The present longitudes are numbered in the relevant sectors.

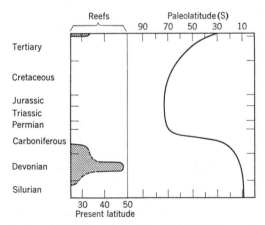

Figure 9.58. Comparison of reef development and paleolatitude in eastern Australia. The reef development is plotted as a function of present latitude on the left [from Teichert (1952)]. Paleolatitude variations for Grafton (eastern Australia) on right.

coal in the Carboniferous to intermediate and high poleolatitude coal in Permian and later time may, therefore, reflect a change in the balance of these two environments **during** the late Carboniferous and Permian. This may arise from organic evolution, or from changes in paleoclimate or land distribution. The reality of the change may find support in the fact that many Carboniferous coals are associated with trees without rings, whereas ringed trees are common in most Permian and later coal measures. Furthermore, the locations of this latter group are consistent with present conditions, since nowadays peat is rare in the equatorial regions, but abundant in latitudes of 50° to 70° N. Finally, the frequency minimum at roughly 25°, which separates the two distributions, corresponds remarkably well with the present arid zone (Figures 9.3 and 9.73a) in which coal formation would be most unlikely. The comparative absence of values between 12° and 30° is good evidence for supposing that since the later Paleozoic there has been a persistent arid zone between these latitudes, but it does not preclude the possibility of extensions of this zone into higher or lower latitudes at particular times.

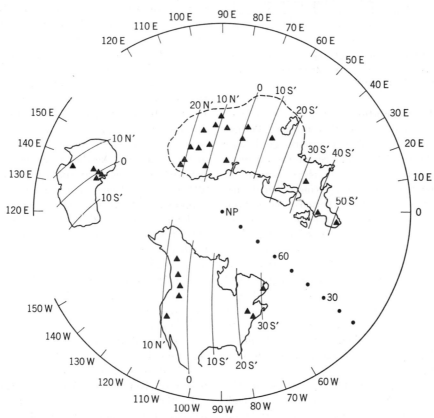

Figure 9.59. The distribution of Archeocyathinae (triangles). North America, Australia, and the Europe–northern Asian region are plotted on a polar equal-area projection in arbitrary longitudes. Longitude scales marked in the appropriate sectors. Relative present latitudinal positions are correct; the latitude scale to be reckoned south for Australia and north for other regions. The distribution of Archeocyathinae is plotted in generalized fashion from a reference list compiled by Professor A. D. Brown of the Australian National University, and I am very grateful to him for allowing me to use this list.

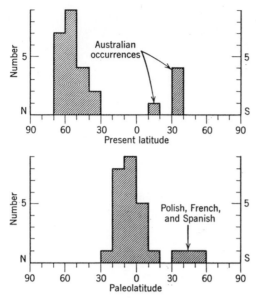

Figure 9.60. Equal-angle latitude histograms for **27** Archeocyathinae occurrences; (*a*) present, (*b*) paleolatitude.

§ 9.18 Glaciations

Paleomagnetic evidence related to the Precambrian, Permo-Carboniferous, and Quaternary glaciations is available. The evidence for the existence of extensive glaciers at these periods in some parts of the world is considered strong. Glaciations at other periods have been mooted, because of the presence of boulder beds once thought to be tillite, but now attributed to origins other than glacial activity. For example, the Upper Paleozoic Squantum "Tillite" was regarded as glacial by Sayles (1914, 1916), but Dott (1961), after detailed study and review, shows that it has "so many features in common with well-established subaqueous gravity-massflow deposits" that a glacial origin is now very unlikely.

Quaternary. Low-level glaciation in the Quaternary occurred predominantly in high or intermediate latitudes. The correlation of low level glaciation with high to intermediate paleolatitude is shown by the *glaciation index* in which the proportion of total land to that covered by ice is expressed as a percentage (Figure 9.66). A similar analysis, relative to present latitude, would

yield the same result. There is a sharp cut-off between 40° and 45° N', and above 70° N' virtually all land was covered sometime during the Quaternary. A similar analysis for the southern hemisphere Quaternary glaciation is not possible, because of the general absence of land in the critical latitudes between 45° and 65° S'.

Late Paleozoic Glaciations. The Carboniferous and Permian sequences of South America, Antarctica, Africa, India, and Australia contain evidence of glaciation. The occurrences range from within 5° of the south geographic pole in Antarctica (Long, 1962) to 34° N in India (Wadia, 1953). Beds deposited in this time range in Europe and North America, in regions often closely antipolar to the glacial occurrences, contain organic reefs, desert sandstones, and evaporites, indicative of warm climate. Explanations for this asymmetry may be considered in terms of three hypotheses. (1) Asymmetrical climate: it may be supposed that the Earth's climate was grossly asymmetrical relative to the equator, allowing the development of ice sheets in low latitudes, while at the same time the climate in the northern hemisphere was comparatively mild (Brooks, 1949). (2) Polar-wandering: it may be supposed that the glaciations were confined to high or intermediate latitudes, as in the Quaternary glaciation, and that during the Carboniferous and Permian the pole moved a great deal, occupying positions successively nearer to each of the southern continents. (3) Continental drift: it may be supposed that during the Upper Carboniferous and Permian, India and the southern continents were arranged around and close to the south pole, and have since moved, relative to the pole and to each other, into their present positions (Köppen and Wegener, 1924).

If the first hypothesis is correct, the paleomagnetic poles from all places should agree with one another and with the present pole. If the second is correct, large variations should be observed *within* the Upper Carboniferous and Permian in each region, and all traces of pole paths should coincide. On the third hypothesis there should be little variation within the Upper Carboniferous and Permian in each region, the paleolatitudes should be high or intermediate, and the poles for different regions should disagree. At the present time this rather decisive test cannot be applied in full, since paleomagnetic results from the sequences containing glacial evidences are as yet available only from Australia. There are some very preliminary results from Africa and South America but none from Antarctica and India. Although the paleomagnetic study of these Gondwana glacial sequences has barely been initiated its potential importance to paleogeographic problems is great, and for this reason the available results are set out in some detail.

The paleomagnetic work in Australia was carried out in the standard sections (Table 9.2). Beds of supposed glacial origin which occur at several levels interbedded with normal marine and freshwater sediments con-

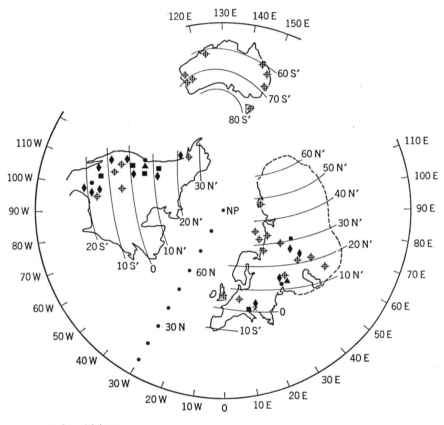

× Sumatrininae
▲ Verbeekininae
■ Neoschwagerininae
◆ Parafusulina, Triticites, Polydiexodina, Pseudoschwagerina, and Rugofusulina
● Ozawainella, Reichelina, Rauserella, and Dunbarula
⊕ All groups absent from Permian marine outcrops

Figure 9.61. Permian marine localities with and without fusulinids. The localities of certain fusulinid groups and the localities of marine outcrops without fusulinids are marked from Stehli (1957) on equal-area paleolatitude maps. North America and the Europe–northern Asian land mass are in their correct relative positions. Australia is in the correct latitude but arbitrary longitude. Latitude scale to be reckoned south for Australia and north for other regions.

Table 9.2   Rock Groups in the "Glacial" Sequences in New South Wales. *Groups containing levels with glacial evidence have an asterisk. Appendix numbers to paleomagnetic work are given.*

Narrabeen Series [8.28]	Lower Triassic
Upper Coal Measures	
Upper Marine Series * [7.42]	
Lower Coal Measures	Permian
Lower Marine Series * [7.43]	
Upper Kuttung * [6.58, 59]	Upper Carboniferous
Lower Kuttung [6.60]	Lower Carboniferous (Viséan?)

suggests that "there is now no evidence of Dinantian glaciation anywhere in the southern hemisphere." In sections where fossil control is good, he suggests that glaciation began in the late Namurian or early Westphalian and continued into the Stephanian. Further glacial levels occur in the Lower and Upper Marine Series, and these are tentatively considered to be the time equivalents in part of the Sakmarian, Artinskian,

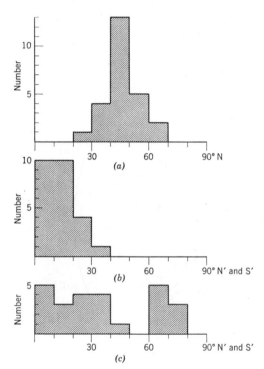

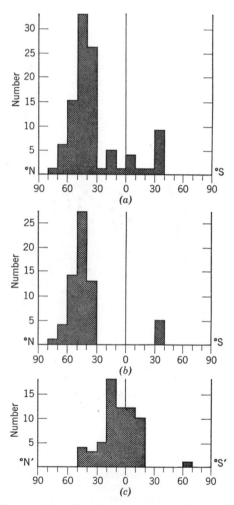

Figure 9.62. Equal-angle latitude histograms for Permian marine localities with and without fusulinids (a) Present latitudes of localities with fusulinids ($N = 25$), (b) paleolatitudes of localities with fusulinids, (c) paleolatitudes of barren localities. The values in (b) and (c) are plotted irrespective of whether in the northern or southern hemisphere.

Figure 9.63. Equal-angle latitude histograms for red beds ($N = 64$). (a) Representative values from all continents (present latitude); (b) present latitude of those for which paleomagnetic control is available; (c) paleolatitudes. Simplified from Briden and Irving (1964).

taining coals. A glacial level in the Lower Kuttung (Lower Carboniferous) was indicated by David and Sussmilch (1931); however, on the basis of subsequent study, and review of previous work, Campbell (1962)

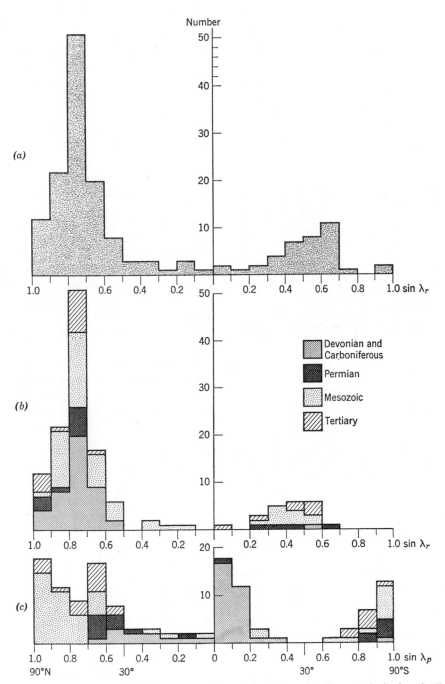

Figure 9.64. Equal-area latitude histograms of coal deposits. (*a*) Present latitude of all coals in a representative list; (*b*) present latitude of coals for which there is paleomagnetic control; (*c*) paleolatitudes. From Briden and Irving (1964).

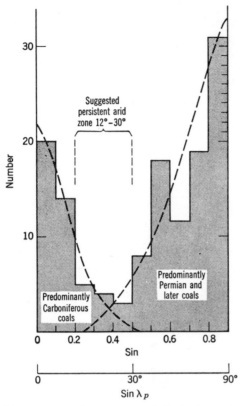

Figure 9.65. Equal-area paleolatitude histogram of coal deposits. Values plotted irrespective of sign. The dashed line gives the tentative division into two time groups centered near the equator and poles respectively. From Briden and Irving (1964).

from the glacial varvoids themselves in the Main Glacial Stage of the Upper Kuttung and from the volcanics in both Marine Series. The directions of the stable remanence are in good agreement with steep positive inclinations. The glacial occurrences lie between 17° and 43° S present latitude, whereas their paleolatitudes range from 59° to 80° S' (Figure 9.67). The comparison with the Quaternary glaciation index is noteworthy (Figure 9.66). A further notable point is that Compston (1960) has recorded a paleotemperature of 6°C from a level 20 ft above a tillite in Western Australia. The directions of ice flow relative to the ancient meridians (Figure 9.67) show a general northerly tendency, the average being N'40° W'. This evidence is consistent with the hypothesis (3) above, and with the view that the late Paleozoic glaciation in Australia arose because this region was at that time near to the southern geographic pole.

Precambrian Glaciations. There are paleomagnetic results related to the glaciations which are thought to have occurred in the late Precambrian of Europe and Greenland,

and possibly the Kungurian (David, 1950), but correlations with the standard Russian section are difficult because of faunal differences. Radiometric ages for levels in the Upper Marine gave 250 m.y., or Middle to Upper Permian on Kulp's 1961 Time Scale (Evernden and Richards, 1962). It appears probable, therefore, that glacial activity recurred throughout much of the Upper Carboniferous and Lower and Middle Permian, covering a period of time of the order of 50 m.y. Glacial activity was not constant but occurred at separated periods. Interbedded marine beds and marine "tillites" occur, indicating that the glaciated areas were near sea level.

Paleomagnetic results have been obtained

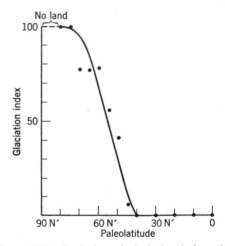

Figure 9.66. Variation of glaciation index with paleolatitude for the northern hemisphere Quaternary glaciation. The ratio, expressed as a percentage, of the total land distance along lines of paleolatitude to that covered by low level ice at some time during the Quaternary.

and in the middle Precambrian of the Canadian Shield; these occurrences are in regions glaciated in the Quaternary. No results are yet available relevant to the Precambrian glacial occurrences in Africa and Australia.

Samples from late Precambrian sequences in Norway and western Greenland give low inclinations, indicative of low paleolatitudes varying from 10° to 40° S′ for the European occurrences, and 0° to 5° S′ for the Greenland beds (Figure 9.68). Harland and Bidgood (1959) suggest the possibility of a

widespread glaciation of exceptional severity extending over much of the Earth in the late Precambrian, and state that "it is probable that marine tillites were formed near the equator in late Precambrian time." But it should be noted that their paleomagnetic results are based on only a few widely scattered directions (the circular standard deviation in both cases being about 30°) as yet unchecked by magnetic or thermal cleaning. Therefore, until results of high reliability are available it seems wise to regard this as a speculation of potential interest requir-

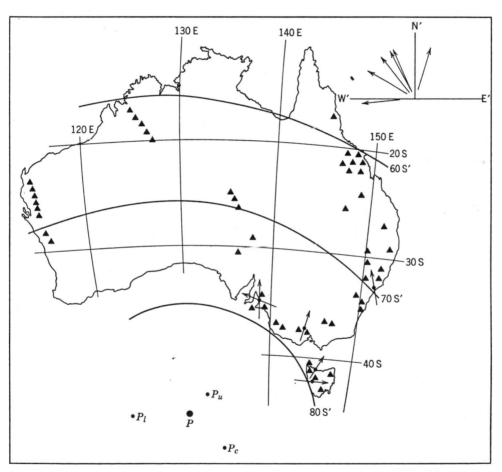

Figure 9.67. Paleolatitude of Australia during the late Paleozoic glaciation. Glacial occurrences (triangles) and directions of ice movement inferred from striated pavements are from David (1950) and Banks and Ahmed (1962). The direction of ice movement relative to the paleomeridian (N′) are plotted at the top right. P_c, P_l, P_u are the poles for the Upper Kuttung sediments, Lower Marine Basalt, and Upper Marine Latites, respectively, which do not differ significantly from one another; P is the mean of these, and the paleolatitudes are drawn with respect to this mean pole.

ing confirmation or rejection by further work.

The Huronian of Canada contains evidence of glaciation (middle Precambrian Gonganda Formation [Coleman, 1926]). The paleomagnetism of the nearby Sudbury Nickel Irruptive has been studied, and this is thought to have been emplaced within the period 1800–1200 m.y., a time range also associated with Huronian sedimentation. A tentative comparison therefore appears in order, although it is highly desirable to get results from the glacial beds themselves. The estimated paleolatitude of 65° to 68° N′ for these occurrences is to be regarded as provisional.

§ 9.19   Paleotemperatures and Paleolatitudes in the Cretaceous

Urey, Lowenstam, Epstein, and McKinney (1951) have shown that estimates of absolute paleotemperature may be made from measurements of the relative abundance of the oxygen isotopes O^{18} and O^{16} in the calcium carbonate of shelly fossils. By comparing paleotemperatures from fossil localities with the paleolatitude of these localities, the variation of temperature with latitude in the geological past may be studied; in particular, it is of much importance to compare the nonglacial or normal climatic regime under which the latitude gradient is supposed to have been small, with the present-day glacial regime (§ 9.05). Of most interest in this context are paleotemperatures from the interval of supposed normal climate from Jurassic to Lower Tertiary, and from the Permo-Carboniferous glacial period. Except for one result already mentioned from the Permian of Australia (§ 9.18) there are no reliable values prior to the Jurassic. There are only a few results from the Lower Tertiary and Jurassic, but data of high quality are available from the Cretaceous, and for this reason the comparisons made here are confined to these.

These values are not, of course, direct measures of past temperatures, but are estimates subject to certain assumptions which have received detailed study (see, for example, Epstein and Lowenstam, 1953; Lowenstam and Epstein, 1954). In the absence of secondary effects the $O^{18}:O^{16}$ ratio is related to the temperature of the equilibrium reaction in which the animal extracts calcium carbonate from the sea water and deposits it in its skeleton. On the basis of certain calibration experiments performed in

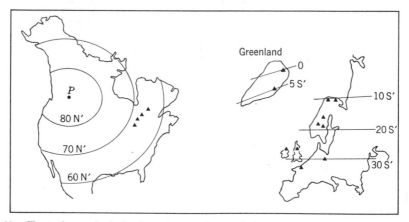

Figure **9.68.**   Tentative paleolatitudes of some Precambrian glacial occurrences. On the left the Huronian glacial occurrences of Canada are marked together with paleolatitudes from the paleomagnetic studies of the Sudbury Irruptive [1.49]. On the right the late Precambrian glacial occurrences in Greenland and Europe are taken from Schwarzbach (1961*b*); paleolatitudes for Europe are from paleomagnetic studies of the Norway Sparagmites [1.04] and those of Greenland from the Tillite Formation [1.56].

controlled conditions, and of reasonable assumptions about the isotopic composition of ancient sea water, it is possible to estimate paleotemperatures from the measured $O^{18}:O^{16}$ abundances. Subsequent recrystallization or secondary deposition of calcium carbonate distorts the record. Such secondary effects tend to give values which are higher than the true paleotemperature. Further uncertainties are: that additions to the skeleton did not occur during the full temperature range of its environment so that a biased value is obtained; that deposition was selective with respect to the isotopes; and that the animal was migratory so that the record may have been transported from some other place. Yet despite these uncertainties in an individual datum, the repeatability of values from different specimens from the same locality (usually better than 2°C in those cases where detailed and careful work has been carried out), the agreement among different localities of the same age, and the broad similarity in the time variations found within the Cretaceous in the U.S.A. and Europe, indicate that a true temperature record is obtained.

Not all results are of equal value. Belemnite guards give the most consistent results; the detailed variation shown by their "annular" banding is reminiscent of seasonal temperature changes and is an impressive test of reliability (Urey and others, 1951). Brachiopod and oyster shells seem often but not always to give values 5°C or so higher than those for belemnites, and this is thought to arise from secondary changes (Lowenstam and Epstein, 1954). Therefore the following comparisons are confined to results from Cretaceous belemnites, which form a homogeneous group, yielding data of high internal consistency. The values are plotted against present latitude and paleolatitude in Figure 9.69. Where work at one locality has been repeated the latest values are used. Not all published data are included, the selection being made according to these numerical criteria: only those results are used in which there are two or

more observations at a locality, and in which the range of values did not exceed 5°C. This range was chosen since it embraces the annular variations through a belemnite guard and which is therefore taken to be a reasonable estimate of the seasonal variations to be expected. Variations greatly in excess of this may be due to secondary effects or to migrations—both undesirable. Most values obtained in this way (31 out of 37) are from the detailed and critical researches of Lowenstam and Epstein.

The values from Europe (14° to 24°C) have a similar range to those from the U.S.A. (16° to 23°C), although the present latitude of the collecting localities differs by about 20°. The range in each is due to a systematic time change, so that the values at any stage within the Cretaceous are remarkably constant. A single locality in Greenland (76° N) gave values within the same range, suggestive of a mild climate in high latitudes, but values from two localities in Australia (21° to 28° S) gave rather lower values, which was unexpected in view of their present climates.

The grouping becomes different when paleotemperatures are plotted against paleolatitude. The results from Europe and U.S.A., formerly separated, are now a single group, confined for the most part between 30° and 40° N'. The agreement is very impressive when results from a single stage are considered, and as an example the temperatures from Maestrichtian belemnites are given in Figure 9.70. The generally lower Australian paleotemperatures are in intermediate to high paleolatitudes. The Greenland result at an estimated 45° N' is close to the main European and North American group. (There are no Cretaceous paleomagnetic results for Greenland but the poles for Europe and North America are near together and it therefore seems legitimate to use these; they give paleolatitudes for the collecting locality of 48° and 43° N' and the mean is used.) The somewhat paradoxical condition arises that evidence for a mild climate in high latitudes in the Cretaceous is not to be sought for in Greenland, but in Australia.

On the basis of present facts it is tentatively suggested that the good agreement between the paleotemperature results from Europe, the U.S.A., and Greenland, is to be correlated with the similarity in the paleolatitudes of the collecting sites, the range of paleolatitude (irrespective of sign) studied so far in the Cretaceous (30° to 62°) being less than the present latitude spread of lo-

calities (21° to 76°). The Maestrichtian values of 16° to 19°C at paleolatitudes of between 31° and 42° N′ is comparable to the present mean surface temperature of the oceans in such latitudes, but sea temperatures of 14° to 16°C in paleolatitudes of about 60° S′ observed from Australian fossils are much higher than those encountered in comparable latitudes today, even in the favored Gulf Stream.

These comparisons serve to indicate criti-

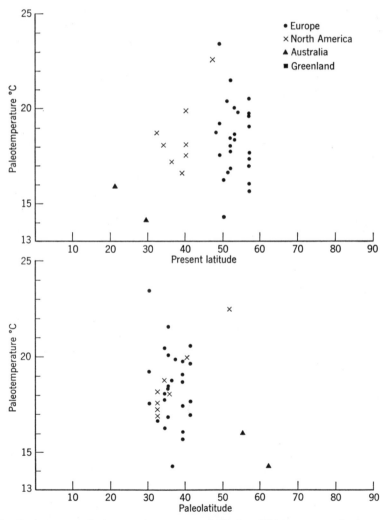

Figure 9.69. Cretaceous paleotemperatures versus latitude. Thirty-seven paleotemperature estimates from Cretaceous belemnites are plotted against present latitude (upper) and paleolatitude (lower). No distinction is made between northern and southern hemisphere values. The values have been abstracted from these originals: Urey and others, 1951; Lowenstam and Epstein, 1954, 1959; Dorman and Gill, 1959a; Bowen, 1961.

cal problems for future study. It would seem that paleotemperatures from the Cretaceous faunas of Alaska, NW Canada, and Australia are critical for high latitude studies. An investigation of the Cretaceous paleolatitude gradient across North America northwestward from Florida should provide critical data. Results from lower paleolatitudes (less than 30°) are also needed—from the Caribbean and Mediterranean regions. These, together with similar studies of Jurassic and Lower Tertiary fossils, should provide data of crucial importance to the hypothesis of a geocentric axial dipole field and for the question of the latitude versus temperature gradient in nonglacial periods.

§ 9.20 Desert Sandstones and Paleowind Directions Wind direction is governed to some extent by the Earth's rota-tion, so that a relation between the wind directions in the geological past and the paleomagnetic results may be expected if the magnetic and spin axes have coincided. Studies of their relationship are therefore relevant to this assumption and to paleogeography. Paleowind directions may be inferred from cross stratification in dune-bedded sandstones, from the detritus distribution around islands, and from directional growth due to heliotropism in fossil skeletons—for instance in stromatoliths (Vologdin, 1961).

Sand is swept up the back slope of dunes and comes to rest on the lee or slip face at the angle of repose for dry sand, which ranges up to 33° (Bagnold, 1941). The cross stratifications observed in aeolian sandstones are considered to be the remnants of successive slip faces of advancing

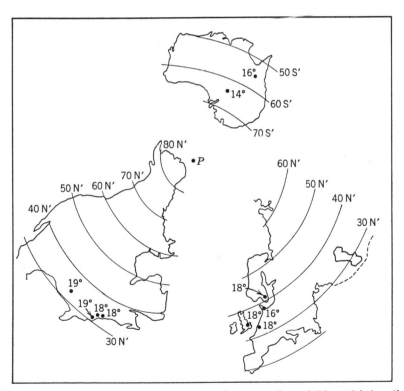

Figure 9.70. Lower Cretaceous paleotemperatures for Australia and Maestrichtian (late Upper Cretaceous) paleotemperatures from North America and Europe. The continents are arranged so that the Cretaceous paleomagnetic poles *P* for each region coincide—the "north" pole for Europe and North America and "south" pole for Australia.

dunes. Thus the average direction of the dip of such faces observed through a sedimentary member may be expected to give the average direction of sand transport, and therefore of the wind under whose influence the beds were laid down. The variation in individual observations is determined by the variation in dune shape and in wind direction. Broad uniformity of average directions are sometimes observed over a wide area and through thick sequences, and this, coupled with the aridity required for the accumulation of desert sandstones, has lead many geologists to suggest conditions of deposition similar to those characteristically found in the modern deserts of the trade wind belt. Perhaps the best example of such broad consistency is that found in late Paleozoic and early Mesozoic aeolian sandstones in the western U.S.A., a region now well north of the trade wind zone; on an average the dune beds dip to the south, indicating that the wind blew from north to south (Figure 9.71). Poole (1957) suggests a northerly extension of the trade wind zone at that time. Another possibility is that the region was in a lower latitude and has since rotated clockwise relative to the meridian. An informative procedure, which serves as a test for these ideas, is to compare the occurrences against the paleolatitudes and paleomeridian directions estimated from the paleomagnetic evidence (Opdyke and Runcorn, 1960; Opdyke, 1961*b*).

Taking a simple view, the trade winds now may be thought of as blowing toward the equator from regions of high barometric pressure at latitudes of about 30°, and being deflected by the Coriolis force which imparts a westerly component. A consistent regime of this type is found in the Pacific, in the Atlantic, in Africa north of the Sahara, and in the south Indian Ocean. Regional variability in the distribution and intensities of low and high pressure areas causes much variability; for instance, in Brazil, and the north Indian Ocean in the northern summer, the prevailing winds blow away from the equator. At the poleward limit of the trades there is a change to a westerly direction, usually between latitudes of 30° and 40°. This is called the *wheel round* and is well marked in the NE Sahara, being mirrored there by the direction of modern dune movement. Therefore when comparing paleowind directions and paleomeridians no perfectly consistent geometrical relationship is to be anticipated; the most that can be expected is that the relationships are within the range of variability encountered today. In the following descriptions the inferred mean direction of sand transport, and thus of the paleowind, is specified either by the angle ∂ relative to the present meridian and which is enclosed by the compass points N and E indicating that the directions are reckoned E of present true north, or by the angle ∂_p relative to the paleomeridian enclosed in the ancient compass points N' and E' (Figure 9.2).

The number of sandstone formations which are considered to be fossilized desert dunes are not numerous, but those which have been identified are often thick and widespread. Major occurrences are marked in Figures 9.36 to 9.47, 9.71, and 9.72. They do not seem to occur prior to the late Carboniferous. The longest time sequence available is in the western U.S.A., where there is a range from the Pennsylvanian through to the Tertiary, with large developments in the Permian and Jurassic. In Europe they are restricted to the Permian and Triassic, in South America and Africa to the late Triassic, but none is known from Australia.

North America (Figure 9.71). The oldest beds studied are the Casper, Tensleep, and Weber Sandstones cited by Opdyke and Runcorn (1960) to be of Permo-Pennsylvanian age. The Casper sandstone of Wyoming, in studies by Knight (1929) at 2 localities gave a mean direction of sand transport of N214° E, and by Opdyke and Runcorn (1960) at 3 localities gave a mean of N207° E; the localities are spread over a distance of about 200 km and the mean for the unit is N210° E. The Tensleep Sandstone studied at 8 localities in Wyoming spread over a distance of about 300 km gives a mean direction N200° E (Opdyke and Runcorn, 1960). The Weber Sandstone studied at 5 localities in northeastern Utah and northwestern Colorado yields an average direction of N216° E (Opdyke and Runcorn,

1960). The paleolatitudes are about 6° N′, and the angles (∂_p) made with the paleomeridian are respectively N′259° E′ (Casper), N′248° E′ (Tensleep), and N′264° E′ (Weber), with an average N′257° E′.

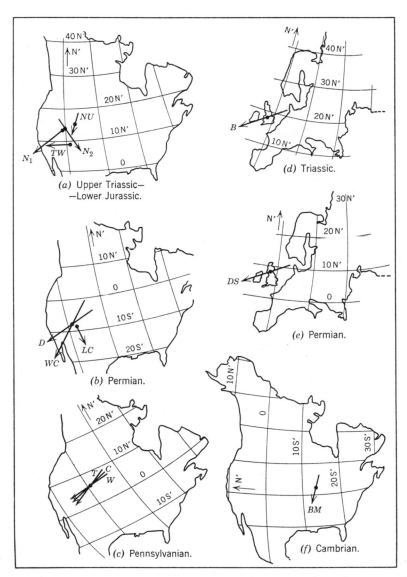

Figure 9.71. Paleowind directions in North America and Europe. Directions are indicated by bold arrows the dot on each being roughly central to the region of observation. The arrows N′ point to paleonorth. The wind directions are labeled as follows: (a) *NU* Nugget Formation, N_1 Upper Navajo (Kiersh), N_2 Middle Navajo (Kiersh), *TW* type Wingate; (b) *D* De Chelly; *WC* western Coconino, *LC*, Coconino of the Little Colorado; (c) *C* Casper, *T* Tensleep, *W* Weber; (d) *B* Bunter Sandstone; (e) *DS* Dumfries Sandstone; (f) *BM* Baraboo monadnock.

Reiche (1938) has studied the Permian De Chelly and Coconino Sandstones. Observations on the De Chelly Sandstone are from 5 localities in the Navajo and Hopi Reservations of northeastern Arizona spread over a distance of roughly 150 km; the directions are consistently to the southwest with an average N214° E. Reiche divides the localities of study of the Coconino Sandstone into two groups: first the western Coconino, which was studied at 9 localities spread widely over a distance of about 300 km in northwestern Arizona and around Flagstaff, and which gave consistent southerly directions with an average N187° E; second, the Coconino of the Little Colorado River, studied at 8 localities to the southeast of Flagstaff spread over a more restricted distance of about 50 km, and which gave scattered directions with an easterly component averaging N134° E. The paleolatitudes are about 8° S′, and the angles to the paleomeridians are, for the De Chelly N′247° E′, the western Coconino N′221° E′, and for the "Little Colorado" Coconino N′169° E′. The directions in general point away from the paleoequator.

The Glen Canyon group of Lower Jurassic age contains two sandstone units of predominantly aeolian origin: the Wingate Sandstone overlain by the Navajo Sandstone. The Wingate Sandstone (which may be of Lower Triassic age) gives a paleowind direction of N247° E for the type section in northwestern New Mexico (Reiche, 1938). The Middle and Upper Navajo Sandstone has been studied by Kiersh (1950) in the region of the San Raphael swell in central Utah over a distance of roughly 10 km. For 3 localities in the Upper Navajo, Kiersh gave a mean direction of N200° E, but an analysis of his data given by Runcorn (1961) gave N210° E. From 3 localities in the Middle Navajo, Kiersh obtained a mean direction N140° E and reanalysis gave N126° E (Runcorn, 1961). The later values are accepted here. Observations on dune bedding in the Navajo from the Navajo reservation in Arizona by Harshbarger (1949) gave mean direction N152° E (Run-

corn, 1961). The Nugget Formation, which is the equivalent of the Navajo in Wyoming, has been studied at 2 localities, giving a mean direction N186° E (Opdyke and Runcorn, 1960). Unfortunately no paleomagnetic results are available from the Jurassic of North America, and so the directions are compared with Triassic results, which contain numerous data of high reliability from Upper Triassic beds which may not be far removed in time from the Wingate and Navajo Sandstones. Such a procedure is not above criticism, and may need modification when suitable Jurassic results become available. The paleolatitudes of the above occurrences range from 8° to 15° N′. The angles to the paleomeridians are, for the type Wingate N′268° E′, the Upper Navajo of Kiersh N′235° E′, for the Middle Navajo of Kiersh N′151° E′, for the Navajo of Harshbarger N′174° E′, and for the Nugget Formation N′198° E′. Harshbarger (1949) has also studied the Upper Jurassic Entrada and Cow Springs Sandstones of Arizona, which give mean directions of N171° E and N201° E respectively (Runcorn, 1961). But comparisons with paleomagnetic results are not yet possible.

Another result of interest from the western U.S.A. is that from the Chuska Sandstone on the borders of Arizona and New Mexico (Wright, 1956); the directions are scattered, but give a mean N19° E, the values relative to the paleomeridian being the same. This direction is close to the direction of dune transport in this region nowadays. The Chuska Sandstone is considered to be Miocene (?) on the basis of physiographic evidence.

From the study of the distribution of detritus in the Middle Silurian coral reef zone of the Great Lakes area, Lowenstam (1957) has suggested that the southerly reefs "were located in the path of the southerly wind and storms." This would be the equivalent of a westerly wind at 10° S′ relative to paleolatitudes (Figure 9.56). The Baraboo Range in Wisconsin consists of hard Precambrian rocks lapped around by Paleozoic marine sediments, and it is thought to have been an island at that time in a largely unbroken shallow sea. Raasch (1958) suggests, from a study of the ancient shore features and detritus, that it is possible to delineate the lee and windward shores, and thus estimate the direction of the prevailing wind. Consistent directions are obtained and he argues that such constancy "in an open marine situation is found today chiefly in the trade wind belts." He tentatively suggests, therefore, that in Cambrian time the "Baraboo monadnock" "lay within a trade wind belt in which the prevailing wind direction was a few degrees east of north." The paleolatitude (Figure 9.71) of 13° S' is consistent with his view. The paleowind direction is a little south of (paleo) east and is consistent with a position in the southerly trades.

Europe (Figure 9.71). Estimates of paleowind directions are available from the Permian and Triassic. It appears that the best established result in the Permian is that from the Dumfries Sandstone of Scotland (Shotton, 1956) which gave a mean direction N249° E. The paleolatitude is 8° N', and the angle to the paleomeridian N'241° E', which is comparable to that of modern trade winds. Schwarzbach (1961b) quotes results from the Permian of Germany as "Rotliegendes of the Nahe basin; wind from SW; Zechstein of Central Germany: SSW to ESE" which are inconsistent with those from Britain. Triassic directions are available from the Bunter Sandstone of the English Midlands (Shotton, 1937), which are in paleolatitudes of 18° N'; the mean direction is N251° E and the direction to the paleomeridian N'231° E'.

South America (Figure 9.72). Studies by Bigarella and Salamuni (1961) following work by Almeida have yielded a pattern of directions from the Botucatú Sandstone of Brazil, and its equivalent, the Tacuarembo Sandstone, of Uruguay. This is compared with the paleolatitudes obtained from paleomagnetic results from the Serra Geral Formation which is closely related in time to the Botucatú. The paleolatitudes are not greatly different from the present latitudes;

the known extent of the Botucatú ranged from 11° to 29° S'. Working southward the directions are at first from the north and away from the paleoequator, but at a latitude of about 25° S and a paleolatitude of about 22° S' the directions swing around to westerly. This pattern is similar to the present circulation, but the comparison goes no further, since the rainfall which the present circulation brings is 100 to 250 cm, far wetter, it may be presumed, than the conditions under which the Botucatú accumulated; although the wind directions are comparable, the paleogeographic setting was probably different from that at present.

Africa (Figure 9.47). Upper Triassic terrestrial sandstones containing components of aeolian origin occur toward the top of the Karroo System. Paleowind directions are not yet available. The distribution is compared with the paleolatitudes estimated from the somewhat younger Karroo Basalts and Dolerites (late Triassic to early Jurassic) which have been studied in the same general region; their approximate range of 24° to 30° S' is not much different from their present latitude range.

Discussion. At present, dune-bedded desert sandstones occur most commonly between latitudes of 18° and 40°. Considering more generally the occurrences of modern sandy and stony deserts, these are confined within latitudes of 10° to 50° with the maximum frequency at roughly 23° (Figure 9.73). The present latitudes of fossil desert sandstones range 55° N to 35° S with maximum frequency between 30° and 60°. Their paleolatitudes are low (with the exception of the Tertiary Chuska Sandstone they are all less than 30°), and there appears to be a trend with time. The paleolatitudes of the Pennsylvanian and Permian are all less than 10°, indicating extensive dune formation nearer to the equator than at present. Mesozoic occurrences lie mainly within the range 10° to 30°, which is comparable to the present-day situation. The mean paleolatitude of the late Paleozoic occurrences is 7°, compared with 17° for the Mesozoic deposits, and roughly 23° for modern desert sands. It may be noted that the wheel round observed in the Botucatú is some 8° nearer the equator than that at present, and this is consistent with this trend.

The relationships of the paleowind and paleomeridian directions are complex. There is no general pattern of NE or SE paleo-trade winds, but there are several examples which conform to this. The variability of patterns, however, is within that observed today. Sometimes the directions point away from the paleoequator (for example, in the Botucatú (Figure 9.72) and the Coconino (Figure 9.71b) Sandstones); sometimes they point towards the equator as would be expected for trade winds (for example, the Bunter Sandstone, Figure 9.71d). Some of these complications may arise from the limited areal extent of the observations in some formations or to errors in the paleomagnetic

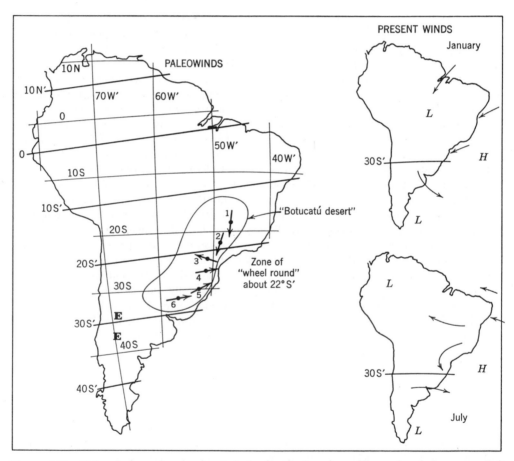

Figure 9.72. Paleowinds and present winds in South America. The paleowind arrows (left figure) are the means for observations from the Botucatú Sandstone in the states of (1) Minas Gerais, (2) São Paulo, (3) Parana, (4) Santa Catarina and (5) Rio Grande do Sul in Brazil, and (6) Uruguay; from Bigarella and Salumuni (1961). The outline of the known distribution of the aeolian sandstone is marked. The paleolatitudes are in thicker line and are derived from the work of Creer [9.36]. E indicates evaporite deposits, the occurrence in Neuquen (the more southerly) is from Harrington (1956), and the other from Cristi (1956). The two smaller maps show the present wind directions in January and July (compiled from the *Times Atlas*, 1958, vol. 1) and the centers of high (*H*) and low (*L*) pressure which control them.

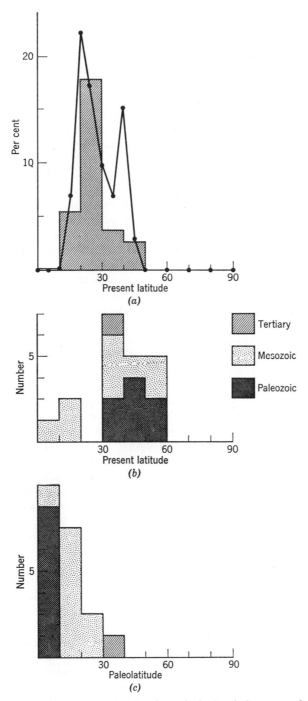

Figure 9.73. Equal-angle histograms (irrespective of sign) of desert sands. (a) Latitude of sandy and stony deserts: the shaded histogram gives the area of such deserts occurring in the given latitude interval using an arbitrary vertical scale; the dots give the proportion (expressed as per cent) occupied by such deserts to total land around every 5° line of latitude (compiled from the *Times Atlas*, 1958, vol. 1); (b) present latitudes of fossil desert sandstones listed in the text; (c) paleolatitudes of same.

239

determinations and these and other uncertainties are now considered.

§ 9.21　Discussion of Uncertainties　The comparisons made in this chapter yield three main results.

(1) Time variations of paleolatitude relative to certain land masses are broadly consistent with the paleoclimatic variations suggested by the geological evidence in the *same* region.

(2) Compilations of the paleolatitude spectra of paleoclimate indicators show that the latter are all latitude dependent. Broadly speaking, geological features, which are supposed by analogy with present conditions to be indicators of warm climate, occur in regions which at the time of their formation are estimated to have been in low paleolatitudes, and features indicative of cool or cold climate occur in intermediate or high paleolatitudes.

(3) The paleolatitude dependence of some indicators varies with time. The effect is negligible in marine deposits, and most noticeable in certain continental deposits. For example, the paleolatitudes of carbonates generally, and of the Archeocyathinae, and of organic reefs, are predominantly within the range 0° to 30°; their distribution is approximately symmetrical about the paleoequator, being similar to that of modern carbonates and reefs about the present equator. Furthermore the paleolatitudes of Permian fusulinids are predominantly within the range of 30° either side of the paleoequator where their frequency is a maximum, and this is consistent with their supposed preference for warm water. On the other hand the paleolatitudes of evaporites and desert sandstones are mostly within the range 30° either side of the paleoequator, systematically lower than the latitude of their modern equivalents; this is particularly marked in the Upper Paleozoic and less so in the Mesozoic.

If these results are correct they imply, (*a*) that the Earth's field has had the general form of an axial geocentric dipole since the Precambrian, (*b*) that the apparent

polar-wanderings, set out in § 6.10, are in fact true movements of the coupled paleomagnetic and paleogeographic poles relative to the regions of observation, and (*c*) that these regions have moved relative to one another, because the various paths of apparent polar-wandering do not agree. It is therefore necessary to ask what causes, other than real paleolatitude changes and rotations, could produce the observed effects. There are several possibilities: there are the possible errors in the paleomagnetic inclination causing errors in the paleolatitude estimates; there are the effects of the incompleteness of the record; and there is the possibility that the results arise from special circumstances in the distribution of suitable depositional environments.

The inclination in sediments may be lower than that of the applied field due to depositional and compaction effects (§ 2.12). The vital test for assessing natural effects is to compare (irrespective of sign) the directions in igneous rocks and sediments of the same general age, for igneous rocks are not subject to these effects. Excellent agreement occurs in the Permian and Triassic of Europe, and in the Triassic of North America. The question does not arise in the African, Indian, and Australian data which are derived mainly from igneous rocks or from sediments with good "igneous" control. Nevertheless many more comparisons of this type are urgently needed. It might be noted that no results have yet been reported from igneous rocks in the Paleozoic of North America, the results being based entirely on observations from red sediments.

A further source of inclination error is partial instability, due to remagnetization in the Earth's field recently or in the remote past. Effects from this source may be minimized where results are obtained by combining positive and negative polarities (§ 5.03), but in the Permian, where only the latter occur, systematic effects might be present. Although in many cases thermal and magnetic cleaning (§ 5.09) of specimens has been carried out, many more such studies are needed; for example no systematic magnetic cleaning has yet been reported from rocks from the Paleozoic of North America.

There is the further possibility that the observed paleolatitude spectra arise from incompleteness of the geological or paleomagnetic record, or to special features of past land and sea distribution. First, there is the possibility that the sample of a feature for which paleolatitude can be estimated is not representative of the feature generally. This possibility can be studied by comparing the present latitude distribution of all listed occurrences with that of the occurrences for which paleolatitude estimates have been made. This is done for evaporites and coals (Figures 9.48 and 9.64) and in these the two distributions are very similar, suggesting that the occurrences used are representative.

Second, it may be argued that, since the paleolatitudes of Europe and the U.S.A. were low during the Paleozoic and early Mesozoic, then low latitude spectra must inevitably be obtained. Furthermore, one may say that the occurrence of particular sediments and fossils in Europe and the U.S.A. merely indicates that the correct depositional setting was present, and that this may be connected with local physiography rather than with climate. What then is the frequency of these sedimentary and fossil types in regions of high paleolatitude? The places and times for which relevant information is at present available are Siberia (Permian to Cretaceous, Figures 9.38 to 9.41), Australia (Upper Carboniferous to Cretaceous, Figures 9.38 to 9.42), and western Canada (Cretaceous, Figure 9.38). It is useful therefore to recall some of the results from these critical paleolatitudes.

In the Permian and Mesozoic of Siberia, there appear to be no recorded organic reefs, desert sandstones, or evaporites. Limestone deposits are much less extensive than farther west, in Europe. It seems unlikely that this is due to the absence of suitable depositional settings since thick deposits of these ages, both of continental and shallow water marine origin, occur, for example, in the Velui Basin.

In Australia, in the periods Upper Carboniferous to Cretaceous no organic reefs are known (Figure 9.58). Carbonates are generally rare, the limited red beds that occur in the Lower Triassic (Narrabeen Chocolate Shales) may be partly tuffaceous in origin (David, 1950), and evaporites are represented only by a very small accumulation of gypsum in the Cretaceous of central Australia. It is most unlikely that this absence of features is due to the absence of suitable depositional settings, for the Great Artesian Basin (and others of smaller extent) is one of the largest basins in the world that received shallow water marine and terrestrial sediments through much of the Mesozoic. Yet in the recorded geology there are no thick evaporites, few limestones, no desert sandstones, and no organic reefs, such as occur abundantly in the Mesozoic sequences of Europe and North America which nowadays are in similar or higher latitudes. It would be a coincidence if this absence were not somehow related to the estimated high paleolatitude.

Finally, the extensive Cretaceous deposits of western Canada are made up largely of terrigenous sediments, with no recorded major limestones, no red beds, evaporites, or organic reefs.

Recalling two detailed points and referring first to the distribution of the Permian fusulinids (Figure 9.61), the correlation in northern Siberia and Australia of Permian marine deposits barren of these fossils with intermediate or high paleolatitude, and the correlation of localities which have yielded fusulinids with low paleolatitudes suggests that there is a real latitude effect. Second, the very good agreement between Cretaceous paleotemperature values in similar paleolatitudes indicates the reliability of the paleomagnetically determined paleolatitudes.

Thus, there is a great deal of circumstantial evidence in favor of the view that the paleolatitude histograms describe, at least in approximate fashion, the paleolatitude spectra of the geological features in question. The results of the comparisons set out in this chapter are all consistent with the view that the Earth's field has on average had the form of an axial dipole since the Precambrian. If this is correct then several points relating to the paleoclimatic zonation of the Earth arise.

§ **9.22**   **Paleoclimatic Zones**   When sufficient results are forthcoming it ought to be possible to build up a record, period by period, of the paleolatitude distribution of each paleoclimatic indicator, and thus to surmise the time variations in paleoclimatic zones. The results available at present are set out in schematic fashion in Figure 9.74. This is intended only as a crude model and will doubtless require modification in the future. The points of note are: the low latitude distribution of carbonates, the high paleolatitudes of post-Carboniferous coals, and the low, often near equatorial values for late

Paleozoic and early Mesozoic evaporites and desert sandstones.

The evidence suggests that there have always been latitude-dependent climatic zones. That there has always been a persistent arid zone in the latitudes 12° to 30° is suggested by the evidence from coals (§ 9.17). In the Maestrichtian (Cretaceous), marine paleo-temperatures of 16° to 19°C in paleolatitudes of 31° to 42° are comparable with present temperatures, but values of 14° to 16°C at paleolatitudes of 60° are much higher than at present, and this is consistent with the previously stated view (§ 9.05) that in nonglacial periods the paleolatitude versus temperature gradient is much less than at present.

The time differences that occur in spectra from the terrestrial occurrences may reflect changes in past land distribution, which have

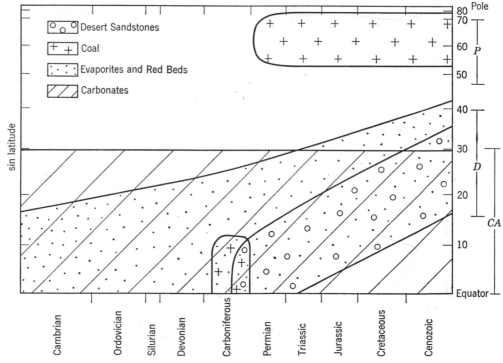

Figure 9.74. Highly schematic and speculative representation of the variation through time of the paleolatitudes of certain sediments. Only the largest formations are taken into account. On the right the range of some present-day counterparts is marked; desert sands (*D*), shallow marine carbonates (*CA*) and peat (*P*). Red beds and evaporites are grouped together, because their distributions are very similar at this level of generality. Based on the speculations of Briden and Irving (1964).

progressively influenced the development of arid and semi-arid belts. In the Lower Carboniferous and earlier Paleozoic the land masses of Europe, northern Asia, Australia, and North America were in low paleolatitudes. Other land masses may also have shared this low paleolatitude, but this will only become clear as more paleomagnetic results are obtained. This large area of land favored the development of dry conditions. For western Europe and North America this situation persisted into the later Paleozoic: red beds, desert sandstones, and evaporites were laid down on land, and marine red beds and carbonate rocks were deposited in the peripheral seas. In the later Paleozoic, eastern Siberia and Australia were in intermediate and high paleolatitudes, and this continued into the Mesozoic. In the Mesozoic in western Europe and North America the paleolatitude increased slowly; evaporites, red beds, carbonates and desert sandstones are abundant at first, but diminish in frequency later. Such is the broad and highly generalized picture which emerges from the data at present available.

§ 9.23 The Axial Geocentric Dipole Model

The hypothesis that, when viewed from the Earth's surface and averaged over periods of several thousand years, the paleogeomagnetic field has been that of an axial geocentric dipole is a fundamental concept in paleomagnetic work, and in several places in this book tests have been made to check its applicability. Essentially this model is that devised by Gilbert in 1600 (§ 3.4). Tests for the model arise from different approaches, some being concerned with the internal consistency of the paleomagnetic data itself, and others with the correspondence of paleomagnetic results with those from other scientific fields. Information at present available is consistent with the model being broadly correct since the middle of Paleozoic time and perhaps also for earlier periods. But at this comparatively early stage in the development of paleomagnetic work it is clear that more evidence is needed before the matter can be dealt with in an entirely satisfactory way. The tests are now summarized.

(1) The mean directions in rock units laid down in the last 7000 years or so, and whose individual time spans were about 2000 years or more, are accurately aligned along the axial geocentric dipole field direction. This is also true for rock units deposited during the past few million years, and with less accuracy, but usually within the permissible statistical errors, for rock units ranging back into the Upper Tertiary (§ 6.02). Thus the hypothesis is accurately correct for the recent past, and broadly correct for the past 20 m.y. or so.

(2) The field, as viewed from regions of continental extent, in periods ranging back to the middle of the Paleozoic, is consistent with that of a geocentric dipole; that is, the scatter of paleomagnetic poles obtained from different rock units belonging to the same system in the same land mass is small, and comparable to that observed for the later Cenozoic (Figure 6.6).

(3) The variation with paleolatitude of the dispersion in rock units (that found between observations from different collecting sites in the same rock unit (§ 4.06)) is consistent with that obtained from a latitude versus dispersion analysis of the 1945 field (§ 3.7). Both paleomagnetic and geomagnetic dispersions may be explained by supposing that they arise from an axial geocentric dipole field perturbed by randomly directed components (§ 3.8). The ratios (F_d/F_o) of the magnitude of the perturbing field to the steady dipole field at the equator are 0.38 and 0.396 respectively, which is very good agreement (§ 6.12).

(4) The fourth test (Wilson, 1961) is to study the intensity of the paleogeomagnetic field as a function of paleolatitude, since if the field were dipolar the intensity should vary as equation (3.1). As yet there is no substantial evidence relating to this important matter.

(5) The rate of change in the paleomagnetic directions since the Carboniferous observed in Australia, is roughly one half that observed in Europe and North America, and

this is consistent with the field being a geocentric dipole, since in the former case the change is from steep to intermediate inclinations, and in the latter from low to intermediate inclinations (§ 6.08).

(6) The paleolatitude changes calculated for observing regions on the assumption of an axial geocentric dipole field are broadly consistent with the paleoclimatic changes inferred for these regions and this supports the assumption made.

(7) The paleolatitude spectra of various paleoclimatic indicators are all latitude dependent and this is consistent with the hypothesis of an axial geocentric dipole field.

(8) Finally the study of paleotemperatures (determined from oxygen isotopes) as a function of paleolatitude determined paleomagnetically on the basis of the axial geocentric dipole hypothesis, yields a test of great power. Although at present the information available is not great, the concurrence of Maastrichtian (Cretaceous) paleotemperatures obtained from localities in similar paleolatitudes in North America and Europe illustrates the usefulness of this approach, and points the way to important developments in the study of the variations in the Earth's temperature regime in the geological past.

CHAPTER TEN

Special topics

In this chapter the applications of paleomagnetism to certain problems in geology and geophysics are set out. The items are of a miscellaneous nature indicating the state of flux of these studies. They cover a wide field, including structural geology, stratigraphy, paleogeography, the origin of certain deposits, the detection of changes in the Earth's radius and the question of the magnetic fields in extraterrestrial bodies. The basic assumption made in most of these applications is that paleomagnetic results provide reliable indicators of the paleogeomagnetic field, just as in the applications of paleontology to geological problems, it is assumed that fossils provide a record of past life. For the most part the descriptions are made in terms of examples, which are to be regarded as illustrations of the various applications and not proven cases of general significance.

10A APPLICATIONS TO STRUCTURAL PROBLEMS

§ **10A.1 General Statement** Some application to structural problems on a sub-continental scale are set out here, the application to tectonics on a larger scale being considered later (§ 10B). The principle is that structural deformation may be expected to affect the directions of fossil magnetism, and a study of these should yield information about the form and timing of such deformations. Relative movement of parts will show itself in the observed magnitude of the dispersion of directions. The total movement undergone may be measured if information regarding the undeformed state is available. The latter step may not be vital for the practical problem in hand, but it is preferable to be able to refer to control observation on rocks which have not been deformed, as the following example illustrates.

§ **10A.2 Detection of Broken Ground** (Jaeger and Green, 1958; McDougall and Green, 1958) Steep slopes are often covered with talus which moves slowly downhill. In some circumstances it may be important to know the depth to the *in situ* bedrock. It may not be possible, because of vegetation cover, to establish this by direct mapping, and in such cases the slope is usually drilled, and an attempt made to estimate the depth of talus from core, taking into account such features as bedding, rock type, degree of weathering, etc. If this should fail then the remanent magnetism may be studied with profit.

The example is from the Western Tiers of Tasmania (Figure 10.1). The Hydro-electric Commission of Tasmania was anxious to construct a tunnel through the Tiers to carry water for power generation and it was important to ensure that the tunnel was in undisturbed bedrock. The Tiers consist of dolerite resting on sediment. The direction of NRM of the dolerite *in situ* in the immediate area of the Tiers, and in its outcrop over much of Tasmania, was previously known to have a steep inclination, on average about 5° from vertical [9.30]. Drilling yields core of fresh homogenous dolerite, and normal methods of study show no changes such as may be interpreted as indicating the boundary between talus and rock *in situ*. But magnetic study yields a sharp change. Nearby vertical magnetizations occur throughout the length of hole 5086 sited near the summit of the Tiers. Other cores, farther down the slope, have scattered low inclinations becoming steep and uniform at depth; the transition is sharp, and can be recognized to an accuracy of a few feet. The parent dolerite at the crest has strong vertical jointing, and when left unsupported laterally, breaks away into columns, which move down the steep slope and come to rest subhorizon-tally producing flat inclinations. Over much of the slope the depth of broken ground is about 200 ft and tunneling must therefore be carried out below this level.

§ 10A.3   Variable Attitude of Layers

Within a rock unit there is often much variability in the attitude of bedding planes in sediments, or in the planes of layering in igneous rocks, and a question which often confronts a geologist is—were these planes originally variable, or were they originally horizontal? In the former case the NRM, if acquired at the time of formation, should be uniform in direction; in the latter case the directions will be scattered by the same amount as the scatter of poles of the bedding (or layering) surfaces.

The first example taken is from the work of Hood (1961) and Sopher (1963) on the Sudbury Nickel Irruptive [1.46–49; 1.87, 88]. This body, which has an apparent thickness of 1 to 2 miles, consists of an inner layer of micropegmatite separated by a transition zone from an outer layer of norite (Figure 10.2). The outcrop is roughly oval and encloses the Whitewater volcanics and sediments. The long sides of the oval are referred to as the North and South Ranges. The dips are variable but are generally in-

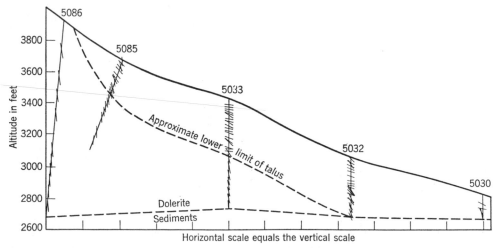

Figure 10.1. Inclination of NRM in bore core in a talus slope. The drill holes are vertical or steeply inclined. The angle which the direction makes with the hole is shown by short line. The approximate lower limit of talus is marked. Redrawn from McDougall and Green (1958), with the kind permission of Stephen Austin and Sons, Hertford, and the authors.

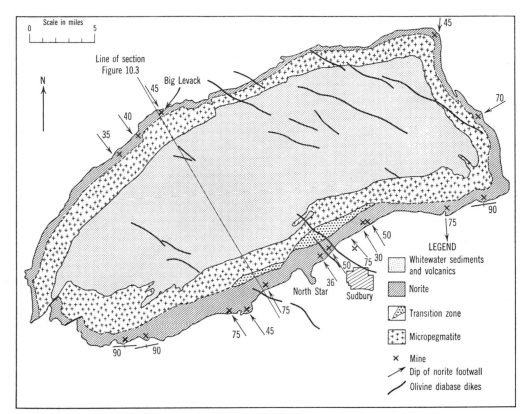

Figure 10.2. Geological sketch map of the Sudbury Nickel Irruptive. Redrawn with simplifications from Sopher (1963), with the kind permission of the Director of the Geological Survey of Canada, and the author.

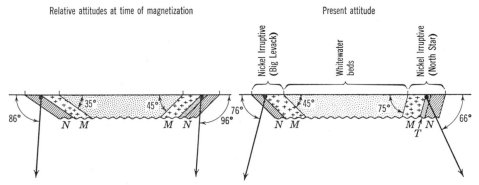

Figure 10.3. Schematic sections through the Subury Nickel Irruptive. The line of section is shown in Figure 10.2. *M* is micropegmatite, *N* norite, and *T* the transition zone. The arrows show the mean directions of magnetization. Compiled from Sopher (1963).

ward, the North Range values being about 30° less than those in the South Range. The origin of the attitude is in dispute, and without attempting a full review it is convenient to recognize two extreme hypotheses: the first (*A*) assumes that the irruptive was an originally flat volcanic or sill-like body which has since been deformed, and the second (*B*) assumes that body was emplaced in its present configuration. The mean remanence directions are in the plane (line of section, Figure 10.2) perpendicular to the strike, the divergence between the Ranges being about 40°—a factor 3 less than the divergence in dip. Thus, at the time of magnetization the angle between the irruptive in the North and South Ranges was about 80° (Figure 10.3). This result may be interpreted as follows: (1) that the remanence is secondary—an originally horizontal body being deformed to give an 80° angle between Ranges, then magnetized, and then deformed again to produce the present angular difference of 120°; (2) that the remanence is primary, and that there was an original 80° angular difference between Ranges, subsequent deformation increasing this to 120° without affecting the remanence. It would be natural to relate the secondary magnetization in (1) to the phase of dike intrusion (Figure 10.2) which may have been accompanied by general heating, but Sopher shows [1.89] that the mean remanence direction in these dikes (260, −2; $a_{95} = 11°$) is parallel to that in norite baked by them (256, 0; $a_{95} = 11°$) so that the magnetization of the main irruptive body almost certainly predated the phase of dike intrusion. The observed divergences *in situ* show that hypothesis *B* is inadequate, but the magnitude of the divergence is too small for hypothesis *A* unless it is assumed that the magnetization is secondary. Hypothesis *A* cannot be entirely discounted until the magnetization is shown to be primary which has not yet been done. A compromise suggested by Sopher is that the body was initially an asymmetrical funnel-shaped intrusion and that "post-irruptive slumping and folding towards the interior of the basin resulted in the present attitudes." Although

paleomagnetism has not, as yet, provided a decisive answer it does give useful information that complements geological observations.

The method may also apply where the variability of planes is much less than in the above example. In a sedimentary body some variability of dip generally occurs, amounting to 10° or so, even in the most regular sequence. It may be of interest to know whether this was depositional or whether it arose from subsequent tilting or differential compaction. If the body is well exposed the answer will generally be clear from field observation, but if it is not, it may be impossible to decide. A comparison of the dispersion of paleomagnetic directions, corrected first to the individual bedding plane at each level, and then to some common plane (say the present horizontal or the average bedding plane) should yield a solution; if the dispersion is least in the first case then it appears that the variability is tectonic, and vice versa. No results related to this problem are yet available.

A similar problem sometimes arises in intrusives. In cases where the country rock is dipping it is uncertain whether tilting occurred after injection or prior to it. Relevant results are available from the Great Whin Sill [7.15]. This is intruded into tilted Carboniferous sediments whose dips are low (generally less than 10°) and variable. The directions of NRM *in situ* are rather less scattered than when corrected for the bedding of adjacent sediments, indicating that intrusion occurred after tilting of the sediments. Such information about the relative order of events may assist the field geologist.

Finally, there is the question of the original dip of lava flows. Modern lavas may solidify on slopes ranging up to 10° or 20° or more, and in older sequences, in the absence of interbedded sediments or such features as half-filled vesicles, it is difficult to decide whether the dips of planes between flows are original or tectonic. Some relevant results have been obtained from the Tertiary lavas of Skye [11.012]. The lavas at The Storr, in Trotternish, have a westerly dip of 14°. The mean direction of 21 igneous units *in situ* is 191, −62, and after correction for the westerly dip this becomes 162, −62. At Oisgill Bay, 35 km to the west, the mean direction from 6 level igneous units is 190, −62, no different from that *in situ* at The Storr. Thus the inference that the flow dips at The Storr are original, is strong. This concurs with the views of geologists based on independent evidence, and makes clear the potential usefulness of paleomagnetic methods in cases where the geological evidence is less definitive.

§ 10A.4 Detection of Relative Rotations about Vertical Axes

Paleomagnetic directions are sometimes out of line with the characteristic directions found in rocks of similar age in the same general region. This may be due to rotations relative to the main body of the region, such as may have occurred in once mobile belts within a now consolidated continental framework, or in areas currently mobile and situated between or on the borders of more stable blocks. The criterion by which such rotations may be recognized is that the divergence should affect the declination but not inclination. The method depends on the accuracy with which the declination is measured. In general $\delta D = a_{95} \sec I_m$, so that when the inclination is steep the declination is poorly defined. The method may be used to test for rotations postulated on geological grounds, and especially to study the origin of the curvature of orogenic belts. The descriptions in the following two sections relate to this interesting question which is now briefly outlined.

Many workers, for example J. T. Wilson (1954), believe that this curvature is of *primary* origin. His ideas are an extension of the contraction theory of mountain building developed by Jeffreys (1959) which supposes that in a cooling Earth the outer 70 km is in compression resulting from shrinkage of the deeper parts. Failure in this outer shell may occur in conical zones (Scheiddeger, 1958) which have arcuate surface traces marking the sites of geosynclines and subsequent mountain chains.

Carey (1958), on the other hand, suggests that the curvature is *secondary* and arises from bending in plan at a late stage in the history of the geosyncline. These bends he calls *oroclines* and the larger oroclines he thinks arise from continental drift—for example, the great bend in the Alaskan Range is thought to have arisen as a result of the moving apart of North America and Europe.

§ 10A.5 Siletz River Volcanics

Two divergent results are available from the Eocene of North America—from the Green River Formation of Colorado (Torreson, Murphy, and J. W. Graham, 1949 [11.101]) and the Siletz River Volcanics (Cox, 1957 [11.098]). The divergence could be due to a clockwise rotation of part of western Oregon. If this rotation did in fact occur, then it seems likely that it happened prior to the extrusion of the Columbia River basalts which give directions aligned roughly on a north-south axis, so that the time limits to the rotation are middle Eocene to Miocene. Working independently, and using geological evidence only, Carey sites an orocline, the Mendocino orocline, in this region (Figure 10.4). He contends that this was once approximately straight, and if this is correct the region from which the samples of Siletz lava have been obtained has rotated approximately 63° clockwise. Reversing this rotation brings the paleomagnetic direction (declination now 7° ± 12) into line with true north and with the directions from Colorado. Although further checks are needed the paleomagnetic evidence as it is known at present is consistent with Carey's view as to the structural history of this region.

§ 10A.6 Bending of Japan

(Kawai, Ito, and Kume, 1961) The mean declinations of NRM from the southwest and northeast trending arms of the Japanese arc differ by 58° (Table 10.1), to be compared with the present angle of 57° between the axes (AA', BB') of the arms (Figure 10.5). The mean directions for Cenozoic rocks are in good agreement in both declination and inclination. These authors attribute this divergence "to the deformation of the Japanese

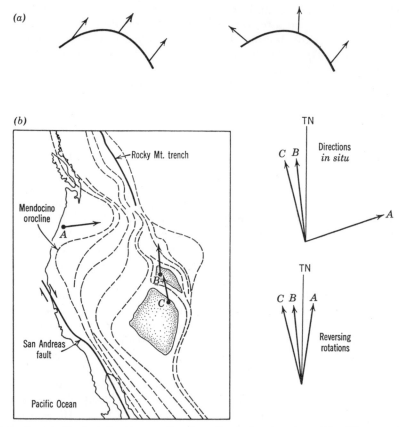

Figure 10.4. In (a) the test for the orocline hypothesis is set out, and in (b) a possible application of this test is given (see text). In (a) the heavy line represents the plan of a bent orogen—on the left the paleomagnetic criterion for disproving the hypothesis is indicated, and on the right the criterion for its corroboration. Also, in (a) the direction A is derived from work on the Siletz River Volcanics and the directions B and C from studies of the Green River Formation.

Islands." They point to the vulcanism and high seismicity of the *fossa magna*, and the occurrences of high density material in the sector to the south, suggesting that this is "a mass of basic rocks intruded into the fracture zone which resulted from the bending of the Japanese Islands along this line." They consider that the movement occurred in "early Tertiary times." The reason for the difference of 21° between the inclinations is obscure, since it is not to be expected that bending would be accompanied by much relative latitudinal movement. Carey had previously postulated bending of Japan on tectonic evidence, and his reconstruction

gives good agreement for the pre-Tertiary declinations.

Divergences from the present meridian

Table 10.1 Comparison of Directions in the Two Arms of Japan. *Computed from data of Kawai, Ito, and Kume (1961).*

	NE Arm	SW Arm
Cenozoic [9.21, 22]	10, +50	9, +50
Late Paleozoic to Mesozoic [11.060, 061]	332, +61	30, +47

occur in Cenozoic rocks in the region of the *fossa magna*, suggesting that movements along this line occurred during the later Cenozoic, and may be still continuing. For example, Ito (1963) has recorded declinations in 5 plutonic bodies in the *fossa magna* ranging from 20° E to 31° W, and he attributes this scatter to relative rotations since emplacement [11.118–123]. Secondly, in the Pliocene, easterly declinations occur over widely scattered localities [11.067, 068], but in the Pliocene Enrei Formation from the Suwa Lake region the mean declination is westerly [11.077]. Third, Quaternary rocks in the Yamaguchi Prefecture [12.37] have declinations along the present meridian, whereas the Quaternary rocks of the North Izu and Hakone volcanic region yield a declination of 343° [12.38]. The Enrei Formation and the North Izu and Hakone volcanics are both situated in the unstable zone of the *fossa magna* (Figure 10.5).

§ **10A.7 Lewis Thrust** (Norris and Black, 1961) The Lewis thrust in the Canadian Rockies was formed during the Laramide orogeny. Its surface trace has a variable direction (Figure 10.6). Beginning in the north the trend is at first north-south, and then in the region of the North Kootenay Pass there is a swing to the southeast. The origin of this change is uncertain; it may be due to differential erosion, or rotation of the thrust plate. Paleomagnetic results are available from 3 localities in the Kintla Formation (Precambrian) which can be mapped without interruption throughout the plate. Reversals occur, but irrespective of sign, the declinations of the means at each locality are the same within the statistical errors. The inclinations are also in good agreement. If the trend change at the North Kootenay Pass were due to differential rotation, declination differences of about 35° would be expected. The authors conclude that the observed structural and stratigraphic continuity within the sheet, together with the agreement in declinations "suggest that the plate moved as a single coherent, tectonic unit," and, that "it ap-

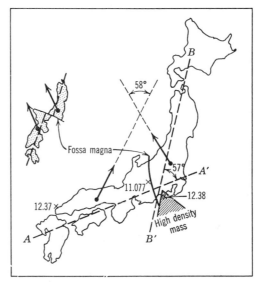

Figure 10.5. The supposed bending of Japan. The arrows give the mean declinations of NRM of rocks of pre-Tertiary age in the SW and NE arms of the arc. The lines *AA'*, *BB'* are the axes of these arms. On the left the Japanese arc after the reversal of deformations proposed by Carey (1958) is given. The crosses indicate sampling localities 12.37 Yamaguchi Basalts, 11.077 Enrei Formation, 12.38 North Izu and Hakone volcanics.

pears, therefore, that the Clark and Lewis Ranges were always structurally farther east than the Flathead Ranges."

§ **10A.8 The Origin of the Red Sea** The main faulting associated with the Red Sea was initiated in middle Tertiary times. A depression was present during the Oligocene which deepened during the Miocene. It is likely that this depression represented an initial stage, and that the Red Sea, as it is today, was formed later. It is convenient to recognize three possible modes of formation. (1) Compressional rifting; in which it is assumed that the Red Sea is a depressed crustal segment bounded by reversed faults. (2) Tensional rifting; in which it is assumed that the Red Sea is a sunken crustal segment bounded by normal faults. (3) Dilatation of tensional faults; in which it is supposed that Arabia and

Africa moved apart, leaving between them subcrustal material, which, because of its greater density, remained at a lower level. (1) and (2) imply that Africa and Arabia have moved only a small distance (order of 1 km) relative to each other. In contrast, (3) requires relative movements of the order of 100 km. It is of some general importance to test hypothesis (3) since it is often adopted as a starting point in the development of arguments about continental drift: in these it is contended that the African Rift Valleys are the first stage of break-up, the Red Sea the second, and the Atlantic or Indian Oceans the third stage in which dilatation has been long continued.

Some help has been provided by gravity and aeromagnetic observations (Girdler, 1958), but such results provide evidence about the present situation only. The need is for an historical study, by means of which the magnitude of the past relative movements may be estimated, and paleomagnetism is a possibility. The Red Sea depression, and its continuation into the Jordan Valley, pinches out northward. Assuming dilation, a movement apart in the south of about 300 km, is reduced to zero in Syria by an anticlockwise rotation of the Arabian peninsula about some point in Syria, and the paleomagnetic directions in rocks laid down prior to this movement should show systematic divergences in declination, but not in inclination, as between Africa and the

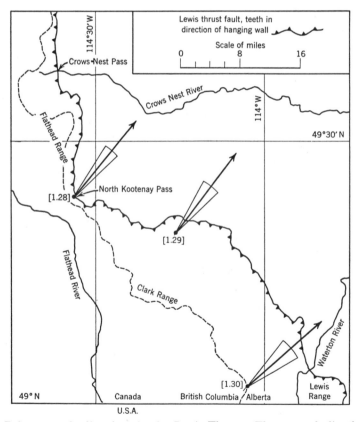

Figure 10.6. Paleomagnetic directions in the Lewis Thrust. The mean declinations at 3 localities [1.28, 1.29, and 1.30] are shown with their statistical errors respectively 7°, 10°, and 12° ($\wp = 0.05$). The dotted line is the provincial boundary between British Columbia and Alberta, and the southern edge of the sketch is the 49th parallel. Redrawn with directions added from Norris and Black (1961), with the kind permission of the Editor of *Nature* and the authors.

Arabian peninsula. No divergences will be present if no such movement has occurred. A full paleomagnetic survey of rock formations from both sides of the Red Sea will be necessary to complete the test, but results of high precision are available from the Aden Volcanics [12.42], which demonstrate its feasibility.

These volcanics show reversals, and the inclination of the mean irrespective of sign (+24.0) is the same as that of the geocentric axial dipole field (+24.4) but the declination is westerly (353 ± 4°) diverging significantly from the present meridian. The amount and sense of the divergence is right for closure of the Red Sea, assuming Africa unmoved. In Figure 10.7a the present coastlines and the meridian (45° E) through Aden are shown. The arrowed direction is the paleomagnetic meridian. In (b) the Arabian peninsula is moved, first by a rotation about a point in southern Syria, and then translated southward approximately 150 km so that the opposite coastlines of the Red Sea fit together; the paleomeridian is now parallel to the present meridian. The southwestern tip of the peninsula overrides a portion of Africa that consists of very young rocks thought to have been formed since the movement. Although the paleomagnetic results are consistent with this movement, which is similar to that required by Carey (1958), they do not, of course, prove that it did occur. There is, for example, the alternative possibility that the main field has moved relative to the Earth as a whole, or that Aden itself has rotated relative to Arabia, and to decide between these possibilities it will be necessary to obtain results from northeast Africa.

§ **10A.9   Alpine Orogenic Zone of Europe**   Studies of the Stephanian and Permian of Scotland, France, Norway, Germany, and Russia, have yielded directions of high internal consistency (§ 6.05). These results are from the "stable block" of northern Europe, the region being stable in the sense that it has not been disturbed internally by major orogenic movements since the Up-

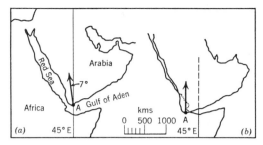

Figure 10.7.   Closure of the Red Sea.   (a) Shows the present coast lines; Aden is marked A and the arrow is the paleomeridian. In (b) the Red Sea is closed. Redrawn from Irving and Tarling (1961), with the kind permission of the American Geophysical Union.

per Carboniferous. In contrast, results from Permian rocks in the southern European zone of Tertiary deformation, although they share the same general trend, are more scattered than the directions farther north. The ages of these rocks are not known with great accuracy, but it seems probable that they are predominantly Lower Permian, and so were laid down in the interval for which uniformity occurs in northern Europe.

The declinations from the "stable block" are southerly (Figure 10.8). The inclinations are generally low and the mean deviation from the paleoisoclines calculated from the mean Permian pole for Europe is 9°. This is a measure of the deviations from the average pattern to be expected from individual results; it is comparable in magnitude to the statistical errors, and there is therefore no reason to regard them as physically significant. In the alpine belt the directions, although still southerly, have scattered declinations, and the inclinations deviate from the paleoisoclines calculated from the data from northern Europe by an average of 21°, which is over twice the mean deviations encountered farther north. The deviations of declination and inclinations are considered separately, since they may have differing origins.

The declinations in the Esterel [7.04, 05] are rather more westerly than those farther north, but the difference is not great. There are two results from the quartz-porphyrites of Bolzano in which the declinations differ by 14° [7.19, 20]. The deviation in the Spanish result from Huesca Province is of special interest because Carey has postulated a 35° anticlockwise rotation of Spain since the Mesozoic, and his restoration brings the declination into good agreement with those from northern Europe (Figure 10.9).

The situation becomes more complicated when the inclinations are considered. The

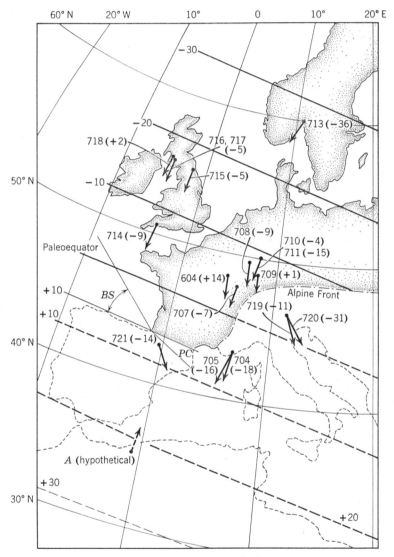

Figure 10.8. Paleomagnetic direction in rocks of late Carboniferous and Permian age in western Europe. The arrows give the declination, and the inclination is given in brackets after the appendix reference number. The paleoisoclines are from van Hilten (1962a) and have been calculated from a mean pole of 43° N, 169.5° E, which is close to, and not significantly different from, the mean pole for the European-north Asian region (Table 6.2). The north European "stable block" is stippled, and the paleoisoclines properly refer only to this area. *BS* is the Biscay sphenochasm, *PC* is the zone of Pyrennean compression, and *A* is van Hilten's proposed Permian position for the Bolzano quartz-porphyries.

inclination measured from the Pyrenees (−14), Esterel (−16, and −18), and from Bolzano (−11 and −31) all indicate paleo-latitudes appropriate to those of northern Europe at that time, which is absurd. An alternative, suggested by van Hilten (1962a), is to postulate a position such as A (Figure 10.8) for the Bolzano region, moving the sampling region south of the paleoequator and rotating dextrally through an angle of 150°! This means also that the Earth's field at the time was negative, whereas the evidence favors a positive polarity (§ 7.7). It seems more likely that the discrepancy is due to inadequacies in the precision of paleo-magnetic results at present available. The results from the "stable block," with the exception of those from the igneous rocks of the Nahe [7.11] and Oslo [7.13] regions are not based on magnetic or thermal clean-ing. Since all polarities are positive, sec-ondary components along the present field would tend to decrease the inclination. It

is noteworthy that these two results based on detailed studies, do give inclinations sys-tematically higher than the average paleo-isoclinal values. Thus the paleoisoclines extrapolated to southern Europe may be too high, and the paleoequator should be situated farther south. There is the further possibility that the tectonic correction ap-plied to the directions may be in error; the Bolzano results [7.19, 20] are corrected for uniform southerly dips of 10° to 15°, and the assumption that this is tectonic and not depositional has not been checked by meas-urements in adjacent beds of the same age dipping by different amounts in other di-rections (§ 10A.3). These uncertainties are matters of detail, changes in which are not likely to affect the general picture for the Per-mian field in Europe, nor would they grossly affect the paleolatitude analyses given in Chapter Nine since the paleolatitudes change at only half the rate of paleoisoclines in these latitudes.

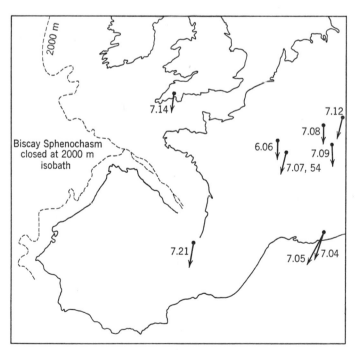

Figure 10.9. Supposed rotation of Spain: Stephanian and Permian data. Outlines redrawn from Carey (1958). The Permian paleomagnetic declinations from Huesca Province [7.21] are rotated with Spain. Recent observations from Huesca Province [7.55] are consistent with [7.21].

Although results are fewer, a comparable situation is found in the Triassic (Figure 10.10). The declinations (irrespective of sign) are northeasterly, except those in Spain, which are northerly, and the latter could be due to a counterclockwise rotation relative to Europe (Clegg, Deutsch, Everitt, and Stubbs, 1957). Carey's proposed closure of the Biscay Sphenochasm brings the declinations into agreement. The Spanish result indicates a paleolatitude well north of Europe at that time, but since it is based entirely on negative directions and there is no cleaning, there is every possibility of this being due to secondary components.

These results yield evidence of counterclockwise rotations of the peninsulas of south west Europe relative to the "stable block" of northern Europe. In view of the uncertainties in the inclination values at present available, the evidence for relative translations is considered slender, but as more precise results become available there seems little doubt that the complex tectonic movements which this zone underwent in the Tertiary will be unraveled.

10B PALEOMAGNETISM AND PALEO-GEOGRAPHIC RECONSTRUCTIONS

§ **10B.1   Introductory Remarks** Paleomagnetism relates to the problem of relative continental displacement (or continental drift) in this way. If there have been no relative displacements, and if the model of a geocentric dipole field for the Earth is correct, then paleomagnetic poles from different regions for the same time interval should agree, and the paleolatitudes (or paleoisoclines) estimated from these same regions should fall on concentric circles about the mean pole. This should apply to individual results from a limited time interval, or, more generally, for a polar sequence obtained from a longer interval. Good agreement is found for the Quaternary, and substantial agreement for the Upper Tertiary, but for the Lower Tertiary, Mesozoic, and Upper Paleozoic the agreement is poor (§§ 6.02 to 6.05). By and large these discrepancies occur only *between* regions; results from the *same* system in the *same* region are of good internal consistency,

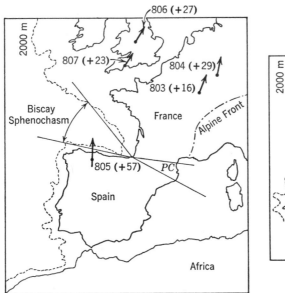
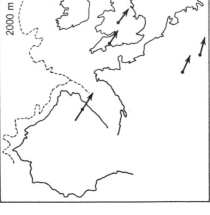

Figure 10.10. Supposed rotation of Spain: Triassic data. Outline from Carey (1958). The arrows show the declination, and each has a reference number followed by the inclination value in brackets.

comparable to that in the Quaternary (Figure 6.6). Reasonable explanations for these results are that the working model of the field is incorrect, or that substantial relative displacements of the continents during or since the Upper Paleozoic and Mesozoic have occurred. It should be noted that this argument relates only to results from the Upper Paleozoic or later. The paleomagnetic case (as it now stands) for the hypothesis of continental drift rests on evidence from the Upper Paleozoic, Mesozoic, and Lower Tertiary. The results from the Lower Paleozoic or Precambrian are either too few, too unreliable, or related to an insufficiently secure time basis, to be useful in this regard; to speculate on the meaning of these earlier results in terms of drift is to speculate in a void. The following discussion therefore is mainly confined to results for the Devonian onward.

During the past century various paleogeographic schemes have been proposed involving large scale relative continental displacements comparable in magnitude to the dimensions of the continents themselves. The essence of all such hypotheses is that the Earth initially possessed either one primitive continent called *Pangaea,* or two, called *Laurasia* and *Gondwanaland,* and at some comparatively late time in geological history these primitive continents broke up and the fragments drifted into their present positions. Different authors have produced different reconstructions based on various types of evidence. Critics of these hypotheses have stressed first, the necessarily incomplete, and contradictory nature of the evidence, and second, the difficulties involved in providing physically satisfactory mechanisms both for the initial break-up and for the subsequent dispersal. But the reality of drift depends on observation and not on theory. There would be no problem if an adequate mechanism were known.

The distinction used here between *polar-wandering* and *relative continental displacements* or *continental drift* has been set out already (§ 6.09) and follows that commonly made in the geological literature. It was,

for instance, made by Wegener (1924) and Köppen and Wegener (1924) who considered, on the basis of the paleoclimatic evidence, that the paleogeographic pole had moved relative to the whole crust, this general movement being in addition to the relative movement between different parts of the crust or continental drift.[1] These workers list the successive paleogeographic pole positions using a coordinate system fixed relative to Africa.

Apparent polar-wandering (§ 6.10) determined paleomagnetically may contain components due to general polar-wandering and to continental drift, and one of the reasons behind any attempt to distinguish between these in the results is that they may arise from different causes. Thus, in a simple-minded way, it may be argued that the broad similarity in the form of the polar paths from North America, Europe, and Australia since the Carboniferous (Figure 6.27) suggest a common geophysical effect, namely, polar-wandering, whereas the differences in their positions suggest displacements among these regions in a longitudinal sense relative to the present frame. But as apparent polar movements become defined in greater detail it may eventually be found to be impossible to make such a clear distinction, in which case it will become necessary to revert to the single hypothesis of continental drift. Yet this author would be reluctant to do this because the drift hypothesis, if applied without limi-

---

[1] The term *continental drift* has not always been used in this way in the paleomagnetic literature. For example, relative changes in paleolatitude and rotations of land masses have sometimes been referred to as continental drift (Blackett, Clegg, and Stubbs, 1960). It is thought preferable to confine the use of the term continental drift to the sense initially meant by Wegener, that is, to the process of relative movements among continents, and to describe the pole changes mapped by the paleomagnetic data (or changes in paleolatitudes and paleomeridians) as *apparent polar-wandering* relative to given regions.

tations to the paleomagnetic results, involves many degrees of freedom, and would yield an infinite number of possible continental distributions (§ 10B.4). The only situation which this author can envisage, in which the possibilities may be reduced to a manageable number, is one in which a component of general polar-wandering is present (10B.4). For this reason, it is of interest to search the data to see if such components do, in fact, exist.

§ **10B.2   Paleoclimatic Aspects**   A test for the hypothesis of continental drift is the external comparison between the paleomagnetic and paleoclimatic evidence already set out (§§ 6.10, 9.03). For this test the paleomagnetic results from a region *A* are referred to a region *B*. The paleolatitude estimated for *B* using the results from *A* should be consistent with the paleoclimatic evidence at *B*, and if a degree of consistency is found it would be evidence against the hypothesis of relative movement between *A* and *B*. On the other hand, gross inconsistency would be evidence in support of relative movements, since there is *internal* consistency between paleoclimate and paleolatitude for the same region. The variations for any place relative to the pole sequence obtained from any other region may be calculated, so that there are a very large number of possible comparisons. Those given in Figure 10.11 are typical. For the sake of completeness Lower Paleozoic values are included, but no weight is placed on them in the arguments.

Paris is taken as representative for western Europe and the paleolatitude variations calculated from the Australian paleomagnetic results are plotted. The Lower Paleozoic values are low. In the late Paleozoic and Mesozoic paleolatitudes range between 50° and 70° N′ and these are correlated with the frequent occurrence of evaporite deposits, desert sandstones, and thick carbonates including coral reefs. The paleolatitude variations for *Peking* calculated from the North American data are plotted in Figure 10.11*b*. High values in excess of 70° N′ are

estimated for the period Carboniferous to Triassic. The climate of this time for North China is described by Kobayashi and Shikama (1961) as "warm and hot," an inference which is based on the occurrence of red beds, bauxitic sediments, and on the large size and abundance of the terrestrial faunas. There are no evidences of glaciation, such as occur elsewhere during this interval, and as might be expected if these estimates of high paleolatitudes were indeed correct. The Indian peninsular region is represented by *Nagpur,* paleolatitude estimates being made from the European poles. The mean value of about 20° N′ in the Late Carboniferous and Permian is to be compared with the evidence of glaciation at this time (Wadia, 1953).

Localities in the southern hemisphere are now considered. *Bloemfontein* is taken as representative for South Africa and paleolatitudes are obtained from the Australian poles. Low values occur for the Upper Carboniferous to Cretaceous. The widespread Upper Carboniferous tillites of the Dwyka Series are considered by Du Toit (1937) to have been deposited by an ice sheet of continental dimensions. The external paleolatitude estimate for the Dwyka glacials is 10° to 20° S′. *Curityba,* capital of Parana state, is the reference locality chosen for southern Brazil. The Upper Carboniferous contains beds interpreted as of glacial origin. Red beds and desert sandstones are widespread in the Permian and Triassic (Oliveira, 1956). The paleolatitude variations estimated from the Australian poles range from 30° N′ to 30° S′; these are consistent with the Permian and Triassic geological record, but not with the supposed glaciation in the Upper Carboniferous. Finally, the paleolatitudes for *Canberra* calculated from the European poles are given. The Upper Carboniferous and Permian glaciations are to be compared with the paleolatitudes estimated externally of less than 20° N′. The paleolatitude increase in the Cenozoic is in contrast to the increase in paleotemperature given by Dorman and Gill (1959*a*) during the Tertiary.

Instead of time variations for reference localities, the space variations at particular times for whole regions may be compared. This is illustrated for the late Carboniferous and Permian in Figure 10.12. The paleomagnetic results for this interval in any one region show uniform directions (§ 6.05). For the eastern hemisphere the pole and paleolatitudes are for the Stephanian and Permian of Europe and northern Asia, so strictly they refer only to this region, but the parallels have been extended over the other continents to see how they compare with their supposed climate at that time. The late Carboniferous and early and middle Permian glacials of Australia, and the late Carboniferous glacial beds of India occur within 20° of the paleoequator, in the same paleolatitude as the evaporites, coral reefs, desert sandstones, and abundant fusulinid faunas in Europe, Sumatra, and northwestern India. The rich fusulinid faunas of Japan extend to 70° N′. The late Carboniferous Dwyka glacials extend from 35° to 65° S′. For the western hemisphere the pole and paleolatitudes are those calculated from the results from the Upper Kuttung (late Carboniferous) and Permian of Australia. Evaporites, organic reefs, desert sandstones, and abundant fusulinid occurrences in North America lie between 40° and 55° N′ in higher paleolatitudes than the late Carboniferous glacials of southern Brazil and Argentina.

These comparisons show that consistency between paleoclimate and paleolatitude determined externally is rare, whereas gross inconsistencies are common, and are therefore in agreement with the hypothesis of continental drift. An alternative is to say that the so-called paleoclimatic indicators are not indicators at all, or that the climate in the past bore no relation to paleolatitude. On the latter view it has to be supposed for example that glaciers, coral reefs, and deserts occurred at the same time in the same low latitude. If there were such a lack of relationship, then there would be evidence of it in the paleolatitude spectra for each paleoclimate indicator, but this is far from the case since all spectra obtained until now have been strongly paleolatitude dependent (Chapter Nine).

The paleomagnetic evidence alone presents us with the alternatives of continental drift or a nondipolar field. The comparisons with the paleoclimatic evidence allow us to assert further that unless continental drift is accepted, the strong paleolatitude dependence obtained for paleoclimatic indicators has to be regarded as entirely fortuitous. This seems improbable.

On these grounds, and with these reservations, it seems reasonable to proceed with the geocentric dipole hypothesis, and to consider the amount of continental drift which the paleomagnetic results thereby imply. The next step is to see to what extent the paleomagnetic data are consistent with the paleogeographic maps drawn by the exponents of continental drift.

§ **10B.3 Comparisons with Some Previous Paleogeographic Hypotheses** The test of drift reconstructions may be made in several ways. In the first place tests may be made of Carey's structural hypothesis (§ 10A.4). The unwinding of the larger oroclines led Carey to postulate large-scale displacements of the continents; for example, straightening of the Alaskan orocline carrying North America with it closes the Atlantic Ocean, and the unwinding of the Baluchistan mountain arc displaces peninsular India southward adjacent to SE Africa. Up to the present, paleomagnetic observations have been made only on some of the smaller of Carey's structural rotations (§§ 10A.5, 10A.6, 10A.8, 10A.9) but these are consistent with his views. A vital test is to follow the paleomagnetic declinations along one of the larger oroclines because if they show a concordance of directions comparable to that observed in the smaller features, then Carey's hypothesis would be corroborated, and the conclusions regarding continental drift which flow from it may be held to be substantially justified. This test has not yet been carried out in its full rigour.

A second procedure is to test the hypothesis of oceanic island drift. The mid-oceanic

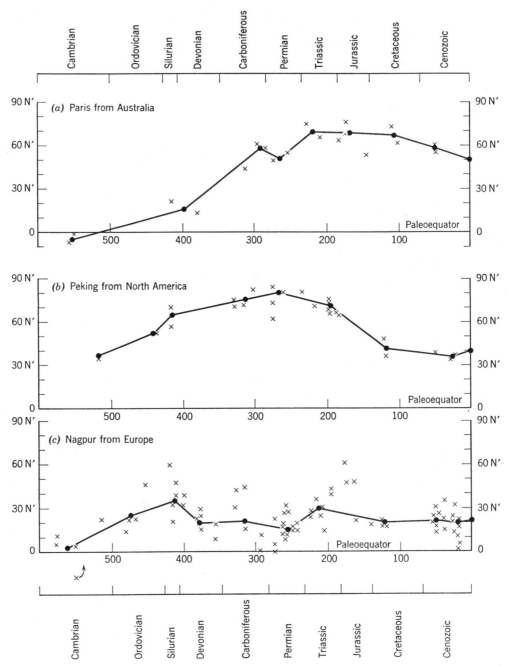

Figure 10.11. Paleolatitude time variations determined externally. Variations for certain reference localities using data from other regions and assuming no relative movement between regions. Crosses indicate values obtained from individual paleomagnetic poles and the dots give values obtained from mean poles for periods (Table 6.2). The reference localities are as follows: (*a*) Bloemfontein (29°12′ S, 26°15′ E), (*b*) Curityba (25°25′ S, 49°45′ W), (*c*) Canberra (35°15′ S, 149°10′ E), (*d*) Paris (48°52′ N, 2°18′ E), (*e*) Peking (39°49′ N, 116°30′ E), (*f*) Nagpur (21°5′ N, 79°5′ E).

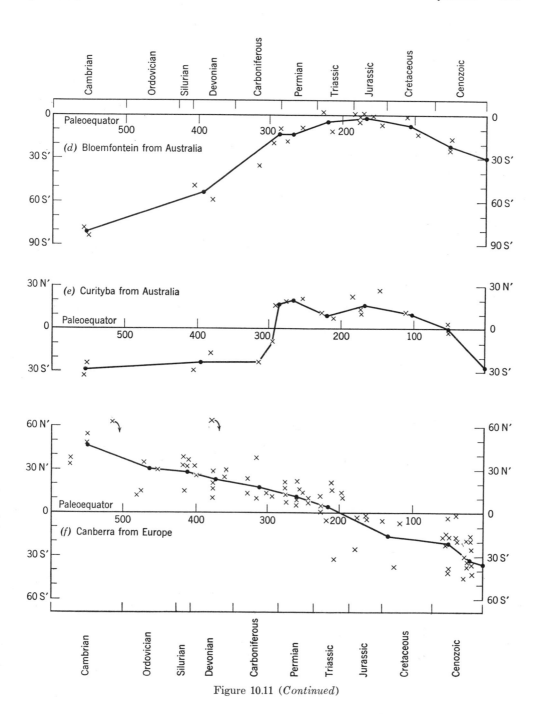

Figure 10.11 (*Continued*)

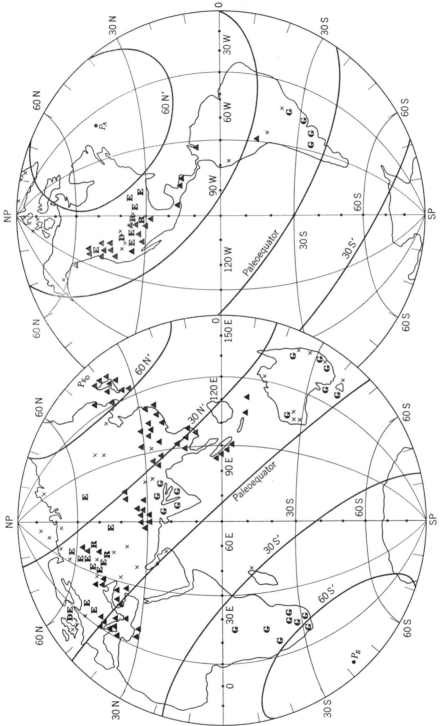

Figure 10.12. Paleolatitudes and paleoclimate of the late Carboniferous and Permian: an external comparison. Continental outlines are plotted on equal-area equatorial projections—the present latitudes and longitudes are added in thin line. In the map of the eastern hemisphere P_E are the mean paleomagnetic poles determined from Europe and northern Asia; the paleolatitude parallels 0°, 30°, and 60° concentric with these are added. In the map of the western hemisphere P_A is the mean paleomagnetic pole determined from Australia with paleolatitudes at 30° intervals plotted. Various paleoclimatic evidences are shown. Triangles are marine localities with fusulinids (certain families) from Stehli (1957); crosses are marine localities without fusulinids also from Stehli. **E** are evaporite occurrences from Lotze (1957). **R** are organic reefs mostly from Hill (1957). **D** are occurrences of desert sandstones (§ 9.20). **G** indicates occurrences of supposed glaciations compiled from David (1950), Hill (1958b), and Du Toit (1937).

ridges often have associated transverse ridges running toward the continental margin. J. T. Wilson (1963), reviving and extending notions of earlier workers (see for example King, 1958 and Carey, 1958), suggests that the transverse ridges mark the paths of continental movements. He shows that, by and large, the ages of the oldest rocks on the islands carried by the transverse ridges increase with distance from the mid-oceanic ridges, and this, Wilson contends, suggests that the islands have a common origin on the mid-oceanic ridges and have since moved outward as the continents drifted apart. The rate of movements is about 3 cm/yr, and they have been occurring since the early Cretaceous. By using the transverse ridges as guide lines, Wilson has given a reconstruction of the continents for the earlier Mesozoic which is similar in essence to that given by Wegener. The reality of this island motion may be tested paleomagnetically if there have been strong N-S components of motion. This condition is not satisfied by the islands of the transverse ridges of the Atlantic but is satisfied for certain islands of the Indian Ocean. For example, for Heard and Kerguelen Islands Wilson's hypothesis predicts a rate of change of the paleomagnetic directions of about 0.5°/m.y. since the early Tertiary. With careful radiometric control of rock ages this change should be detectable. No data are yet available relevant to this interesting test.

A third procedure for testing paleogeographic reconstructions is to take the paleomagnetic results from the stable continental blocks and to recalculate the pole positions, not, as before, with respect to the present positions of the sampling areas, but relative to the past positions using the ancient coordinates of sampling area read from paleogeographic maps. If the reconstructions are valid, the discrepancies obtained from rocks of the same period from different continents should disappear, and paleolatitude parallels or paleoisoclines of equal value should form an ordered sequence concentric about the unified pole. Polar comparisons only are made in this section, but the use of paleo-

latitudes yields the same results. Studies of this problem are, in some cases, rather out-of-date since the paleomagnetic results used have been supplemented since by much new data. The following is a review of what has been done, and no attempt is made here to bring the comparisons completely up-to-date. However, subsequent data would not change the results significantly.

The maps drawn by various exponents of drift are of variable usefulness. The coordinates systems used by Wegener (1924) and Köppen and Wegener (1924) are rather crude for the present purposes, but those of Du Toit (1937), King (1958, 1961), and Carey (1955, 1958) are sufficiently precise. Wegener's maps embrace both northern and southern continents—which he united in Pangaea. Du Toit and King prefer to imagine two primaeval continents: Laurasia, composed of North America, Europe, and northern Asia and brought together by closure of the north Atlantic; and Gondwanaland, which consisted of South America, Africa, Arabia, peninsular India (south of the Indo-Gangetic plain), Madagascar, Australia, and Antarctica, grouped together in a large southern continent. These broke up and dispersed in later Mesozoic and Tertiary time. Du Toit and King have provided separate maps of Laurasia and Gondwanaland in independent coordinates, so that paleomagnetic results from one hemisphere cannot be applied to a reconstruction of the other hemisphere. Carey, on the other hand, has returned to the idea of Pangaea, and has given reassemblies using single maps (Carey, 1958) so that interhemisphere comparisons become possible. If these ideas of continental drift are correct the greatest of all pole discrepancies should be revealed between the fragments of Gondwanaland, and in particular, peninsular India, which is supposed to have suffered at least 6000 km latitudinal translation, should disclose the effect most readily.

Pangaea. Khramov (Table 10.2), using Wegener's reconstruction and applying the results available to him at that time, cal-

Table 10.2 Mean Deviations of Paleo-magnetic Poles. *d_0 calculated on present land distribution, d_p on distribution postulated by Wegener. Compiled from Khramov (1958).*

Period and land regions from which poles were calculated	$d_0°$	$d_p°$
Cretaceous: Europe, North America, India	34	7
Permian: Europe, North America, Australia	47	22

culated the mean deviation of poles obtained from different regions and compared these with the deviation of the poles assuming no relative displacements. The reconstruction yields a lower dispersion of poles. Carey (1958) showed that the paleomagnetic poles relative to the present land distribution may be contained within a circle of 82° radius, but for the same poles plotted relative to his Pangaea, the radius of the containing circle is 47°. An independent recalculation (Irving, 1958a; Jaeger and Irving, 1957) of the same poles relative to Carey's Pangaea yielded a similar over-all reduction in scatter.

Laurasia. Tests of a more specific nature have been made of the Laurasia and Gondwanaland components. Irving (Table 10.3) using the data available in 1957 compared Laurasia reconstructions with the Permian and Triassic determinations. In the first of these reconstructions Du Toit moves North America toward Europe so that the Atlantic is about half closed, Europe is displaced in a northerly direction relative to North America. The fit of poles is not appreciably better than when calculated from the present positions. King closes the Atlantic more tightly and rotates North America approximately 37° counterclockwise relative to Europe; on his map the Triassic poles agree but the fit of Permian poles is not improved. Carey retains more of the Arctic Basin, closes the Atlantic more or less completely, and moves Europe northward with respect to North America; this

brings the Permian and Triassic poles into reasonable agreement.

Gondwanaland. Du Toit's map representing Gondwanaland during the Paleozoic is used, and the poles obtained from the southern dolerites and basalts are marked on it (Figure 10.13). These formations are predominantly of Lower Jurassic age so this comparison may not constitute a fair test of the reconstruction. But Du Toit thought that "the complete break-up of Gondwanaland seems not to have been effected until the Cretaceous-Tertiary," so that the poles, although not necessarily coincident, should be closer together on his reconstruction. Figure 10.13 shows this to be the case. The poles relative to the reconstruction are much closer than on the present distribution. For the reconstruction the average angular separation of poles taken two at a time is 24°, and their circular standard deviation $\Theta_{63} = 16°$ $(K = 25)$. The corresponding values for the pole positions relative to the present land distribution are 52° and $\Theta_{63} = 36°$ $(K = 5)$. The poles for India, South America, and Australia are close together, while those from Africa and Antarctica are some distance away. These divergences could arise from polar-wandering, the rock formations in the various continents not being exactly contemporaneous, or to the initiation of break-up prior to the Jurassic, or to the incorrectness in detail of Du Toit's reconstruction. The first of these is ren-

Table 10.3 The Separation (means of values) at the Perimeters of the Error Zones of the Pole Determinations from Britain and the U.S.A. *Calculated for their present positions and for the positions postulated in three reconstructions. Compiled from Irving (1958a).*

	Triassic (°)	Permian (°)
Present distribution	6	14
Du Toit (1937)	6	12
King (1958)	0	11
Carey (1958)	0	1

dered unlikely by the good agreement between several results from the Jurassic of Australia ranging in age from Lower to Upper Jurassic, and by the contemporaneity of the Antarctic and Tasmanian rocks [9.30, 38].

The above comparisons show broad consistency between the Upper Paleozoic and younger paleomagnetic results and certain aspects of drift reconstructions. The comparisons, although of a preliminary nature, provide illustrations of the way in which paleomagnetism may be used to check such reconstructions.

§ **10B.4   Paleomagnetism as a Basis for Paleogeographic Maps**   The evidence relating to the problem of making paleogeo-

graphic maps from the paleomagnetic data is embodied in the paleolatitude and paleomeridian maps given in § 9.07. In these, each land region is considered separately, and no attempt is made to relate the results from different regions to one another. This may be done by calculating the relative movements necessary to unify equivalent poles (defined later). Alternatively, relative movements may be estimated by drawing the paleolatitudes (or paleoisoclines) on each continent and juggling these until they conform to a geocentric dipole field (van Hilten, 1962*b*). The consideration of results from a single period of time is described first, followed by the more general procedures necessary when results from several periods are available, the latter being of special in-

Figure 10.13. Pole positions from the southern basalts and dolerites relative to Du Toit's reconstruction of Gondwanaland. The continental outlines are plotted on an equal-area projection with 15° graduations. The poles are labeled according to their continent of derivation and are from these rock units: Karroo dolerite and basalt [9.24 to 9.27]; Ferrar dolerite [9.37, 9.38, and 9.43]; Rajmahal Traps [9.23]; Serra Geral lavas [9.36]; Australian Jurassic [9.28 to 9.33]. Sampling localities are indicated by crosses.

terest since they provide an approach to the question of estimating paleolongitude, which, as will be seen, is the major difficulty.

Data for a Single Period. Regard the pole as fixed and the continents as movable, that is, relative continental displacement but no polar-wandering. The paleomagnetic inclination I gives the colatitude p of the sampling area, from this relationship: $\cot p = \tfrac{1}{2} \tan I$. If the possibility of drift is admitted, both rotations and translations of the continents may occur, so that the declination does not fix longitude, and any position on the small circle of radius p around the pole will satisfy the data, provided the land mass is rotated suitably. Similarly, the nth sampling region with inclination I_n may have been situated anywhere on a small circle of radius p_n, so, for sets of data from several continents an infinite number of continental arrangements are possible. This is illustrated in Figure 10.14 using data from three southern continents. All poles are fixed at the

center of the maps and the continents moved accordingly. The paleocolatitudes are approximately 10° for Tasmania, 50° for southern Brazil, and 60° for South Africa. These continents are rotated so that the horizontal component of magnetization lies along the meridian; the rotations are roughly 35° clockwise, 20° counterclockwise, and 30° clockwise respectively. In Figure 10.14*b* the relative longitudes are those of the present day. In the other diagrams the continents are moved along their appropriate paleolatitude lines into different relative longitudes, all consistent with the paleomagnetic results. The situations in (*a*) and (*c*) where the continents are superposed are absurd. Nevertheless there remain numerous solutions of type (*b*) and (*d*) between which the paleomagnetic data cannot discriminate. The distribution (*b*) is that most consistent with the *assumption of minimum movement,* that is, the assumption that the relative continental displacements since the time in

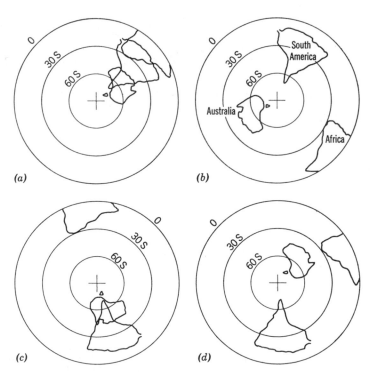

Figure 10.14.   The "indeterminancy" of paleolongitude.   Redrawn from Irving (1957*c*), with the kind permission of Taylor and Francis, London.

question are minimum. This assumption is used frequently here and in §10B.5, and is regarded as a necessary starting point in the discussions.

Data for Several Periods. Restrictions may be imposed when there are results from two or more periods if drift has happened as a discontinuous process, there being intervals of movement separated by defined standstills during which only polar-wandering occurred. Imagine, for example, two regions A and B for which paleomagnetic pole positions a_1, a_2 and b_1, b_2 have been estimated for periods 1 and 2. If, during these periods, A has not moved relative to B, but there has been polar-wandering, so that a_1 differs from a_2, and b_1 from b_2, then the arc angle between the pairs a_1, a_2 and b_1, b_2 will be the same, and the position of A relative to B at that time is determined by simply unifying a_1 and b_1, and a_2 and b_2. Tests of the determination may be made by obtaining measurements from rocks laid down in the interval between periods 1 and 2: the pole $a_{1.5}$ should agree with $b_{1.5}$ if the relative positions of A and B have been determined correctly. It is assumed in this procedure that the pairs a_1, b_1 and a_2, b_2, which may be called *equivalent paleomagnetic poles* (Figure 10.15), are comparable, or, more precisely, that the rock units from which they were obtained were laid down during, but not necessarily covering, the whole of a time interval during which polar-wandering was less than the experimental errors in determining pole positions. At the present stage only comparisons between poles obtained as an average for a geological period can be made. Even with finer subdivision of time, errors may arise from this source, but these will be lost when comparisons between many sets of equivalent poles are made, since errors in age correlations between continents are not likely to be biased one way. In other words it is equally likely that $(t_a - t_b)$ is positive or negative, where t_a and t_b are the true ages of two rock units from A and B, and which are regarded as geologically contemporaneous. The sets $(a_1, a_2, a_3 \cdots)$ $(b_1, b_2, b_3 \cdots)$ are called *polar-wandering sets*

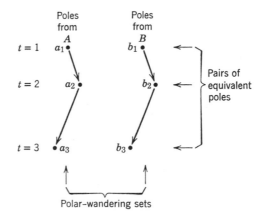

Figure 10.15. Definition of equivalent poles and polar-wandering sets.

and define general polar-wandering (as well as apparent polar-wandering) relative to A and B (Figure 10.15). Two methods of testing the data to see if this condition (polar-wandering but no drift) occurs for certain intervals have been suggested, and are now described.

The Method of Pivot Points (Creer, Irving, Nairn, and Runcorn, 1958). The displacement of a point on the Earth's surface to any other point on that surface can be obtained by a finite rotation about a fixed pole on the surface. Call this the *pivot point*. Consider equivalent poles a_1 and b_1 determined from A and B. Assume B and b_1 fixed relative to the spherical surface, then rotations of this surface made in order to bring b_1 into coincidence with a_1 may be carried out about an infinite number of pivot points, whose locus is the great circle equidistant from a_1 and b_1. The angular rotation necessary to bring the pair together is $2 \tan^{-1} [\tan (q/2) \operatorname{cosec} r]$ where q is the original angular distance between the poles, and r is the angular distance from the pivot point to a point midway between the poles. Consider further equivalent poles a_2, b_2 and a_3, b_3, etc., for time periods 2 and 3; then, if no relative displacement between A and B has taken place between the earliest and latest periods, the loci of pivot points for each period will intersect at a common point, so that the relative movement, since the latest period, has most probably occurred by rotation of A with respect to B about the point of intersection. Runcorn (1956b) suggests that westward movement of North America relative to Europe may be considered to have occurred about a pivot point close to the present pole.

The Method of Paleocolatitude Circles (Irving, 1958b). This method depends on the occurrence of common intersection points of paleocolatitude circles. First assume continent A with successive pole positions a_1, a_2, a_3 $\cdots$ fixed relative to the Earth's crust. Now allow continent B, for which there are pole determinations b_1, b_2, b_3 $\cdots$, for the same time intervals, to move so that equivalent poles coincide. The paleocolatitudes p_1, p_2, p_3 $\cdots$ for B during geological periods 1, 2, 3, $\cdots$ can be calculated from the paleomagnetic inclination I_1, I_2, I_3 $\cdots$ in rock units laid down during these periods. Possible positions of B are represented by a family of small circles of radii p_1, p_2, p_3 $\cdots$ and centers a_1, a_2, a_3 $\cdots$. Let the fixed poles a_1 and a_2 from A with coordinates (λ_1', ϕ_1') and (λ_2', ϕ_2') have small circles of radius p_1 and p_2 obtained from B, around them. The planes containing these small circles are:

$$\left.\begin{aligned} x \sin\lambda_1' \cos\phi_1' + y \sin\lambda_1' \sin\phi_1' \\ + z \cos\lambda_1' = \cos p_1 \\ x \sin\lambda_2' \cos\phi_2' + y \sin\lambda_2' \sin\phi_2' \\ + z \cos\lambda_2' = \cos p_2 \end{aligned}\right\} \quad (10.1)$$

and these, together with the equation of a unit sphere $(x^2 + y^2 + z^2 = 1)$, constitute three simultaneous equations whose solutions give the intersection points. If the circles just touch, the solutions are identical; if they neither touch nor intersect, the solutions are imaginary. If a third pole, a_3, and paleocolatitude value, p_3, are now combined, first with a_1 and p_1, and then with a_2 and p_2, and a common intersection point is found for all three, then it indicates that relative movement between A and B is unlikely to have occurred between times 1 and 3. It is desirable to have a set of three or more

poles and paleolatitude circles each referring to different times, but in most circumstances two (for times t_1 and t_2) provide a useful guide, since of their two possible intersection points, one will involve relative rotation between t_1 and t_2, whereas the other will not, and the former may be discarded on the basis of the assumption of minimum movement.

§ **10B.5   Some Illustrations**   Complicated situations may be envisaged when these methods are applied to actual results, but one may be optimistic and hope that some common intersections [2] occur for some successive time periods. Graphical methods are sufficiently accurate for the present purposes. Figures 10.16 to 10.19 have been drawn from plots on a 19-inch diameter globe, using movable transparencies shaped to the continents and molded round the globe. In Figure 10.16 the Europe-northern Asia region, and its poles are assumed fixed, and the mean poles for periods Permian P, Triassic Tr, Jurassic J, Cretaceous K, and Lower Tertiary T_1 are plotted in the southern hemisphere. Europe, being in the northern hemisphere, is not seen. Reference to Figure 10.17 may clarify the procedure. There is no satisfactory mean Jurassic pole for Europe and northern Asia, and the individual value from Central Asia [9.20] is used. The paleocolatitude circles have been calculated for a reference locality in South Australia (point 4). A common intersection zone for the Permian to Lower Tertiary paleocolatitude circles occurs in the region 12°E,43°S and Australia is drawn in accordingly. The dimensions of this intersection zone are comparable to the statistical error in the determinations of poles and radii of circles. Inter-

---

[2] It is worth noting that *if* Wegener-type drift has occurred, and the primeval continent (or continents) remained as an entity during the early Mesozoic, Paleozoic, and earlier time, then it is a geometrical necessity that common intersections of paleocolatitude circles should occur and thus provide the means of reconstructing the present fragments.

sections between Permian, Jurassic, and Cretaceous circles occur in the region 41°W,55°S (point 5) but the intermediate (in time) Triassic circle is far away. The simplest explanation of this result is that Australia remained fixed relative to Europe in position (1) in the Permian and Triassic and through into the Jurassic, remaining unmoved with respect to Europe during this interval; in the Cretaceous and Lower Tertiary it occupied positions (2) and (3), moving with small clockwise rotation to its present position (4). The rate of movement *relative* to Europe may be calculated as approximately 92° of arc since the Jurassic, or an average of 6 cm/year. Alternatively the position (1) may be maintained from Permian to Lower Tertiary with a 90° counterclockwise rotation in the interval Jurassic to Lower Tertiary; thereafter, Australia moved relative to Europe to position

(4) at an average rate of 20 cm/year. The first alternative seems far more reasonable. Other much more complicated movements, involving considerable rotations, and frequent changes in the direction of translation and sense of rotation, are possible, and may be visualized by selecting points at random on the successive paleocolatitude circles. Such alternatives regard the coincidence in the region (1) as fortuitous, and violate the principle of minimum movement. A further point of interest arises from considering intersection points (1) and (6) between the Permian and Triassic paleocolatitude circles. If only these two circles were available, it may be thought impossible to decide which of these intersection points is the more likely position for Australia. In fact, this is not so, since (1) requires no movement, whereas (6) requires relative rotational movement be-

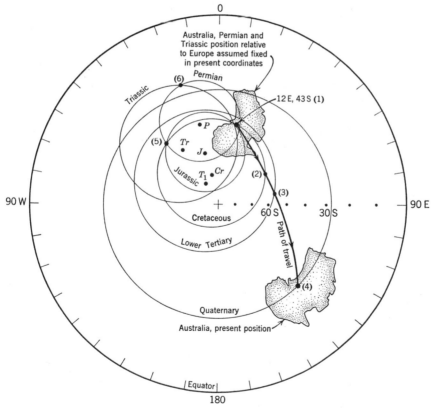

Figure 10.16. Paleocolatitude circles. Stereographic equal-angle net. Proposed path of travel of Australia relative to Europe is given.

tween Permian and Triassic time. On the hypothesis of minimum movement the former is preferable, and this is confirmed by the paleocolatitude circles for later times.

It appears possible therefore that the Permian and Triassic poles for Europe and Australia constitute a polar-wandering set, and so fix the relative position of these two regions during this time interval. With this in mind the relative position of Europe and Australia has been plotted on Figure 10.17

by unifying pole pairs. The pairs have not been placed exactly together, to make clear that there are statistical errors in the determinations, so there is some freedom as to the placing of Australia, but it is clear that if the assumptions made are correct then in the late Paleozoic and Mesozoic Australia must have been in the vicinity of the southern hemisphere European poles since Australian rocks of this age have steep inclinations. The relative latitudes and longitudes

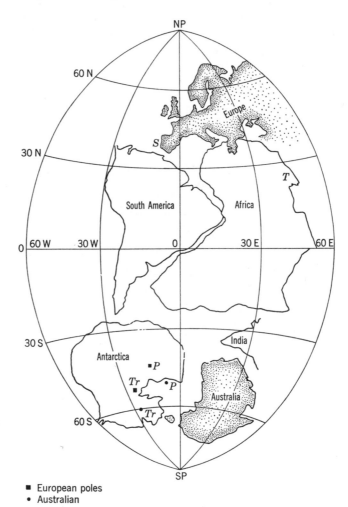

Figure 10.17. Proposed relative position of Europe and Australia in the Permian (*P*) and Triassic (*Tr*). Position obtained by unifying the pole pairs for the Permian and Triassic. Europe and Australia are stippled. India, Africa, Antarctica, and South America are fixed relative to Australia in a manner proposed by Carey (1958). The fit with Europe is rather tight and it appears to be inconsistent with Carey's proposed expansion of the Earth (§ 10E.2). The projection is equatorial equal-area, between longitudes 60° E and 60° W.

of Europe and Australia in the Permian and Triassic may be read off the map.

The Lower Tertiary and Jurassic poles for India and Australia (Table 6.2) have a similar separation and may constitute a desirable polar-wandering set for reconstruction purposes. Assuming this to be true they are unified in Figure 10.18. The relative positions of India and Australia thus obtained are very similar indeed to those suggested by Carey.

A return may now be made to the check made on Du Toit's assembly of Gondwanaland (Figure 10.13) in which certain discrepancies were noted. On Figure 10.19 the poles for the Jurassic results are plotted within a circle of 10° radius, this freedom being allowed because of errors in polar estimates. The land masses are moved accordingly. No control of paleolongitude is possible since only one time period is repre-

sented. India is fixed relative to Australia as for Figure 10.18. South America, Africa, and Antarctica are placed in the paleolongitudes advocated by King (1961) showing that there is no discrepancy between his reconstruction of these three land masses and the paleomagnetic results. The purpose of Figure 10.19 is to show that however much the Australian and Indian poles are moved within this circle it is not possible to bring these land masses alongside Antarctica in the manner desired by the advocates of drift (see for example Figure 10.17). This would seem to support the suggestion already made (p. 264) that the paleomagnetic results for the Jurassic of Gondwanaland indicate either that the break was initiated prior to the Jurassic, or that the relative positions of Antarctica and Australia in Gondwanaland reconstructions require readjustment.

These methods suggest means for drawing

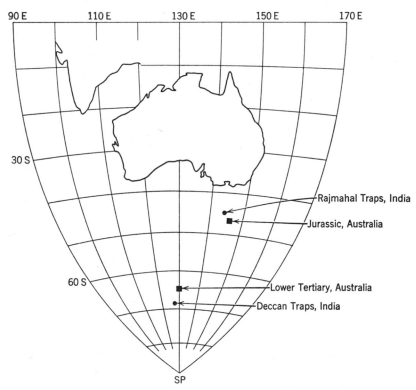

Figure 10.18. Relative positions of India and Australia in the interval Jurassic to Lower Tertiary. Equal-area equatorial projection is used for the southern hemisphere between longitudes 90° and 170° E.

maps showing the relative positions of the continents at past times. It should be stressed that Figures 10.16 to 10.19 are intended only as *illustrations*. Such paleogeographic maps represent *some* of the ways of explaining the paleomagnetic results, but this is not to say that other explanations are not possible. The virtue of these maps is that they can be tested by taking further paleomagnetic observations. When making these reconstructions four important assump-

tions are made: (1) that the paleomagnetic directions reflect the direction of the Earth's field at the time of formation; (2) that the field when averaged over several thousands of years approximates to that of a geocentric dipole; (3) there is the assumption regarding equivalence of poles; and lastly (4) there is the assumption of minimum movement. The assumption of polar equivalence depends primarily on the accuracy of intercontinental correlations and the density of paleomag-

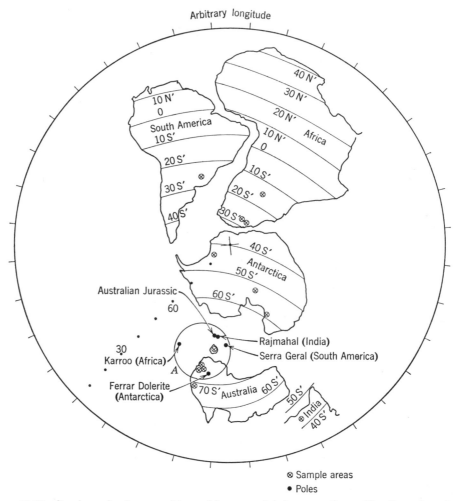

Figure 10.19. Gondwanaland reassembly making use of paleomagnetism. The Jurassic poles for each land component are placed in a circle of 10° radius (labeled *A*). Polar equal-area projection. The paleolatitudes relative to each region are given. The longitude is arbitrary. The figure suggests that Australia and Antarctica were not united at this time. The consistency between King's (1961) South America-Africa-Antarctica reassembly and the paleomagnetic results is notable. Sampling localities are marked by crosses in circles.

netic data. It could be argued that, because of correlation errors and the paucity of data, this assumption is invalid, but the increased use of radioisotope decay schemes for dating rocks should eventually reduce these correlation errors, and the rapid accumulation of paleomagnetic data ought soon to remedy the sampling inadequacies.

The problem of fixing relative paleolongitude is the major difficulty. Doubtless there are many ways of looking at this problem preferable to those of pivot points and paleocolatitude circles and these will come to light in due course. However, if continental drift has happened as periods of movement separated by defined standstills during which the pole wandered, then other coincidences like those for Australia and Europe will arise for all continents. If such coincidences should happen frequently the probability of their being significant becomes very great. It is not improbable that relative paleolongitudes may be closely defined in this way.

10C PALEOMAGNETISM AND STRATIGRAPHIC CORRELATION

§ **10C.1 General Ideas** The direction of the Earth's field, as estimated from particular regions, varies with time, and when these variations have been established in standard sequence the paleomagnetic method can be used in reverse to provide information about rock age.

Paleomagnetism has an everyday application to many problems of a local nature where it may be a useful adjunct to normal stratigraphic methods; in several instances, paleomagnetism has given a lead in age determination problems, and later radiometric work has confirmed its result with added precision. Sometimes, however, it may be of rather more basic importance. Although it may seem presumptuous at this stage to compare paleomagnetism in its application to stratigraphy, with the paleontologic and radiometric methods there are two aspects in which it is likely that paleo-

magnetism has a contribution to make in its own right as a method, which, in these particular aspects, is superior in its effectiveness to other stratigraphic tools. First, in unfossiliferous or poorly fossiliferous sediments, particularly Precambrian sediments and post Precambrian red beds, it is likely to have a valuable application since such beds cannot be dated radiometrically and paleontology is powerless or weak. Second, paleomagnetism could furnish world-wide marker horizons, because the variations in the Earth's field, when averaged over several thousand years, are a planetary rather than a regional phenomenon, and there is the possibility of recognizing synchronous paleogeomagnetic events in all parts of the world.

The standpoints adopted by different workers differ somewhat. It is contended here that the idea of the synchroneity of paleomagnetic direction variations originates in our notions about the form and variation in the Earth's field, and that it is proper that these applications should be argued in terms of models of the field and its variations. Blundell (1961a) on the other hand "stressed that rock magnetism can be applied quite independently of any theory concerning the earth's field." Applications in the latter sense are possible over small areas within which the field varies little, but for correlations on a regional or intercontinental scale it is necessary, in order to make comparisons between different places, to assume some working model of the field. Without this, one is restricted to local problems. The theme in this account is that, although the application of paleomagnetism to local problems is appreciable, it is in the more general questions of regional and intercontinental correlation that paleomagnetism has most to offer the stratigrapher.

There are three types of variation—each related to its own characteristic time scale. First, there is the dispersion of directions about the mean, related to the secular variation. Second, there are changes in the mean directions, or apparent polar-wanderings. Third, there are reversals of sign about the

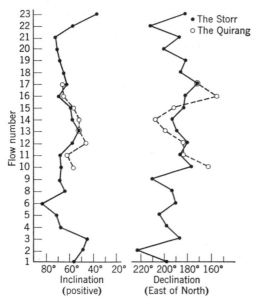

Figure 10.20. Directions of NRM at two localities in the Tertiary lavas of Skye. The flows are numbered in stratigraphic sequence beginning with the oldest. Flow 7 at The Storr is thin and weathered and has not been sampled. Redrawn from Khan (1960), with the kind permission of the Royal Astronomical Society, London, and M. A. Khan.

mean axis arising from the reversal of the field.

§ 10C.2   Use of the Secular Variation

The scatter of directions observed at several sites in the same rock unit is sometimes attributable to the secular variation, and because of the regional character of these variations applications are necessarily local in nature. The range of applicability has not yet been established in practice but probably does not extend more than 1000 km; standard variation scales established in control localities may not reasonably be extrapolated to test localities of unknown age situated more than this distance from the control localities. If paleomagnetic measurements gave an exact record of the field direction, and deposition was continuous, then very detailed correlations between piles of beds at different localities in the same region would be possible by matching the variations

observed in parallel columns. But the statistical and imperfect nature of the paleomagnetic data, and the gaps and irregularities in the stratigraphic record (§ 4.03) render such a test very difficult, and it is only after much detailed work that valuable results can be expected.

Archeomagnetic Dating. Attempts to build up secular variation directional scales using historic lavas and baked clays fired by ancient man, have provided information of much geomagnetic interest (§§ 1.7, 6.13), but little actual use has been made of these for dating purposes. The study has been dependent on archeological dating, so that the flow of useful information has been toward geomagnetism rather than archeology. It is doubtful whether the method is of sufficient precision for it to become a tool of real archeological importance in competition with Carbon 14 dating. Furthermore, the method at its present stage of development appears to be applicable only to a small percentage of baked structures; for example, Cook and Belshé [12.06] in their study of about 50 structures in Britain obtained what they regarded as satisfactory results from only 14 sites, which is not a high return for their labor.

The work of the Thelliers' on the intensity of the field (Chapter Eight) suggests a further possibility, namely, that intensity determinations on rocks or baked clays of unknown age may be compared to the curve of intensity variation established for samples of known age. The possible advantage of this method is, that the decrease estimated by the Thelliers may refer to a decrease in the Earth's dipole moment, in which case the effect should be world-wide, thereby opening up the possibility of world-wide comparisons. But this method needs verification in practice.

Correlation of Lava Flows. There is the possibility of correlating lava sequences in different localities using variations in their remanence directions. An example is given in Figure 10.20 using results from the Tertiary lavas of Skye (Khan, 1960). The sequences on The Storr and The Quirang, which are about 15 km apart, are known, from the field evidence, to be approximately the same age, but no correlation flow-by-flow has been made by normal geological methods. The direction variations in each section were matched by calculating correlation coefficients obtained by equating the oldest flow at The Quirang (8 flows altogether) with each of the lower 15 flows at The Storr (22 flows altogether); in turn, the correlation was only significant when the oldest Quirang flow was correlated with the tenth flow at The Storr. It seems therefore that The Quirang flows correspond to flows 10 to 17 at The Storr.

§ 10C.3 Uses of Apparent Polar-Wandering

In single regions (apart from reversals) a drift of directions with time at rates of the order 0.2°/m.y. is found (§ 6.08). Since differences in mean directions of less than 10° are detected only with some uncertainty, the method applies only to the study of large age differences, say of the order 50 m.y. It is useful for distinguishing Mesozoic from Tertiary rocks, for example, but not generally Oligocene from Miocene. At certain times, however, when rapid changes are in progress, it may be possible to achieve greater precision, and where the changes are abrupt, marker horizons of considerable utility may be identified.

The method may be considered in two stages. In the first place there is the direct comparison of mean directions. This applies only within regions of limited extent over which the field may be expected to have varied by an amount less than the statistical errors. The range of applicability of this method is probably of the order 1000 km, depending on the instance in mind. In the second stage, comparisons over a wider area are made using the technique of paleomagnetic poles. The poles for the control and test localities may be compared, or the direction at the test locality may be compared against that calculated from the control locality pole, using equations 9.1 and

9.2. At present the disagreement between paleomagnetic poles from different regions means that the method is applicable only to regions of continental extent within which relative movement of control and test localities has not occurred. But if, as new data become available, overwhelming evidence in favor of the geocentric dipole hypothesis is presented, then it should be possible to reconstruct the past positions of continents relative to each other and to the paleogeomagnetic axis (§ 10B.4) so that a unified standard scale of direction variations with time could, in principle, be erected for all continents. Certain examples are now described, grouped under two broad headings.

Dating of Intrusive Rocks. The first example concerns the age relations of two groups of small intrusions in Ayrshire, Scotland, which are referred to as kylites and crinanites. A Permian age for the kylites is suggested by their field relationships, but the age of the crinanites is uncertain, although it has been suspected that they are Tertiary. Armstrong (1957) finds that the directions in the kylites [7.18] have a mean of 190, +2 similar to that in the nearby Permian Mauchline lavas and sediments [7.16, 17], and this confirms their age as Permian. The crinanites have directions close to those observed in Tertiary lavas in Scotland and this supports the suggestion that they are of comparable age.

The second example is from the Monteregian Hills near Montreal [10.11, 12] (Larochelle, 1961). These are isolated alkali bodies intrusive into Cambrian and Ordovician sediments in Quebec Province. Because of their petrological similarity they have been considered to be comagmatic, and, further, that alkali rocks further to the east, at Mt. Megantic, are of similar age. The remanence directions of these bodies are in close agreement and this supports the suggestion that they are approximately contemporaneous. The geological age is known from the field evidence to be late Ordovician or younger, and in order to obtain a closer estimate their directions may be compared with those in rocks of known age elsewhere in North America. Because of the large distance between Quebec and most of the paleomagnetic sampling localities this comparison is made using paleomagnetic poles (Figure 6.7). The poles are different from those calculated from Triassic or Tertiary rocks and agrees with that from the Dakota Sandstone [10.13], which thus indicates a Cretaceous age for the intrusions, but since no results are available from the Jurassic there remains the possibility that the intrusions may be of this age. Although the probable ages can only be fixed within fairly wide limits from the paleomagnetic evidence, these are very much more restricted than those set by the geological field evidence. Radioisotope age determinations, made subsequently to the paleomagnetic work, gave a middle Cretaceous age.

Work of a rather similar nature has been carried out on certain hypabyssal intrusions in eastern Australia—the Gibraltar Microsyenite [9.28], the Gingenbullen Dolerite [9.33], the Prospect Dolerite [9.29], and the Cygnet Intrusive Complex [10.09]. These intrusions cut Middle or Upper Triassic sediments, setting a lower limit to their age; the upper limit was not known with certainty, but the intrusions have been generally considered, on petrological grounds, to be Tertiary (David, 1950). The paleomagnetic directions are nearly vertical, different from the directions observed in Cenozoic lavas in southeastern Australia [11.093, 11.094, 11.096, 12.45], but similar to those observed in rocks of known Mesozoic age. A Mesozoic rather than Tertiary age for these intrusives is therefore indicated, although it was not possible to say where, within the Mesozoic, they lie. This conclusion was later confirmed with much added precision by radioisotope age determinations, three bodies being Lower Jurassic [9.28, 29, 33], and one [10.09] late Lower Cretaceous.

The work on the Mesozoic intrusives of Quebec and eastern Australia make an interesting parallel. Paleomagnetism first set limits to their ages, which were confirmed, soon afterwards, by radioisotope methods, narrowing still further their age limits. The consistency between independent physical methods is noteworthy. The radioisotope ages are the more precise, and once established, clearly take precedence, thereby providing an improved age basis for the paleomagnetic result, which then becomes a point on the standard scale of direction variations.

Dating Unfossiliferous Sediments. Extensive studies of the late Precambian Grand Canyon Series of Arizona [1.13 to 20], and the Belt series of Montana and Alberta [1.21 to 32, 1.65 to 73], yield well-grouped paleomagnetic poles (Figure 6.16) and as Collinson and Runcorn (1960) point out, "The inference that the Grand Canyon series and the Belt series are contemporaneous is in agreement with the conclusions of geologists who have studied these formations." The geological opinion is based on lithological comparisons only, so the paleomagnetic result is a substantial confirmation.

The axis transition in the Precambrian Torridonian Sandstone Series of Scotland occurs within and near the top of the lower division, or Diabaig Group [1.01, 02]. Below and above the level the directions persist for 600 m and 4000 m respectively. The axis change of 78° and attendant apparent polar movement of 46° (Figure 6.16) occurs rapidly, compared to the time of duration of the stable directions. If this is a true polar change then the transition should be recognizable in other regions. There is a suggestion of a comparable effect in the North American results. The poles for the Sudbury Nickel Irruptive [1.46 to 48] and the Baraga County Dikes of Michigan [1.34] bear approximately the same relationship to the poles from the Belt and the Grand Canyon Series as the Diabaig pole from the Torridonian [1.02] bears to that from the Applecross and Aultbea Group [1.01]. If there is a similar transition here, and if it can be identified on the ground, as it has been in the Torridonian, then it should be possible to establish a useful marker horizon in the later Precambrian.

§ 10C.4 **Use of Reversals** The essence of this method is to match sequences of polarity changes observed in different sections. The reversal levels constitute marker horizons for stratigraphic purposes. The frequency of reversals varies with time (§§ 7.2, 7.3), and so the types of problem to which the phenomenon is applicable are different for different times. Broadly speaking, the lower the frequency, the more general their application will be. If reversals of polarity are due to reversals of a geocentric dipole field, then the onset of a reversal is, geologically speaking, a simultaneous event in all parts of the world. The time taken for the field to the reverse is not known with certainty and may be variable. For the later Cenozoic, Hospers (1954) estimated the time required as $2 - 20 \times 10^3$ years. This is quite adequate for stratigraphic purposes. Even if a value of 10^6 years is allowed for pre-Cenozoic reversals this is still much less than the errors in radiometric methods, and compares favorably with paleontologic dating even under the most ideal conditions. Serial reversals in the stratigraphic column therefore may provide a larger number of marker horizons which, if they can be identified, constitute a stratigraphic tool of much utility.

In practice, reversals are easily recognized. The change is one of 180°, and if instability problems have been properly attended to (§ 5.09) there is no difficulty in recognizing them. The main problem is to identify the same reversal level in different sections. If in the sections compared, a level of positive polarity is simply followed by a negative one, there is no difficulty. But if several alternating polarity levels occur in each section the problem is more difficult, since the periodicity of reversal is short compared to the time scale of geological events. There may have been as many as 20 reversals since the Miocene (§ 7.2), and except for the last reversal, where it is possible to work back from the present situation, there is as yet no certain way of distinguishing a particular level from any later or earlier level of similar polarity. Measurements of the successive thickness of alternate polarity levels in one section may be matched sideways with thickness patterns in other sections, but this is unlikely to be of much help since rates of deposition differ and, because of nonsequence, whole polarity levels may be absent from a section. The most favorable situation occurs when the time scale of reversals is much longer, so that beds with common polarity cover a span of time comparable to a geological period. The onset of reversal at the upper and lower limits will serve as easily recognized marker horizons, which for all practical purposes may be regarded as synchronous. Certain examples are now described.

Iceland. Hospers (1953) established a sequence of alternating polarities in the Cenozoic volcanic and sedimentary formations of Iceland (Table 7.2). Later work (Einarsson and Sigurgeirsson, 1955; Einarsson, 1957; Sigurgeirsson, 1957; Rutten and Wensink, 1959, 1960) has extended the sequence given by Hospers, and shown how reversals may be used as an adjunct to field mapping for correlating sections. Einarsson refers to this as *magnetogeological mapping.* Workers in Iceland have generally used the symbols N1, R1, N2, R2, etc., to signify the period of negative polarity since the early Pleistocene, the period of positive polarity prior to this, and so on. Comments on this scheme are made later (§ 10C.5). In the majority of cases the determinations of polarity were made in the field on hand samples, and were carried out side by side with field mapping. So far the results have related to correlations within Iceland, but a point of more general interest concerned with the definition of the base of the Quaternary, has arisen from a study of the lavas of the Gray Phase; Hospers (1951) noted the possible importance of reversals in this respect, and Rutten and Wensink (1960) have modified and elaborated his views.

The Gray Phase consists of the youngest of the plateau basalts of Iceland. It is overlain by the Palagonite Formation and interglacial lavas and sediments related to the last glaciation (Table 7.2). The Gray Phase itself contains numerous beds of tillite, and so may on these grounds be considered entirely Quaternary.   However, local glaciations of pre-Quaternary age could occur in these high latitudes without their being similar ice advances in lower latitudes, so that the oldest glacial beds here may correspond to levels much older than the earliest Pleistocene glaciation, say in Central Europe. The Gray Phase overlays unconformably the plateau basalts of the Upper Tertiary, which, in turn, overlay unconformably the main sequence of Tertiary plateau basalts, which are of uncertain age, but which may extend down into the Eocene. None of the basalts beneath the Gray Phase contains glacials. A tentative schematic section based on the sequences of reversals is given in Figure 10.21. This is a composite section drawn up from six localities. It suggests that the base of the Gray Phase has negative polarity, and upward through the section this becomes positive and then negative again. The upper negative po-

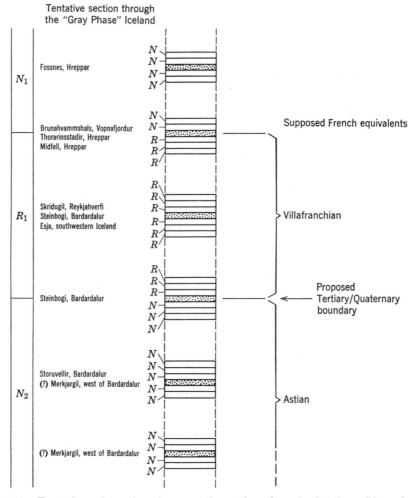

Figure 10.21. Tentative schematic paleomagnetic section through the Gray Phase in Iceland. The polarity zones are given on the left and the polarities observed at the 6 localities in the column. The correlation of this sequence with the sequence in Central France (Table 7.1) proposed by Rutten and Wensink is indicated. Redrawn with modifications from Rutten and Wensink (1960), with the kind permission of the authors.

larities continue into the Palagonite Formation and younger beds through to the present day, so that the upper reversal in the Gray Phase may be correlated with the reversal in the Lower Pleistocene of Central France (Table 7.1). The lower reversal beneath this may therefore correspond to the reversal at the base of the Villafranchian in Central France. Rutten and Wensink contend that the Pliocene-Quaternary boundary should be defined on this lower reversal; that is, the base of the Quaternary should be defined as the change from N2 to R1 on the Icelandic terminology. They argue with good reason that this is preferable to a definition based on the occurrence of glaciations, which are likely to be strongly diachronous as between different parts of the world. If their suggestion is accepted, and if the radiometric dating of the penultimate reversal in the Hawaiian Islands and California can be held substantially correct (§ 7.3), then the Tertiary-Quaternary boundary as here defined is about 2.5 m.y. old.

Turkmenia. Khramov (1958) has reported a reversal sequence in the late Cenozoic sediments of Turkmenia (Figures 7.1 and 7.2). The polarity levels are numbered from 0 to 13 backward in time. The scheme is not independent of the geological evidence. In certain cases much assistance in correlation problems was rendered by paleomagnetism, particularly in the Red Bed sequence [11.043], which is poorly fossiliferous, and where correlation is important because of the potentialities of these beds as oil producers. Khramov relates his scheme to an absolute time scale by assuming that each polarity period had a duration of 0.5 m.y., although he makes clear that this may not be very realistic in view of the apparent variability in the frequency of reversals. One point of some interest is that if the suggestion of Rutten and Wensink as to the definition of the Pliocene-Quaternary boundary is adopted, then this boundary is found between levels 2 and 1 (Figure 7.2) in the sections of the Apsheronsk stage in the Kiurendagh. At present any conclusion is necessarily tentative, but there

seems reason to hope that when the requisite observations become available, the Pliocene and Quaternary sections of Central Asia will be related to those of western Europe by means of reversals with a precision very much greater than that previously possible.

Khramov suggests two possible methods of identifying contemporaneous units of the same polarity in different sections. First, the mean directions of each polarity unit may be compared; there is evidence from the Turkmenian data of systematic differences of about 10° between the mean directions in successive stratal units of the same polarity. Such an effect would arise if the field reversal in any particular instance were not exactly 180°, but, let us say, 175°, the successive axes being 5° out of exact alignment, the reversal only becoming exact when averaged over several such changes. Second, he suggests that comparisons between results from transition zones should be helpful. Since the way in which the field reverses is hardly likely to be repeated exactly each time, then the pattern of changes in each transition zone should be identifiable from section to section. These are brave ideas requiring many years of painstaking observation before they can be tested.

Late Paleozoic Reversals (§ 7.2) The potential usefulness of the reversal levels in the Upper Carboniferous and in the late Permian as intercontinental marker horizons is evident, since the intervening beds with uniform positive polarity should be recognizable in the standard sections of all continents. There seems to be every possibility, for example, of relating the change from positive to negative polarity in the sequences of certain continents to that observed by Khramov in the uppermost Permian (Tartarian) of the type Permian section in the U.S.S.R. It seems probable that the Illawarra Reversal in Australia relates to this level. Similarly, the change from negative to positive, which occurs in the Upper Carboniferous (within the Westphalian or between the Westphalian and Stephanian) in the standard western European sections, may be represented in Australia by the Paterson Reversal. These marker horizons should provide assistance in the difficult problems of correlating the Gondwana beds of the southern continents with their equivalents in the northern continents.

§ **10C.5   Naming Problems**   The same symbol has sometimes been used to denote different things. For example, the first time interval of positive polarity has been designated R_1 in both Iceland and France (Rutten and Wensink, 1959; Rutten, 1960), giving the impression that these are known to be contemporaneous, whereas in fact this is the point that requires verification. A preferable procedure is to use geographical names, both for the levels of reversal and for the intervening beds and their equivalent time periods. This procedure may be illustrated in the case of the late Paleozoic reversals. The reversal levels bounding the beds of positive polarity in the late Paleozoic have been identified on the ground in Australia and have been given local geographic names (§ 7.2). It is proposed that the rocks between these two levels be called the *Kiaman Magnetic Division* and that the time taken for these rocks to be laid down be called the *Kiaman Magnetic Interval* (Irving and Parry, 1963). The name Kiaman was put forward on historical grounds, since it was in a sample from the Upper Marine Latites collected near Kiama, New South Wales, that the French scientist, Mercanton, first reported the occurrence of positive directions for rocks of this age. "Une cube donne sans ambiguité: inclinaison boréale, 87°" (Mercanton, 1926*a*, p. 189). Although, as more data are obtained, there is likely to be much debate as to the exact stratigraphic position of the lower and upper reversal levels in different regions, the term Kiaman should avoid confusion with geological terminology. It would be incorrect to apply the terms "Permian Magnetic Division" or "Permian Magnetic Interval" because the beds with uniform positive polarity are not confined to that system but extend down into the Carboniferous. The definitions

given above are in terms of the Australian Permian section. Although it may be preferable to define the Division in terms of the geologically standard Permian of Russia, there is a clear historical precedent from Mercanton's pioneer work for the use of the Australian name.

Eventually it may be possible to erect a time scale based on paleomagnetic characteristics. Such a time scale should be defined in terms of observations on the ground, and should be independent of geological definitions. A whole sequence of new names may be needed, and to avoid confusion it is desirable that these should be defined in terms of observations in the standard rock sequences in each continent, otherwise much confusion will ensue as to what is observed fact, what is definition, and what is conjecture.

10D   PALEOMAGNETISM AND THE ORIGIN AND HISTORY OF ROCKS

§ **10D.1   General Remarks**   The magnetism of a rock depends on the minerals present, and on its mode of origin and history, so that, in principle, a study of these properties should provide information of interest for theories of origin and subsequent history. But in this present early stage of development, the interpretation of paleomagnetic observations depends heavily on geological ideas about origin and history, so that in general the flow of information has been in the reverse direction. For example, the fossil magnetism (NRM) of igneous bodies is often considered to be thermoremanent (TRM) and the main reason for this view is that the rock is considered from geological evidence to be igneous, and to have cooled from temperatures much higher than the Curie points of its magnetic minerals. In certain cases, studies of igneous contacts and laboratory investigations may support this view (Chapter Five), but such tests have been carried out on only a small proportion of material studied. This is not a criticism of the progress of paleomagnetism, but simply a statement that reflects its youthfulness. Nevertheless, there are certain paleomagnetic results that provide very useful evidence about origin and history for use in conjunction with that obtained by classical geological methods.

§ 10D.2 Applications to Igneous Bodies

The variations in magnetic properties in igneous bodies and their contacts are sometimes germane to such problems as differentiation, the distinction of sills and flows, the problem of the composite nature of intrusions and extrusions, and the question of magma temperatures.

Thick Differentiated Sills. A characteristic trend in magnetic differentiation is toward enrichment in iron, and it is to be expected that the variation of magnetic properties in a thick sill may reflect this process. Most of the studies of variations through thick sills have been done on the Tasmanian Dolerites (Jaeger and Joplin, 1955; Jaeger, 1957*b*; Jaeger and Green, 1958) and the Ferrar Dolerites (Bull, Irving, and Willis,

1962). The individual members of Tasmanian Dolerite are usually so thick that it is difficult in any one place to obtain a record from lower to upper contact, and the pattern of variation is built up by piecing together incomplete sections. Results are given here from two sills, the Mt. Wellington sill, which has been studied at surface exposures in its lower half, and a sill from the Great Lake region (about 100 miles north of Mt. Wellington), which has been studied in bore core through its upper half.

At Mt. Wellington the base of the sill is exposed, but the top contact is not seen. Its total thickness is probably 1200 ft or more. Both intensity and susceptibility values follow the same general trend (Figure 10.22). Beginning at the bottom chilled contact they are first moderate, and then fall to very low values within 100 ft of the base. Above 500 ft they increase sharply, falling again somewhat toward the summit. The iron minerals occur as discrete particles, and as irregular often skeletal crystals in the mesostasis. The high values of intensity and susceptibilty are associated with rocks with

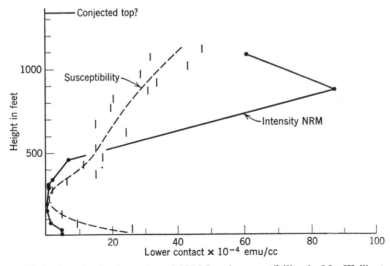

Figure 10.22. Variations in the intensity of NRM and susceptibility in Mt. Wellington Sill, Tasmania. The depths are counted upwards in feet from the lower contact. The NRM is indicated by dots connected by solid line and have been obtained as averages of 3 samples at each level. The susceptibilities are averages for 50-ft intervals and are from Jaeger (1957*b*). Figure redrawn from Bull, Irving, and Willis (1962), with the kind permission of the Royal Astronomical Society, London.

20 to 30 per cent mesostasis (Joplin, 1957), which are late stage differentiates, in places approaching granophyre. The results from the upper 1050 ft of a sill, which is thought from other geophysical evidence to be about 2000 ft thick, is given in Figure 10.23. Again the susceptibility and remanence values follow one another closely. Beginning at the bottom of the core, which is thought to be about the middle of the body, the values are intermediate, and then rise to high values, within about 200 ft of the top of the sill. There is a decrease in values toward the upper contact. The general picture that emerges from these results, and others described in the references cited, is that extensively differentiated sills are characterized by low values for susceptibility and remanent intensity in the lower one-third, and by high values in the upper portions, corresponding to late-stage iron enrichment.

The variations may, in some contexts, be useful for judging vertical position within such intrusions. Once experience has been gained in known situations, the expected magnetic profile may be predicted with some confidence, so that the position of a test sample may be estimated. In the Mt. Wellington sill, for example, the intensities vary by a factor 100 between the lower and the upper portions. Generally speaking it is a matter of experience in Tasmanian dolerite

that specimens with intensities in excess of about 30×10^{-4} emu/cm^3 may, with some confidence, be allocated to the upper portions of intrusions. No firm rules, however, can be laid down for all situations. It is a matter of gaining experience with the material on hand. The magnetic profiles may also be used to investigate the possibility of multiple intrusion; if multiple profiles occur then it suggests that several intrusive phases are present.

"Block-settling" Hypothesis of Dolerite Differentiation (Jaeger and Joplin, 1955). The foregoing account deals with some of the broad scale variations through thick sills. In detail, considerable fluctuations occur. In bore core 5001 in Tasmanian dolerite (Figure 10.23), successive samples yielded systematic variations in distances of the order of tens of feet (Figure 10.24). The values fluctuate by a factor 5, defined peaks being separated by regions with low values. The variations of remanent intensity and susceptibility follow each other closely. This lead Jaeger and Joplin to postulate that in the sill in question, the low regions represented "blocks" which had crystallized early beneath the solidified crust of the sill, and had fallen through the magma chamber as a single entity coming to rest on the solid lower surface of the chamber. The space between "blocks" became filled with late stage differ-

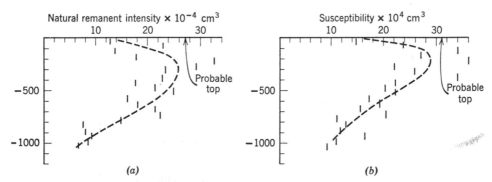

Figure 10.23. Variations in the intensity of NRM (*a*) and susceptibility (*b*) in the bore core 5001 Tasmanian dolerite. The depths are counted downwards in feet from the upper margin. The core is through the upper half of the sill. Measurements were made at approximately every 5 feet or less and averages over 50-ft intervals are given here. Redrawn from Jaeger and Joplin (1955), with the kind permission of the Geological Society of Australia and the authors.

entiates, thus giving the sharp peaks in the magnetic values. This suggestion cuts across current ideas of differentiation, which favor the mechanism of single crystal settling, as a means of achieving progressive change. The "block-settling" idea is also consistent with petrographic and density measurements on this bore core. Furthermore, Jaeger and Joplin present calculations to show that small crystals are not likely to survive a long fall through a hot magma, but that the "block-settling" hypothesis overcomes this difficulty. Their suggestion, being rather radical, has met with serious (Walker, 1956; Hess, 1956) but perhaps not fatal (Jaeger and Joplin, 1956) criticism, and provides an interesting illustration of the way in which magnetic studies provide a new approach to a long-standing geological problem.

Sills or Lava Flows? It is often difficult to tell from field evidence whether an igneous sheet is intrusive or extrusive. In either case the lower contact relations would be comparable, and it is in the upper contact that differences might be expected: if the body is intrusive, signs of heating in the country rock might be expected; if the body is extrusive—the upper surface may be weathered, there will be no evidence of baking of the country rock, and, in some cases, igneous rock fragments similar to the body may occur in the overlying strata, indicating that the latter were derived in part from the body, and are therefore younger. To these Everitt (1960) has added a paleomagnetic criterion. If the rock is intrusive, then upper contact country rock will have a TRM parallel in direction to that of the body. If the country rock is sedimentary, then the intensity of magnetization will be greater, and the directions less scattered at the contact than at a distance from the body. If the country rock is igneous, there may be neither intensity nor dispersion contrast; and if it and the body were formed at a time when the field was not changing, there need be no contrast in properties, and the method fails. The method is most applicable to igneous bodies set in sedimentary rock. Although it applies

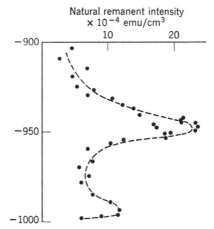

Figure 10.24. Detailed variation of NRM intensity in dolerite sill, bore core no. 5001 Tasmanian dolerite. Redrawn from Jaeger and Joplin (1955) with trend added.

primarily to upper contact relations, it is desirable also to study the lower contact to see if the properties there also conform to the general picture.

The origin of certain igneous bodies associated with Carboniferous sediments in Shropshire has long been in dispute. They are sometimes referred to as the Midland Basalts, although opinions differ as to which are intrusive and which extrusive. The field evidence is not definitive. Everitt studied 7 bodies [6.30–35], such as the one described below. The Titterstone Clee Hill body is saucer-shaped and the mean direction of two samples (5 specimens) was 222, +26 with a mean intensity of 700×10^{-6} emu/g. The country rock is Millstone Grit. A sample in the underlying baked sandstone, 2 ft from the margin, gave a direction 203, +22 with an intensity of 10×10^{-6} emu/g. Two samples from overlying sandstone, one 6 in. and one 5 ft from the contact, gave mean directions 197, +20 and 192, +25 with intensities of 30 and 3×10^{-6} respectively, the fall-off in that distance being by a factor 10. Two samples from country rock 200 ft from the contact gave very widely scattered directions, and intensities of 0.16×10^{-6} emu/g. The enhanced intensity in the contact sandstone and the small scatter of directions parallel to those in the body itself indicate that the body is intrusive. The coverage in terms of samples is small, but the case seems reasonably well established.

Subdivision of Ignimbrite Sheets (Hatherton, 1954a, b). The Patetere ignimbrites cover an area of about 100 by 150 miles in the North Island of New Zealand. The sheet boundaries are difficult to locate, and a broad division into three (lower, middle, and upper) has been recognized geologically. The vertical variation of magnetic properties, expressed as the ratio Q_n (§ 2.02), is plotted in Figure 10.25. The values increase toward those sheet boundaries recognized geologically, and, in addition, a finer subdivision is apparent, indicating that the geologically recognized

sheets are multiple in character. The reason for this variation (in particular the enhanced intensity of NRM towards the margin) is not known. Hatherton presents calculations giving the cooling rate of such a sheet which correlate in form with the variations observed, and this suggests a connection with the particle size spectrum. Variable viscous decay with time may also play a part. Despite the uncertainty in this regard, the effect is of interest for the origin of these ignimbrites, since they set closer limits to the sizes of the units laid down in each outburst.

The Temperature of Clastic Volcanic Deposits. Many types of clastic deposits are produced directly or indirectly from volcanic activity, and it is useful to know the tem-

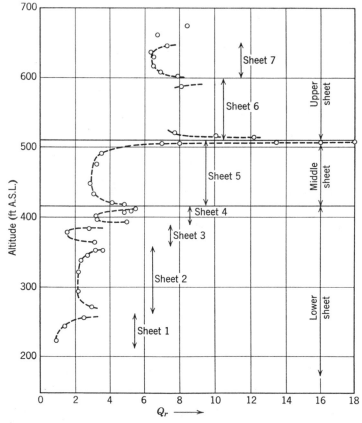

Figure 10.25. Magnetic profile of the Patetere ignimbrites at Waipapa, New Zealand. The Q_n values are measured for $F = 0.5$ oe. The geologically recognized sheets are indicated on the right. Redrawn from Hatherton (1954a), with the kind permission of the American Geophysical Union and T. Hatherton.

perature of their formation. The geological evidence, however, is often qualitative or inconclusive. Some types, such as tuffs, pumice, and scoria, were probably laid down at temperatures only a little less than that of the original magma. Others, such as agglomerate and volcanic mudflows, are thought to have formed at or near atmospheric temperatures. Aramaki and Akimoto (1957) suggest this test: if the fragments were deposited at temperatures above their Curie point then their NRM directions should be uniform and parallel to the Earth's field at the time of cooling, but if fragments had cooled before incorporation in the deposit then the directions would be random. As a test case a study was made of deposits whose origin is clear from the geological evidence (Figure 10.26). The directions in blocks from three *nuée ardente* deposits are uniform and near the present field. The deposits are all recent, and it is known, from beds *in situ* in Japan, that the Earth's field during this time was close to the present field. Thus the fragments in these deposits were at temperatures above their Curie points (estimated to exceed 400°C) when laid down. The directions in blocks from three Pleistocene and Recent mudflow deposits are widely scattered, indicating formation at temperatures

less than 400°C. These results are consistent with the nature of the deposits inferred from geological observations, and it is probable that the method will be useful when applied to situations in which the geological evidence is less clear.

Magma Temperatures. At some distance from an igneous contact the warmed country rock may acquire a partial TRM (§ 5.05). In principle, thermal demagnetization of this component should give the maximum temperature to which the rock was heated. Blundell (1961a) points out that from such a study of a series of samples collected at increasing distance from a contact, it ought to be possible to provide a graph of the maximum temperatures reached at different distances from the contact and thus to infer the temperature of the igneous material. The full test has not been carried out, but Blundell quotes results of Everitt, from a sample of Devonian lava collected 1.4 m from the contact of a Tertiary dike in which the "Tertiary" partial TRM was found to be destroyed at 500°C leaving a magnetization with a "Devonian" direction. This indicates that, during intrusion, the lava at that distance from the contact was only heated to 500°C. There are difficulties in interpreting isolated results, since the laboratory

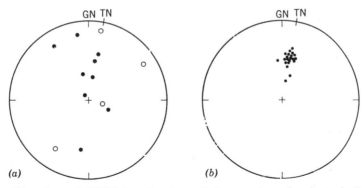

Figure 10.26. Directions of NRM in volcanic mud flows and nueé ardente in Japan. Equal-area projection. (*a*) Direction in different blocks in mud-flows associated with volcanic eruptions: Bandai-san (1888) 4 samples; central core of Hakone volcano (later Pleistocene) 5 samples; Ko-Fuji volcano (later Pleistocene) 4 samples. (*b*) Directions in different blocks in four nueé ardente deposits of the Asama volcano: Kambara (1783) 5 samples; Agatsuma (1783) 12 samples; Oikwake (prehistoric) 4 samples. GN is geomagnetic north and TN true north. Redrawn from Aramaki and Akimoto (1957), with the kind permission of the *American Journal of Science* and the authors.

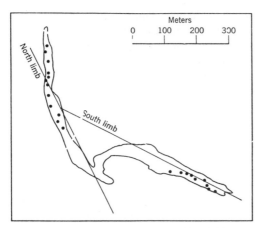

Figure 10.27. Outline of the F'derik hard hematite ore body. Dots are sampling sites. From Gross and Strangway (1961), with the kind permission of the *Journal of Economic Geology* and the authors.

heating may disrupt the record. Furthermore, heating may have occurred over many years and viscous effects may have to be taken into account when interpreting the short-term laboratory experiments.

§ **10D.3 Applications to Banded Iron Formation** (Gross and Strangway, 1961) Banded iron formation may contain 10 per cent of iron, but enrichment must occur to bring the concentration up to 50 per cent or so before it can be exploited commercially. This may occur in various ways. (1) *Syngenetic ore*. If the deposition of gangue material is interrupted, e.g., by wave action, then beds enriched in iron will accumulate. Lowering of water level in a depositing basin might result in enrichment of the exposed beds. (2) *Metamorphic ore*. During metamorphism the iron may be mobilized and migrate to favorable structurally environments. (3) *Magmatic ore*. Magmatic fluids derived from adjacent intrusions could either supply additional iron or remove gangue. (4) *Lateritic ore*. During surface weathering, gangue may be leached, resulting in a soft ore cap.

From the developers' point of view it is very helpful to know which process has been operative. If the ore is syngenetic, then it would be advantageous to reconstruct from field mapping, the form and extent of the original depositing basin. If the ore is metamorphic or magmatic, it is reasonable to expect that secondary structures, such as faults or folds, would act as channels or traps for the ore, and in this case exploitation would be guided by structural considerations. If weathering were the cause of the enrichment then it would be useful to study the topography at the time of enrichment. In many cases this origin cannot be ascertained by means of normal geological methods, and the fossil magnetism of the body may be studied with profit, as the following example indicates.

The plan of the F'derik ore body in the Fort Gouraud deposits of Mauritania is set out in Figure 10.27. It is divided into two limbs intersecting at about 37°. The North limb dips about 65°E and the South limb is nearly vertical. The NRM directions *in situ* fall into 3 groups (Figure 10.28). Group *A*, which is from the North limb, has NE declination with shallow negative inclination. Group *B*, also from the North limb, has westerly directions and is represented by only a few observations. Group *C*, from the South limb, has northerly or southerly directions, which may be a reversed set. The angle between the mean declinations of groups *A* and *C* is 33°, comparable to the angle between limbs, and upon rotating the North limb into alignment with the South limb, and restoring them to the horizontal plane, the directions coalesce into a single group. Gross and Strangway interpret this to mean "that the bulk of the 'deep hematite ore' at F'Derik is either predominantly syngenetic and represents a concentration of iron within the original basin during sedimentation, or that it was formed by the leaching of the iron formation when the beds were flat lying (neglecting any primary dip)." The *B* directions are taken to indicate a subsidiary secondary magnetization developed in some parts of the body during folding and metamorphism, so that although most hematite seems to have formed when the beds were approximately flat, it appears that there was subsidiary redistribution or addition at a later stage. Thus the method appears to be capable of distinguishing between different modes of origin within the same ore body. Moreover, its application is not confined to banded iron ores, but may be useful in nonferrous ore bodies which contain magnetic minerals as accessories. The above results, although of a preliminary nature, point the way to interesting developments.

§ **10D.4 The Paleolatitude of Oil Fields** (Irving and Gaskell, 1962) In Chapter Nine the paleolatitude spectra of various types of sedimentary deposits were described, rather from the standpoint of studying the basic question of the axial symmetry of the field. If the internal consistency of these spectra is considered to justify the method, then the latter may be useful for exploration purposes. Thus, if a

certain useful deposit in known areas is found to have a characteristic paleomagnetic inclination, then this property might be used in regions undergoing exploration. A possible application to oil exploration is now given.

In oil search there are, broadly speaking, two main questions. First, are there structures in which oil can be trapped, and are suitable reservoirs rocks present? Second, is the environment one in which oil may have formed initially? The first may be satisfactorily studied by normal exploration techniques. The second is more difficult, since the mechanism of oil formation and its later possible migration from source bed to reservoir are matters of conjecture. There is no direct method of detecting oil other than by drilling. Thus ideas about the origin of oil affect, to some extent, the method of exploration pursued. It is thought that organic remains in sediments are transformed into petroleum, which later collects into reservoirs. The abundance of suitable organisms

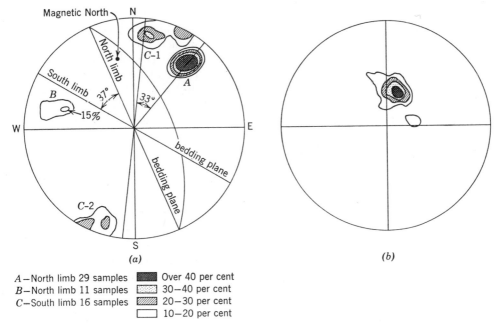

A—North limb 29 samples   ▓ Over 40 per cent
B—North limb 11 samples   ▦ 30—40 per cent
C—South limb 16 samples   ▨ 20—30 per cent
                 □ 10—20 per cent

Figure 10.28. Schematic representation of the NRM directions in the F'derik hard hematite ore body. (*a*) Directions *in situ*. (*b*) Directions of groups *A* and *C* after restoration to horizontal. Directions plotted on equal-area projections as contours within which given proportions of the sample are contained. Redrawn from Gross and Strangway (1961), with the kind permission of the *Journal of Economic Geology* and the authors.

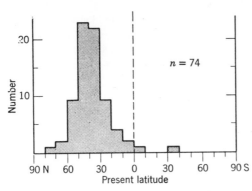

Figure 10.29. Equal-angle latitude histogram of the major oil fields.

may have depended on climate, and it is of some interest to test this point by studying the paleolatitude spectrum of oil occurrences. Few paleomagnetic data have been reported from oil fields themselves, but useful results can be obtained by extrapolating from nearby regions. Attention is confined to important producing fields, and to those for which the paleomagnetic coverage provides estimates of paleolatitudes.

The great majority of oil fields lie in the northern hemisphere (Figure 10.29). Although exploration in the southern hemisphere has been much less extensive, the preponderance of the northern hemisphere fields is so great that the distribution can hardly be entirely a matter of variability in study. Oil fields in Paleozoic beds are mostly between latitudes of 60° and 30°, whereas in the Mesozoic and Tertiary progressively lower values occur. Such features indicate that the causes controlling the occurrence of oil conform to some broad pattern. If the causes were of a local and miscellaneous nature, then it would be more likely that oil would have been found in all latitudes with roughly equal frequency.

The paleolatitudes show a trend with time in the reverse sense to that of present latitudes; the mean values are, for the Paleozoic 3° N′, Mesozoic 25° N′, Tertiary 28° N′. These results suggest that measurements of the paleomagnetic inclination may be a useful tool by which the oil geologist may, along with other criteria, judge the likelihood of any suitable rock structure containing oil. For instance, if Figure 10.30 does in fact contain a representative sample, the best chance of finding oil in useful quantities in Paleozoic beds is in paleolatitudes of less than 30° (inclination 0° to 50°). When λ_p is greater than 40° ($I > 60°$) the chances would appear to be small, and where λ_p exceeds 60° ($I > 74°$), the chances may be remote. These suggestions are based on current data and may require modification as new results come to light.

10E DETECTING CHANGES IN THE EARTH'S RADIUS

§ **10E.1   Introductory**   Paleomagnetism provides means for estimating the Earth's radius, r_p, in the past. The idea is that if the radius has not changed, then the paleomagnetic directions in rocks of the same age at widespread localities within a test region comprising a stable continental block should conform to a geocentric dipole field. If they do not, then either, (1) the radius has changed and these changes may be calculated (§ 10E.3), or (2) the inference that the test region is stable is incorrect, or (3) the field has been nondipolar. Determinations of r_p are, therefore, contingent on assuming a geocentric dipole field, and tectonic stablity of the test region. The procedure is to survey the variations in the rate of change in the paleogeomagnetic field over a test region, and is severely limited by the statistical fluctuations in the paleomagnetic data. The effects will be most noticeable over large test regions, and the only suitable data presently available are from the Devonian, Permian, and Triassic of the Europe-Siberia region. The data from other regions are either too few or insufficiently spaced. The results given here relate only to European-Siberian data and a general analysis including data from other regions will be needed before firm conclusions may be drawn, but the present data appear capable of refuting some of the extreme hypotheses of Earth expansion previously formulated.

§ **10E.2 Hypotheses of an Expanding Earth** Some workers suggest that the Earth has grown in the course of time. Others advocate contraction, but only by small amounts. The essence of expansion hypotheses is that at an early stage in its history the Earth had a radius roughly one-half its present value of about 6370 km, and that it was entirely covered by a sialic crust. Under expansion the crust shattered, and the fragments, which retained their primitive dimensions, became the modern continents. The gaps between fragments enlarged, and the exposed layers, because of their greater density, remained at a lower level and became the ocean basins. Most of the ex-

pansion is reflected in the increase of these, so that the solid angle subtended at the Earth's center by any continent will have diminished in time.

In all expansion hypotheses the total increase in radius is roughly the same, but the rates of increase proposed vary greatly (Figure 10.31). Egyed (1957) advocates a uniform increase in the paleoradius basing his estimates on these four arguments. Taking the present continents (area between 1.5 and 2×10^{18} cm³) as the primitive surface, he calculates an initial radius of 3500–4000 km. If expansion began at an early stage in the Earth's history 4.4×10^9 years ago, then a radius increase of 0.06 cm/year is obtained. Second, he contends that progressive increase of the ocean basins through expansion would cause a progressive emergence of the sialic

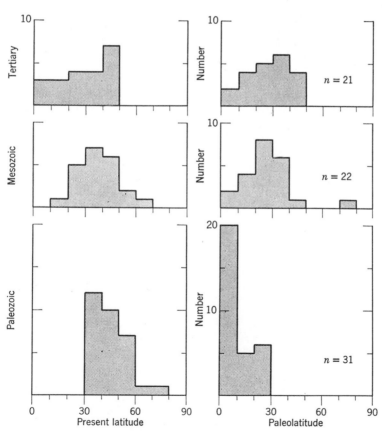

Figure 10.30. Equal-angle histograms of the present and paleolatitude of oil fields. The results are plotted irrespective of whether N or S latitude and are grouped into eras.

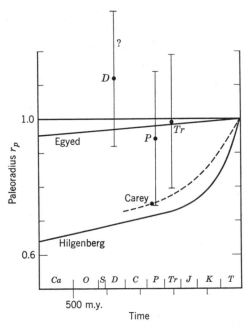

Figure 10.31. Changes in the Earth's radius since the beginning of the Cambrian. Geological time is set out horizontally, and the paleoradius vertically; $r_p = 1.0$ is the present radius. The hypotheses of expansion are as follows: Egyed 0.05 cm/year; Hilgenberg (1962b); Carey (1958) $r_p = 0.75$ for late Paleozoic and the dotted line being surmise from his text. The values determined paleomagnetically by Ward are D Devonian, P Permian, Tr Triassic, the limits being estimates of the standard deviations of the means.

areas, so that the areas of the crust covered by shallow seas should diminish with time. He calculates from paleogeographic maps that such a decrease has occurred, and estimates a radius increase of 0.04 cm/year from the maps of Termier and Termier (1952) since the Middle Ordovician, and 0.07 cm/year since the beginning of the Paleozoic from Strahow's maps. Third, Egyed attributes the supposed decrease in the Earth's angular velocity with time to expansion, and obtains from this a radius increase of 0.05 cm/year. Finally, he assumes the Earth's inner core to consist of "ultra high-pressure phases," formed at the inception of the solar system under pressures much greater than those within the Earth today. The inner core, outer core (assumed silicate),

and mantle are considered to represent progressive steps in a series of irreversible changes towards less dense phases of larger volume. On this assumption Egyed calculates a radial increase of 0.05 cm/year. These diverse arguments yield estimates in good agreement and give a mean rate of increase of 0.05 cm/year.

On the other hand Hilgenberg (1962a, b) and Carey (1958) prefer that the rate of change increase with time. Hilgenberg suggests a more or less constant rate up to the early Mesozoic of about 0.17 cm/year, and thereafter a rapid increase, the average rate since the Jurassic being 1.1 cm/year. Carey believes that the primitive diameter "was less than half its present diameter and its surface was less than a quarter of its present surface." He says that "the surface area has roughly doubled since the Paleozoic and that the Late Paleozoic diameter was about ¾ of the present diameter." This represents an increase of about 1600 km and an average rate of increase in radius of roughly 0.5 cm/year since the late Paleozoic. Carey's desire for an expanding Earth arises out of his studies of relative continental displacements. When attempting to reassemble the continents on the basis of his orocline concept, he finds that he is unable to do this satisfactorily on a globe or projection whose size bears the same relationship to his model continents as the present Earth does to the present continents. These difficulties, he contends, vanish when the reassembly is attempted on a smaller globe, and so rather than abandon the reassembly he resorts to the further hypothesis of a growing Earth. The rapid increase in the rate of change is required to account for the large dispersion of the continents after break-up in the Mesozoic, and seems to be thought of by him as the cause of continental drift.

§ 10E.3   **Estimates of Paleoradius.** The difference in the paleomagnetic inclination between two places depends on the difference in their paleolatitudes and not on the absolute distance between them, so that if the Earth has expanded then the rate of change of paleomagnetic inclination with distance in a paleomeridional direction will have decreased with time. Thus one procedure for detecting changes in the paleoradius is to compare this rate of change with that of a geocentric dipole field on an Earth of the present radius (Egyed, 1960). Suppose the paleomagnetic inclinations (I_1 and I_2) are known at two stations, and that they both refer to the field at geological time t when the field had a constant configuration relative to the stations. Assume that the configuration was that of a geocentric dipole, and that the stations have not moved relative to each other since t, then the paleoradius (r_p) at time t is given by

$$r_p = \Delta l(\lambda_{p1} - \lambda_{p2})^{-1} \qquad (10.2)$$

Δl is the distance between the paleolatitude circles on which the stations lie, and λ_{p1} and λ_{p2} are the paleolatitudes estimated from I_1 and I_2 by equation (3.3). The method only applies when the stations are situated on a crustal block which has retained its primitive dimensions. If, during expansion, each station moves radially outwards, like marks on the skin of a balloon, then their geographical coordinates would be unchanged and paleomagnetism would not reveal a radial increase. The measurement is one of the variations of a rate of change, and because of statistical fluctuations is subject to much uncertainty, as this illustration shows. The rate of change of inclination per degree of latitude is larger in low latitudes than in high, so that the strongest effects are felt in low latitudes. The inclination differences between stations in a favorable test region spaced 3340 km apart along a meridian (30° of arc on the present radius) one at the equator and the other at a latitude 30° on an Earth the present size, is 49°. When the stations are the same distance apart on a reduced Earth of radius 5370 km, one at the equator and the other at latitude 36° the difference increases by 6° to 55°. Thus statistical fluctuations (expressed as standard deviations of the means) in the determinations of I_1 and I_2 of 10° for example, such as commonly occur, means that radius

Table 10.4   The Earth's Paleoradius, r_p.
Results for 3 periods are compared against the expansion advocated by previous hypotheses. E using calculation method of Egyed (1960); E_1 value obtained by Cox and Doell (1961). W values using Ward's method, Ward (1963) and based on A group data. Present radius taken as unity.

	r_p, paleo-magnetic	r_p, expansion hypotheses		
		Hilgen-berg	Egyed	Carey
Triassic (E)	1.13			
Triassic (W)	0.99	0.73	0.98(5)	0.78
Permian (E_1)	0.99			
Permian (E_2)	0.96	0.72	0.98(1)	0.75
Permian (W)	0.94			
Devonian (E)	1.23			
Devonian (W)	1.12	0.69	0.96	—

changes of less than 20 per cent are unlikely to be detected.

Paleoradius estimates using paleomagnetic results from Europe and Siberia are listed in Table 10.4. Stations in this region have been arranged into broad geographical groups, and from these, data have been selected in pairs for use in equation (10.2). The separation (Δl) was obtained trigonometrically by calculating the distance between the paleolatitude circles through each locality about the average paleomagnetic pole (Table 6.2) using an Earth radius of 6370 km. The standard deviations are large (the order of 30 per cent) so that the estimates do not differ significantly from the present radius. Results from three periods are given, the spread of sampling localities for other periods and places being insufficient for these purposes.

Egyed (1961) and Ward (1963) have suggested more generalized procedures not restricted to results from stations lying roughly on the same paleomeridian. Ward uses the criterion that the most probable paleoradius is that for which the dispersion of paleomagnetic poles is a minimum. The procedure is to vary the paleoradius arbitrarily, recalculating the poles for each station for each value of r_p until minimum pole dispersion is achieved. The method has the considerable advantage that it relates the data to their correct spherical environment. The values for three periods are given in Table 10.4 and plotted in Figure 10.31—the standard deviations (about 20 per cent) being appreciably less than before, since the data are more fully utilized. There is no systematic trend of the mean values with time. The results are inconsistent with the hypotheses of Hilgenberg and Carey,[3] but their precision is insufficient to test for the slow rate of increase advocated by Egyed. The inconsistency with Carey's hypothesis is substantial and appears therefore to invalidate Earth expansion as a cause of continental drift. It should be noted that the Devonian determination is based on the *A* group data, and the inconsistencies which have now appeared in the Devonian data from Europe and northern Asia (§ 6.05) may invalidate it.

10F   EXTRATERRESTRIAL PALEOMAGNETISM

Meteorites are samples of extraterrestrial material and their natural remanent magnetization (NRM) may provide information relevant to theories of their origin. There are three broad classes of meteorites, the *irons* composed of nickel-iron, the *stones* composed chiefly of silicates, and the *stony-irons* composed of nickel-iron and silicates. The stony meteorites are divided into the *chondrites,* which possess a characteristic spheroidal texture, and the *achondrites,* in which this texture is absent. Meteorites are believed by many investigators to have originated from the disruption of a parent body (or bodies) in the asteroid zone of the solar system, the iron and stony varieties being derived respectively from the core and mantle

[3] Recently, van Hilten (1963) has given results of calculations of paleoradius based on paleomagnetic data, which indicate an expansion by the amounts advocated by Hilgenberg and Carey. It is understood that van Hilten's results, which contradict those of Ward although based on approximately the same data, are to be discussed shortly in the *Geophysical Journal.*

of the parent. The irons are thought to have cooled very slowly from high temperatures, so that the parent was apparently solid before disruption. This is a much oversimplified picture, and there is no general agreement about the details of meteoritic history; some may have come directly from the parent, others may have passed through intermediate cycles prior to their arrival on Earth. But there is one general point to which their magnetic properties may refer, and this is the question of whether or not the parent(s) possessed a molten core. If such a core were present it may have generated a magnetic field comparable to the Earth's. As the core solidified the field would disappear, and it is not to be expected that the iron meteorites would have a remanence dating from that time. But part, at least, of the parent mantle may have cooled through the Curie point while the core was still fluid, and thereby acquired a thermoremanent magnetization (TRM). If remanence of TRM type were found in stony meteorites supposedly derived from the parent mantle, then it would indicate that a molten core was originally present. The absence of such components would not disprove the hypothesis of a molten core since this core may not have generated a field in the first place; moreover the original TRM may have been destroyed during the violent history of these bodies.

One potential source of error is the disturbing effect of heating during passage through the atmosphere. Lovering, Parry, and Jaeger (1960) show that in iron meteorites the temperature at depths of 3 cm or more beneath the fused crust never rose above 100°C, which is low compared to the Curie points observed for meteorites (see below). Moreover, the effect is likely to be less in stony meteorites, which have lower thermal conductivities. This conclusion is borne out by observations on the *Brewster chondrite* (Weaving, 1962a). This body has a diameter of 15 cm. The intensity of NRM at the edge is 0.29 emu/g, which falls in a distance of 1.2 cm, to a roughly constant value of 0.005 emu/g. The surface magnetization is of IRM type, and although its precise cause is uncertain it is considered by Weaving to be connected with ablation during fall. Thus, it is important when studying meteorites, to obtain specimens from depths sufficient to avoid these effects, and the following descriptions relate to specimens taken from several centimeters beneath fused surfaces.

The iron meteorites cannot be expected to provide much evidence, since they are coarsely crystalline, and therefore soft magnetically. This is shown by studies of the *Bingara* (*No. 2*) *iron meteorite* whose NRM falls to 7 per cent of its initial value in alternating magnetic fields of 100 oe peak value. Comparable instability of NRM is also shown by certain stony meteorites. For example, the *Moore County eucrite* (Lovering, 1959), which is an achondrite, loses its NRM after demagnetization in alternating magnetic fields of 50 oe, and that of the *Mokoia chondrite* disappears on heating to 200°C (Stacey, Lovering, and Parry, 1961). In these cases the NRM is probably a viscous magnetization acquired recently in the geomagnetic field, and there is certainly no detectable memory of extraterrestrial magnetic fields. Mokoia is a carbonaceous chondrite, which as a class, are believed by some workers to be primitive types which have probably not been strongly heated since formation; the absence of a stable remanence is consistent with this view.

On the other hand, components of high magnetic stability have been found in four other stony meteorites—all chondrites and all magnetically anisotropic.

Specimens of the *Mt. Browne, Farmington,* and *Homestead chondrites,* taken from 5 cm or more beneath fused crusts, have been studied (Stacey and Lovering, 1959; Stacey, Lovering, and Parry, 1961). The major magnetic phase (determined from J_s/T curves, § 2.08) responsible for 80 to 90 per cent of the saturation magnetization is kamacite, which is the α-phase iron-nickel alloy with 5 to 6 per cent nickel, and which has a Curie point of 750°C. Thermal demagnetization of NRM reveals three components. First, there are low temperature components, which disappear between 100° and 200°C, and which are considered to have been acquired isothermally in the Earth's field since fall. Second, there are medium temperature components, which are lost between 550° and 650°C and which, it is thought, were acquired either thermoremanently or by phase change in the presence of a field; these components are due either to taenite, plessite, or metakamacite, which are unstable on heating, probably due to their tendency to diffuse into the much more abundant kamacite. Third, there are high temperature components, which disappear between 720° and 780°C at the α-γ transition of kamacite; this is not a true remanence but arises from anisotropy of the kamacite phase. The medium temperature components are the most important paleomagnetically, and granted they were acquired during cooling, then comparison of their natural magnitudes with the TRM acquired in known fields in the laboratory shows that the strength of the magnetic field of the parent body was between 0.1 and 1.0 oe. Stacey, Lovering, and Parry conclude that "the magnetic evidence is consistent with the supposition that the chondrites once formed parts of the mantle of a body with a fluid metal core which produced a magnetic field of terrestrial type."

The fourth chondrite studied is the *Brewster meteorite* (Weaving, 1962*a*, *b*), which, in its central portions, gives results corresponding broadly to those just described. The magnetic phase has a wide range of Curie points, with notable values in the 500° to 650°C and 750° to 770°C ranges. The dominant component of NRM has disappeared at 600°C, and corresponds to the medium temperature range above; this component is stable with respect to alternating magnetic fields, and produces demagnetization curves of the TRM type. The magnitude of this component indicates that it was acquired initially in a field of 0.1 oe, similar to that for the three other chondrites. No high temperature anisotropy component was detected.

Reference list of
paleomagnetic results

The results are presented as a table with explanatory notes. The results are not all of equal value; some are based on detailed studies of numerous samples from rock units of well-defined geological age, whereas others are based on a preliminary study of a few samples whose ages may be known only within wide limits. The notes are intended to describe this variability. Results which do not fulfill the minimum reliability criteria are entered in brackets.

The results are arranged into 12 period-groups as follows: 1 Precambrian, 2 Cambrian, 3 Ordovician, 4 Silurian, 5 Devonian, 6 Carboniferous, 7 Permian, 8 Triassic, 9 Jurassic, 10 Cretaceous, 11 Tertiary, 12 Quaternary. Each period-group contains results from rock units which, on the basis of their geological age, are here assigned to one of these periods. In many cases the age of the rock unit is defined only within ranges which are not confined within a single geological period; in such cases the results are listed in one period-group with cross-references in other appropriate period-groups. Within period-groups the results are arranged according to the geographic location of the rock units as follows: Europe, Asia, Africa, Australia, North America, South America, the Arctic regions, Antarctica, and the Oceanic Islands. The results in each period-group are in two parts—a main part containing the results available to the author up to November 1962, and a supplement containing results which became available to the author between then and October 1963. In a few in-stances late additions have been made to the main part rather than to the supplement. The table contains 11 columns. The detail given in originals is not always sufficient to allow entries to be made in all columns.

Column 1 contains the reference number of the result. This number consists of the period-group number (listed above) followed by the result number.

Column 2 gives the location of the rock unit specified by country and geographical coordinates. If the area is large, either the mean geographical position or a range is specified. In some cases the coordinates were not given in the original, and where possible they have been read from standard atlases. The values have been quoted to the maximum accuracy permitted by the descriptions in originals, but never to better than 0.1°.

Column 3 gives the name of the rock unit studied. Where possible a specific geological name is given. In other cases, due either to the absence of a specific geological name, or to inadequate descriptions in originals, a convenient descriptive name is adopted.

Column 4 gives the age of the rock unit studied. The geological age is specified by these period symbols: Precambrian Pc, Cambrian C, Ordovician O, Silurian S, Devonian D, Carboniferous C, Permian P, Triassic Tr, Jurassic J, Cretaceous K, Tertiary T, Quaternary Q. Subdivisions of periods from Cambrian to Cretaceous, where recognized, are denoted by u, m, or l. Epochs within the Tertiary (Paleocene, Eocene, etc.) are denoted by Tpa, To, Te, Tm, and Tp. The Quaternary is divided into Recent (Qr), and Pleistocene (Qp). Subdivision of the Precambrian is not attempted. Estimates of the absolute age of the rock units are also given. These estimates were obtained in one of two ways. If radiometric determinations are available the values are entered and indicated by an asterisk. Otherwise the geological age (or age range) has been translated into absolute values using Kulp's 1961 Time Scale (Kulp, 1961). For epoch boundaries prior to the Tertiary the values are read from Kulp's Time Scale, then 5 m.y. is added or subtracted in such a way as to provide a wider time range. For epochs in the Tertiary a similar procedure is adopted, except that the leeway allowed is 2 m.y.

Column 5 contains an estimate of the mean direction of magnetization. The declination D_m is reckoned clockwise east from geographic north, and I_m, the inclination, is regarded as negative if the direction is upward and positive when below the horizontal. For rock units in which the beds are undisturbed the horizontal is the present-day horizontal, but if the beds have been tilted the horizontal is assumed to be the bedding plane which, in the case of igneous rocks, is obtained from adjacent sediments. If the results contain directions of both positive and negative polarity (see Column 8) the estimate of the mean irrespective of sign is given, the direction quoted being that which points toward the northern hemisphere paleomagnetic pole (see Column 9). Values are quoted to the nearest whole degree.

Columns 6 and 7 contain estimates of the precision of the observations and the error in the mean. These values have usually been obtained by Fisher's analysis (§ 4.07). The precision is an estimate, k, of Fisher's κ and describes the distribution of points about the mean direction (D_m, I_m). The circle of confidence a_{95} is the half-angle (quoted to the nearest degree) of the cone whose axis is the direction (D_m, I_m) and within which the true mean lies with a probability of 95 per cent. The precision and error are not always comparable as between different entries, since they have been calculated using differing schemes for weighting according to the number of specimens, samples, and collecting sites, and ac-

cording to variation in the within-sample, within-site, and between-site precision. The procedures used are indicated in the notes when adequate information is available in the original.

Column 8 records the polarity of the directions, the convention being described in § 4.13. The occurrence of both (or mixed) polarities is denoted by M.

Column 9 gives estimates (to the nearest degree) of the paleomagnetic pole position specified by its northern hemisphere coordinates. Estimates of the error in the pole position are given in brackets. If the pole position was calculated directly from D_m, I_m, the errors δp and δm are the semi-axes of the elliptical error area round the pole at a probability of 95 per cent, δp in the colatitude direction and δm perpendicular to it (method I, § 4.12). If the pole was calculated by the application of Fisher's statistics to poles obtained at a lower sampling level the error area is a circle of radius δp ($= \delta m$) (method II, § 4.12).

Columns 10 and 11 give the reference numbers used in previous lists—(*GSAB*) that in the *Bulletin of the Geological Society of America* (Cox and Doell, 1960), and (*GJ*) those in the *Geophysical Journal of the Royal Astronomical Society* (first list, **3**, 96–111; second list, **3**, 444–449; third list, **5**, 72–79; fourth list, **6**, 263–267; fifth list, **7**, 263–274; sixth list, **8**, 249–257; seventh list, **9**). Complete numerical data are not always given in originals and many supplementary calculations have been made by the above-mentioned compilers, and their results are often used in this reference list. In addition this reference list contains the results of many new calculations. When there is overlap the values in this and previous lists will correspond exactly or approximately, but differences may arise through the adoption of different methods of combining data, or through errors in computation, or through the incorporation of data not at the time available to earlier compilers. By and large these differences are geophysically unimportant. The history of any particular result may be traced by reference to the original, to the above-mentioned compilations using the numbers in Columns 10 and 11, and to the notes given on pp. 316–362.

Reference List of Paleomagnetic Directions and Pole Positions

Reference Number	Rock Units Studied — Location	Name	Age	Directions of Magnetization — D_m, I_m	k	a_{95}	Polarity	Paleomagnetic Pole — λ', $\phi'(\delta p, \delta m)$	Previous Reference Numbers — BGSA	GJ
PRECAMBRIAN (OLDER THAN ABOUT 600 M.Y.)										
1.01	Scotland 58N, 6W	Torridonian Sandstone Series (upper)	Pc	123, +44	12	5	M	06, 43E (4, 6)	B1-12	1/126
1.02	Scotland 58N, 6W	Torridonian Sandstone Series (lower)	Pc	307, +34	40	7	−	35, 118W (5, 8)	B13-16	1/127
1.03	England 53N, 3W	Longmyndian	Pc	114, +29	5	12	M	02, 120W (7, 13)	B17-21	1/128
2.01	Scotland	Younger Gabbros, Aberdeenshire		see entry **2.01**					—	2/40
1.04	Norway 60.5N, 11E	Sparagmites	Pc	11, −21	7	24	M	18, 179E (12, 25)	—	2/40
2.13	Czechoslovakia	Barrandian Porphyrites		see entries **2.10** to **2.14**						
1.05	U.S.S.R. 60N, 117E	Sinian Sediments	Pc-€	35, −07			−	21, 101W (4, 9)	—	6/69
1.06	South Africa 26S, 28E	Pilansberg Dikes	Pc (1290 *)	24, +69	124	6	−	08, 43E (9, 10)	B89, 90	1/141
1.07	South Africa 25.5S, 28E	Bushveld Gabbro	Pc (1920 *)	11, +59	70	9	−	23, 36E (12, 12)	B91, 92	1/142
1.08	Australia 13S, 132E	Edith River Volcanics	Pc	90, +48		18	+	06, 14W (15, 24)	B87, 88	1/145
1.09	Australia 21S, 120E	Nullagine Lavas	Pc	143, +64		8	+	51, 18W (10, 13)	B86	1/144
1.10	Australia 14S, 132E	Buldiva Quartzite	Pc	243, +38		12	−	30, 121W (8, 14)	B85	1/143
1.11	U.S.A. 31N, 105W	Hazel Formation (flat-lying)	Pc	(316, +56)	(35)	(6)	−	(53, 173W (7, 9))	B68, 69	1/135
1.12	U.S.A. 31N, 105W	Hazel Formation (folded)	Pc	(328, +37)	(3)	(17)	−	(60, 154E (12, 20))	B70, 71	1/136
1.13	U.S.A. 36N, 109W	Bonito Canyon Quartzite	Pc	31, −25	19	4	−	33, 34E (2, 4)	B79	3/87
1.14	U.S.A. 36N, 112W	Bass Limestone	Pc	225, +34			+	21, 22E	B64, 65	3/86
1.15	U.S.A. 36N, 112W	Bass Limestone and Hakatai Shales	Pc	205, +65	6	21	+	04, 52E (27, 33)	B58-61	1/138
1.16	U.S.A. 36N, 112W	Hakatai Shales (1)	Pc	268, +73	22	5	+	30, 150W (9, 10)	B54-57	1/137
1.17	U.S.A. 36N, 112W	Hakatai Shales (2)	Pc	245, +31			+	09, 6E	B62, 63	3/84
1.18	U.S.A. 36N, 112W	Shinumo Quartzite	Pc	246, +33			+	07, 7E	B66, 67	3/83
1.19	U.S.A. 36N, 112W	Grand Canyon Series combined	Pc	237, +48	12	23	+	03, 23E (26, 26)	—	—
1.20	U.S.A. 36N, 112W	Precambrian of Arizona combined	Pc	231, +45	11	21	M	08, 25E (23, 23)	—	—
1.21	U.S.A. 47N, 114W	Belt Series, McNamara Formation	Pc	26, −43	30	4	+	14, 42E (3, 5)	B72	3/77
1.22	U.S.A. 47N, 114W	Belt Series, Miller Peak Formation	Pc	234, +30	20	7	+	11, 14E (4, 8)	B73	3/78
1.23	U.S.A. 47N, 112W	Belt Series, Spokane Shale (1)	Pc	232, +55	18	4	+	05, 152W (4, 6)	B75	3/79
1.24	U.S.A. 49N, 114W	Belt Series, Spokane Shale (2)	Pc	206, +39	10	8	+	16, 41E (6, 10)	B76	3/80
1.25	U.S.A. 49N, 114W	Belt Series, Grinnel Formation	Pc	225, +48	15	6	+	02, 28E (5, 8)	B78	3/81
1.26	U.S.A. 49N, 114W	Belt Series, Appekunny Formation	Pc	223, +29	15	6	+	15, 24E (4, 7)	B77	3/82
1.27	U.S.A. 48N, 114W	Belt Series of Montana combined	Pc	221, +42	35	12	M	09, 29E (11, 11)	—	—
1.28	Canada 49.4N, 114.6W	Belt Series, Kintla Formation (1)	Pc	39, −40	23	6	M	11, 30E (5, 7)	—	5/89
1.29	Canada 49.3N, 114.3W	Belt Series, Kintla Formation (2)	Pc	38, −49	24	7	M	03, 34E (6, 9)	—	5/90
1.30	Canada 49.0N, 114.0W	Belt Series, Kintla Formation (3)	Pc	50, −38	40	10	M	07, 21E (8, 12)	—	5/91
1.31	Canada 49.2N, 114.3W	Belt Series, Kintla Fm. combined	Pc	43, −43	111		M	07, 28E	—	—
1.32	North America 48N, 114W	Belt Series of Montana and British Columbia combined	Pc	42, −42	49	7	M	08, 29E (7, 7)	—	—
1.33	North America	Precambrian of Arizona and Belt Series combined	Pc	—	—	—	M	12, 29E (13, 13)	—	—

No.	Location	Age	Rock Name	Dir.	N₁	N₂	±	Pole	B	Ref.
1.34	U.S.A. 46.5N, 88.5W	Pc	Baraga County Dikes	82, −86	82	1	+	45, 99W (2, 2)	B33	1/129
1.35	U.S.A. 47N, 88.5W	Pc	Chequamegon Sandstone	(30, +74)	(47)	(6)	−	(69, 47W (10, 11))	B22, 23	1/130
1.36	U.S.A. 47N, 88.5W	Pc	Jacobsville Sandstone, Keweenawan Peninsula	250, −11	11	13	−	18, 14E (7, 13)	B24, 25	1/131
1.37	U.S.A. 47N, 88.5W	Pc	Freda Sandstone, and Nonesuch Shale	285, −01	26	3	−	09, 170E (2, 3)	B26-28	1/132
1.38	U.S.A. 47N, 88.5W	Pc	Copper Harbor Sediments and Lavas	294, +32	20	7	−	29, 176E (4, 7)	B29, 30	1/133
1.39	U.S.A. 47N, 88.5W	Pc	Portage Lake Lavas	282, +44	47	4	−	26, 169W (3, 5)	B31, 32	1/134
1.40	U.S.A. 47N, 88.5W	Pc	Upper Keweenawan combined	277, +50	7	—	—	11, 178W	—	—
1.41	U.S.A. 44N, 75W	Pc	Adirondack Gneisses	(145, +50)	—	—	M	—	B34	—
1.42	Canada 45N, 77.5W	Pc	Boulter Intrusive	297, +55	19	5	−	42, 157W (5, 7)	B35	5/93
1.43	Canada 45N, 78W	Pc	Umfraville Intrusive	115, +43	8	7	−	01, 22W (6, 9)	B36, 37	5/94
1.44	Canada 45N, 77.5W	Pc	Thanet Intrusive	93, +62	5	14	−	28, 23W (18, 22)	B38, 39	5/94
1.45	Canada 44.5N, 77.5W	Pc	Tudor Intrusive	328, +11	5	9	−	42, 149E (5, 9)	B42, 43	5/95
1.46	Canada 46.6N, 81.4W	Pc (1200-1800 *)	Sudbury Nickel Irruptive (North)	320, +70	20	5	−	64, 141W (8, 9)	B44	5/92
1.47	Canada 46.5N, 81.0W	Pc (1200-1800 *)	Sudbury Nickel Irruptive (South)	183, +68	49	2	−	08, 82W (2, 3)	B45-51	5/92
1.48	Canada 46.6N, 81.2W	Pc (1200-1800 *)	Sudbury Nickel Irruptive combined (1)	245, +82	—	—	—	39, 99W	B52	5/92
1.49	Canada 46.6N, 81.2W	Pc (1200-1800 *)	Sudbury Nickel Irruptive combined (2)	300, +78	—	—	—	53, 115W	B53	5/92
1.50	Canada 49N, 79W	Pc	Diabase Dikes (1)	(258, −48)	(13)	(19)	+	(29, 1W (17, 27))	—	6/70
1.51	Canada 49N, 79W	Pc	Diabase Dikes (2)	(10, −15)	(14)	(21)	M	(33, 91E (11, 21))	—	6/71
1.52	Canada 47N, 53W	Pc	Signal Hill Sandstone	283, +20	21	11	−	16, 145W (6, 12)	B82, 83	1/139
1.53	Canada 47N, 53W	Pc	Blackhead Sandstone	232, +51	25	10	−	02, 95W (9, 13)	B80, 81	1/140
1.54	Canada 47N, 53W	Pc	Signal Hill and Blackhead Ss. combined	262, +39	8	14	−	11, 122W (10, 16)	B84	—
1.55	Greenland 73N, 25W	Pc	Multicolored Series	110, +36	31	9	−	13, 39E (5, 10)	—	4/34
1.56	Greenland 73N, 25W	Pc	Tillite Formation	135, +16	5	18	M	04, 161W (10, 19)	—	4/33

PRECAMBRIAN SUPPLEMENT

No.	Location	Age	Rock Name	Dir.	N₁	N₂	±	Pole	B	Ref.
1.57	U.S.S.R. 58N, 95E	Pc	Lower Angara Suite	6, −28	—	—	—	17, 93W	—	7/56
1.58	U.S.S.R. 59N, 92E	Pc	Koninsk Suite	(12, +12)	—	—	—	(35, 103W)	—	7/57
1.59	India 26N, 73E	Pc	Malani Rhyolites	353, +56	—	10	—	78, 45E (11, 15)	—	7/61
1.60	India 26N, 78E	Pc	Bijawar Traps	70, +03	—	18	—	19, 176E (9, 18)	—	7/60
1.61	India 25N, 73E	Pc	Mundwarra Complex	329, −24	—	21	—	42, 65W (12, 22)	—	7/58
1.62	India 14N, 78E	Pc	Cuddapah Traps	scattered directions					—	7/59
1.63	S. Rhodesia 18.5S, 30.3E	Pc (2150 *)	Great Dike (1)	218, −59	68	6	+	21, 62E (9, 9)	—	7/62
1.64	S. Rhodesia 18.5S, 30.3E	Pc (2150 *)	Great Dike (2)	236, −61	12	20	+	11, 69E (23, 31)	—	7/63
1.65	Canada 49.3N, 114.6W	Pc	Kintla Formation (C)	221, +49	14	8	+	03, 31E	—	—
1.66	Canada 49.3N, 114.2W	Pc	Sill in Kintla Formation (B)	(18, −12)	(24)	(19)	−	(31, 44E)	—	—
1.67	Canada 49.2N, 114.3W	Pc	Kintla Formation (A)	46, −34	25	9	−	12, 21E	—	—
1.68	Canada 50.3N, 114.3W	Pc	Purcell Lava	25, −18	4	18	−	29, 36E	—	—
1.69	Canada 49.2N, 114.1W	Pc	Upper Siyeh Formation	(47, −24)	(34)	(16)	−	(16, 18E)	—	—
1.70	Canada 49.2N, 114.1W	Pc	Grinnel Formation	212, +51	52	5	+	05, 37E	—	—
1.71	Canada 49.1N, 114.1W	Pc	Waterton Formation	202, +33	25	7	M	20, 43E	—	—
1.72	Canada 49N, 114W	Pc	Purcell System combined (1)	216, +42	10	6	M	10, 32E (4, 7)	—	7/79
1.73	Canada 49N, 114W	Pc	Purcell System combined (2)	33, −32	21	14	M	18, 33E (9, 16)	—	7/79
1.74	Canada 47.0N, 84.5W	Pc	Jacobsville Sandstone, Sault Ste. Marie	289, −21	11	14	—	05, 164E (7, 15)	—	7/67

Reference List of Paleomagnetic Directions and Pole Positions (Continued)

Reference Number	Rock Units Studied — Name	Location	Age	Directions of Magnetization D_m, I_m	k	a_{95}	Polarity	Paleomagnetic Pole $\lambda', \phi'(\delta p, \delta m)$	Previous Reference Numbers BGSA	GJ
PRECAMBRIAN SUPPLEMENT (continued)										
1.75	Orienta Sandstone	U.S.A. 47.0N, 91.0W	Pc	273, −05	7	22	(?)	00, 176E (11, 22)	—	7/64
1.76	Amnicon Formation	U.S.A. 47.0N, 91.0W	Pc	scattered directions					—	7/65
1.77	Eileen Sandstone	U.S.A. 47.0N, 91.0W	Pc	300, −18	18	7	—	13, 151E (4, 7)	—	7/66
1.78	Sediments, Sault Ste Marie	Canada 47.0N, 84.5W	Pc	(306, +19)	(25)	(17)	—	(31, 165E (9, 18))	—	7/68
1.79	Duluth Gabbro	U.S.A. 47.0N, 92.0W	Pc	286, +33	17	9	—	23, 180 (6, 10)	—	7/69
1.80	Mamainse Point Lavas	Canada 47.0N, 84.5W	Pc	292, +40	19	10	+	32, 173W (9, 12)	—	7/70
1.81	Logan Diabase, Group I	Canada 48.5N, 89.0W	Pc	117, −76	13	5	+	54, 130W (8, 8)	—	7/72
1.82	Logan Diabase, Group II	Canada 48.0N, 89.5W	Pc	288, +48	21	7	+	33, 172W (6, 8)	—	7/73
1.83	Sibley Series	Canada 48.5N, 89.0W	Pc	78, −51	23	8	M	16, 149W (8, 10)	—	7/74
1.84	Alona Bay Lavas	Canada 47.0N, 84.5W	Pc	50, −84	12	14	+	39, 95W (25, 25)	—	7/71
1.85	Sandstone Dikes	Canada 47.0N, 84.5W	Pc	(243, +66)	(14)	(26)	—	(19, 123W)	—	7/75
1.86	Grenville Rocks	Canada	Pc	(287, −44)			+	(07, 18W)	—	7/80
1.87	Sudbury Nickel Irruptive (North)	Canada 46.5N, 81.1W	Pc (1200–1800 *)	310, +73		5	+	58, 130W (8, 9)	—	7/76
1.88	Sudbury Nickel Irruptive (South)	Canada 46.5N, 81.1W	Pc (1200–1800 *)	173, +64		4	—	03, 86W (5, 6)	—	7/77
1.89	Diabase Dikes, etc., Sudbury	Canada 46.5N, 81W	Pc	258, −01	35	7	++	08, 17E (4, 7)	—	7/78
1.90	Red Sediments	Argentina 25S, 65W	Pc	196, −32		25	++	45, 43W	—	6/72
1.91	Red Sediments	Brazil 25S, 49W	Pc	210, −71			+	06, 32W	—	6/73
CAMBRIAN (600 (?)–500 M.Y.)										
2.01	Younger Gabbros, Aberdeenshire	Scotland 57.5N, 2.5W	Pc-D	182, +51	13	9	++	01, 176E (8, 12)	—	2/39
2.02	Caerbwby Sandstone	Wales 52N, 5W	€l (600–560)	187, +39	32	8	++	15, 169E (6, 9)	C41–45	1/121
2.03	Hartshill Quartzite	England 52.5N, 1.5W	€l (600–560)	193, +34	12	16	—	18, 165E (10, 18)	—	5/83
2.04	Barrandian Porphyries Group C	Czechoslovakia 50.0N, 13.7E	€u-O (535–425)	26, +33		12	—	52, 147E (8, 13)	—	5/86
2.05	Barrandian Porphyries Group D	Czechoslovakia 50.0N, 13.7E	€u-O (535–425)	208, −12		15	+	40, 156E (8, 15)	—	5/86
2.06	Barrandian Porphyries Group E	Czechoslovakia 50.0N, 13.7E	€u-O (535–425)	226, −14		15	+	32, 136E (8, 15)	—	5/86
2.07	Barrandian Porphyries Group F	Czechoslovakia 50.0N, 13.7E	€u-O (535–425)	188, +16		25	+	30, 185E (13, 26)	—	5/86
2.08	Barrandian Porphyries C-F combined	Czechoslovakia 50.0N, 13.7E	€u-O (535–425)	27, +11	10	—	M	40, 157E	—	5/86
2.09	Barrandian Porphyrite Group B	Czechoslovakia 50.0N, 13.7E	€ (600–500)	192, +66		9	—	09, 6E (12, 14)	—	5/87

No.	Location	Rock Unit	Age	D, I			Pol.	Pole (°lat, °long)	C-No.	Ref.
2.10	Czechoslovakia 50.0N, 13.7E	Barrandian Porphyrites Group A₁	Pє-Є (>500)	97, −22	—	21	+	13, 78W (12, 22)	—	5/88
2.11	Czechoslovakia 50.0N, 13.7E	Barrandian Porphyrites Group A₂	Pє-Є (>500)	123, +08	—	16	+	17, 105W (8, 16)	—	5/88
2.12	Czechoslovakia 50.0N, 13.7E	Barrandian Porphyrites Group A₃	Pє-Є (>500)	17, +35	—	9	+	66, 134E (6, 11)	—	5/88
2.13	Czechoslovakia 50.0N, 13.7E	Barrandian Porphyrites Group A₄	Pє-Є (>500)	108, −14	—	8	+	17, 86W (4, 9)	—	5/88
2.14	Czechoslovakia 50.0N, 13.7E	Barrandian Porphyrites Groups A₁, A₂ and A₄ combined	Pє-Є (>500)	109, −09	16	—	+	16, 88W	—	5/88
2.15	U.S.S.R. 49N, 25E	Sediments, Dniester Region	Є (600-500)	233, +51	—	—	−	02, 16W	—	5/85
3.03	U.S.S.R.	Ukrainian Basalt		see entry 3.03						
2.16	U.S.S.R. 61N, 116E	Verkholensk Suite	Єu (535-500)	1, +16	—	8	M	37, 64W (4, 8)	—	5/84
1.05	U.S.S.R.	Sinian Sediments		see entry 1.05						
2.17	Australia 16S, 126E	Antrim Plateau Basalts	Єl (600-560)	53, −02	—	12	M	36, 154W (6, 12)	C56	1/125
2.18	Australia 16S, 126E	Elder Mountain Sandstone	Єm (570-525)	231, −15	—	10	+	34, 164W (5, 10)	C54, 55	1/124
2.19	U.S.A. 30.5N, 99W	Wilberns Formation	Єu (535-500)	98, +24	—	—	?	00, 158E	C47	1/123
2.20	U.S.A. 39N, 106.5W	Sawatch Sandy Dolomite	Єu (535-500)	(148, −15)	(44)	(4)	+	(47, 125E (2, 4))	C48, 49	1/122
2.21	U.S.A. 41N, 110W	Lodore Formation, negative	Є (600-500)	59, +04	14	8	−	—	C50	3/76
2.22	U.S.A. 41N, 110W	Lodore Formation, positive	Є (600-500)	234, +13	25	13	−	—	C51	3/76
2.23	U.S.A. 41N, 110W	Lodore Formation combined	Є or Єl	56, −05	(16)	(7)	M	23, 6E (4, 7)	C52	3/76
2.24	U.S.A. 42N, 107W	Deadwood Formation	Є (600-500)	(151, −14)	—	—	+	(47, 117E (4, 7))	C53	3/75
2.25	U.S.A. 36N, 114W	Bright Angel Shales	Єl (600-560)							—
2.26	U.S.A. 36N, 114W	Tapeats Sandstone						(22, 27E)	C46	—
9.40	Antarctica	Basement Dikes		see entry 9.40						
9.41	Antarctica	Admiralty Granites	Є?	see entry 9.41						
CAMBRIAN SUPPLEMENT										
2.27	U.S.S.R.	Aldan Stage	Єl (600-560)	close to present field		10	M		—	7/55
2.28	U.S.S.R.	Upper Lena Stage	Єl (600-560)	163, +03	—	(47)	—	30, 67W (5, 10)	—	7/54
2.29	Argentina 24.5S, 65W	Red Sediments	Є-O (600-500)	(24, +18)	—	(26)	—	(49, 28W)	—	6/67
2.30	Argentina 24.5S, 65.5W	Red Sediments	Є-S(?)	(24, +17)	—	—	—	(50, 28W)	—	6/68
2.31	Antarctica 68S, 67W	Older Intrusives		scattered directions				—	—	7/53
ORDOVICIAN (500-425 M.Y.)										
2.01	Scotland	Younger Gabbros, Aberdeenshire	Pє-D	see entry 2.01						
2.08	Czechoslovakia	Barrandian Porphyries	Єu-O	see entries 2.04 to 2.08						
3.01	U.S.S.R. 60N, 30E	Tremadocian Sediments	Ol (500-460)	{38, +41 / 211, −35}	—	18	M	42, 169E (13, 22)	C32-36	2/38
3.02	U.S.S.R. 51N, 26E	Ukrainian Basalt	O?	255, +57	23	12	−	20, 29W (12, 17)	C30, 31	3/70
3.03	U.S.S.R. 51N, 26E	Ukrainian Basalt	O or Є?	140, +75	40	11	−	28, 46E (18, 20)	C28, 29	3/71
3.04	U.S.S.R. 54N, 57E	Asha Stage	O (500-425)	253, −27	—	—	+	21, 152E (4, 8)	—	5/79
3.05	U.S.S.R. 60N, 118E	Sediments, Lena Region	Om (470-435)	352, +16	—	4	M	22, 53W (2, 4)	—	5/80

Reference List of Paleomagnetic Directions and Pole Positions (Continued)

Reference Number	Location	Rock Units Studied — Name	Age	Directions of Magnetization D_m, I_m	k	a_{95}	Polarity	Paleomagnetic Pole $\lambda', \phi'(\delta p, \delta m)$	BGSA	GJ
ORDOVICIAN (500–425 M.Y.) *(continued)*										
3.06	U.S.A. 40N, 79W	Juniata Formation	Ou (445–425)	131, +26	6	8	+	20, 153E (5, 9)	C40	3/74
3.07	U.S.A. 42.5N, 75W	Trenton Group (conglomerate)	Om (470–435)	(177, +71)	(23)	(6)	—	(09, 74W (8, 10))	C37	3/72
3.08	U.S.A. 43.5N, 75W	Trenton Group	Om (470–435)	(179, +82)	(23)	(5)	—	(27, 75W (10, 10))	C38	3/73
9.40	Antarctica	Basement Dikes		see entry **9.40**						
3.09	Antarctica 69S, 40E	Antarctic Gneisses	O (470 *)	(343, +53)	(128)	—	—	(14, 154W)	—	2/41
ORDOVICIAN SUPPLEMENT										
3.10	U.S.S.R.	Lugov Suite	Ol (500–460)	157, +19	—	13	M	21, 61W (7, 13)	—	7/52
2.30	Argentina	Red Sediments		see entry **2.30**						
2.31	Antarctica	Older Intrusives		see entry **2.31**						
SILURIAN (425–405 M.Y.)										
4.01	Wales 52N, 5W	Ludlow Series	Su (415–405)	205, −36	33	14	+	52, 134E	C16, 17	3/68
2.01	Scotland	Younger Gabbros, Aberdeenshire		see entry **2.01**						
4.02	U.S.S.R. 49N, 26E	Silurian, Dniester Region (1)	Su (415–405)	74, +10	—	—	M	14, 124E (10, 18)	—	7/48
4.03	U.S.S.R. 49N, 26E	Silurian, Dniester Region (2)	S (425–405)	214, −20	—	—	+	40, 160E	—	7/49
4.04	U.S.S.R. 49N, 26E	Silurian, Dniester combined	S (425–405)	—	—	—	M	29, 140E	—	—
4.05	U.S.S.R. 67N, 66E	Ural Peridotites	S (425–405)	98, +38	—	—	—	16, 140E	C18	3/69
4.06	U.S.S.R.	North Urals	Su–Dl (415–385)	95, +44	—	21	—	22, 141E (16, 26)	—	6/65
4.07	U.S.S.R. 61N, 116E	Red Sandstones, Lena Region	Sl (425–410)	197, +46	—	—	?	00, 101E (7, 11)	—	7/50
4.08	China 40N, 97E	Red Siltstones of Kansu	Sm (425–405)	(294, +55)	(16)	(9)	—	(39, 25E (9, 12))	C26, 27	1/119
4.09	South Africa 34S, 18E	Table Mountain Series	Su–Dl (415–385)	162, −04	—	5	—	50, 11W (3, 5)	—	4/32
5.30	Australia 35S, 149E	Canberra Igneous Rocks		see entry **5.30**						
4.10	Australia 34.7S, 148.9E	Duro Porphyry	Sm (425–405)	306, −11	18	18	—	32, 97E (9, 18)	C19–21	3/67
4.11	U.S.A. 39.5N, 79W	Rosehill Formation	Sm (425–405)	325, −39	33	13	+	20, 136E (10, 15)		1/117
4.12	U.S.A. 33.6N, 86.7W	Clinton Iron Ore	Sm (425–405)	143, +19	107	12	M	34, 139E (7, 12)	C22, 23	1/118
4.13	U.S.A.	Silurian Sediments combined	Sm (425–405)	324, −30	—	—	M	27, 137E	—	—
9.40	Antarctica	Basement Dikes		see entry **9.40**						
SILURIAN SUPPLEMENT										
4.14	U.S.S.R.	Chergaka Suite	Su (415–405)	142, +32	—	13	+	13, 48W (9, 15)	—	7/51
4.15	Argentina 19S, 58W	Jacadigo Series	O?	60, +39	—	19	—	19, 0	—	6/66
5.49	Brazil	Sediments		see entry **5.49**						
2.31	Antarctica	Older Intrusives		see entry **2.31**						

No.	Location	Rock Unit	Age	D, I	N	k	Pol	Pole	Ref	No.
5.01	West Germany 51N, 6E	Eifel Sandstone	Dl-m (405-360)	(197, -11)	(15)	(23)	+	(42, 163E (4, 8))	—	4/29
5.02	United Kingdom 52N, 3W	Old Red Sandstone	D (405-345)	(196, -04)	(19)	(5)	+	(38, 156E (3, 5))	C4-13	1/114
5.03	England 52N, 3W	Brownstone Series	Dl (405-385)	(233, -22)	(4)	(12)	+	(31, 111E (7, 12))	C1-3	1/115
5.04	Scotland 57N, 2W	Igneous Rocks, Midland Valley	D (405-345)	46, -54			M	10, 39W	—	—
5.05	Scotland 57N, 2.5W	Lower Old Red Sandstone Lavas	Dl (405-385)	35, +05	25	11	+	29, 136E (7, 11)	—	4/30
5.06	Scotland 55.5N, 2.5W	Upper Old Red Sandstone Sediments	Du (370-345)	188, +22	7	9	+	23, 169E (5, 10)	—	4/31
2.01	Scotland	Younger Gabbros, Aberdeenshire		see entry **2.01**						
5.07	U.S.S.R. 59N, 33E	Famennian Sediments	Du (370-345)	221, -12 / 38, +33	—	10	M	34, 158E	—	4/26
5.08	U.S.S.R. 57N, 31E	Upper Frasnian Sediments	Du (370-345)	34, +10	—	10	M	31, 164E (5, 10)	—	4/27
5.09	U.S.S.R. 60N, 33E	Middle Frasnian Sediments	Du (370-345)	221, -16	—	10	+	28, 159E (5, 10)	—	4/28
5.10	U.S.S.R.	Sediments, Russian Platform combined	Du (370-345)	38, +16	133	—	M	31, 160E	—	—
5.11	U.S.S.R. 49N, 25E	Sediments, Dniester Region	D (405-345)	201, -22	—	—	+	50, 175E	—	5/61
5.12	U.S.S.R. 49N, 25E	Sediments, Dniester Region	D (405-345)	210, -13	—	—	+	40, 165E	—	5/62
5.13	U.S.S.R. 49N, 25E	Sediments, Dniester Region	D (405-345)	202, -22	—	—	+	46, 172E	—	5/63
5.14	U.S.S.R. 49N, 25E	Sediments, Dniester Region	D (405-345)	212, -16	—	—	+	40, 162E	—	5/64
5.15	U.S.S.R. 49N, 25E	Sediments, Dniester Region	D (405-345)	209, -12	—	—	+	41, 166E (4, 8)	—	5/65
5.16	U.S.S.R. 49N, 25E	Sediments, Dniester Region combined	D (405-345)	207, -17	145	6	+	43, 168E (6, 6)	—	—
5.17	U.S.S.R. 60N, 60E	Bauxite of the North Urals	D (405-345)	227, -23	—	4	+	31, 178W (2, 4)	—	5/66
4.06	U.S.S.R.	North Urals		see entry **4.06**						
5.18	U.S.S.R. 56N, 93E	Chargin Series	Du (370-345)	102, +53	—	—	M	23, 154E	—	5/67
5.19	U.S.S.R. 55N, 95E	Chargin, Amonash, and Lovat Series	Du (370-345)	113, +51	—	—	M	15, 150E	—	5/68
5.20	U.S.S.R. 56N, 93E	Tatysheva Series	Du (370-345)	103, +61	—	—	M	28, 147E	—	5/69
5.21	U.S.S.R. 56N, 93E	Kunguss Series (1)	Dm-u (395-345)	97, +53	—	—	M	24, 157E	—	5/70
5.22	U.S.S.R. 55N, 95E	Kunguss Series (2)	Dm-u (395-345)	104, +65	—	—	M	30, 146E	—	5/71
5.23	U.S.S.R. 55.5N, 94E	Kunguss Series combined	Dm-u (395-345)	101, +59	—	—	M	27, 151E	—	—
5.24	U.S.S.R. 56N, 93E	Chasovennay Series	Dm-u (395-345)	98, +59	—	—	M	28, 152E	—	5/72
5.25	U.S.S.R. 56N, 93E	Red Sediments, Krasnoyarsk Region	Dm-u (395-345)	285, -56	—	—	+	23, 150E	—	5/73
5.26	U.S.S.R. 56N, 93E	Karymov and Ivashikhin Series	Dm (395-360)	89, +55	—	—	M	29, 163E	—	5/74
5.27	U.S.S.R. 55N, 95E	Anzhin Series	Dm (395-360)	86, +50	—	—	M	28, 168E	—	5/75
5.28	U.S.S.R. 56N, 93E	Byskar Series (1)	Dl-m (405-360)	88, +53	—	—	M	32, 162E	—	5/76
5.29	U.S.S.R. 55N, 95E	Okler and Penov Series	Dl (405-385)	86, +66	—	—	M	39, 154E	—	5/77
5.30	U.S.S.R. 56N, 98E	Sediments, Krasnoyarsk Region	D (405-345)	311, +27 / 115, +04	—	—	M	28, 155E	—	5/78
5.31	U.S.S.R. 56N, 94E	Sediments, Siberian Platform combined	D (405-345)	97, +57	119	4	M	27, 155E (5, 5)	—	—
4.09	Africa	Table Mountain Series		see entry **4.09**						
5.32	Australia 35.2S, 149.0E	Canberra Igneous Rocks	Su-Dl (415-385)	12, -37	6	21	M	71, 172W (14, 24)	—	3/66
5.33	Australia 34.7S, 148.8E	Murrumbidgee Series	Dm (395-360)	40, -29	10	10	—	49, 139W (5, 11)	—	3/65
5.34	Australia 33S, 149E	Catombal Formation	Du (370-345)	(1, -67)	(75)	(5)	—	(73, 33W (6, 8))	—	3/62
5.35	Australia 37S, 150E	Nethercote Sediments	Du (370-345)	(15, -64)	(10)	(13)	—	(76, 77W (17, 20))	—	3/63
5.36	Australia 37S, 150E	Yalwal Stage Basalts	Du (370-345)	5, -23	29	14	M	65, 160E (8, 15)	—	3/64
5.37	Australia 37S, 147E	Red Beds of Victoria	Du-Cl (370-330)	(17, -65)	ns		—	(74, 79W)	—	3/61
5.38	U.S.A. 42.5N, 74W	Onondaga Limestone	Dl-m (405-360)	(177, +79)	(19)	(4)	—	(21, 73W (7, 7))	C14	3/60

Reference List of Paleomagnetic Directions and Pole Positions *(Continued)*

Reference Number	Location	Name	Age	D_m, I_m	k	a_{95}	Polarity	$\lambda', \phi'(\delta p, \delta m)$	BGSA	GJ
		Rock Units Studied		Directions of Magnetization				Paleomagnetic Pole	Previous Reference Numbers	

DEVONIAN (405–345 M.Y.) (continued)

9.39	Antarctica	Beacon Group Sediments	see entry **9.39**							
9.40	Antarctica	Basement Dikes	see entry **9.40**							

DEVONIAN SUPPLEMENT

5.39	U.S.S.R. 48N, 74E	Kazakhstan Porphyrites	D (405–345)	218, −23	—	—	+	43, 159W	— —	6/60
5.40	U.S.S.R.	Okler Series	Dl (405–385)	91, +51	—	—	M	25, 163E	— —	7/43
5.41	U.S.S.R.	Sediments	Dl (405–385)	115, +26	—	—	M	04, 24W	— —	7/47
5.42	U.S.S.R.	Byskar Series (2)	Dl (405–385)	88, +53	—	—	M	32, 162E	— —	7/46
5.43	U.S.S.R.	Sediments	Dm (395–360)	87, +57	—	—	M	32, 162E	— —	7/45
5.44	U.S.S.R.	Kunguss Suite (3)	Du (370–345)	100, +59	—	—	M	27, 152E	— —	7/44
5.45	U.S.S.R.	Sediments	Du (370–345)	106, +55	—	—	M	28, 150E	— —	—
5.46	U.S.S.R.	Siberian Sediments combined	D (405–345)	95, +56	194	7	M	28, 156E (8, 8)	— —	6/61
5.47	China 31N, 111E	"Hematite" Rocks	D (405–345)	(350, +06)	—	(32)	—	(61, 49W)	— —	6/62
5.48	Argentina 24S, 65.5W	Sediments	D (405–345)	28, +47	—	18	—	31, 37W (15, 23)	— —	6/63
5.49	Uruguay 30S, 65.5W	Sediments	D (405–345)	(2, −36)	—	(34)	—	(80, 46W)	— —	6/64
5.50	Brazil 25S, 50W	Sediments	S–D	(150, +41)	—	—	+	(62, 144W)	— —	—

CARBONIFEROUS (345–280 M.Y.)

6.01	West Germany 49N, 7E	Stephanian Sandstones (1)	Cu (300–280)	180, 00	16	6	+	41, 173W (3, 6)	— —	4/23
6.02	France 47N, 4.5E	Stephanian Sandstones (2)	Cu (300–280)	180, +20	12	5	+	33, 175W (3, 6)	— —	4/24
6.03	France 45.4N, 4.5E	Stephanian Sandstones (3)	Cu (300–280)	181, +22	4	22	+	33, 176W (12, 23)	— —	4/25
6.04	France and W. Germany	Stephanian Sandstones combined	Cu (300–280)	180, +14	44	19	+	36, 175W	— —	—
6.05	Scotland 56N, 3W	Kinghorn Lavas, beds 9–15	Cl (345–315)	12, −18	—	—	—	—	— —	—
6.06	Scotland 56N, 3W	Kinghorn Lavas, beds 16–20	Cl (345–315)	170, +24	—	—	+	—	— —	—
6.07	Scotland 56N, 3W	Kinghorn Lavas, bed 21	Cl (345–315)	(55, +19)	—	—	—	—	— —	—
6.08	Scotland 56N, 3W	Kinghorn Lavas, beds 25–48	Cl (345–315)	13, −35	—	—	+	—	— —	—
6.09	Scotland 56N, 3W	Kinghorn Lavas, beds 50–55	Cl (345–315)	205, +41	—	—	+	—	— —	—
6.10	Scotland 56N, 3W	Kinghorn Lavas, bed 69	Cl (345–315)	15, −35	32	14	M	17, 167E (9, 16)	D21–31	1/99–101
6.11	Scotland 56N, 3W	Kinghorn Lavas combined	Cl (345–315)	10, −31	—	—	—	—	— —	—
6.12	Scotland 56N, 3W	Kinghorn Sill, bed 65	?	(15, +14)	—	—	+	—	— —	4/22
6.13	Scotland 55.5N, 2.5W	Southdean Basanite Plug	C (345–280)	227, −38	13	10	+	41, 112E (7, 12)	— —	—
7.15	England	Great Whin Sill	see entry **7.15**							
6.14	England 54N, 3W	Carboniferous Limestone	Cl (345–305)	41, +34	13	9	M	43, 119E (6, 10)	—	5/47
6.15	England 54N, 3W	Lancashire Sediments, negative	C (320–280)	24, +22	—	—	—	43, 144E	D10, 11	1/103
6.16	England 54N, 3W	Lancashire Sediments, positive	C (320–280)	184, +23	—	—	+	24, 173E	D10, 11	1/103

6.17	England 54N, 3W	Lancashire Sediments combined	C (320–280)	14, −01	—	—	M	34, 160E	—	—
6.18	England 53N, 2W	Keele Beds (1)	Cu (310–280)	220, −20	67	10	+	37, 126E (5, 10)	—	4/19
6.19	England 53N, 2W	Keele Beds (2)	Cu (310–280)	199, +34	—	—	+	16, 159E	—	4/20
6.20	England 53N, 2W	Keele Beds combined	Cu (310–280)	19, −06	—	—	+	28, 144E	—	—
6.21	England 53N, 1.5W	Derbyshire Sediments, negative	C (330–280)	37, +39	—	—	−	48, 128E	D13–17	1/103
6.22	England 53N, 1.5W	Derbyshire Sediments, positive	C (330–280)	197, +37	—	—	+	15, 162E	D18–20	1/103
6.23	England 53N, 1.5W	Derbyshire Sediments combined	C (330–280)	28, +01	—	—	M	33, 148E	—	—
6.24	England 53.5N, 1.5W	Tideswelldale Igneous Unit	Cm (330–300)	218, +36	—	—	+	—	D7–9	1/97
6.25	England 53.5N, 1.5W	Tideswelldale Baked Rocks	Cm (330–300)	221, +34	—	—	+	—	D7–9	1/97
6.26	England 53.5N, 1.5W	Tideswelldale combined	Cm (330–300)	220, +35	—	—	+	09, 162E	—	—
6.27	England 53N, 1.5W	Derbyshire Lava, negative	Cl (345–305)	(48, −45)	—	—	+	—	D18–20	1/102
6.28	England 53N, 1.5W	Derbyshire Lavas, positive	Cl (345–305)	(200, +29)	—	—	+	—	D18–20	1/102
6.29	England 53N, 1.5W	Derbyshire Lavas combined	Cl (345–305)	33, −37	—	—	M	10, 147E	D18–20	1/102
6.30	England 52.5N, 2W	Midland Sills	Cu (315–280)	198, +15	12	23	M	—	D4–6	1/96
6.31	England 52.5N, 2W	Midland Baked Sediments	Cu (315–280)	199, +12	59	10	+	—	D4–6	1/96
6.32	England 52.5N, 2W	Midland Sills and Baked Sediments	Cl (315–280)	199, +13	22	11	M	28, 157E	D4–6	1/96
6.33	England 52.5N, 2.5W	Little Wenlock Lava	Cl (345–305)	(356, +15)	—	—	−	—	—	—
6.34	England 52.5N, 2.5W	Little Wenlock Baked Sediments	Cl (345–305)	(359, −07)	—	—	−	—	—	4/20
6.35	England 52.5N, 2.5W	Little Wenlock combined	Cl (345–305)	205, +49	—	—	+	(39, 172W)	—	4/20
6.36	Wales 51.2N, 3.5W	Sediments	C (345–280)	(33, +35)	—	—	−	06, 155E	—	—
6.37	England 51.5N, 2.5W	Pennant Sandstone	Cu (315–280)	20, −33	(13)	(11)	M	(49, 126E (7, 12))	D1–3	—
6.38	England 54N, 3W	Carboniferous of Britain combined (1)	C (345–280)	37, +31	31	10	M	16, 159E (8, 8)	—	—
6.39	England 54N, 3W	Carboniferous of Britain combined (2)	Cu (345–280)	218, −15	48	11	+	43, 126E (6, 6)	—	—
6.40	U.S.S.R. 48N, 38E	Araucarite Stage, Donbas	Cu (315–280)	209, −08	—	—	+	38, 168E (1, 2)	—	5/48
6.41	U.S.S.R. 48N, 38E	Avilov Stage, Donbas	Cu (315–280)	213, −12	—	—	+	39, 179E (2, 4)	—	5/49
6.42	U.S.S.R. 48N, 38E	Upper Carboniferous Donbas combined	Cu (315–280)	38, +38	—	—	+	39, 173E	—	—
6.43	U.S.S.R. 59N, 34E	Oka-Serpukhov Stage, Tikvin	Cl (345–305)	41, +29	—	—	M	43, 162E (4, 7)	—	5/50
6.44	U.S.S.R. 59N, 34E	Tula Horizon, Tikvin	Cl (345–305)	78, +25	—	—	M	37, 162E (4, 7)	—	5/51
6.45	U.S.S.R. 59N, 34E	Tournai Stage, Tikvin	Cl (345–305)	53, +32	—	—	M	17, 127E (2, 4)	—	5/52
6.46	U.S.S.R. 59N, 34E	Carboniferous Tikvin combined	Cl (345–305)	243, −30	16	13	M	34, 148E	—	—
6.47	U.S.S.R. 54N, 57E	Tournai Stage, South Urals	Cl (345–315)	142, +87	—	—	+	29, 159E (6, 11)	—	5/53
6.48	U.S.S.R. 53N, 91E	Carboniferous, Siberia (1)	Cl (345–305)	100, +50	—	—	−	48, 98E	—	5/54
6.49	U.S.S.R. 55N, 90E	Carboniferous, Siberia (2)	Cl (345–305)	82, +78	—	—	−	20, 153E	—	5/55
6.50	U.S.S.R. 53N, 91E	Carboniferous, Siberia (3)	Cl (345–305)	92, +70	—	—	−	49, 129E	—	5/56
6.51	U.S.S.R. 55N, 91E	Carboniferous, Siberia (4)	Cl (345–305)	103, +45	—	—	−	41, 141E	—	5/57
6.52	U.S.S.R. 54N, 92E	Carboniferous, Siberia (5)	Cl (345–305)	120, +84	—	—	−	12, 156E	—	5/58
6.53	U.S.S.R. 54N, 92E	Carboniferous, Siberia (6)	Cl (345–305)	121, +84	—	—	−	46, 110E	—	5/59
6.54	U.S.S.R. 54N, 91E	Carboniferous, Siberia (7)	Cl (345–305)	101, +72	—	—	−	46, 110E	—	5/60
6.55	U.S.S.R.	Carboniferous, Siberia combined	Cl (345–305)		22	13	−	40, 131E (18, 18)	—	—
9.22	Japan	Late Paleozoic and Mesozoic Intrusives		see entry 9.22						
6.56	S. Rhodesia 18S, 29E	Dwkya Varved Sediment, negative	Cu (315–280)	(0, −81)	(84)	(5)	−	(36, 151E (10, 10))	D52	1/112
6.57	S. Rhodesia 18S, 29E	Dwkya Varved Sediment, positive	Cu (315–280)	(333, +76)	(57)	(7)	+	(07, 17E (12, 13))	D53, 54	1/113
5.37	Australia	Red Beds of Victoria		see entry 5.37						
6.58	Australia 31.6S, 151.4E	Upper Kuttung Sediments	Cu (315–280)	213, +79	114	6	+	48, 46W (11, 11)	D50	1/110
6.59	Australia 32.6S, 151.7E	Paterson Toscanite	Cu (315–280)	2, −67	ns	3	−	73, 33W (4, 5)	—	—

Reference List of Paleomagnetic Directions and Pole Positions (Continued)

Reference Number	Location	Name	Age	D_m, I_m	k	a_{95}	Polarity	$\lambda', \phi' (\delta p, \delta m)$	BGSA	GJ
		Rock Units Studied		Directions of Magnetization				Paleomagnetic Pole	Previous Reference Numbers	

CARBONIFEROUS (345–280 M.Y.) (continued)

6.60	Australia 32.6S, 151.5E	Lower Kuttung Lavas	Cu (288 *)	187, +50	50	11	+	84, 134W (10, 15)	—	—
6.61	U.S.A. 31N, 99W	Barnett Formation, negative	Cl (345–305)	319, +08	200	4	−	41, 144E (2, 4)	D44, 45	1/107
6.62	U.S.A. 31N, 99W	Barnett Formation, positive	Cl (345–305)	149, +19	11	6	+	39, 123E (3, 6)	D42, 43	1/106
6.63	U.S.A. 31N, 99W	Barnett Formation, combined	Cl (345–305)	322, −05			M	41, 135E		
6.64	U.S.A. 36N, 113W	Naco Formation, Carizzo Creek	Cu (315–280)	150, −03	40	4	+	46, 113E (2, 4)	D37–39	1/105
6.65	U.S.A. 34N, 112W	Naco Formation, Fossil Creek	Cu (315–280)	125, +16	22	7	+	23, 130E (4, 7)	D40	2/59
6.66	U.S.A. 35N, 112.5W	Naco Formation combined	Cu (315–280)	137, +06			+	35, 122E		—
2.24	U.S.A.	Deadwood Formation	€ or C	see entry 2.24						
7.51	U.S.A.	Sangre de Cristo Formation	Cu–Pl	see entry 7.51						
7.50	U.S.A.	Supai Formation	Cu–P	see entry 7.50						
6.67	Canada 48N, 59W	Codroy Group	Cl (345–305)	166, +08	38	8	+	37, 139E (4, 8)	D46, 47	1/108
6.68	Canada 48N, 66W	East Canadian Sediments	C (345–280)	164, +20		5	+	30, 133E (3, 5)	D48, 49	1/108
9.39	Antarctica	Beacon Group Sediments	D–Tr	see entry 9.39						
9.40	Antarctica	Basement Dikes	D–C	see entry 9.40						

CARBONIFEROUS SUPPLEMENT

6.69	U.S.S.R.	Krasnotsvet Clay, Gzhelian Stage	Cu (315–280)	208, −32			+	47, 178E		6/54
6.70	U.S.S.R.	Sediments	Cl (345–305)				?	38, 127E (6, 6)		7/41
6.71	China 40N, 116E	Sediments	C (345–280)	(5, +52)		(34)	−	8, 95W		6/55
6.72	Peru 12S, 75W	Grey Tuffs	Cl (345–305)	315, +75			+	(82, 94W)		6/58
6.73	Argentina 24S, 65W	Sediments	Cl (345–305)	(180, +55)			+	(78, 115E)		6/59
6.74	Peru 12S, 75W	Mitu Formation	Cu (315–280)	76, −52			M	18, 47E		6/56,57

PERMIAN (280–230 M.Y.)

7.01	France 43.5N, 6.8E	Esterel Pyromeride R4	P (280–230)	210, −16			+	46, 142E	E9–11	1/78
7.02	France 43.5N, 6.8E	Esterel Rhyolite R3	P (280–230)	217, −23	69	5	+	45, 131E (3, 5)	E15, 16	1/79
7.03	France 43.5N, 6.8E	Esterel Dolerite	P (280–230)	175, −13	20	18	+	53, 165E (9, 18)	E12–14	1/80
7.04	France 43.5N, 6.8E	Esterel Igneous Rocks combined	P (280–230)	201, −18	14		+	50, 146E		—
7.05	France 43.5N, 6.8E	Esterel Igneous and Sedimentary Rocks	P (280–230)	207, −16	59	5	+	47, 145E (3, 5)	E17, 18	1/81
7.06	France 46.5N, 4.5E	Monteenis Sandstone	Pm (265–240)	(197, +06)	(93)	(4)	+	(38, 162E (2, 4))	E25, 26	1/83
7.07	France 48N, 6E	Nideck Porphyry (1)	P(m?) (265–230)	193, −07	22	5	+	43, 168E (3, 5)	E23, 24	1/82
7.08	West Germany 49.5N, 7E	St. Wendel Sandstone	Pl (280–255)	181, −09	27	4	+	45, 175W (2, 4)	E27, 28	1/84
7.09	West Germany 48–49N, 7–8E	Rotliegende Sediments and Lavas	Pl (280–255)	177, +01	27	18	+	40, 170W (14, 14)		4/15–18
7.10	West Germany 50N, 8E	Nahe Igneous Rocks (1)	P (280–230)	195, −04	5		+	40, 168E		2/37

No.	Location	Formation	Age	Pole			Pol	VGP	E	Ref
7.11	West Germany 50N, 8E	Nahe Igneous Rocks (2)	P (280–230)	195, −15	54	13	+	46, 167E (7, 13)	—	5/36
7.12	West Germany 50N, 8E	Nahe Igneous Rocks combined	P (280–230)	195, −10	21	1	+	43, 167E	—	—
7.13	Norway 59.7N, 10.4E	Igneous Complex of Oslo	Pl (270 *)	204, −36	15	20	+	47, 157E (1, 2)	E19, 20	5/37
7.14	England 51N, 4W	Exeter Traps	Pl (270 *)	189, −09	34	4	+	43, 164E (10, 20)	E1-4	1/73
7.15	England 55N, 2W	Great Whin Sill	Cu-Pl (281 *)	188, −05	9	8	+	37, 169E (3, 3)	—	2/36
7.16	Scotland 55.4N, 4.5W	Mauchline Lavas	P (280–230)	180, −04	5	12	+	36, 175E (4, 8)	E7, 8	1/74
7.17	Scotland 55.4N, 4.5W	Mauchline Sediments	P (280–230)	187, −06	5	12	+	37, 167E (6, 12)	E5, 6	1/75
7.18	Scotland 55.4N, 4.5W	Ayrshire Kylites	P (280–230)	190, +02	—	8	+	34, 163E (6, 12)	E21, 22	1/76
7.19	Italy 46.6N, 11.2E	Bolzano Quartz-Porphyry (1)	Pl (280–255)	164, −11	—	4	+	45, 146W (4, 8)	—	6/49
7.20	Italy 46.5N, 11.4E	Bolzano Quartz-Porphyry (2)	Pl (280–255)	150, −31	—	—	+	51, 119W (3, 4)	—	6/50
7.21	Spain 42.7N, 0.5W	Pyrenean Rocks	P (280–230)	159, −14	—	—	+	52, 154W	—	—
7.22	U.S.S.R. 61N, 46E	Upper Tartarian Sediments (1)	Pu (245–230)	42, +48	—	—	M	48, 165E (9, 14)	—	5/38
7.23	U.S.S.R. 59N, 51E	Upper Tartarian Sediments (2)	Pu (245–230)	42, +48	—	—	M	49, 169E (5, 7)	—	5/39
7.24	U.S.S.R. 53N, 52E	Upper Tartarian Sediments (3)	Pu (245–230)	46, +46	—	—	M	48, 162E (8, 11)	—	5/40
7.25	U.S.S.R.	Upper Tartarian combined	Pu (245–230)	43, +47	1722	—	M	48, 165E	—	—
7.26	U.S.S.R. 54N, 52E	Lower Tartarian Sediments (1)	Pu (245–230)	222, −39	—	—	+	45, 171E (7, 10)	—	5/41
7.27	U.S.S.R. 61N, 45E	Lower Tartarian Sediments (2)	Pu (245–230)	220, −35	—	—	+	41, 172E (6, 11)	—	5/42
7.28	U.S.S.R. 57N, 54E	Lower Tartarian Sediments (3)	Pu (245–230)	226, −44	—	—	+	45, 167E (7, 11)	—	5/43
7.29	U.S.S.R.	Lower Tartarian combined	Pu (245–230)	223, −39	255	—	+	44, 170E	—	—
7.30	U.S.S.R. 59N, 50.5E	Tartarian undifferentiated	Pu (245–230)	{ 038, +57 / 211, −38 }	—	18	M	52, 176E (9, 13)	E31	2/33
7.31	U.S.S.R.	Upper and Lower Tartarian combined	Pu (245–230)	42, +44	189	4	M	47, 169E (4, 4)	—	2/34
7.32	U.S.S.R. 57.5N, 55E	Kazanian Red Sediments (1)	Pu (255–235)	222, −42	—	—	+	46, 173E	—	5/44
7.33	U.S.S.R. 57N, 55E	Kazanian Red Sediments (2)	Pu (255–235)	229, −44	—	—	+	44, 167E (7, 11)	—	—
7.34	U.S.S.R. 57N, 55E	Kazanian combined	Pu (255–235)	227, −43	—	—	+	45, 170E	—	—
7.35	U.S.S.R. 57.5N, 56E	Ufimian Red Sediments (1)	Pu (260–245)	220, −38	—	—	+	43, 179E	E29, 30	2/35
7.36	U.S.S.R. 56N, 55E	Ufimian Red Sediments (2)	Pu (260–245)	228, −40	—	—	+	43, 168E (6, 9)	—	5/45
7.37	U.S.S.R. 57N, 55.5E	Ufimian combined	Pu (260–245)	224, −39	—	—	+	43, 173E	—	—
7.38	U.S.S.R. 48N, 38E	Donbas Red Sediments	Pl (280–255)	225, −09	—	—	+	33, 161E (5, 9)	—	5/46
7.39	U.S.S.R. 72N, 102E	Ultrabasics of Maymecha-Kotuy	Pm-u (250 *)	295, −68	—	5	+	40, 150E (7, 8)	—	3/55
9.22	Japan	Late Paleozoic and Mesozoic Intrusives	see entry 9.22	see entry 9.22						
7.40	Kenya 3S, 39E	Maji Ya Chumvi Formation	Pu (250–230)	267, +38	9	11	+	04, 150E (8, 13)	E63	1/92
7.41	Kenya 3S, 39E	Taru grit	Pl (280–255)	87, +61	23	16	?	00, 87E (19, 25)	E64	1/93
7.42	Australia 34.6S, 150.8E	Upper Marine Latites	Pm-u (248 *)	232, +81	26	6	+	44, 48W (12, 12)	E61	1/94, 7/39
7.43	Australia 32.7S, 151.6E	Lower Marine Basalt	Pl (280–255)	230, +76	170	5	+	46, 58W (9, 9)	E62	1/95, 7/40
8.30	U.S.A.	Chugwater Formation	see entry 8.30	see entry 8.30						
7.44	U.S.A. 39.6N, 107.4W	Culter Formation (1)	P (280–230)	140, +06	—	10	+	34, 123E	E32, 33	1/86
7.45	U.S.A. 37.0N, 107.0W	Culter Formation (2)	P (280–230)	161, +33	96	—	+	33, 92E	E34	—
7.46	U.S.A. 38N, 109W	Culter Formation combined	P (280–230)	130, +20	—	—	+	34, 107E	E35	—
7.47	U.S.A. 34.4N, 106.4W	Abo Formation (1)	Pl (280–260)	149, +08	5	18	+	42, 117E (9, 18)	E56, 57	1/87
7.48	U.S.A. 35.3N, 108.4W	Abo Formation (2)	Pl (280–260)	160, +55	7	12	+	17, 88E (12, 17)	E58	—
7.49	U.S.A. 35N, 107W	Abo Formation combined	Pl (280–260)	153, +32	—	—	+	30, 100E	E59	—
7.50	U.S.A. 35.5N, 105.2W	Yeso Formation	Pl-m (280–250)	143, −01	99	3	+	41, 127E (2, 3)	E54, 55	1/85
7.51	U.S.A. 34-36N, 109–112W	Supai Formation	Cu-P (290–250)	150, +11	35	10	+	40, 110E (9, 9)	E37-53	{ 1/88-91 / 3/56-58 }

Reference List of Paleomagnetic Directions and Pole Positions (Continued)

Reference Number	Location	Name	Age	Directions of Magnetization D_m, I_m	k	a_{95}	Polarity	Paleomagnetic Pole $\lambda', \phi' (\delta p, \delta m)$	Previous Reference Numbers BGSA	GJ
PERMIAN (280–230 M.Y.) *(continued)*										
7.52	U.S.A. 35.4N, 105.3W	Sangre de Cristo Formation	Cu-Pl (290–250)	175, +31	9	11	+	38, 81E (7, 11)	E60	—
7.53	Greenland 72.5N, 23.5W	Sediments	P (280–230)	175, −37	50	7	+	38, 163E (5, 8)	—	4/14
9.39	Antarctica	Beacon Group Sediments		see entry **9.39**						
PERMIAN SUPPLEMENT										
7.54	France 53.9N, 5.7E	Volcanics, Nideck-Donon (2)	P (280–230)	193, −13	134	4	+	41, 169E (2, 4)	—	7/35
7.55	Spain 43N, 1W	Andesites, Huesca Province	P-Tr	152, −22	65	5	+	51, 133W (3, 5)	—	7/36
7.56	Spain 43N, 1W	Red Sediments, Huesca Province	P-Tr	(250, +51)	(7)	—	−	(08, 54W)	—	7/37
7.57	U.S.S.R.	Beloyarsk Suite	Pl (288–255)	—	—	—	M	43, 157E	—	7/38
7.58	China 36N, 117E	Sediments	P (280–230)	(270, −29)	—	(38)	+	(09, 165W)	—	6/52
7.59	China 30N, 103E	Basalts	P (280–230)	(32, −4)	—	(40)	+	(50, 130W)	—	6/51
7.60	Brazil 25S, 50W	Corumbatai Formation	Pu (250–230)	180, +60	—	—	+	74, 130E	—	6/53
TRIASSIC (230–180 M.Y.)										
8.01	France 49N, 7E	Vosge Sandstone, negative	Trl (230–210)	10, +40	9	23	−	62, 167E (17, 28)	F13, 14	4/7
8.02	France 48N, 7E	Vosge Sandstone, positive	Trl (230–210)	218, +09	2	11	+	28, 143E (6, 12)	—	1/63
8.03	France 48.5N, 7E	Vosge Sandstone combined	Trl (230–210)	25, +16	—	—	M	44, 151E	—	1/65
8.04	Germany 45.5–50N, 7.5–9E	Bunter Sandstone	Trl (230–210)	17, +29	36	13	M	55, 159E (10, 10)	—	4/8–12
8.05	Spain 43N, 5W	Sandstone	Tr (220–180)	353, +57	—	—	−	82, 131W	F15, 16	—
8.06	England 53N, 2W	Keuper Marls	Tru (200–180)	33, +27	18	12	M	43, 131E (6, 12)	F1–12	1/64
8.07	England 50.7N, 3.2W	Keuper Marls (Sidmouth)	Tru (200–180)	30, +23	3	21	M	44, 134E	—	1/65
8.08	Scotland 55.6N, 5.3W	New Red Sandstone, Arran	Tr (230–180)	214, −48	—	—	M	54, 118E	F17–20	2/32
8.09	U.S.S.R. 59N, 50E	Vitloosian Sediments	Trl (230–210)	222, −19	—	—	+	31, 180	—	5/23
8.10	U.S.S.R. 48N, 38E	Serebryansk Suite	Trl (230–210)	39, +57	—	—	M	60, 135E (4, 6)	—	5/24
8.11	U.S.S.R. 48N, 47E	Bashunchak Suite	Trl (230–210)	42, +56	—	—	+	57, 142E (4, 6)	—	5/25
8.12	U.S.S.R. 49N, 52E	Tananyk Suite	Trl (230–210)	45, +46	—	—	M	49, 158E (5, 9)	—	5/26
8.13	U.S.S.R. 53N, 52E	Buzuluk Suite	Trl (230–210)	220, −51	—	—	+	54, 164E (15, 19)	—	
8.14	U.S.S.R.	Lower Triassic combined	Trl (230–210)	—	—	—	M	51, 159E	—	
8.15	U.S.S.R.	Siberian Traps (1)	Trl-m (230–195)	67, +84	—	3	M	61, 117E (6, 6)	—	5/27
8.16	U.S.S.R. 66N, 88E	Siberian Traps (2)	Trl (230–195)	90, +71	—	4	−	48, 148E (8, 10)	—	3/31
8.17	U.S.S.R. 67.0N, 88.8E	Siberian Traps (3)	Trl (230–195)	62, +76	—	9	−	65, 156E (15, 16)	—	3/32
8.18	U.S.S.R. 67N, 92E	Siberian Traps (4)	Trl (230–195)	92, +80	—	12	M	60, 133E (23, 23)	—	5/28
8.19	U.S.S.R. 63N, 114E	Siberian Traps (5)	Trl (230–195)	179, +87	—	13	M	59, 114E (25, 25)	—	5/29
8.20	U.S.S.R.	Siberian Traps combined	Tr (230–195)	—	—	—	M	60, 133E (11, 11)	—	—

No.	Location	Formation	Age (M.Y.)	Pole		N		Direction	F	Ref.
8.21	U.S.S.R. 75N, 108E	Taimyr Peninsula, Red Sandstone	Tr (230–180)	130, +68	—	6	—	40, 147E (8, 10)	—	5/33
8.22	U.S.S.R. 71N, 101E	Siberian Platform, Dolerites (1)	Tr (230–180)	286, −59	—	5	+	32, 163E (6, 8)	—	5/30
8.23	U.S.S.R. 71N, 101E	Siberian Platform, Dolerites (2)	Tr (230–180)	117, +64	—	4	—	35, 150E (5, 6)	—	5/31
8.24	U.S.S.R. 71N, 101E	Siberian Platform, Dikes	Tr (230–180)	303, −64	—	5	+	34, 146E (6, 8)	—	5/32
8.25	U.S.S.R. 71N, 101E	Siberian Platform Rocks combined	Tr (230–180)	115, +63	264	—	M	34, 153E	—	—
9.21	Japan	Late Paleozoic and Mesozoic Intrusions		see entries 9.21, 9.22						
8.26	Bechuanaland 23S, 27E	Cave Sandstone	Tru (205–180)	325, −13	7	8	—	53, 44W (5, 9)	F108, 109	1/71
8.27	Rhodesia	Sandstone	Tru (205–180)	(352, −31)	(100)	(7)	—	(84, 8W (4, 8))	—	2/31
8.28	Australia 33.9S, 150.9E	Chocolate Shale	Trl (230–210)	338, −82	ns	7	—	49, 20W (14, 14)	—	7/34
8.29	Australia 27.8S, 153E	Brisbane Tuff	Trm (215–195)	11, −74	145	6	—	57, 37W (10, 11)	—	7/33
8.30	U.S.A. 41–45N, 106–109W	Chugwater Formation	Tr–P (260–200)	334, +17	51	5	M	48, 112E (5, 5)	F41–79	3/45–54
8.31	U.S.A. 36–41N, 109–112W	Moenkopi Formation	Trl–m (230–195)	338, +19	21	13	M	57, 107E (10, 10)	F80–91	3/37–44
8.32	U.S.A. 37N, 113W	Springdale Sandstone	Tru (205–180)	338, +16	—	—	—	55, 107E	F21–24	1/69
8.33	U.S.A. 36N, 111W	Chinle Formation (Shinarump)	Tru (205–180)	(355, +43)	(27)	(7)	M?	(79, 90E (5, 8))	F37, 38	—
8.34	U.S.A. 35N, 105W	Chinle Formation (Las Vegas)	Tru (205–180)	(33, +47)	(12)	(16)	—	(61, 10W (14, 21))	F27, 28	—
8.35	U.S.A. 39N, 109W	Chinle Fm. (Colorado N.M. (1))	Tru (205–180)	(356, +66)	(25)	(5)	—	(81, 125W (7, 9))	F33, 34	3/36
8.36	U.S.A. 39N, 109W	Chinle Fm. (Colorado N.M. (2))	Tru (205–180)	(34, +60)	(14)	(7)	—	(64, 35W (8, 11))	F35, 36	3/35
8.37	U.S.A. 35N, 105W	Chinle Formation (Romeroville)	Tru (205–180)	16, +09	14	9	M	56, 47E (4, 9)	F 26	3/34
8.38	U.S.A. 39N, 109W	Chinle Formation (Moab (1))	Tru (205–180)	156, −07	—	—	+	49, 109E	F29, 30	3/33
8.39	U.S.A. 39N, 109W	Chinle Formation (Moab (2))	Tru (205–180)	160, −10	—	—	M?	50, 114E	F31, 32	3/33
8.40	U.S.A.	Chinle Formation combined	Tru (205–180)	—	—	—	M	55, 93E	—	—
8.41	U.S.A. 40N, 77W	New Oxford Formation	Tru (205–180)	334, +48	36	7	—	66, 174E (6, 8)	F99, 100	1/70
8.42	U.S.A. 40.5N, 74.9W	Newark Group, New Jersey	Tru (190 *)	359, +25	49	4	—	63, 108E (3, 4)	F97, 98	{ 1/66, 5/34
8.43	U.S.A. 42N, 73W	Connecticut Valley Rocks	Tru (205–180)	12, +14	—	15	M	54, 86E (8, 15)	F94–96	1/67
8.44	U.S.A. 42N, 72.5W	Massachusetts Lavas	Tru (205–180)	10, +16	41	10	—	55, 88E (6, 11)	F92, 93	{ 1/68, 5/35
9.36	Uruguay	Tacuarembo Sandstone	Tru	see entry 9.36						
8.45	Greenland 72N, 23W	Kapp Biot Sediments	Trm–u (215–180)	358, +68	41	3	M	68, 160E (4, 5)	—	4/14
9.39	Antarctica	Beacon Group Sediments	D–Tr	see entry 9.39						

TRIASSIC SUPPLEMENT

No.	Location	Formation	Age (M.Y.)	Pole		N		Direction	F	Ref.
7.55	Spain	Andesites and Sediments		see entries 7.55, 7.56						
8.46	China	Dolerite	Tr (230–180)	(63, +18)	(32)	—	—	(27, 143W)	—	6/44
8.47	Argentina 33S, 69W	Las Cabras Formation	Tr (?)	(2, −27)	(26)	—	—	(71, 64W)	—	6/46
8.48	Argentina	Rio Blanco Formation	Tr (?)	scattered directions						
8.49	Argentina 24S, 65W	Red Sediments	Tr (230–180)	198, +56	16	16	+	70, 68E (16, 23)	—	6/45
8.50	Colombia 6.5N, 74.5W	Giron Beds	Tr (?)	3, +26	17	17	—	82, 50W (10, 18)	—	6/47
8.51	Venezuela 8N, 71W	La Quinta Formation	Tr–J	254, −41	24	24	+	18, 3W (18, 29)	—	6/48

JURASSIC (180–135 M.Y.)

No.	Location	Formation	Age (M.Y.)	Pole		N		Direction	F	Ref.
9.01	England 52N, 1W	Northants Iron-stone	Jm (175–155)	(341, +56)	—	—	—	(70, 133W)	—	—
9.02	England 51N, 2.5W	Bridport Sands	Jl (180–165)	(23, +60)	(73)	(5)	—	(71, 111E (6, 8))	—	—

Reference List of Paleomagnetic Directions and Pole Positions (Continued)

Ref-erence Num-ber	Location	Rock Units Studied Name	Age	Directions of Magnetization			Polar-ity	Paleomagnetic Pole	Previous Reference Numbers	
				D_m, I_m	k	a_{95}		λ', ϕ'(δp, δm)	BGSA	GJ

JURASSIC (180–135 M.Y.) *(continued)*

Ref-erence Num-ber	Location	Rock Units Studied Name	Age	D_m, I_m	k	a_{95}	Polar-ity	λ', ϕ'(δp, δm)	BGSA	GJ
9.03	England 51N, 2.5W	Yeovil Sands	Jl (180–165)	(359, +64)	(57)	(6)	−	(85, 175W (8, 9))	—	—
9.04	England 51N, 2.5W	Midford Sands	Jl (180–165)	104, +70	10	7	−	33, 41E (11, 13)	G6	2/24
9.05	England 51N, 2.5W	Cotswold Sands, negative	Jl (180–165)	(7, +66)	(22)	(6)	−	(85, 115E (8, 10))	G7	2/23
9.06	England 51N, 2.5W	Cotswold Sands, positive	Jl (180–165)	263, −64	7	10	+	38, 59E (13, 16)	—	—
9.07	England 51N, 2.5W	Midford and Cotswold Sands combined	Jl (180–165)	91, +67			M	36, 50E	—	—
9.08	England 54.5N, 0.5W	Blea Wyke Beds (1)	Jl (180–165)	(10, +67)	(46)	(4)	−	(82, 124E (5, 7))	—	—
9.09	England 54.5N, 0.5W	Blea Wyke Beds (2)	Jl (180–165)	(349, +66)	(18)	(9)	−	(81, 128W (12, 14))	—	—
9.10	England 54N, 1W	Yorkshire Sediments	J (180–135)	(3, +67)	(88)	(5)	−	(85, 150E (6, 8))	G1, 2	4/6
9.11	Scotland 57.5N, 5W	Scottish Sediments	Jl (180–165)	(234, −66)	(33)	(7)	M	(56, 76E (9, 11))	G3–5	1/51
9.12	France 43.0N, 1.6E	Pyrenean Tuffs	Jl (180–165)	(55, +59)	(17)	(6)	−	(49, 77E (6, 9))	G8	2/25
9.13	Austria 47.6N, 12.6E	Alpine Red Limestone	Jl (180–165)	48, +51	71	7	−	51, 109E (6, 9)	G11, 12	1/53
9.14	Austria 47.6N, 12.6E	Alpine Radiolarite	Jm (175–155)	37, +48	100	6	−	56, 122E (5, 7)	G9, 10	1/52
9.15	Austria 47.6N, 12.6E	Alpine Sediments combined	Jl-m (180–155)	42, +50			−	54, 115E	—	—
9.16	U.S.S.R.	Armenian Porphyrites (1)	Jl (180–165)	(43, +71)			−		—	—
9.17	U.S.S.R.	Armenian Porphyrites (2)	Jm (175–155)	(43, +53)			−		—	—
9.18	U.S.S.R.	Armenian Porphyrites (3)	Ju (165–135)	(61, +58)			−		—	—
9.19	U.S.S.R. 40N, 45E	Armenian Porphyrites combined	J (180–135)	(50, +61)	(58)		−	(53, 115E)	—	—
9.20	U.S.S.R. 39.5N, 54.5E	Turkmenian Sediments	Jm-u (175–135)	32, +40	11	17	−	59, 165E	—	2/21
9.21	Japan 37N, 140E	Mesozoic Intrusive, NE Japan	Tr-K (230–63)	332, +61	15	16	−	68, 73E (20, 25)	—	5/14
9.22	Japan 35N, 134E	Late Paleozoic and Mesozoic Intrusives, SW Japan	C-K (350–63)	30, +47			−	63, 130W (14, 21)	—	5/13
9.23	India 25.0N, 87.9E	Rajmahal Traps	J (?) (<180)	327, −64	36	4	−	13, 69W (5, 6)	H8–10	1/54
9.24	Rhodesia 18S, 26E	Karroo Basalt	Tru-Jl (200–160)	332, −40	19	5	−	63, 79W (4, 6)	G32–36	1/55
9.25	South Africa	Stormberg Lavas	Tru-Jl (200–160)	340, −49	9	14	M	72, 72W (13, 19)	—	4/4
9.26	South Africa 30.3S, 28.5E	Karroo Dolerite (surface)	Tru-Jl (190–154 *)	172, +62	—	12	M	76, 128W (14, 19)	G31	1/56
9.27	South Africa	Karroo Dolerite (mines)	Tru-Jl (190–154 *)	160, +60	52	9	M	68, 78W (14, 14)	G22–30	1/57–60
9.28	Australia 34.5S, 150.4E	Gibraltar Microsyenite	Jl (178 *)	27, −86	9	12	−	41, 34W (24, 24)	—	5/20
9.29	Australia 33.8S, 150.8E	Prospect Dolerite	Jm (168 *)	359, −81	28	7	−	51, 29W (13, 13)	—	5/21
9.30	Australia 42S, 147E	Tasmanian Dolerite, general	Jm (167 *)	319, −84	111	3	−	51, 20W (6, 6)	G5	1/61, 7/26
9.31	Australia 43S, 148E	Tasmanian Dolerite, Red Hill	Jm (167 *)	294, −75	70	7	−	—	—	7/27
9.32	Australia 26.4S, 153.1E	Noosa Heads Intrusive Complex	Ju (140 *)	51, −79	48	13	M	36, 48W (24, 25)	—	7/28
9.33	Australia 34.4S, 150.3E	Gingenbullen Dolerite	J	191, +80	23	8	+	53, 36W (15, 15)	—	5/19
9.34	U.S.A. 37N, 111.5W	Kayenta Formation	Jl (180–165)	(4, +50)	(36)		−	(83, 39E)	G13–20	3/27–30
9.35	U.S.A. 39N, 109W	Carmel Formation	J (180–135)	(349, +63)	(10)	(9)	−	(80, 160W (11, 14))	G21	3/26
9.36	Uruguay 29S, 57W	Serra Geral Formation (1)	Tru-J (200–135)	354, −43	24	3	M	83, 112 W(2, 3)	G37–52	1/62
9.37	Antarctica 78S, 161E	Ferrar Dolerite (1)	Jm (163–127 *)	255, −76	52	3	−	58, 38E (5, 5)	—	2/27

No.	Locality	Rock Unit	Age	D, I	N	k	P	Pole		Ref.
9.38	Antarctica 77.4S, 161.6E	Ferrar Dolerite (2)	Jm (163–127) *	250, −68	63	3	—	45, 39E (3, 4)	—	6/36
9.39	Antarctica 78S, 161E	Beacon Group Sediments	D-Tr	(254, −76)	(62)	(10)	—	(58, 35E (13, 16))	—	2/29, 6/38
9.40	Antarctica 77.5S, 161.6E	Basement Dikes	€-C	(247, −64)	(67)	(4)	—	(40, 40E (5, 6))	—	2/30, 6/37
9.41	Antarctica 77.4S, 161.9E	Admiralty Granites	€?	(257, −77)	(23)	(9)	—	(60, 37E (12, 15))	—	6/39
9.42	Antarctica 79–82S, 25W	Dolerite Intrusions	Tr-J?	64, −68	—	12	M	54, 44E	—	2/26

JURASSIC SUPPLEMENT

No.	Locality	Rock Unit	Age	D, I	N	k	P	Pole		Ref.
9.43	China 29N, 106E	"Dark red hematite"	J (180–135)	(261, +34)	—	(54)	—	(01, 37E)	—	6/34
9.44	India 25N, 91E	Sylhet Traps (NW group)	>Ku	322, −59	—	7	—	16, 60W (8, 11)	—	7/31
9.45	India 25N, 91E	Sylhet Traps (SW group)	>Ku	243, −60	—	16	+	36, 147E (18, 24)	—	7/32
10.15	Mozambique	Lupata Vols. and related (?) sediments		see entries 10.15, 10.16						
9.46	Basutoland 29.6S, 29.3E	Stormberg Lavas, Sani Pass	Tru-Jl	329, −54	66	4	—	64, 78W (3, 4)	—	6/40
9.47	Basutoland 29.4S, 27.8E	Stormberg Lavas, Maseru Pass	Tru-Jl	330, −50	40	5	—	64, 74W (5, 7)	—	6/41
9.48	Basutoland 29.6S, 29.3E	Stormberg Lavas, Maseru Pass	Tru-Jl	162, +54	18	11	+	74, 84W (11, 16)	—	6/42
9.49	Basutoland 29.4S, 27.8E	Stormberg Lavas, Maseru Pass	Tru-Jl	178, +66	36	10	+	71, 147W (13, 16)	—	6/43
9.50	Basutoland 29.5S, 28.5E	Stormberg Lavas combined	Tru-Jl	338, −56	68	—	M	71, 91W (15, 15)	—	—
9.51	S. Africa and S. Rhodesia	Karroo Lavas and Dolerites	Tru-Jl				M	69, 97W (8, 8)	—	—
8.15	Venezuela	La Quinta Formation	J	see entry 8.51						
9.52	Argentina 39S, 71W	Kimmeridgian Sediments, Neuquen	J	(04, −57)	—	(23)	M	(86, 8W (24, 33))	—	6/33
9.53	Brazil and Uruguay	Serra Geral Formation (2)	Tru-J (200–135)	347, −38	22	6	M	78, 126W (6, 6)	—	6/35
9.54	Antarctica 63S, 60W	Upper Jurassic Volcanic Group	Ju (165–135)	scattered directions						7/29
9.55	Antarctica 63S, 60W	Dikes	J(?)	scattered directions						7/30
9.56	Antarctica 84S, 165E	Ferrar Dolerite (3)	Jm (163–127) *	244, −75	18	11	—	59, 41E (18, 20)	—	—

CRETACEOUS (135–63 M.Y.)

No.	Locality	Rock Unit	Age	D, I	N	k	P	Pole		Ref.
10.01	England 50.5N, 1.5E	Wealden Sediments	Kl (135–100)	(345, +63)	(260)	(2)	—	(79, 115W (2, 3))	H1, 2	3/25
10.02	England 51N, 0.5E	"Iron grit," negative	Kl (135–100)	3, +68	20	6	—		—	5/15
10.03	England 51N, 0.5E	"Iron grit," positive	Kl (135–100)	185, −72	10	7	+		—	5/16
10.04	England 51N, 0.5E	"Iron grit" combined	Kl (135–100)	359, +70	—	—	M	87, 11W	—	—
10.05	U.S.S.R. 39.5N, 54.5E	Lr. Albian Sediments	Kl (125–105)	{ 26, +46 / 211, −34 }	—	—	M	62, 169E	—	2/21
10.06	U.S.S.R. 39.5N, 55E	Up. Cretaceous Sediment	Ku (105–63)	32, +42	—	—	—	60, 165E	—	2/20
10.07	Japan 34.5N, 131.5E	Inkstone Series	Kl-m (135–90)	58, +50	—	2	—	42, 153W (2, 3)	H14–20	2/19
9.21	Japan	Late Paleozoic and Mesozoic Intrusives		see entries 9.21, 9.22						
11.079	India	Deccan Traps	K-Te	see entries 11.079–11.091						
10.08	Madagascar	Lavas and Dikes	Ku (105–63)	314, −85	776	5	—	68, 168W	H11–13	1/50
10.09	Australia 43.2S, 147.1E	Cygnet Alkaline Complex	Kl (109–99) *	19, −79	47	5	M	50, 22W (10, 10)	—	6/31
10.10	Australia 36S, 150E	Mt. Dromedary Igneous Complex	Kl (93 *)		8	18	M	56, 42W (9, 9)	—	7/23
10.11	Canada 45.5N, 73E	Monteregian Hills Intrusives	Kl (122–100) *	{ 340, +57 / 142, −62 }	8	9	+	65, 157W	—	5/17
10.12	Canada 45.5N, 71W	Mt. Megantic Intrusive	Kl (115 *)	157, −52	44	7	+	69, 172E (7, 10)	H3, 4	5/18
10.13	U.S.A. 34N, 110W	Dakota Sandstone	K (135–63)	(164, −62)	—	—	+	(75, 160W (9, 11))		1/49

309

Reference List of Paleomagnetic Directions and Pole Positions *(Continued)*

Reference Number	Location	Rock Units Studied — Name	Age	Directions of Magnetization D_m, I_m	k	a_{95}	Polarity	Paleomagnetic Pole $\lambda', \phi'(\delta p, \delta m)$	Previous Reference Numbers BGSA	GJ
CRETACEOUS SUPPLEMENT										
10.14	U.S.S.R. 41N, 45E	Volcanics, Georgia	K (135–65)	(13, +54)	—	(22)	—	(78, 165E (22, 31))	—	7/20
10.15	Mozambique 16.7S, 34.2E	Lupata Alkaline Volcanics	J-K	336, −54	339	3	—	62, 101W (4, 4)	—	7/21
10.16	Mozambique 16.2S, 34.2E	Red Siltstone	J-K	359, −46	160	6	—	79, 142W (5, 8)	—	7/22
10.17	Canada 78.7N, 103.7W	Isachsen Diabase	K (see notes)	284, +80	20	8	—	69, 180 (14, 14)	—	7/25
10.18	U.S.A. 37.8N, 119.6W	Granite Plutons, Sierra Nevada	Ku (79–89 *)	335, +61	202	4	—	70, 171E (8, 10)	—	7/24
10.19	Argentina 39S, 71W	Huitrinian Sediments, Neuquen	Ku (105–65)	(341, −38)	—	(14)	—	(66, 118W (13, 13))	—	6/32
11.126	Antarctica	Andean Intrusive Suite		see entry 11.126						
TERTIARY (63–1 M.Y.)										
11.001	France 45.8N, 3.1E	Gergovie Intrusives	To (38–23)	201, −57	24	11	+	72, 115E (12, 16)	A47–49	1/34
11.002	France 46N, 3E	Limagne Basalt	Tm (27–11)	180, −73	—	—	-	77, 3E	A44–46	1/35
11.003	France 45.1N, 3.0E	Upper Miocene Lavas, Cantal	Tm (27–11)	329, +41	—	—	-	57, 119W	—	3/21
11.004	France 46N, 3E	Upper Miocene Lavas, Limagne	Tm (27–11)	158, −35	—	—	+	57, 133W	—	3/22
11.005	France 45.5N, 3E	Upper Miocene Lavas combined	Tm (27–11)	332, +39	62	10	M	57, 124W (8, 12)	—	—
11.006	France 45.6N, 3.0E	Lavas of Mt. Dore and the Limagne	Tm-p (27–1)	177, −51	27	14	+	76, 164W (13, 19)	A30, 32	1/24
12.01	France	Auvergne Lavas		see entry 12.01						
11.007	Germany 50.5N, 7E	Bonn Intrusives	To-m (38–11)	188, −63	16	14	+	82, 142E (17, 22)	—	4/3
11.008	Germany 50.5N, 9E	Vogelsberg Rocks, negative	T (63–1)	9, +73	23	11	-	—	—	4/4
11.009	Germany 50.5N, 9E	Vogelsberg Rocks, positive	T (63–1)	177, −57	10	12	+	—	—	4/4
11.010	Germany 50.5N, 9E	Vogelsberg Rocks combined	T (63–1)	2, +65	—	—	M	86, 168E	—	—
11.011	Germany 50.5N, 9.5E	Vogelsberg Basalt	Tm (27–11)	8, +58	—	6	M	76, 160E	A35–40	3/23
11.012	Scotland 57.4N, 6.3W	Skye Lavas and Intrusives	Te-o (60–23)	186, −60	60	3	+	74, 157E (4, 5)	—	2/13
11.013	Scotland 56.7N, 6.2W	Ardnamurchan Gabbro	Te-o (60–23)	184, −55	62	16	+	69, 165E (15, 22)	—	2/14
11.014	Scotland 57.0N, 6.4W	Rum Gabbro	Te-o (60–23)	181, −55	97	9	+	69, 171E (10, 14)	—	2/15
11.015	Scotland 56.4N, 5.8W	Mull Lavas	Te-o (60–23)	166, −73	11	18	+	82, 69W (28, 31)	I 6–8	1/30
11.016	Scotland 56.4N, 5.8W	Mull Intrusives	Te-o (60–23)	16, +60	70	9	M	72, 133E (11, 14)	I 4, 5	1/31
11.017	Scotland 55.5N, 7.2W	Arran Dikes	Te-o (60–23)	7, +63	35	10	M	78, 149E (12, 15)	I 3	1/32
11.018	N. Ireland 55.1N, 6.4W	Antrim Lower Basalts (1)	Te-o (60–23)	194, −60	31	5	+	73, 135E (6, 8)	I 9–12	1/29
11.019	N. Ireland 55.1N, 6.4W	Antrim Lower Basalts (2)	Te-o (60–23)	173, −65	13	10	+	80, 158W (12, 15)	I 13, 14	2/18
11.020	N. Ireland 55.1N, 6.4W	Antrim Lower Basalts combined	Te-o (60–23)	183, −63	—	—	+	79, 162E	—	—
11.021	N. Ireland 55.1N, 6.4W	Antrim Upper Basalts	Te-o (60–23)	206, −62	18	16	+	69, 109E (19, 25)	I 15, 16	2/17
11.022	N. Ireland 55.1N, 6.4W	Antrim Non-Igneous Rocks	Te-o (60–23)	184, −63	20	9	+	79, 158E (11, 13)	I 17, 18	2/16
11.023	N. Ireland 55.1N, 6.4W	Antrim Non-Igneous Rocks	Te-o (60–23)	191, −62	13	8	+	76, 138E (9, 14)	—	—
11.024	N. Ireland 55.1N, 6.4W	Antrim Igneous Suite combined	Te-o (60–23)	188, −63	18	4	+	78, 145E (5, 6)	—	—
11.025	Britain 55.5N, 3W	North-west Dikes	Te-o (60–23)	174, −73	—	16	+	85, 47W (25, 28)	A41–43	2/12
11.026	British Isles 56N, 5W	Tertiary Igneous Rocks combined	Te-o (60–23)	6, +63	123	4	M	78, 153E (5, 6)	—	—

No.	Locality	Rock Unit	Age	D, I				Pole		
11.027	England 51.2N, 4.7W	Lundy Dikes	T (<50 *)	194, −59	64	7	+	75, 130E (8, 11)	I1, 2	1/33
11.028	U.S.S.R. 41N, 45E	Georgian Igneous Rocks	Tp (15-1)	356, +56	—	7	—	67, 124W	—	7/9
11.029	U.S.S.R. 42N, 43E	Georgian Andesites	Tp (15-1)	332, +55	—	8	—	85, 110E (7, 9)	—	7/11
11.030	U.S.S.R. 42N, 45E	Georgian Andesite-Basalts	Tp (15-1)	186, −23	—	—	—	68, 52W (8, 11)	—	7/10
11.031	U.S.S.R. 42N, 43E	Georgian Andesites	Tp (15-1)	354, +46	13	—	+	60, 152W	—	—
11.032	U.S.S.R. 42N, 44E	Georgian Pliocene combined	Tp (15-1)	(40, +37)	—	—	M	74, 115W	—	—
11.033	U.S.S.R.	Armenian Granodiorite	Te (60-34)	(35, +47)	—	(3)	—	—	—	—
11.034	U.S.S.R.	Armenian Porphyrite (1)	Te (60-34)	(193, −65)	—	(2)	—	—	—	—
11.035	U.S.S.R.	Armenian Diabase	Te (60-34)	(207, −45)	—	(1)	+	—	—	—
11.036	U.S.S.R.	Armenian Andesite Breccia-Tuff	Te (60-34)	(164, −38)	—	(2)	+	—	—	—
11.037	U.S.S.R.	Armenian Porphyrites (2)	Te (60-34)	(186, −56)	—	(5)	+	—	—	—
11.038	U.S.S.R.	Armenian Augite-Porphyrites	Te (60-34)	(17, −09)	—	(15)	+	—	—	—
11.039	U.S.S.R.	Armenian Porphyrite (3)	Te (60-34)	(19, +50)	(21)	—	+	—	—	—
11.040	U.S.S.R. 40N, 45E	Armenian Eocene Igneous combined	Te (60-34)	15, +43	—	—	M	(72, 161E)	—	3/24
11.041	U.S.S.R. 40N, 44E	Armenian Pliocene Lavas	Tp (15-1)	3, +38	—	5	M	70, 178W (4, 6)	—	—
11.042	U.S.S.R. 40N, 45E	Armenian Andesites	Tp (15-1)	see entry 12.20	—	—	M	71, 143W	—	—
12.20	U.S.S.R.	Armenian Plio-Pleistocene Lavas		13, +37	7	4	M	69, 162W (3, 5)	—	2/5
11.043	U.S.S.R. 39.5N, 54E	Red-colored Sequence	Tp (15-5)	see entry 12.30	—	—	M	—	—	—
12.30	U.S.S.R.	Apsheronsk and Akchagylsk Stages		34, +44	—	—	M	—	—	—
11.044	U.S.S.R. 39.5N, 55E	Turkmenian Sediments (1)	Tpa-o (63-23)	22, +50	10	9	M	60, 158E (6, 10)	—	2/6
11.045	U.S.S.R. 36N, 62E	Turkmenian Sediments (2)	To (38-23)	10, +42	25	15	M	70, 162E (9, 14)	—	6/14
11.046	U.S.S.R. 41N, 71E	N. Ferghana Sediments	To-m (38-11)	2, +40	200	12	M	71, 138W (9, 15)	—	6/19
11.047	U.S.S.R. 41N, 71E	N. Ferghana Pliocene Sediments (1)	Tp (15-1)	4, +31	100	6	M	72, 115W (4, 7)	—	6/17
11.048	U.S.S.R. 41N, 71E	N. Ferghana Pliocene Sediments (2)	Tp (15-1)	4, +38	75	8	M	65, 118W (5, 9)	—	6/18
11.049	U.S.S.R. 41N, 71E	N. Ferghana Pliocene Sediments (3)	Tp (15-1)	1, +44	50	8	M	69, 122W (6, 10)	—	6/16
11.050	U.S.S.R. 41N, 71E	N. Ferghana Pliocene Sediments (4)	Tp (15-1)	3, +38	21	10	M	75, 112W (8, 13)	—	6/15
11.051	U.S.S.R. 41N, 71E	N. Ferghana Pliocene Sediments combined	Tp (15-1)		—	6	M	70, 117W (5, 7)	—	—
11.052	U.S.S.R. 49N, 136E	Khabarovsk Basalt	Tm-p (27-1)	7, +66	—	5	M	86, 129W (7, 8)	—	6/22
11.053	U.S.S.R. 44N, 132E	Primore Oligocene Basalts	To (38-23)	52, +76	—	5	M	55, 172E (9, 9)	—	6/21
11.054	U.S.S.R. 43N, 131E	Primore Neogene Basalts	Tm-p (27-1)	0, +64	—	5	M	89, 131E (7, 8)	—	6/20
11.055	U.S.S.R. 49N, 141E	Sakhalin Basalts	Tp (15-1)	352, +70	—	3	M	83, 100E (4, 5)	—	6/23
11.056	U.S.S.R. 55N, 161E	Kamchatka Sediments	Tm-p (27-1)	338, +67	—	16	—	76, 58E (21, 26)	—	6/25
11.057	U.S.S.R. 55N, 161E	Kamchatka Basalts	Tm-p (27-1)	344, +63	—	—	—	76, 27E (10, 13)	—	6/24
11.058	U.S.S.R. 55N, 161E	Kamchatka Rocks combined	Tm-p (27-1)	342, +65	—	—	—	76, 43E	—	—
11.059	U.S.S.R. 55N, 158E	Kamchatka Andesite-Basalt	Tp (15-1)	356, +65	—	6	M	82, 4W (8, 10)	—	6/26
12.34	Japan (etc.)	Igneous Rocks		see entry 12.34	—	—	M	—	—	—
11.060	Japan 35N, 134E	Cenozoic Rocks SW Japan	T-Q (<63)	9, +50	48	8	M	81, 109W (7, 10)	—	5/11
11.061	Japan 37N, 140E	Cenozoic Rocks NE Japan	T-Q (<63)	10, +50	68	9	—	80, 96W (8, 11)	—	5/12
11.062	Japan 36N, 138E	Late Tertiary Volcanics	Tm-p (27-1)	350, +48	37	13	M	79, 13E (11, 16)	A86	—
12.35	Japan 35N, 140E	Sediments of the Boso Peninsula	Tm-Qp	see entry 12.35	—	—	M	—	—	—
11.063	Japan 34.5N, 135.5E	Lavas and Tuffs	Tm-p (27-1)		—	—	M	—	—	—
11.064	Japan	Miocene Igneous Rocks (1)	Tm (23-11)	27, +59	—	3	M	68, 152W (4, 5)	A91	2/9
11.065	Japan	Miocene Igneous Rocks (2)	Tm (27-20)	32, +40	—	11	M	59, 113W (8, 13)	A92	2/10
11.066	Japan	Miocene Igneous Rocks combined	Tm (27-11)		—	—	—	73, 144W (22, 22)	A93	—

Reference List of Paleomagnetic Directions and Pole Positions (Continued)

Reference Number	Name	Location	Age	Directions of Magnetization D_m, I_m	k	a_{95}	Polarity	Paleomagnetic Pole $\lambda', \phi'(\delta p, \delta m)$	BGSA	GJ
TERTIARY (63–1 M.Y.) *(continued)*										
11.067	Pliocene Lavas (1)	Japan	Tp (10–1)	3, +42	—	2	M	79, 57W (2, 3)	A88	2/7
11.068	Pliocene Lavas (2)	Japan	Tp (15–5)	14, +52	—	4	M	77, 109W (4, 6)	A89	2/8
11.069	Pliocene Lavas combined	Japan	Tp (15–1)	—		—	—	80, 89W (10, 10)	A90	—
11.070	Komoro and Shigarami Volcanics	Japan	Tp (15–1)	see notes						
11.071	Enrei Formation (1), Wada-toga Rocks	Japan	Tp (10–1)	(169, −47)	(6)	(26)	+	—	—	—
11.072	Enrei Formation (2)	Japan	Tp (10–1)	182, −38	16	18	+	—	—	—
11.073	Enrei Formation (3)	Japan	Tp (10–1)	194, −39	13	22	+	—	—	—
11.074	Enrei Formation (4)	Japan	Tp (10–1)	(150, −61)	(8)	(28)	+	—	—	—
11.075	Enrei Formation (5)	Japan	Tp (10–1)	168, −19	—	—	+	—	—	—
11.076	Enrei Formation (6)	Japan	Tp (10–1)	153, −26	76	—	+	—	—	—
11.077	Enrei Formation combined	Japan 36N, 138E	Tp (10–1)	172, −43	9	10	—	77, 8W (8, 13)	—	6/27
11.078	Takoasan Andesite	Japan	Tp (5–1)	35, +70						
11.079	Deccan Traps, general	India 18N, 74E	Ku-Te (95–34)	149, +56	21	14	M	28, 78W (14, 20)	I 29, 30	1/38
11.080	Deccan Traps, Linga	India 22W, 79E	Ku-Te (95–34)	164, +48	—	2	+	37, 83W (2, 3)	I 31, 32	1/39
11.081	Deccan Traps, Khandala	India 18.7N, 73.4E	Ku-Te (95–34)	147, +58	—	3	+	25, 79W (3, 4)	I 33/34	1/40
11.082	Deccan Traps, Khambatki Ghat	India 17.5N, 74.0E	Ku-Te (95–34)	176, +60	—	5	+	31, 103W (6, 8)	I 36/37	1/41
11.083	Deccan Traps, Igatpuri Ghat	India 19.6N, 73.6E	Ku-Te (95–34)	161, +51	—	—	+	36, 87W	I 38, 39	1/42
11.084	Deccan Traps, Nipani (upper)	India 16.4N, 74.4E	Ku-Te (95–34)	338, −32	—	5	—	50, 72W (3, 5)	I 43–45	1/44
11.085	Deccan Traps, Nipani (lower)	India 16.5N, 74.3E	Ku-Te (95–34)	168, +60	—	4	+	32, 95W (5, 6)	I 40, 41	1/43
11.086	Deccan Traps, Amba Ghat (upper)	India 17.0N, 73.8E	Ku-Te (95–34)	335, −26	—	7	—	51, 64W (4, 8)	I 49–51	1/46
11.087	Deccan Traps, Amba Ghat (lower)	India 17.0N, 73.8E	Ku-Te (95–34)	144, +60	—	4	+	23, 77W (5, 6)	I 46–48	1/45
11.088	Deccan Traps, Mt. Pavagadh	India 22.5N, 71.6E	Ku-Te (95–34)	351, −16	—	8	—	58, 91W (4, 8)	I 52–54	1/47
11.089	Deccan Traps, negative	India	Ku-Te (95–34)	342, −25	52	7	—	54, 75W	I 58	—
11.090	Deccan Traps, positive	India	Ku-Te (95–34)	160, +57	93	7	+	31, 87W (10, 10)	I 59	—
11.091	Deccan Traps combined	India	Ku-Te (95–34)	161, +46	20	8	M	39, 84W (9, 9)	—	—
11.092	Mt. Pavagadh Acid Tuffs	India 22.5N, 71.6E	T (<63)	335, +17	—	7	—	75, 89W (4, 7)	I 55–57	1/48
12.42	Aden Volcanics	Aden		see entry **12.42**						
11.093	Older Volcanics Victoria (1)	Australia 38.0S, 145.5E	Te-o (60–23)	17, −73	35	7	M	67, 57W (11, 12)	I 27	1/37
11.094	Tertiary Basalts New South Wales	Australia	Te-o (60–23)	190, +70	16	14	+	63, 43W (20, 20)	—	5/10
11.095	Tasmanian Basalt, boreore	Australia	T (<63)	—		—	—	—	I 28	—
11.096	Tasmanian Basalts	Australia 42S, 147E	T (<63)	12, −72	29	—	—	73, 55W	I 28	6/28
12.45	Newer Volcanics Victoria	Australia		see entry **12.45**						
11.097	Duchesne River Formation	U.S.A. 40N, 110W	T (<63)	(2, +65)	(14)	(5)	—	(83, 99W (6, 8))	A67	3/20
11.098	Siletz River Volcanics	U.S.A. 45N, 123.5W	Te (60–50)	70, +55	50	7	M	37, 49W (7, 10)	I 21, 22	1/36
11.099	Wasatch Formation	U.S.A. 44.5N, 109W	Te (60–34)	(351, +64)	(30)	(17)	—	(84, 180E (20, 27))	I 26	3/19
11.100	Green River Formation	U.S.A. 39.5N, 108W	Te (60–34)	345, +65	168	5	—	78, 158W (6, 7)	I 25	3/17
11.101	Green River Formation (Laney)	U.S.A. 41.5N, 109.5W	Te (60–34)	(355, +63)	(28)	(6)	—	(85, 168W (8, 9))	I 23, 24	3/18

11.102	U.S.A. 44N, 103W	Arikee Formation	Tm (27-11)	(66, +69)	(3)	(26)	–	(47, 49W (37, 44))	A66	3/16
11.103	U.S.A. 37.5N, 122W	Neroly Formation	Tm (20-11)	(7, +58)	(89)	(3)	–	(85, 42W (3, 4))	A55, 56	3/13
11.104	U.S.A. 46N, 120W	Ellensburg Formation	Tm-p (20-10)	1, +69	12	9	–	85, 115W (13, 15)	A64, 65	3/15
11.105	U.S.A. 43N, 115W	Payette Formation	Tm-p (27-1)	(1, +62)	(240)	(3)	–	(89, 44W (3, 5))	A57	3/14
11.106	U.S.A. 46.5N, 120.5W	Columbia River Basalts	Tm (27-1)	7, +65	29	9	M	85, 43W (9, 14)	A58-65	1/26
11.107	Canada 61N, 134W	Tertiary Basalts	Tm-p (27-1)	349, +75	28	4	M	85, 150E (5, 6)	A53, 54	1/27
11.108	Iceland 65.2N, 20.0W	Miocene Lavas	Tm (27-11)	2, +78	7	6	M	89, 5E (10, 10)	A33, 34	1/25
11.109	Greenland 68.2N, 31.7W	Skaergaard Ferro-Gabbro	Te	193, -71		5	+	76, 114E (8, 9)	—	6/30
12.49	Iceland	Pliocene and Pleistocene Lavas	see entries 12.49, 12.50							
12.55	Antarctica	Cenozoic Lavas of Cape Hallet	see entry 12.55							
12.59	U.S.A.	Hawaiian Lavas	see entries 12.59–12.62							

TERTIARY SUPPLEMENT

11.110	Germany 50.3N, 7.0E	Igneous Rocks, Eifel	To-Qr (<47)	26, +66	58	7	M	73, 92E (9, 11)	—	6/11
11.111	Germany 50.7N, 8.0E	Igneous Rocks, Westerwald	To-m (47-18)	23, +55	20	15	M	68, 132E (15, 21)	—	6/13
11.112	Germany 50.7N, 7.5E	Igneous Rocks, Siebengebirge	To-m (47-18)	34, +61	65	7	M	65, 104E (8, 10)	—	6/12
11.113	Germany 50.6N, 7.5E	Igneous Rocks, Rheinland Pfalz	To-Q (47-18)	28, +62	38	5	M	70, 108E (6, 8)	—	—
11.114	Germany 51.4N, 9.8E	Volcanics, Gottingen (1)	Tm-p (16-6)	188, -63	—	11	+	81, 151E (14, 17)	—	7/6
11.115	Germany 51.4N, 9.8E	Volcanics, Gottingen (2)	Tm-p (16-6)	184, -64	14	11	M	83, 163E (14, 17)	—	7/7
11.116	Germany 51.3N, 9.4E	Tuffs and Lavas, Habichtswald	Tm-p (16-6)	358, +66	24	19	M	87, 141W (25, 31)	—	7/8
11.117	U.S.S.R. 42N, 43E	Volcanics and Sediments, Georgia	Te (60-34)	356, +45	10	15	M	75, 123W (12, 19)	—	7/12
12.67	U.S.S.R.	Dolerite, Georgia	see entry 12.67							
11.118	Japan 37N, 139E	Quartz Diorite, Shimizu tunnel	Tm?	3, +52	—	7	–	—	—	—
11.119	Japan 36.6N, 138.3E	Intrusives, Susaka	Tm?	20, +55	—	8	–	—	—	—
11.120	Japan 36.0N, 138.1E	Quartz Diorite, Lake Suwa	Tm?	329, +45	—	9	–	—	—	—
11.121	Japan 35.7N, 138.6E	Gabbro, Kofu	Tm?	357, +45	—	6	–	—	—	—
11.122	Japan 36N, 139E	Quartz Diorite, Tanzawa	Tm?	359, +52	—	12	–	—	—	—
11.123	Japan 36.3N, 138.6E	Intrusives of Fossa Magna combined	Tm?	357, +51	41	12	–	85, 9W (11, 16)	—	7/13
11.124	Australia 38.0S, 145.5E	Older Volcanics of Victoria (2)	Te-o (60-23)	10, -77	—	9	M	63, 40W (16, 16)	—	7/14
11.125	Argentina 38S, 71W	Lavas	T (63-1)	181, +73	—	4	+	69, 108E (6, 7)	—	6/29
11.126	Antarctica	Andean Intrusive Suite	Ku-Te (95-43)	351, -77	253	3	M	86, 178E (6, 6)	—	7/19

QUATERNARY (LESS THAN 1 M.Y.) AND PLIO-PLEISTOCENE

12.01	France 45.1N, 3.5E	Auvergne Lavas	Tp-Qp	197, -63	28	13	++	78, 93E (16, 20)	A20/21	1/21
12.02	France 45.5N, 3.0E	Plateaux Basalts	Qp	206, -64	—	—	++	72, 84E	A18, 19	3/10
12.03	France 45.5N, 3.0E	Chaîne des Puys Lavas	Qp	353, +62	—	—	–	85, 106W	A14, 15	3/9
12.04	Germany 49.9N, 4.7E	Roman Kiln, Tréves	Qr	359, +61	933	4	–	83, 172W (5, 6)	—	—
12.05	Western Europe and Africa:	Archeomagnetic determinations of intensity and inclination of the field (see Chapter 8)								
12.06	England 52N, 0E	Archeological Baked Clays (1)	Qr	0, +66	242	2	–	87, 180(3, 3)	A7	—
12.07	England 52N, 1W	Archeological Baked Clays (2)	Qr	3, +58	174	5	–	77, 170E (6, 7)	—	5/1
12.08	England 52N, 1W	Archeological Baked Clays combined	Qr	1, +64	149	3	–	82, 172E (4, 5)	—	—
12.09	Italy 37.7N, 15.0E	Mt. Etna Lavas	Qr	4, +56	50	7	–	86, 126E (7, 10)	A1-3	1/1
12.10	Sweden	Glacial Varves	Qp	356, +69	23	12	–	84, 141W (14, 14)	A13	1/4

Reference List of Paleomagnetic Directions and Pole Positions (Continued)

QUATERNARY (LESS THAN 1 M.Y.) AND PLIO-PLEISTOCENE (*continued*)

Reference Number	Location	Name	Age	D_m, I_m	k	a_{95}	Polarity	λ', $\phi'(\delta p, \delta m)$	BGSA	GJ
		Rock Units Studied		Directions of Magnetization				Paleomagnetic Pole	Previous Reference Numbers	
12.11	Sweden 63.2N, 16.0E	Glacial Varves (2)	Qp	359, +71	—	—	—	82, 160W (5, 6)	—	1/5
12.12	Sweden 63.1N, 17.7E	Postglacial Varves (1)	Qr	357, +73	42	3	—	86, 142W (5, 6)	A5, 6	1/2
12.13	Sweden 63.1N, 17.7E	Postglacial Varves (2)	Qr	2, +75	34	4	—	89, 156E (7, 8)	A8, 9	1/3
12.14	Sweden 63N, 18E	Postglacial Varves (3)	Qr	338, +77	477	—	—	80, 49W	A13	—
12.15	Sweden 63N, 18E	Postglacial Varves combined	Qr	353, +75	—	—	—	87, 84W	—	—
12.16	U.S.S.R. 42N, 45E	Georgian Andesite-Basalt	Q	5, +30	—	16	—	63, 144W (10, 17)	—	6/6
12.17	U.S.S.R. 41N, 44E	Georgian Dolerite	Q	171, −54	—	7	+	80, 90W (7, 10)	—	6/4
12.18	U.S.S.R. 43N, 45E	Georgian Andesites	Q	18, +57	—	11	—	74, 155E (12, 16)	—	6/5
12.19	U.S.S.R. 42N, 45E	Georgian Igneous Rocks combined	Q	7, +47	26	—	M	75, 159W	—	—
12.20	U.S.S.R. 40N, 45E	Armenian Plio-Pleistocene Lavas	Tp-Qp	192, −45	—	2	+	74, 175W (2, 3)	—	3/3
12.21	U.S.S.R. 40N, 45E	Armenian Lavas and Tuffs	Q	0, +58	—	3	—	88, 135W (3, 4)	—	3/2
12.22	U.S.S.R.	Armenian Volcanic Tuffs	Q	(347, +55)	—	—	—	—	—	6/1
12.23	U.S.S.R.	Armenian Volcanic Tuffs	Q	(353, +48)	—	—	—	—	—	6/3
12.24	U.S.S.R.	Armenian Andesite-Basalt	Q	(3, +44)	—	—	—	—	—	—
12.25	U.S.S.R.	Armenian Andesite-Basalts	Q	(330, +50)	—	—	—	—	—	—
12.26	U.S.S.R.	Armenian Dacites and Andesite Dacites	Q	(8, +44)	—	—	—	—	—	6/2
12.27	U.S.S.R. 40N, 45E	Armenian Igneous combined	Q	(353, +49)	(55)	(10)	—	(78, 103W (9, 13))	—	—
12.28	U.S.S.R. 39.5N, 53E	Khazar Beds	Q	(2, +53)	—	—	—	(87, 160W)	—	2/2
12.29	U.S.S.R. 39.5N, 53.2E	Baku Beds	Q	11, +54	26	4	M	81, 168E (4, 6)	—	2/1
12.30	U.S.S.R. 39N, 54E	Apsheronsk and Akchagylsk Stages	Tp-Qp	359, +42	9	8	M	75, 122W (6, 10)	A26-29	2/3, 4
12.31	U.S.S.R. 53N, 159E	Kamchatka Andesite-Basalts	Q	15, +61	—	3	—	75, 69W (3, 5)	—	6/7
12.32	U.S.S.R. 57N, 161E	Sheveluch Volcanic Domes	Qr	4, +62	—	6	—	77, 20W (7, 9)	—	3/1
12.33	U.S.S.R. 49N, 154E	Kurile Island Lavas	Q	345, +65	—	5	—	80, 64W (5, 7)	—	3/4, 6/8
12.34	Japan (etc.)	Igneous Rocks	T-Q	11, +61	5	11	M	80, 173E (13, 17)	A84	4/2
12.35	Japan 35N, 140E	Sediments of the Bōsō Peninsula	Tm-Qp	(356, +34)	(70)	(11)	—	(73, 27W)	—	—
12.36	Japan 35N, 140E	Sediments of the Bōsō Peninsula	Qp	(5, +58)	—	—	—	—	—	—
12.37	Japan 34.5N, 131.5E	Yamaguchi Basalt	Qp	0, +57	18	4	M	87, 132E (4, 6)	—	3/8
12.38	Japan 35N, 139E	North Izu and Hakone Rocks	Qp-r	343, +51	10	7	M	78, 46E (7, 7)	A82, 83	1/7-15
12.39	Japan 36N, 138E	Quaternary Volcanic Rocks	Q	359, +47	18	11	—	83, 35W (10, 15)	A85	3/7

	Location	Description	Age	D, I	N	Pol.	Pole	A	Ref.
12.40	Japan	Historic Lavas	Qr	357, +46	100	4	—	82, 25W (4, 6)	—	3/6, 5/2
12.41	Japan	Archeological Baked Clays	Qr	356, +53	17	3	—	86, 19W (3, 4)	—	3/5
12.42	Aden 12.8N, 45.0E	Aden Volcanics	T-Q	353, +24	340	3	M	83, 50W (2, 3)	—	4/1
12.43	Tunisia 37N, 10E	Archeological Baked Clays	Qr	359, +54	—	3	—	88, 155W	A4	3/12
12.44	Algeria 23N, 5E	Ahaggar Basalts	Q	345, +32	24	14	—	74, 104W (9, 16)	—	6/9
12.45	Australia 38.0S, 143.5E	Newer Volcanics Victoria	Tp-Qr	3, −60	37	5	M	86, 78W (6, 7)	A76-78	1/23
12.46	New Zealand 38S, 176E	Ignimbrites	Q	(350, −65)				(79, 35E)	A79-80	1/28
12.47	U.S.A. 43N, 73W	New England Glacial Varves	Qp	355, +51	50	10	—	79, 128E (9, 13)	A50-52	1/6
12.48	Argentina 38S, 70W	Neuquen Lavas	Qp	1, −61	15	5	M	86, 100E (6, 8)	A68-75	1/22
12.49	Iceland 65N, 22W	Lavas, negative	Tp-Qp	—	—	—	—	77, 74E (6, 6)	A22, 23	1/19, 20
12.50	Iceland 65N, 22W	Lavas, positive	Tp-Qp	—	—	—	—	88, 149E (7, 7)	A24, 25	1/19, 20
12.51	Iceland 64.6N, 22.0W	Early Quaternary Lavas	Qp	181, −75	9	7	+	87, 149E (12, 13)	A16, 17	1/18
12.52	Iceland 64N, 19W	Postglacial Lavas (1)	Qr	1, +74	—	8	—	86, 152E (13, 15)	A11, 12	1/17
12.53	Iceland 64N, 19W	Postglacial Lavas (2)	Qr	—	—	—	—	89, 54E (6, 6)	A10	—
12.54	Iceland 64N, 19W	Postglacial Lavas combined	Qr	—	—	—	—	88, 135E	—	—
12.55	Antarctica 72S, 171E	Lavas, Cape Hallet	T-Q	28, −80	48	4	M	81, 86W (8, 8)	—	2/11
12.56	U.S.A. 19.6N, 155.6W	Historic Lavas, Hawaii	Qr	9, +38	416	3	—	81, 77W (2, 4)	—	5/3
12.57	U.S.A. 19.6N, 155.6W	Puna Volcanic Series, Hawaii	Qp-r	4, +42	116	3	—	84, 115W (2, 4)	—	5/4
12.58	U.S.A. 19.6N, 155.6W	Kahuku Volcanic Series, Hawaii	Qp	8, +24	31	5	—	79, 26W (3, 5)	—	5/5
12.59	U.S.A. 19.6N, 155.6W	Hamakua Volcanic Series, Hawaii	Tp-Qp	13, +52	65	4	—	73, 116W (4, 5)	—	5/6
12.60	U.S.A. 19.6N, 155.6W	Pololu Volcanic Series, Hawaii	Tp(?)	6, +32	60	3	—	84, 45W (2, 3)	—	5/7
12.61	U.S.A. 19.6N, 155.6W	Ninole Volcanic Series, Hawaii	Tp(?)	1, +25	33	5	—	84, 19W (3, 5)	—	5/8
12.62	U.S.A. 19.6N, 155.6W	Hawaiian Lavas combined	Tp(?)-Qr	6, +34	29	2	—	84, 57W (1, 2)	—	5/9
12.63	Samoa 14S, 172W	Samoan Lavas, negative	Q	1, −30	15	14	—	88, 13W (9, 16)	—	—
12.64	Samoa 14S, 172W	Samoan Lavas, positive	Tp-Qp	191, +35	35	10	+	79, 53W (7, 11)	—	—

QUATERNARY AND PLIO-PLEISTOCENE SUPPLEMENT

	Location	Description	Age	D, I	N	Pol.	Pole	A	Ref.
11.110	Germany	Igneous Rocks, Eifel	Tp-Qp	see entry 11.110					
12.65	U.S.S.R. 41N, 45E	Dolerite, Georgia	Qr	358, +60	—	6	M	88, 70E (7, 9)	—	7/5
12.66	Antarctica 63S, 61W	Volcanics, South Shetland Is., exc.	T-Q	15, −74	333	3	M	82, 51E (6, 6)	—	7/4
12.67	Antarctica 58S, 26W	Volcanics, South Sandwich Is.	T-Q	(19, −69)	(123)	(6)	—	(78, 45E (9, 10))	—	7/3
12.68	U.S.A. 19.5N, 155.5W	Historic Lava Flows, Hawaii	Qr	10, +36	643	2	—	80, 71W (2, 2)	—	7/1
12.69	Canada and U.S.A.	Silts	Qp	—	—	—	—	(87, 166E (22, 22))	—	6/10

315

Explanatory Notes

PRECAMBRIAN (OLDER THAN ABOUT 600 M.Y.)

1.01–02 *Torridonian Sandstone Series* Late Precambrian (Irving and Runcorn, 1957; Irving, 1957a) These beds are divided into 3 groups called, from the oldest to youngest, Diabaig, Applecross, and Aultbea. The rocks are mostly brown, red, or purple arkoses. Corrections for tilting improve the precision of the mean site directions, indicating that the magnetization predates the tilting, which is Paleozoic or earlier. The directions along the arch of a sharp fold of Caledonian age were scattered *in situ* but came together after correction to bedding, indicating that the directions remained unchanged during and since that orogeny. See §§ 5.04, 5.06, 5.12, 10C.3 for other results. These results from field tests, and from the main sequence (described below), are based on over 400 oriented samples from 116 sites.

1.01 *Torridonian Sandstone Series* (*upper*) A total of 205 samples (1300 specimens) were collected from 81 sites spread laterally over 110 km and stratigraphically through about 3000 m spanning much of the Applecross and Aultbea Groups. Twenty-eight sites were positive and 53 negative. The means of positive and negative groups are not exactly antiparallel and this is probably due to small components imposed by the present field, the effect of which will be diminished in the average obtained irrespective of sign. Sites were given unit weight in the analysis ($N = 81$). Stability is indicated by field tests, by the divergences from the present field, by thermal demagnetization (Figure 5.28), and by the occurrence of reversals. Oblique directions were obtained at 11 other sites, 2 of which were sandwiched between zones of opposed polarity. At 3 further sites the directions were along the present field and were excluded from the analysis.

1.02 *Torridonian Sandstone Series* (*lower*) Thirty-two samples (280 specimens) were collected from 13 sites (red arkoses) in the Diabaig Group spread laterally over 90 km and stratigraphically through 500 m. Stability is indicated by the field tests (see above) and by

the divergence from the present field. Sites were given unit weight in the analysis ($N = 13$). Directions at 2 other sites (green siltstones) gave directions along the present field (Table 5.6) and were excluded from the analysis.

1.03 *Longmyndian* Late Precambrian (Creer, 1957a) About 40 samples (about 200 specimens) were collected from 12 sites in steeply dipping beds over a distance of 40 km. Both polarities occur. The magnetization of test specimens is unchanged in *ac* fields of 300 oe. Stability is indicated by this, by the divergences from the present field, and by the reversals.

1.04 *Sparagmites* Late Precambrian (Harland and Bidgood, 1959) Twenty-nine samples were collected from near Lake Mjösen. Eighteen were too weakly magnetized for measurement, and 4, directed close to the present field, were excluded. Of the remainder, 5 were positive and 2 negative. This reversal, and the divergences from the present field indicate stability. Unit weight was given to each sample in the analysis ($N = 7$).

1.05 *Sinian Sediments* Precambrian to Cambrian (Khramov quoted in Kalashnikov, 1961; Yanovsky and others, 1963) The Sinian complex of the Siberian platform is "placed between Paleozoic and Proterozoic as an independent division" (Nalivkin, 1960, p. 20). This result is based on 30 samples from the R. Patom. It is stated that stability is determined by the "circle of remagnetization."

1.06 *Pilansberg Dikes* Precambrian (Gough, 1956) Radioisotope age determinations (Rb-Sr on biotite) gave a value of 1290 ± 180 m.y. (Schreiner, 1958a). One hundred and sixty-nine samples from 5 dikes (5–53 samples per dike) in deep mines over a distance of 85 km gave well-grouped directions. Most specimen directions were unchanged in *ac* fields of 100 oe, which, with the divergence from the present field, indicates stability. Mean dike directions were given unit weight in the analysis ($N = 5$). Samples from surface outcrops were scattered and detailed work suggests that this is due to lightning strikes (§ 5.13).

1.07 *Bushveld Gabbro* Precambrian (Gough and van Niekerk, 1959) Radioisotope age determinations (Rb-Sr) gave 1920 ± 130 m.y. (Schreiner, 1958b). This is a large basin-shaped body 150×300 km in extent. Ninety-nine samples (about 200 specimens) were collected from 5 quarries over a distance of 200 km. The site directions, when combined giving each unit weight ($N = 5$), give a mean 16, $+70$, $k = 26$, $a_{95} = 15°$. Directions in a quartzite xenolith were parallel to those in the gabbro. After correction for the pseudo-stratification the values listed in this entry were obtained ($N = 5$), the precision being much improved. Stability is indicated by the divergence from the present field. The pole was calculated as a mean of site poles giving each unit weight ($N = 5$, $K = 40$).

1.08 *Edith River Volcanics* Early Upper Precambrian (Irving and Green, 1958) The precision of directions at 10 sites (1 sample at each) in folded lavas improves after correcting for tilt. Unit weight was given to each site in the analysis ($N = 10$). Stability is indicated by the divergence from the present field.

1.09 *Nullagine Lavas* Late Precambrian (Irving and Green, 1958) Five samples (15 specimens) were studied, unit weight being given to each specimen ($N = 15$) in the analysis. Stability is indicated by the divergence from the present field.

1.10 *Buldiva Quartzite* Late Precambrian (Irving and Green, 1958) Eight samples (8 specimens) were studied, unit weight being given to each sample in the analysis ($N = 8$). Stability is indicated by the divergence from the present field.

1.11–12 *Hazel Formation* Precambrian (Howell, Martinez, and Statham, 1958) A study [**1.11**] of flat-lying beds (15 samples, 5 localities) gave closely grouped directions. The directions [**1.12**] in folded beds (37 samples, 9 localities) were highly scattered after correction for tilt. The latter result suggests that the magnetization occurred after folding, and the results are bracketed. Unit weight given to samples in the analysis.

1.13–20 *Precambrian of Arizona* Studies were made of the Bonito Canyon Quartzite and of 3 units in the Grand Canyon Series. The 3 units are respectively, from oldest to youngest, Bass Limestone, Hakatai Shales, Shinumo Quartzite. The Bonito Canyon Quartzite is considered older than the Grand Canyon Series.

1.13 *Bonito Canyon Quartzite* (Collinson and Runcorn, 1960) Result based on 16 sam-

ples (74 specimens) spaced through a 30 m section at Fort Defiance. The divergence from the present field indicates stability. Specimens were given unit weight in the analysis ($N = 74$).

1.14 *Bass Limestone* (Collinson and Runcorn, 1960) Fourteen samples (43 specimens) spaced through a 92 m section in the Grand Canyon gave the mean direction 232, $+52$ ($k = 23$, $a_{95} = 5°$, $N = 43$). The individual directions were smeared toward the Earth's field. An estimate (given in this entry) was made of the direction of the stable component.

1.15 *Bass Limestone and Hakatai Shales* (Doell, quoted in Cox and Doell, 1960) These formations are conformable, the contact being gradational. Ten samples, spanning 140 m stratigraphically, were collected from the Bright Angel and Kaibab trails in the Grand Canyon. Samples were given unit weight in the analysis ($N = 10$). Stability is indicated by the divergence from the present field.

1.16–17 *Hakatai Shales* In addition to **1.15**, which was based partly on samples from the Hakatai Shales, 2 further results are available from these sediments.

1.16 *Hakatai Shales (1)* (Runcorn, 1956a) Fifteen samples (34 specimens) were collected from the Bright Angel Trail down the Grand Canyon. Specimen observations were given unit weight in the analysis ($N = 34$).

1.17 *Hakatai Shales (2)* (Collinson and Runcorn, 1960) Fourteen samples (41 specimens) spanning a 10 m section in the Grand Canyon gave a mean direction of 291, $+58$. The directions were smeared toward the present field and an estimate of the direction of the stable component was made and is given in this entry.

1.18 *Shinumo Quartzite* (Collinson and Runcorn, 1960) Fourteen samples (61 specimens), spanning a 30 m section in the Grand Canyon, gave a mean direction of 288, $+65$. The directions are smeared toward the present field. An estimate of the direction of the stable component was made and is given in this entry.

1.19 *Grand Canyon Series combined* The directions in entries **1.14–18** are combined, giving each unit weight ($N = 5$). The pole is the average of the poles (those which fall in what is now the central Pacific Ocean) in entries **1.14–18** ($N = 5$, $K = 9$).

1.20 *Precambrian of Arizona combined* The directions in entries **1.13–18** are combined irrespective of sign, giving each unit weight ($N = 6$). The pole is the average of the poles (those which fall in what is now the central Pacific Ocean) in entries **1.13–18** ($N = 6$, $K = 9$).

1.21–27 *Belt Series of Montana* Precambrian (Collinson and Runcorn, 1960) An illite shale from the Siyeh Formation was dated radiometrically as 750 m.y. (Goldich, Baadsgaard, Edwards, and Weaver, 1959), suggesting a late Precambrian age. Magnetic results from 6 localities are listed [**1.21–26**]. Specimen observations were given unit weight in the analysis. Stability is indicated by the divergences from the present field, and by the reversal.

1.21 *McNamara Formation* Twenty samples (53 specimens) spanning 25 m.

1.22 *Miller Peak Formation* Fourteen samples (23 specimens) spanning 20 m.

1.23, 24 *Spokane Shale* (1) Thirty-nine samples (71 specimens) from Prickly Pear Canyon span 120 m. (2) Five samples (19 specimens) from McDonald Creek span 15 m.

1.25 *Grinnel Formation* Sixteen samples (44 specimens) span 21 m.

1.26 *Appekunny Formation* Fifteen samples (38 specimens) span 33 m.

1.27 *Belt Series of Montana combined* The directions in entires **1.21–26** are combined, irrespective of sign, giving each unit weight ($N = 6$). The pole is the average of poles (those which fall in what is now the Central Pacific) for each locality ($N = 6$, $K = 37$).

1.28–31 *Belt Series, Kintla Formation* Precambrian (Norris and Black, 1961) Results were obtained from 3 localities in the Lewis Thrust sheet of the Canadian Rockies. All specimens have been partially demagnetized in an *ac* field of 156 oe (peak). Stability is indicated by laboratory studies, by the divergences from the present field, and by the occurrence of reversals. The sampling is as follows: **1.28**, 27 samples, 54 specimens; **1.29**, 24 samples, 48 specimens; **1.30**, 8 samples, 16 specimens. See **1.65–73** and § 10A.7.

1.31 *Kintla Formation combined* The directions in entries **1.28–30** are combined irrespective of sign, giving each unit weight ($N = 3$). The pole is the average of poles in these entries ($N = 3$, $K = 110$).

1.32 *Belt Series of Montana and British Columbia combined* The directions in entries **1.21–26**, **1.28–30** were combined giving each

unit weight ($N = 9$). The pole is the average of the poles in these entries ($N = 9$, $K = 52$).

1.33 *Precambrian of Arizona and the Belt Series combined* This pole was obtained by applying Fisher's statistics to the poles in entries **1.13–18**, **1.21–26**, **1.28–30** giving each unit weight ($N = 15$, $K = 9$).

1.34 *Baraga County Dikes* Precambrian (J. W. Graham, 1953) Five diabase dikes in Baraga County, Michigan, were studied. Samples from 2 dikes gave scattered directions, but in the other 3 the grouping was good. This result is based on 36 directions observed from 2 dikes, 20 from a dike ½ m wide, and 16 from a dike 12 m wide. The dikes are 10 km apart. The direction in 1 sample was unchanged after partial demagnetization in an *ac* field of 493 oe. This test and the divergence from the present field indicate stability. In the analysis, unit weight was given to each of the 36 observations ($N = 36$).

1.35–40 *Keweenawan* Late Precambrian (P. M. Du Bois, 1957, 1962) Results are available from several formations. They are arranged stratigraphically, **1.35** being the youngest. **1.35**, 15 samples from 2 localities. **1.36**, 15 samples. **1.37**, 68 samples from 12 localities spanning 2950 m. **1.38**, 25 samples from 4 localities spanning 490 m. **1.39**, 31 samples from 6 localities spanning 560 m. In the analyses each sample was given unit weight. Directions in the 4 lowest groups diverge strongly from the present field indicating stability, and substantial stability is indicated by certain thermal demagnetization tests (Figure 5.28), by the scattered directions observed in lava boulders in the Copper Harbour conglomerates, by the increase in precision after correction for variable dips in the Freda Sandstone and Nonesuch Shales, and by the good agreement between directions in sediments and lavas of the Copper Harbour Group. The variation in directions between these 4 groups could be due to small unstable components (the mean directions in **1.36–39** fall approximately on a great circle through the present field) or to field changes during the period of deposition. The suggestion of a limited degree of partial instability is not inconsistent with the field stability tests, which refer only to special cases and not to all samples. The directions in the Chequamegon Sandstone are clustered around the present field, and it is doubtful whether the mean differs significantly from it; for this reason the result is entered in brackets. See **1.74–85.**

1.40 *Keweenawan* (*excluding Chequamegon Sandstone*) *combined* The directions in **1.36–39** were averaged giving each unit weight ($N = 4$). A pole was calculated from this mean direction.

1.41 *Adirondack Gneisses* Precambrian (Balsley and Buddington, 1954, 1958, 1960) A total of 128 gneiss samples were collected from the Russell "Border Belt." These rocks are considered to have "undergone more or less homogeneous metamorphism probably within the temperature range 400° to 550°C." The directions fall into 2 groups—one with north-seeking poles down, and one with poles upward and widely scattered directions. The samples of the first group have magnetite as the predominant magnetic mineral, and in those of the second group titaniferous hematite predominates. The mean for the first group is given here. This result is bracketed since the authors consider that the remanence directions are controlled by the mineralogy.

1.42–45 *Gabbro Intrusives of Bancroft* Precambrian (Hood, 1958, quoted in Cox and Doell, 1960) Four intrusions from the Grenville Province in the Bancroft area of Ontario were studied. Radioisotope ages from this part of the Grenville Province range between 1000–1200 m.y. (Shillibeer and Cummings, 1956; Wilson, 1958). Specimen observations were given unit weight in the analyses. In some cases partial demagnetization in *ac* fields was used to decrease scatter. Stability is indicated by the divergences from the present field. The numbers of samples and specimens are as follows: **1.42,** 8 samples, 43 specimens; **1.43,** 12 samples, 58 specimens; **1.44,** 6 samples, 28 specimens; **1.45,** 11 samples, 68 specimens.

1.46–49 *Sudbury Nickel Irruptive* Precambrian (Hood, 1961) Radiometric age determinations (K-Ar and Rb-Sr) indicate that the irruptive was emplaced 1200–1800 m.y. ago (Wetherill, Davis, and Aldrich, 1957). Sixty samples (37 from the norite) were collected from 1 traverse of the North Range, and 4 traverses of the South Range. The spread of localities is 44 km. The results are based on 14 samples (41 specimens) from the North Range, and 33 samples (155 specimens) from the South Range. In some cases partial demagnetization in *ac* fields was used to diminish scatter. In the analyses, unit weight is given to specimens. The directions *in situ* in the North and South

Ranges (entries **1.46, 47**) differ by about 40°. The results are combined in 2 ways: (1) **1.48,** by assuming equal tilting about the long axis of the basin so that the mean is midway between the directions in entries **1.46** and **1.47;** (2) **1.49** by assuming 10° tilt on the North Range and 30° tilt on the South Range about the long axis of the basin, as is indicated by certain geological evidence. See § 10A.3 and **1.87, 88.**

1.50–51 *Diabase Dikes of Ontario and Quebec* Precambrian (Strangway, 1961) Samples were collected from 14 sites over a distance of 500 km. Those from 3 sites were too weak for measurement. The dikes are "of widely differing ages and belong to several swarms having widely different directions." Dispersion was decreased by magnetic cleaning in 100–200 oe. Stability is indicated by the laboratory studies and by divergence from the present field. The directions after partial demagnetization fall into 2 groups: **1.50** with 5 sites showing westerly declinations and upward inclinations; and **1.51** with 5 sites aligned along a N-S axis with low inclinations, down to the south. The dispersion within each group is not excessive. The grouping is made here entirely on the basis of directions. In the original it was suggested that the magnetization was acquired parallel to the internal field of the dikes at the time of cooling, which was nearly in the plane of the dikes and not necessarily parallel to the Earth's field. For this reason these results are entered in brackets.

1.50 (1) Mean of 6 sites mean directions (nos. 1, 2, 3, 5, 8, and 11 of Strangway) giving each unit weight ($N = 6$). This result is based on 43 samples.

1.51 (2) Mean of 5 site mean directions (nos. 4, 6, 7, 9, and 10 of Strangway) giving each unit weight ($N = 5$). This result is based on 73 samples.

1.52–53 *Signal Hill and Blackhead Sandstones* Precambrian (Nairn, Frost, and Light, 1959) These 2 formations from Newfoundland are separated by about 2500 m stratigraphically, the former being older. A single locality was sampled in each case. Stability is indicated by the divergence from the present field. Nairn and others suggest a counterclockwise rotation of Newfoundland of 20° to bring these poles into better agreement with the poles from the Hakatai Shales of Arizona [**1.15–17**], but the reasons for doing this are not compelling since the time correlation with the Hakatai Shales is conjectural, and the discrepancy could, in any case, arise from the limited sampling of these beds.

1.52 *Signal Hill Sandstone* Nine samples (36 specimens) Samples given unit weight in the analysis ($N = 9$).

1.53 *Blackhead Sandstone* Ten samples (40 specimens). Samples given unit weight in the analysis ($N = 10$).

1.54 *Combined* Results **1.52** and **1.53** combined giving each sample unit weight ($N = 19$).

1.55–56 *Multicolored Series and Tillite Formation* Precambrian (Bidgood and Harland, 1961) The Multicolored Series, which is 1000 m beneath the base of the Cambrian, is part of the Eleonore Bay Formation of East Greenland. The latter passes upward conformably into the Tillite Formation and then into the Cambrian.

1.55 *Multicolored Series* Ten samples of red mudstone from 2 outcrops gave negative polarities. The divergence from the present field indicates stability. Unit weight was given to samples in the analysis ($N = 10$).

1.56 *Tillite Formation* In a collection of 54 samples from both limbs of an anticline many were too weak for measurement or had directions close to the present field, but 16, with directions divergent from the present field, were combined to give this result. Samples were used as units in the analysis ($N = 16$). It is stated that reversals are present, and that the "use of the tectonic check" indicates stability; in view of the high dispersion ($\theta_{63} = 36°$) it is doubtful whether such a test could be decisive.

PRECAMBRIAN SUPPLEMENT

1.57–58 *Late Precambrian Iron Formations of the Yenesei Ridge* (Vlassov and Aparin, 1963) Age cited as Sinian. Treatment of test specimens in 200 oe *ac* field yielded no appreciable change.

1.57 *Lower Angara Suite* Based on numerous samples from the Angara-Pit beds of hematite ore. Good agreement with **1.05.** $H_{cr}' = 700$–1000 oe. The divergence from the present field and laboratory tests indicates stability.

1.58 *Koninsk Suite* Result based on 23 samples. $H_{cr}' = 40$ oe. Divergence from the present field might be taken as evidence for stability, but the beds have been metamorphosed to some extent, and the authors' account is taken to imply that this result does not reflect the field direction at the time of formation, so the entry has been bracketed.

1.59–60 *Precambrian of India* (Athavale, Radhakrishnamurty, and Sahasrabudhe, 1963) Magnetic and thermal cleaning was undertaken (although details are not reported) and, in certain cases, stability is indicated by this, and by the departures from the present field.

1.59 *Malani Rhyolites* It is stated that "these are generally grouped with lower Vindhyan rocks." They overlie the Aravali System and are overlain by upper Vindhyan sandstones. Sixty samples (170 specimens) were collected from 9 sites.

1.60 *Bijawar Traps* Basic igneous rocks "associated with unmetamorphosed sedimentary rocks." Seven samples (25 specimens) taken from a quarry near Gwalior Fort.

1.61 *Mundwarra Complex* Eight samples (25 specimens) collected from a "basaltic exposure."

1.62 *Cuddapah Traps* Numerous results (72 samples, 245 specimens) from 10 sites were highly scattered. Demagnetization did not decrease the scatter.

1.63–64 *Great Dike* A complex, layered, ultramafic to mafic intrusion, about 500 km long, and with an average width of 6 km. There are satellite dikes. The layers are warped downwards, having synclinal forms. The contacts dip towards the axis. Age determinations (Rb-Sr) give an age of 2110 ± 350 m.y. (Faure and others, 1962, 1963).

1.63 (1) McElhinny and Gough (1963) Altogether 105 cores were taken at 9 sites spanning about 300 km of the outcrop; 7 sites are in the main dike and 2 in satellite dikes. Fifteen cores were unsuitable and this result is based on 90 cores (about 140 specimens). The NRM directions were scattered (scatter attributed to lightning) at all but 1 site, but became closely grouped after magnetic cleaning in 150–600 oe. The detailed demagnetization studies and the strong discordance with the present field indicate stability. In the analysis sites were given unit weight ($N = 9$).

1.64 (2) Nairn (1963) Over 50 samples were collected from 20 sites but few gave useful results. This result is based on 10 magnetically cleaned samples (250–700 oe) from 6 sites. In the analysis sites were given unit weight ($N = 6$). The precision is markedly less than in **1.63.**

1.65–73 *Purcell System* (Black, 1963) Precambrian of SE British Columbia and SW

Alberta. About 16 samples were not used, being too weakly magnetized. In addition to the values listed, 2 samples from 1 site were measured from the Appekunny Fm. All specimens were magnetically cleaned, usually in 156 oe. It is not made clear in the original how this work relates to that published earlier [**1.28–31**]. Results based on fewer than 5 samples are entered in brackets. **1.65,** 25 samples of red sediment from 2 sites. **1.66,** 4 gabbro samples from 1 site. **1.67,** 13 samples of red sediment from 3 sites. **1.68,** 22 lava samples from 5 sites. **1.69,** 4 samples of red sediment from 2 sites. **1.70,** 16 samples of red sediment from 3 sites. **1.71,** 17 samples of red sediment from 3 sites. Stability is indicated by the departures from the present field, by the broad agreement between igneous and sedimentary rocks, and by the reversals.

1.72 Black's combination of entries **1.65, 1.67, 1.69–71** giving samples unit weight ($N = 75$).

1.73 Combination, irrespective of sign, of the directions in entires **1.65–71** giving each unit weight ($N = 7$). A pole is calculated from the over-all mean.

1.74–85 *Keweenawan* (P. M. Du Bois, 1962) Precambrian. Samples given unit weight in the analyses. See entries **1.35–40** where the evidence for stability is discussed; in addition, entry **1.81** has a contact test.

1.74 Result based on 14 samples from 2 sites.

1.75 Result based on 8 samples; 5 other samples gave directions scattered around the present field. The Orienta is the lowest member of the Bayfield Group and overlies **1.76.**

1.76 Six samples, dispersion high. The Amnicon overlies **1.77.**

1.77 Result based on 28 samples from 5 sites spanning about 500 m.

1.78 Keweenawan sediments possibly of Freda age. Result is based on only 4 samples (2 sites) and is therefore entered in brackets.

1.79 *Duluth Gabbro* dated by K-Ar methods as 1120 m.y. by Goldich and others (1957), and by Rb-Sr methods as 980 m.y. (Faure and others, 1962). Result based on 18 samples collected from 9 sites near Duluth.

1.80 Twelve samples.

1.81–82 Results from the *Logan Diabase* are divided into two groups on the basis of the direction of NRM. Group I is based on 80 samples from 18 localities including 4 samples from a baked contact showing good agreement

with the diabase. Group II is based on 25 samples from 15 localities. In addition there were several samples with divergent directions.

1.83 Based on 18 sedimentary samples (13 positive, 5 negative) from 4 sites at 2 localities. Results from 2 samples baked by an intrusion, and 4 with divergent directions, were not included.

1.84 Twelve samples.

1.85 Four samples from 2 dikes near Sault Ste. Marie. The result is entered in brackets because the error exceeds 25°, and because the sampling coverage is inadequate.

1.86 *Grenville Gneisses and Pyroxenites* (P. M. Du Bois, 1962) Directions of 16 samples from 3 widely separated sites were corrected to 45° N, 78.5° W. Some samples were treated in *ac* fields. Samples given unit weight in the analysis ($N = 16$). The history of these metamorphic rocks is complex and the result is entered in brackets.

1.87–88 *Sudbury Nickel Irruptive* (Sopher, 1963) See **1.46–49** and § 10.A3. Samples of norite and micropegmatite from the North (about 68 samples) and South (about 39 samples) Ranges gave these direction *in situ*. All samples were magnetically cleaned. Stability is indicated by the divergence from the present field and the *ac* demagnetization studies.

1.89 *Diabase Dikes and Heated Norite, Sudbury* (Sopher, 1963) Precambrian dikes cutting the Sudbury Nickel Irruptive. All samples have been magnetically cleaned. Seven samples from the dikes gave a mean direction parallel to 6 samples in the heated norite (p. 247). The divergence from the present field, and the *ac* demagnetization studies suggest that the magnetization is stable, and the contact test indicates that the remanence was acquired at the time of intrusion. In this analysis unit weight was given to each sample ($N = 13$).

1.90 *Red Sediments, Jujuy Province* Precambrian (Creer, 1962*d*) Seven samples (21 specimens). Stability indicated by departure from present field. Pole calculated from the direction and locality coordinates given.

1.91 *Red Sediments, Parana* Precambrian (Creer, 1962*d*) This result, which is based on only 3 samples, is bracketed.

CAMBRIAN (600(?)–500 M.Y.)

2.01 *Younger Gabbros of Aberdeenshire* (Blundell and Read, 1958) These intrusives are younger than the regional metamorphism of the Dalradian country rock, and older than the deposition of the Middle Old Red Sandstone. In a collection of over 50 samples, 21 only were considered to give reliable results. The satisfactory samples were obtained from several sites in 6 intrusive masses. The directions are not dissimilar to those observed in the Caerbwby Sandstone [**2.02**], which is of known Cambrian age.

2.02 *Caerbwby Sandstone* Lower Cambrian (Creer, 1957*a*) This sandstone is in the lower part of the Caerfai Series. Twelve samples (72 specimens) of red sandstone were collected at 10 levels in a section 106 m thick. The directions diverge from the present field indicating stability. In the analysis samples were given unit weight ($N = 12$).

2.03 *Hartshill Quartzite* Lower Cambrian (Bidgood, 1961) Seven samples, magnetically cleaned in 100 oe, gave directions divergent from the present field, indicating stability. Four samples of the interbedded *Hyolithus* Limestone gave directions close to those observed in the New Red Sandstone in England and these were thought to have been acquired during deep weathering in Triassic time.

2.03–14 *Barrandian Eruptives* Late Precambrian to Ordovician (Bucha, 1961) Studies were made of groups *A–F* of the Barrandian Eruptives in the Krivoklat-Rokycany Range. In all groups except A_3 stability is indicated by strong divergence from the present field and by the occurrence of reversals.

2.03–08 *Barrandian Porphyries, Groups C–F* Upper Cambrian or Ordovician The numbers of samples obtained from each group are 10, 16, 13, and 9, respectively, a total of 48. Both polarities occur. In **2.08** the mean directions from each group are combined, irrespective of sign, giving unit weight to each group ($N = 4$), and a pole is calculated from the over-all mean.

2.09 *Barrandian Porphyrite, Group B* Cambrian Thirty-seven samples.

2.10–14 *Barrandian Porphyrite, Group A* Precambrian to Middle Cambrian Four subdivisions were studied, the number of samples being 14, 15, 12, and 16, respectively. In **2.14** the mean directions for divisions A_1, A_2, and A_4 are combined and a pole is calculated from this over-all direction. A_3 is considered by Bucha to be possibly unstable and is not therefore used in this combination.

2.15 *Sediments of the Dniester Region* Cambrian (Kruglyakova quoted in Kalashnikov, 1961) Stability is indicated by the divergence of the directions from the present field.

2.16 *Verkholensk Suite* Upper Cambrian (Khramov and Sidorova quoted in Kalashnikov, 1961) Forty-seven samples collected from the red sandstones in the middle reaches of the Lena River. It is stated that stability was determined by use of the "circle of remagnetization."

2.17–18 *Cambrian of Australia* Two results of a preliminary nature are available. Stability is indicated by the broad agreement between lavas and sediments, by the presence of reversals, and by the divergence from the present field.

2.17 *Antrim Plateau Basalts* (Irving and Green, 1958) These flat-lying lavas are overlain conformably by dated Middle Cambrian sediments and overlie late Precambrian beds. They are generally regarded as Lower Cambrian but could be Precambrian in part. Seven samples (28 specimens) from 3 sites gave negative directions at 1 site, and positive at the others. The mean direction *in situ* and irrespective of sign is given, specimens being used as units ($N = 28$).

2.18 *Elder Mountain Sandstone* (Irving and Green, 1958; Irving, 1959) Three samples, 18 specimens (§ 5.13).

2.19 *Wilbern's Formation* Upper Cambrian (Howell and Martinez, 1957) A total of 185 samples collected from 10 sites in the Point Peak Shale member of the Wilbern's Formation in the Llano uplift area. The directions give a streaked distribution. The direction given is an estimate of the stable component being that of a group of measurements farthest from the present field. The pole is that given in the original.

2.20 *Sawatch Sandy Dolomite* Upper Cambrian (Howell and Martinez, 1957; Howell, Martinez, and Statham, 1958) In a collection of 36 samples from 2 localities in Colorado, 5 gave directions close to the present field and an analysis ($N = 31$) of the remainder gave this result. Petrological examination suggests that these sediments were dolomitized long after deposition, possibly later in the Paleozoic, and this was accompanied by the partial replacement of glauconite by hematite. The directions may therefore be related to the Earth's field at a period much later than the Cambrian. It may be noted that the directions are not dissimilar to those observed in Carboniferous rocks in the U.S.A. (see entries

6.62–67). The result is entered in brackets because of the uncertainty in the age of the magnetization.

2.21–23 *Lodore Formation* Cambrian (Collinson and Runcorn, 1960) Thirteen samples were obtained from a 60 m section near Vernal on the north flank of the Uinta Mts., Utah. With the exception of 2 samples, which were not considered in the analysis, the directions occur in distinct positive and negative groups (stated as 7 and 26 specimens respectively in Table 1 in the original), the means of which are listed. The over-all mean direction giving each group unit weight ($N = 2$) is given in entry **2.23**; the pole in entry **2.23** is that given in the original and is approximately consistent with this direction. Stability is indicated by the reversal and by the strong divergence of all directions from the Earth's field.

2.24 *Deadwood Formation* (Collinson and Runcorn, 1960) The age is cited as Mississippian in the original on the basis of certain recently discovered bone fragments. But Cox and Doell (1960) state that it is "definitely regarded as Cambrian by the U.S. Geological Survey." Seven samples (34 specimens) collected from a 15 m section gave positive directions indicating stability. In the analysis, specimens ($N = 34$) are given unit weight. It is noteworthy that the directions are not greatly different from those observed in Carboniferous beds in the U.S.A. (see entries **6.62–67**). The result is entered in brackets because of the age uncertainty.

2.25 *Bright Angel Shales* Cambrian (Collinson and Runcorn, 1960) Twenty samples (44 specimens) gave scattered directions with some indication of smearing. No statistical analysis was made.

2.26 *Tapeats Sandstone* Lower Cambrian (Collinson and Runcorn, 1960) Directions in 15 samples (47 specimens) were mostly near the present field with a few smeared towards the direction in entry **2.21**. No statistical analysis of this data was made. An earlier result was obtained by Runcorn and quoted in a conference report (Day and Runcorn, 1955); it is stated in Creer, Irving, and Runcorn (1957), p. 146, to be based on "inadequate data" and is therefore entered here in brackets.

CAMBRIAN SUPPLEMENT

2.27 *Aldan Stage* Lower Cambrian (Popova, 1963) Eleven samples of red sediment

from the Lower Angara River area gave directions close to the present field.

2.28 *Upper Lena Stage* (Popova, 1963) Of 26 samples of red sediment from the Lower Angara River, 7 were close to the present field and were discarded, and 19 (7 negative, 12 positive) were aligned along a NW/SE axis with low inclination. The mean, irrespective of sign, is given. Stability is indicated by the reversals and the divergence from the present field.

2.29 *Red Sediments* Cambrian (Creer, 1962*d*) Seventeen samples each given unit weight in this analysis. The circle of confidence exceeds 25° and so the entry is bracketed.

2.30 *Red Sediments, Salta Province* (Creer, 1962*d*) Age cited as "Cambro-Ordovician." Twenty samples (76 specimens) each given unit weight in this analysis. The result is entered in brackets since the circle of confidence exceeds 25°.

2.31 *Older Intrusives, Marguerite Bay* (Blundell, 1962) Age is pre-Upper Jurassic, and is regarded as Lower Paleozoic. Twenty-two samples (44 specimens) from 3 sites gave highly scattered directions; *ac* demagnetization tests showed that the remanence was unstable.

ORDOVICIAN (500–425 M.Y.)

3.01 *Tremadocian Sediments* (Khramov, 1958) The directions in 29 samples of sands and clays spanning 10 m were smeared toward the present field and estimates of the stable magnetization directions were approximately reversed from one another.

3.02–03 *Ukrainian Basalts* (Komarov, 1959) **3.02,** eight samples from 2 quarries gave negative directions, and the pole when compared with the European polar curve is considered by Komarov to suggest an Ordovician age. **3.03,** six samples from one quarry gave positive directions, and the pole position is considered by Komarov to suggest a Cambrian age. In the analyses samples were given unit weight.

3.04 *Asha Stage, Kurkuaut Suite* Ordovician (Khramov quoted by Kalashnikov, 1961) Sixty samples were collected from the southern Urals. It is stated that stability was determined by use of "the circle of remagnetization."

3.05 *Sediments of the Lena Region* Middle Ordovician (Khramov and Sidorova, quoted by Kalashnikov, 1961) Eighty-seven samples of brown-red aleurolites and sandstones were collected. It is stated that stability was determined by use of "the circle of remagnetization."

3.06 *Juniata Formation* Upper Ordovician (Collinson and Runcorn, 1960) A sequence of red beds 425 m thick near Bedford, Pennsylvania, was spanned by 12 samples (56 specimens). The directions are somewhat dispersed but the divergence from the present field indicates stability. In the analysis specimens were given unit weight.

3.07–08 *Trenton Group* Middle Ordovician.

3.07 (J. W. Graham, 1956) Directions from 28 samples, each from different limestone cobbles in a conglomerate at Sprakers, New York, were in good agreement, indicating that the magnetization is not that of the parent body but was acquired at some unknown time after the deposition of the Trenton Group. The result is entered in brackets.

3.08 (J. W. Graham, 1954a) At Trenton Falls, New York, 35 measurements (presumably samples) from stratified flat-lying beds and 10 from blocks of rock in a zone of penecontemporaneous distortion gave similar directions; moreover, directions in blocks in the distorted zone were less scattered than the bedding poles of these blocks. The magnetization of the distorted zone and probably also that of the flat-lying beds is postdepositional. The directions in this result and in **3.07** are similar to those observed in the Devonian Onondaga Limestone of New York State (see entry **5.38**).

3.09 *Antarctic Gneisses* Ordovician (Nagata and Shimizu, 1959, 1960; Nagata and Yama-ai, 1961) Radioisotope age studies gave 470 m.y., which is Lower Ordovician on Kulp's 1961 Time Scale. Thirty samples, collected from 3 localities near the Japanese IGY base of Syowa, gave directions with vertical components in the opposite sense to the present field. The direction given in this entry is the average of the means (*in situ*) for localities giving each unit weight ($N = 3$). A pole calculated from this is given. Stability was checked by several laboratory tests. The result is entered in brackets because it is uncertain which is the correct reference plane for this result. In the originals a pole is given (3 N, 107 W) based on directions corrected to the gneissose planes assuming that these were

horizontal when the rocks were magnetized. Other samples collected were magnetized along the present field and were shown to be unstable by laboratory tests.

ORDOVICIAN SUPPLEMENT

3.10 *Lugov Suite of the Ust-Kutsk Stage* Lower Ordovician (Popova, 1963) A collection of 28 sedimentary samples (19 positive, 9 negative) from 2 outcrops along the Angara and Biryusa Rivers gave this mean direction irrespective of sign. Stability is indicated by the reversals and the divergence from the present field.

SILURIAN (425–405 M.Y.)

4.01 *Ludlow Series* Upper Silurian (Creer, 1955; Creer, Irving, and Runcorn, 1954) Seven samples (14 specimens) spanning a 22 m section in red sediments at Freshwater East, Pembrokeshire. Samples were given unit weight in the analysis. The divergence from the present field indicates stability.

4.02–04 *Silurian of the Dniester Region*
4.02 (1) (Khramov and Kruglyakova, quoted by Kalashnikov, 1961) Age cited as Upper Silurian. Rock types not described. It is stated that stability is determined by the "circle of remagnetization." Twelve samples were studied. **4.03** (2) (Kruglyakova, quoted by Kalashnikov, 1961) Age cited as Silurian. Rocks studied include limestones and clay marls. Stability is indicated by the divergence from the present field.

4.04 *Combined* Mean pole of **4.02** and **4.03**.

4.05 *Ural Peridotites* Silurian (Komarov, 1959) Six samples from 1 quarry gave directions divergent from the present field indicating stability.

4.06 *Rocks from North Urals* (Komarov quoted by Kalashnikov, 1961).

4.07 *Red Sandstones of the Lena Region* Lower Silurian (Khramov quoted by Kalashnikov, 1961) Result based on directions in 12 samples. It is stated that stability is determined by the "circle of remagnetization."

4.08 *Red Siltstones of Kansu* Middle Silurian (Chang Wen-You and Nairn, 1959) This result, based on only 3 samples (17 specimens) from 1 site, is entered in brackets.

4.09 *Table Mountain Series* Upper Silurian-Lower Devonian (K. W. T. Graham, and Hales, 1961) Age cited in the original as "probably Silurian." It could be lower Devonian but not younger than this. This result is based on 8 cores (107 specimens) from a 2 ft red siltstone bed in a road cutting at Chapman's Peak, Cape Peninsula. The siltstone bed is in the Lower Shale division of the Series. The mean, giving unit weight to each core ($N = 8$), is given. Stability is indicated by the divergence from the present field. Results from "surface" samples (that is in natural exposures and not in deep road cutting) were widely scattered.

4.10 *Duro Porphyry* Middle Silurian (Green, 1959) Result based on 7 samples (14 specimens) from 2 exposures 200 m apart. Specimens given unit weight in the analysis. The divergence from the present field indicates stability.

4.11 *Rose Hill Formation* Early Middle Silurian-Lower Niagaran Series (J. W. Graham, 1949) Thirty-five samples were collected on the limbs of small folds at 2 localities and on the steep limbs of large folds at 4 other localities. The localities are spaced over a distance of 40 km. The directions, which are widely scattered with the beds *in situ,* are nearly parallel after correction for dip (Figure 5.5). The folding is late Paleozoic and stability since that time is indicated. The analysis was carried out, giving unit weight to each site ($N = 5$) ignoring the site labelled *A* in the original at which the direction was anomalous.

4.12 *Clinton Iron-Ore* Middle Silurian-Niagaran Series (Howell, Martinez, and Statham, 1958) Result based on 7 samples (16 specimens) from 1 site (lateral extent 100 m) in Alabama. The statistics were obtained giving unit weight to each specimen. The directions are approximately opposed to those in entry **4.11,** the imperfection in the alignment may not be significant in view of the small stratigraphic coverage of the Clinton result. Stability is indicated by the divergence from the present field.

4.13 *Middle Silurian Sediments combined* The averages, irrespective of sign, of the directions and poles in entries **4.11** and **4.12** are given.

SILURIAN SUPPLEMENT

4.14 *Chergaka Suite* (Popova, 1963) Upper Silurian of the Tuvinian trough. About 20 samples from 2 outcrops along the Yenesei River gave directions toward the SE, strongly divergent from the present field and indicative of stability; this mean direction was calculated from these. About 8 samples from 1 outcrop along the Elegest River gave directions along the present field and were rejected.

4.15 *Jacadigo Series* (Creer, 1962*d*) Age cited as "Silurian" by Creer, but Ahlfeld (1956) says that, "Its age is questionable though it presumably is Ordovician." About 13 sedimentary specimens from Corrego das Pedras, Corumba. Unit weight given to specimens in the analysis. Stability indicated by divergence from the present field.

DEVONIAN (405–345 M.Y.)

5.01 *Eifel Sandstones* Lower to Middle Devonian (Nairn, 1960*a*) This result is based on 4 samples (16 specimens) and is bracketed.

5.02 *Old Red Sandstone* Devonian (Creer, 1957*a*) Thirty-five samples from different levels in flat-lying beds at 6 localities in the Welsh cuvette gave this result. Samples were given unit weight in the analysis. Stability is indicated by the divergence from the present field. Samples from 11 other localities (68 samples) in folded beds gave rather scattered directions after correction for folding, which is late Paleozoic in age, suggesting that the magnetization in these folded beds is predominantly Permian or younger. Recent thermal demagnetization studies by Chamalaun and Creer (1963) suggest that the NRM in both folded and flat-lying beds is predominantly of late Paleozoic age but that there are small pre-folding components of high stability. In view of this new evidence the result is bracketed, but it has been included in that part of Table 6.2 made prior to the publication just mentioned.

5.03 *Brownstone Series* Lower Devonian (Clegg, Almond, and Stubbs, 1954*a, b*) The Brownstones are in the Lower Old Red Sandstone. The number of samples (3 samples, 39 specimens) is <5 and the result is entered in brackets.

5.04 *Igneous Rocks of the Midland Valley* Devonian (Stubbs quoted in Blackett, Clegg, and Stubbs, 1960) Result based on 147 lava specimens (samples ?). The mean, irrespective of sign, is given in this entry.

5.05 *Lower Old Red Sandstone Lavas* Lower Devonian (Nairn, 1960*a* and 1961*a*) Nine samples (49 specimens) from 5 or 6 flows near Ethie. The divergence from the present field indicates stability. Stability in *ac* fields of 250 oe was also shown. Sample means were given unit weight.

5.06 *Upper Old Red Sandstone Sediments* Upper Devonian (Nairn, 1960a and 1961a) Ten samples (46 specimens) from the valley of the R. Jed. The divergence from the present field indicates stability.

5.07–10 *Upper Devonian Sediments of the Russian Platform* (Lin'kova, 1960, 1961, 1963) About 650 samples (about 1400 specimens) were collected from 64 sites in beds of Frasnian and Famennian ages. Many samples (30 per cent) were too weakly magnetized for measurement and others were rejected as unstable. The directions are aligned along a NE + ve/ SW − ve axis. The divergence from the present field and the reversals indicate stability.

5.10 *Combined* The mean of the directions ($N = 3$) and poles ($N = 3$, $K = 397$) in **5.07–09** is given allowing unit weight to each.

5.11–16 *Sediments of the Dniester Region* Devonian (Kruglyakova, and Khramov and Kruglyakova, quoted in Kalashnikov, 1961; Yanovsky and others, 1963) At one locality [**5.15**] 80 samples were collected and it is stated that stability is determined by the "circle of remagnetization." The number of samples obtained at the other 4 localities is not stated. The agreement between sites and the divergence from the present field indicate stability.

5.16 *Combined* The mean of the locality directions ($N = 5$) and poles ($N = 5$, $K = 192$) is given allowing unit weight to each entry.

5.17 *Bauxites of the North Urals* Devonian (Ivanov and Ryazanova, quoted by Kalashnikov, 1961; Yanovsky and others, 1963) The divergence from the present pole implies some degree of stability of the observed directions.

5.18–31 *Sediments of the Siberian Platform* Devonian (Vlassov, Popova, Zvegintsev, and Rodicheva (1961) entries **5.18–24** and **5.26–29**; Vlassov, quoted by Kalashnikov (1961) entry **5.30**; Khramov, quoted by Kalashnikov (1961) entry **5.25**) Twelve results are available from rocks ranging in age from Lower to Upper Devonian and sampled in the region of Krasnoyarsk. Entry **5.25** is based on 28 samples and it is stated that stability is determined by the "circle of remagnetization." In the other entries the number of samples is not stated although it is implied that they are numerous. The pole [**5.30**] is inconsistent with the direction and location stated. The

mean value of H_{cr}' is 60 oe. Heating of test specimens to 100°C did not change the magnetization. The agreement between results, the reversals, and the divergence from the present field indicate stability. See **5.40–45**.

5.31 *Combined* The mean of the directions ($N = 11$) and poles ($N = 11$, $K = 87$) for each result excluding **5.30** are given, allowing unit weight to each result.

5.32 *Igneous Rocks of the Canberra Region* Upper Silurian to Lower Devonian (Green, 1961) About 40 samples (about 80 specimens) were studied from 8 volcanic and intrusive units covering a long time span. Directions in 7 units were negative, the other being positive. Divergence of directions from the present field indicates stability. The two-tier analysis was used. The wide dispersion may be attributed to the long time span covered by these results.

5.33 *Murrumbidgee Series* Middle Devonian (Green, 1961) Result based on 11 samples (21 specimens) collected from a 30 m section of red marine sediments. The divergence from the present field indicates stability.

5.34 *Catombal Formation* Upper Devonian (Green, 1959) Eighty samples (150 specimens) were collected from 16 sites in folded red sediments. The stratigraphic thickness spanned is 460 m, and the lateral spread 110 km. The two-tier statistical analysis was used. The mean direction with the beds *in situ* is along the present field and the between-site precision k_B is 75; after correction for folding the directions become widely dispersed ($k_B = 4$). The magnetization is therefore of comparatively recent origin, and not indicative of the Devonian field direction. The results are entered in brackets.

5.35–36 *Yalwal Stage* Upper Devonian (Green, 1959, 1961) Results are available from sediments [**5.35**] and basalts [**5.36**]. Red marine sediments [**5.35**] (14 samples, 45 specimens) from several sites spaced over 2 km gave direction along the present field. The two-tier analysis was used. Directions in 14 pebbles of similar rock type in overlying Upper Devonian beds are not random. The magnetization is recent and not indicative of the Devonian field direction. The results are therefore entered in brackets. The *Nethercote Basalts* [**5.36**], which overlie these sediments, were sampled (19 samples, 45 specimens) at 7 sites spaced over 5 km and covering a stratigraphic thickness of 180 m. The number of flows studied is uncertain but is not less than 2 and is probably more. Five sites were negative and 2 positive. Stability is indicated by the divergence from the present field and the reversals. The two-tier analysis was used.

5.37 *Red Beds of Victoria* Upper Devonian to Lower Carboniferous (Green, 1959) Eleven sites were sampled but only 8 gave consistent results, the directions at the others being random. The 8 sites (40 samples, 113 specimens) are spread over a distance of 160 km and through a stratigraphic thickness of about 550 m. The bedding dips are small. The directions *in situ* are close to the present field and the between-site precision is not significant. The magnetization is considered by Green to be post-depositional and probably recent and the result is bracketed.

5.38 *Onondaga Limestone* Lower to Middle Devonian (J. W. Graham, 1956) Sixty-five samples from 2 localities in New York State gave directions which were uniform (in mean and in dispersion) in both stratified beds and in beds showing penecontemporaneous deformation. In the analysis unit weight is given to each sample the results from stratified and deformed beds being lumped together ($N = 65$). The divergence from the present field indicates the stability of the NRM, but its age certainly post-dates the deformation. The result is not considered to provide information about the Devonian field and is bracketed.

DEVONIAN SUPPLEMENT

5.39 *Kazakhstan Porphyrites* (Russinov and Sholpo, 1962) Age cited as Devonian. Twenty-two samples from 1 locality gave widely scattered directions which after magnetic cleaning (100–200 oe) became well-grouped. The results were corrected for tilt inferred from other localities not at the collecting locality, and this is a possible source of error. Other samples had anomalous intensities and are thought to have been struck by lightning.

5.40 *Okler Series* (*Reversal Transitions*) (Vlassov and Kovalenko, 1963) Age cited as Lower Devonian. The directions in test specimens were unchanged in *ac* fields of 500 oe. Stability is indicated by this test, and by the occurrence of reversals about an axis strongly inclined to the present field. The average of the negative directions is 94, +56 and of

the positive directions 268, −47, and the mean of these irrespective of sign is given here. See § 7.6.

5.41–46 *Siberian Sediments* (Popova, 1963) Mostly red sediments. The author does not state how these results relate to those reported earlier from this region [**5.18–29**]; some duplication of data seems possible, since entries **5.28** and **5.42** are identical. Several samples, directed along the present field, were discarded. Evidence of stability in the remaining samples is provided by the occurrence of reversals and by the divergence from the present field. Entries **5.42–45** are consistent. **5.41** diverges from this group, but its pole agrees well with the work of Stubbs on Scottish lavas [**5.04**]. **5.41**, 18 samples from outcrops on the Elegest and Yenesei Rivers ($H_{cr}' = 45$ oe). **5.42**, 21 samples (13 negative, 8 positive) from the Rybinsk basin. **5.43**, 18 samples (11 negative, 7 positive) of Givetian age from the Rybinsk basin. **5.44**, 17 samples (9 negative, 8 positive) from the Rybinsk basin; the Kungus Suite is stated to be bottom Frasnian. **5.45**, samples from the Rybinsk and Minusinsk basins and near Lake Varcha; age cited as Upper Frasnian. **5.46**, mean of directions and poles in entries **5.42–45** giving each unit weight ($N = 4$). Precision of poles $K = 120$.

5.47 *"Hematite" Rocks* (Wang, Teng, Li, and Yeh, 1960) Six samples from the Sanshia region, Hupeh province. The circle of confidence exceeds 25° and the result is bracketed.

5.48 *Red and Purple Sandstones, Salta and Jujuy Provinces* (Creer, 1962d) Results from 22 samples (75 specimens) each given unit weight in the analysis ($N = 22$). Divergence from the present field indicates stability.

5.49 *Sediments* (Creer, 1962d) Results from 6 samples (about 50 specimens) of red and purple sediments were each given unit weight in the analysis. A pole is calculated from the mean and location coordinates given. Creer states that the samples "are likely to have been magnetized in recent geological time" and because of this and the large circle of confidence (>25°) the result is entered in brackets.

5.50 *Sediments* (Creer, 1962d) Age cited as "Devonian-Silurian." Three samples (20 specimens). Result entered in brackets since fewer than 5 samples were studied and because Creer states that the samples "are likely to have been remagnetized in recent geological time."

CARBONIFEROUS (345–280 M.Y.)

6.01–04 *Stephanian Sandstone* Upper Carboniferous (Nairn, 1960a) Thirty-two samples (130 specimens) were collected from 3 sites in central and eastern France and in the Saar. The within-site dispersions are sometimes large but the agreement between-sites is good. The divergence from the present field and the uniformity in direction over a wide area indicate stability.

6.04 *Combined* The average of the mean site directions, without correction for difference of location, is given, the precision and error being calculated giving unit weight to each site ($N = 3$). The average of the poles for each site is given ($N = 3$, $K = 288$).

6.05–6.11 *Kinghorn Lavas* Lower Carboniferous (Everitt and Belshé, 1960; preliminary account in Clegg, Deutsch, Everitt, and Stubbs, 1957) Numerous flows occurring in the Calciferous Sandstone Series were studied. The flows have been numbered by geologists from the bottom up. Fifty-six samples from 28 sites were collected, and, of these, 43 from 21 sites were accepted as suitable material. The beds are arranged in the groups of alternating polarity listed in **6.05–10**; directions based on fewer than 5 samples are bracketed The directions are aligned approximately along NE − ve/SW + ve axis. The results from 8 beds were obtained after thermal or magnetic cleaning. The laboratory studies, the reversals, and divergence from the present field indicate stability.

6.11 *Combined* The mean direction of **6.05, 6.06, 6.08–10** ($N = 5$) is given irrespective of sign. Entry **6.07** is excluded, since it was considered by Everitt and Belshé to be a possible transition direction between reversals. Recently published studies (Wilson and Everitt, 1963), including thermal cleaning and studies of baked contacts, which are based on 33 specimens from 17 flows, yielded the mean direction 16, −29 which is not notably different from that calculated in this entry.

6.12 *Kinghorn Sill* (Everitt and Belshé, 1960) This bed is stated to be "a sill of uncertain age." The result is based on only 2 samples from a single site and is bracketed.

6.13 *Southdean Basanite Plug* Carboniferous (Nairn, 1960a) Result based on 5 samples (19 specimens) from a site at Jedburgh. The divergence from the present field indicates stability.

6.14 *Carboniferous Limestone* Lower Carboniferous (R. L. DuBois, 1961) In a collection of 19 samples, 14 (22 specimens) were sufficiently magnetic to be measurable; 4 samples (4 specimens) are negative, 10 samples (18 specimens) are positive. The mean irrespective of sign is given, each specimen being assigned unit weight ($N = 22$). The divergence from the present field and the reversal indicate stability.

6.15–16 *Lancashire Sediments* (Everitt and Belshé, 1960; preliminary account in Belshé, 1957a) The age of these beds is stated to lie in the range Carboniferous Limestone to Millstone Grit. The departures from the present field indicate stability. The directions are grouped into 2 sets whose means are not 180° apart, the misalignment is as if components parallel to the Earth's field are present.

6.15 *Lancashire Sediments, Negative Directions* Fourteen samples from 4 sites. The directions in both limbs of the Pendle monocline are stated to agree "more closely relative to the bedding-planes than to the present horizontal, although since the directions are only a few degrees from the strike axis this test is not absolutely decisive."

6.16 *Lancashire Sediments, Positive Directions* Ten samples were collected from 3 sites.

6.17 *Lancashire Sediments combined* The means irrespective of sign of the directions and poles in entries **6.15** and **6.16** are given on the assumption that secondary components directed approximately along the present field occur.

6.18–20 *Keele Beds* Upper Carboniferous Two results are available: **6.18** (Nairn, 1960a) 17 samples (34 specimens) from several sites, and **6.19** (Everitt and Belshé, 1960) 7 samples from 1 site. The divergences from the present field direction indicate stability, but the discrepancy between the results could be due to the presence of a large secondary component of magnetization imposed by the present field.

6.20 *Combined* The mean, irrespective of sign, of the directions in **6.18** and **6.19** is given assuming secondary components along the Earth's field present.

6.21–23 *Derbyshire Sediments* (Everitt and Belshé, 1960; preliminary account in Belshé, 1957a) The age of these beds is stated to lie in the range Carboniferous Limestone to Millstone Grit. The departures from the present field indicate stability. The directions are grouped into 2 sets whose means are not 180° apart; the misalignment is as if components parallel to the present field are present.

6.21 *Negative Directions* Thirteen samples collected from 3 sites.

6.22 *Positive Directions* Eleven samples collected from 3 sites.

6.23 *Combined* The means, irrespective of sign, of directions and poles in **6.21** and **6.22** are given assuming secondary components along the present field occur.

6.24–26 *Tideswelldale Igneous Rocks and Associated Baked Sediments* Middle Carboniferous (Everitt and Belshé, 1960; preliminary account in Clegg, Deutsch, Everitt, and Stubbs, 1957) Igneous rocks (7 samples) and associated baked sediments (6 samples) from 1 site gave similar directions. This agreement, and the divergence from the present field, provide strong evidence of stability. It is stated, in the original, that it is uncertain whether the igneous body is a lava or an intrusive.

6.26 *Combined* The average of the directions in **6.24** and **6.25,** and the pole calculated from this are given.

6.27–29 *Derbyshire Lavas* (Everitt and Belshé, 1960; preliminary account in Belshé, 1957a) Age of the lavas, sometimes called Toadstones, is cited as Carboniferous Limestone. Three samples from 1 site [**6.27**] had negative directions and 3 samples from 2 sites [6.28] were positive. The directions in 2 of the lavas are values after thermal cleaning to within 100°C of the Curie temperature. This test, the reversal, and the divergence from the present field, indicate stability.

6.29 *Combined* The directions in **6.27** and **6.28** were averaged and a pole calculated from this mean.

6.30–32 *Midland Sills and Associated Baked Sediments* (Everitt, 1960; Everitt and Belshé, 1960; preliminary account in Clegg, Deutsch, Everitt, and Stubbs, 1957) The age of the sills is cited as late Carboniferous by Everitt and Belshé. Studies were made of 6 igneous bodies in the English Midlands (Titterstone Clee Hill, Kinlet, Shatterford, Barrow Hill, Pouk Hill, and Rowley Regis).

6.30 *Midland Sills* Eight igneous samples (49 specimens) from 5 bodies gave predominantly positive directions although negative directions were recorded in 2 samples from

Shatterford. No results were obtained from Pouk Hill. The mean direction, giving unit weight to each body ($N = 5$), is listed.

6.31 *Midland Baked Sediments* Ten samples (73 specimens) of baked sandstones, mudstones, and shales, collected within less than 2.1 m from igneous contacts, all gave positive directions. No results were obtained from Barrow Hill. The mean direction, giving unit weight to the results from each baked envelope ($N = 5$), is listed.

6.32 *Combined* This average result was obtained by giving unit weight ($N = 10$) to the mean from each igneous body and from their baked envelopes. The agreement between the directions in igneous and baked rocks, and the divergence from the present field, indicate stability.

6.33–35 *Little Wenlock Lava and Baked Sediments* Lower Carboniferous, Carboniferous Limestone (Everitt, 1960; Everitt and Belshé, 1960) Results were obtained from 2 samples (20 specimens) of lava, and 2 samples (14 specimens) of underlying baked sediments. The mean is given in **6.35.** The number of samples is <5 and the results are entered in brackets.

6.36 *Welsh Sediments* Carboniferous (Everitt and Belshé, 1960) This result is based on 18 samples from 2 sites. Divergence from the present field indicates stability. In addition 73 samples from 10 sites gave unreliable results and were discarded.

6.37 *Pennant Sandstone* Upper Carboniferous (Clegg, Almond, and Stubbs, 1954a) This result, based on only 1 sample (14 specimens) from Gloucestershire, is entered in brackets. In the analysis specimens were given unit weight.

6.38–39 *Carboniferous of Britain combined* The directions fall into 2 groups. Examples from both groups may be found in the Lower and Upper Carboniferous. The results **6.35** and **6.37** are not considered, since each is based on fewer than 5 samples.

6.38 (1) The directions along an axis NE − ve/SW + ve are averaged irrespective of sign, and without correction for differences in location. Unit weight was given to each of these entries ($N = 8$): **6.11, 16, 19, 22, 26, 29, 32,** and **36.** The pole was calculated as the mean of poles for these entries ($N = 8$, $K = 48$).

6.39 (2) The directions along a NE + ve/SW − ve axis are averaged, irrespective of sign, and without correction for differences of location. The entries averaged are **6.13, 14, 15, 18,** and **21,** each given unit weight ($N = 5$). The pole was calculated as a mean of poles for these entries ($N = 5$, $K = 71$).

6.40–42 *Upper Carboniferous of the Donbas* (Khramov, quoted in Kalashnikov, 1961) Two results from red sediments. Stability is indicated by the divergence from the present field.

6.40 *Araucarite Stage* Result based on 76 samples.

6.41 *Avilov Stage* Result based on 48 samples. It is stated that stability is determined by the "circle of remagnetization."

6.42 *Combined* The average of the directions in entries **6.40** and **6.41** ($N = 2$) and the pole calculated from this mean are given.

6.43–46 *Lower Carboniferous of the Tikvin District* (Khramov, quoted in Kalashnikov, 1961; Yanovsky and others, 1963) Red sandstones. Stability is stated to be determined by the "circle of remagnetization."

6.43 *Oka-Serpukhov Stage* Forty samples.

6.44 *Tula Horizon* Eighteen samples.

6.45 *Tournai Stage (1)* Seventeen samples.

6.46 *Combined* The directions in **6.43–45** are averaged, irrespective of sign, giving each unit weight ($N = 3$). The pole was calculated from this average direction.

6.47 *Tournai Stage, South Urals* Ten samples.

6.48–55 *Lower Carboniferous Sediments of Siberia* (Vlassov and Kovalenko, quoted in Kalashnikov, 1961) The good agreement between these 7 localities and the divergence from the present field indicate stability.

6.55 *Combined* The directions were obtained by averaging the directions in **6.48–54** giving each unit weight ($N = 7$). The pole is the mean of the poles for each locality ($N = 7$, $K = 12$).

6.56–57 *Dwyka Varved Clays* Upper Carboniferous (Nairn, 1960*b*) These results, based on only 4 samples (19 specimens, 10 negative and 9 positive) from Sebungwe, are bracketed.

6.58–59 *Upper Kuttung Series* Upper Carboniferous This Series is about 1200 m thick in the Hunter Valley. These results are from the Paterson Toscanite, which is about halfway up the Series, and from sediments of the Main Glacial Stage in the Hunter Valley and northern New South Wales.

6.58 *Upper Kuttung Sediments* Result based on 40 samples (138 specimens) from 9 sites. All specimens were thermally cleaned in 300°C (see § 5.10; account of earlier work in Irving, 1957*b*).

6.59 *Paterson Toscanite* This is a flow about 100 m thick. It was sampled at 4 sites (12 samples, 33 specimens) spread over a distance of 13 km. The enclosing sediments dip to the south and the directions were corrected for this. The initial site directions are scattered but after treatment in *ac* fields of 225 oe (peak) the between-site disperson is not significant. The divergence from the present field of the direction *in situ* indicates stability.

6.60 *Lower Kuttung Lavas* Results from 3 sites (8 samples, 21 specimens) one in each of the 2 toscanite and 1 felsite flow which occur towards the top of the Lower Kuttung in the Hunter Valley. The sites span 180 m stratigraphically. The Lower Kuttung has been tentatively placed in the Viséan (David, 1950, p. 330). Radioisotope age determinations (K-Ar) by Evernden and Richards (1962) confirmed this age for the andesites which make up the lower part of the sequence. However, determinations for the 2 toscanites gave values of 307 and 288 m.y., which place these beds at a much younger level towards the top of the Carboniferous on the Kulp 1961 Time Scale. The mean direction given is that obtained after magnetic cleaning of specimens in *ac* fields of 300 oe. The analysis was carried out giving equal weight to each site ($N = 3$). Stability is indicated by the departure from the present field.

6.61–63 *Barnett Formation* Mississippian (Martinez and Howell, 1956; Howell and Martinez, 1957) Sixty samples from 8 sites gave positive directions and 8 samples from 1 site were negative. Three measurements gave directions close to the present field and were discarded. The sites are spread over a distance of 120 km in the Llano uplift of western Texas. Samples of limestone, shale, and calcareous concretions were studied. The lack of alignment of the 2 opposed groups is in the correct sense to be due to small viscous components imposed by present field. The reversal and the divergence from the present field are indicative of stability. The magnetization of the concretions is considered to be of chemical origin (CRM).

6.61 *Negative Directions* Mean values giving each sample unit weight ($N = 8$).

6.62 *Positive Directions* Mean values for the positive directions giving each sample unit weight ($N = 60$).

6.63 *Combined* A mean direction is calculated, irrespective of sign, giving equal weight to positive and negative groups ($N = 2$). This gives too much weight to the negative result, but has the advantage of correcting to some extent for any small viscous components imposed by the present field.

6.64–66 *Naco Formation* Pennsylvanian (Runcorn, 1956a; Collinson and Runcorn, 1960) Sedimentary samples from 2 localities (**6.64** Carizzo Creek, 8 samples, 31 specimens spanning 60 m; **6.65** Fossil Creek, 9 samples, 20 specimens spanning 45 m) gave positive directions whose divergence from the present field indicates stability. The localities are about 200 km apart. Specimens were used as units in the analysis. An over-all mean direction giving unit weight to each locality ($N = 2$) is given in entry **6.66.**

6.67 *Codroy Red Beds* Mississippian (Nairn, Frost, and Light, 1959) Nine samples (36 specimens) from Newfoundland gave positive directions, whose divergence from the present field indicates stability. Samples used as units in the calculations.

6.68 *Bonaventure, Kennebecasis and Bathurst Formations* Carboniferous (P. M. Du Bois, 1959c) Bonaventure is late Mississippian or early Pennsylvanian. Kennebecasis is Pennsylvanian. Forty-six samples (92 specimens) were collected from sites spanning 400 km in Gaspé and New Brunswick. The divergence from the present field indicates stability. Samples were used as units in the analysis ($N = 46$).

CARBONIFEROUS SUPPLEMENT

6.69 *Krasnotsvet Clay, Gzhelian Stage* Middle stage of Upper Carboniferous (Andreeva, 1961) Forty samples from the Moscow Basin were studied. $H_{cr}' = 50$–100 oe. Ac fields of 100 oe reduce intensity by no more than 10 per cent. The divergence from the present field indicates stability. Pole calculated assuming sampling region near Moscow (55.4 N, 37.5 E).

6.70 *Sediments, Minusinsk Basin* (Popova, 1963) Result based on about 10 samples from the Bystryansk Suite and other beds. No directions reported. $H_{cr}' = 60$ oe. Stability indicated by the departure of this pole from the present pole.

6.71 *Sediments* Carboniferous (Wang, Teng, Li, and Yeh, 1960) Four samples of red-grey and purple-grey sandstone from the Western Hills, Peking, gave this result. The entry is bracketed since the circle of confidence exceeds 25° and the samples are fewer than 5 in number. Eight other samples gave discordant results.

6.72 *Grey Tuffs* Lower Carboniferous (Creer, 1962d) About 12 specimens gave smeared directions and this is an estimate, made by Creer, of the stable direction.

6.73 *Sediments, La Rioja Province* (Creer, 1962d) Three samples (9 specimens) gave this result, which is entered in brackets because fewer than 5 samples have been studied, and because the circle of confidence exceeds 25°.

6.74 *Mitu Formation* Upper Carboniferous (Creer, 1962d) Twenty-seven samples (80 specimens) fall into negative (mean 76, −44) and positive (mean 258, +60) groups. The average of these directions giving each unit weight is entered here ($N = 2$). Stability is indicated by the positive directions.

PERMIAN (280–230 M.Y.)

7.01–05 *Permian of Esterel*

7.01–04 *Esterel Igneous Rocks* (Roche, 1957; Rutten, v'Everdingen, and Zijderveld, 1957) Twenty-two samples were collected from 3 rock members [pyromeride (5 samples), dolerite (3 samples), and rhyolite (14 samples)]. The directions in the rhyolite were shown to be stable by treatment in ac fields. The magnetization of the dolerite samples was not changed by heating to 300°C and cooling in zero field. The divergence from the present field and the laboratory tests indicate stability.

7.04 *Combined* Means of directions and poles in **7.01–03.**

7.05 *Esterel Igneous and Sedimentary Rocks* (As and Zijderveld, 1958) Fourteen samples of dolerite, rhyolite, pelites, and arkoses from several levels, which may overlap stratigraphically those above [**7.01–04**]. Partial demagnetization in ac fields of 300 oe (peak) at 150°C reduces scatter. The application of the fold test, the general agreement between results from igneous and sedimentary rocks, and the divergence from the present field indicate stability. Sample measurements were given unit weight in the analysis ($N = 14$).

7.06 *Montcenis Sandstone* Saxonian, Middle Permian (Nairn, 1957b) This result is based on only 3 samples (14 specimens) from the Morvan and is bracketed. Specimen measurements were used as units in the analysis ($N = 14$).

7.07 *Nideck Porphyry* Saxonian? (Nairn, 1957b) Fourteen samples (49 specimens) collected from the Vosges gave directions whose divergence from the present field indicates stability. Specimens were used as units in the analysis ($N = 49$). See **7.54.**

7.08 *St. Wendel Sediments* Autunian (Nairn, 1957b) Five samples (27 specimens) from the Saar gave directions whose divergence from the present field indicates stability. Specimen measurements were used in the analysis ($N = 27$).

7.09 *Rotliegende Sediments and Lavas* Lower Permian (Nairn, 1960a) Thirty-six samples (144 specimens) from 4 localities in the Saar, Pfalz, Baden-Baden, and Freiburg, spaced over about 100 km, gave directions whose divergence from the present field indicates stability. The mean giving each site unit weight is given ($N = 4$). The pole was obtained by averaging the poles for each locality ($N = 4$, $K = 43$).

7.10–12 *Igneous Rocks of the Nahe Region* Permian

7.10 (1) Schmucker (1959) Result based on 18 samples from 4 igneous members spread over a distance of 40 km. Laboratory tests indicated their stability. In the analysis unit weight was given to the mean for each member ($N = 4$). The directions in 2 other igneous members were considered unstable.

7.11 (2) Nijenhuis (1961) Result based on 75 samples collected over a distance of 30 km. Components imposed by the present field were removed by magnetic cleaning. Detailed work was carried out on 2 flows, and less detailed work on 1 flow and 2 sills. The age of the flows is cited as lower Middle Permian. The intrusives, although Permian, are less accurately dated. In the analysis unit weight was given to each igneous unit ($N = 5$). The cleaned directions diverge strongly from the present field, and this, and the laboratory studies, indicate stability.

7.12 *Combined* Means of directions and poles in **7.10** and **7.11.**

7.13 *Igneous Complex of the Oslo Region* (v'Everdingen, 1960; preliminary results in Rutten, v'Everdingen, and Zijderveld, 1957) Fossils in associated sediments indicate age limits of Upper Carboniferous to Middle Permian. Radioisotope studies give values around 270 m.y. (Davis and others, 1956) and indicate a Lower Permian age. At least 6 samples were collected from each of 27 igneous units, 538 altogether, including some interbedded sediments; 54 samples proved to be unsuitable. The stratigraphic thickness covered was about 1000 m. Magnetic cleaning in 950 oe (peak) was carried out. The analysis was made giving unit weight to each rock unit. The divergence from the present field and the laboratory tests indicate stability. See Figure 4.2b.

7.14 *Exeter Traps* Permian (Creer, 1957a) Result based on 34 samples from 5 flows. The divergence from the present field indicates stability. The statistics were calculated giving unit weight to the mean of each flow ($N = 5$). Radiometric (K-Ar on biotite) ages for the Killerton lava member of the traps (also studied paleomagnetically) gave 279 ± 6 m.y. (Miller, Shibata, and Munro, 1962).

7.15 *The Great Whin Sill* (Creer, Irving, and Nairn, 1959) Geological evidence indicates a late Carboniferous-early Permian age and radioisotope (K-Ar) studies suggest emplacement 281 ± 5 m.y. ago (Miller and Mussett, 1963). This sill has an average thickness of about 30 m. It was sampled (34 sites, 102 samples, 102 specimens) along its outcrop over a distance of 120 km. Demagnetization by ac fields yields decay curves characteristic of a stable TRM. H_{cr} values range about 350 oe. Baked sediments at contacts are strongly magnetized parallel to the sill directions. These features, and the strong divergence of the directions from the present field, indicate stability. The pole was calculated by averaging poles for sites ($N = 34$, $K = 80$).

7.16–17 *Mauchline Sediments and Lavas* Permian (P. M. Du Bois, 1957) The result is based on measurements of 34 lava [**7.16**] and 26 red sedimentary [**7.17**] specimens (samples?) from Ayrshire. The lava samples span a thickness of about 100 m, but the stratigraphic coverage of the sediments is not stated. In the analysis unit weight was given to each specimen. The divergence from the present field and the good agreement between results from sediments and lavas indicate stability.

7.18 *Ayrshire Kylites* (Armstrong, 1957) The age is presumed to be Permian since the bodies intrude Upper Carboniferous sediments and are pierced by Permian volcanic necks, and also on account of their petrological similarity to the Mauchline lavas [**7.16**]. Partial *ac* demagnetization diminishes scatter. In the analysis the result from each intrusive (7 samples) was given unit weight ($N = 5$). Stability is suggested by the divergence from the present field.

7.19–20 *Bolzano Quartz-porphyry Series* Lower Permian. Results are available from 2 studies in adjacent areas near Bolzano. In each case components directed along the Earth's field were reduced by partial demagnetization in *ac* fields of 900 oe (peak). Stability is indicated by the resistance to demagnetization and by the divergence from the present field. The results, although obtained in the same laboratory (Royal Netherlands Meteorological Institute, De Bilt), are not concordant, and van Hilten (1960) explains this by saying that Dietzel's samples "were taken from a more weathered rock" and that a stable CRM is present.

7.19 (1) Dietzel (1960) Fifty-one samples were collected from 25 exposures over a distance of about 20 km. Means for each exposure were taken as units in the analysis ($N = 25$).

7.20 (2) Van Hilten (1960, 1962*a*) In a collection of 39 samples, 6 were not considered suitable. The samples were spread over a distance of 30 km and through a thickness exceeding 1000 m. Samples were given unit weight in the analysis ($N = 33$). Results corrected for a tectonic dip of "10°–15° south-dipping inclination."

7.21 *Pyrenean Rocks* Permian (Van der Lingen quoted in van Hilten, 1962*a*) Sediments and igneous rocks from north of Canfranca, Huesca Province. See **7.55, 7.56.**

7.22–31 *Tartarian Sediments* Upper Permian Red sediments were studied at several localities over a wide area. It is stated that stability at localities **7.21** to **26** is determined by the "circle of remagnetization." The directions at different localities are in good agreement (irrespective of sign) and are combined in **7.25, 29,** and **31** as detailed below. The Lower Tartarian is characterized by positive polarities. In the Upper Tartarian both polarities occur. Stability is indicated by the reversals, and by the divergence from the present field.

7.22–25 *Upper Tartarian* (Khramov, quoted in Kalashnikov, 1961) **7.22** R. Sukhona, 49 samples; **7.23** R. Vyatka, 34 samples; **7.24** Transvolga Region, 35 samples.

7.25 *Upper Tartarian combined* Means of locality directions and poles ($N = 3$, $K = 1140$) in **7.22–24.**

7.26–29 *Lower Tartarian* (Khramov quoted in Kalashnikov, 1961) **7.26** Transvolga region, 19 samples; **7.27** R. Sukhona, 37 samples; **7.28** Kama district, 35 samples.

7.29 *Lower Tartarian combined* Means of locality directions and poles ($N = 3$, $K = 731$) in **7.26–28.**

7.30 *Tartarian undifferentiated* (Khramov, 1958) The directions in 74 samples collected from 3 localities spread over a distance of the order of 100 km near the R. Vyatka give scattered directions. The samples cover 485 m stratigraphically. The relationship of this result to that in entry **7.23** is not stated.

7.31 *Upper and Lower Tartarian combined* Mean of the locality directions and poles ($N = 7$, $K = 295$) listed in **7.22–24, 7.26–28** and **7.30.**

7.32–34 *Kazanian Red Sediments* Upper Permian Two results whose relationship is not made clear in the originals.

7.32 Khramov (1958) A thickness of 90 m was sampled (24 samples) at 2 localities about 100 km apart in the Perm region. Smearing occurs and an estimate of the stable direction was made by rotating directions along great circles away from the present field.

7.33 Khramov (Quoted in Kalashnikov, 1961) Fifteen samples collected from the Kama district.

7.34 *Combined* Means of directions and poles for **7.32** and **7.33.**

7.35–37 *Ufimian Red Sediments* Upper Permian Two results whose relationship is not made clear in the originals.

7.35 Khramov (1958) Twenty samples from 2 localities near Perm showed smearing. The direction given is an estimate of the stable direction, obtained by rotating directions away from the present field. The localities are about 100 km apart and the samples cover a stratigraphical thickness of 70 m.

7.36 Khramov (Quoted in Kalashnikov, 1961) Thirty-one samples.

7.37 *Combined* Means of directions and poles for entries **7.35** and **7.36.**

7.38 *Donbas Red Sandstone* Lower Permian (Khramov quoted in Kalashnikov, 1961) Result based on 34 samples. Stability is indicated by divergence from the present field.

7.39 *Ultrabasics of Maymecha-Kotuy* (Gusev, 1959) Oriented samples (1600) were obtained from 6 igneous groups in northern Siberia (olivinites, diabasic basalts, pyroxenites, ultra-basic dikes and Meymechites). This result is based on 388 sample observations. The age of the intrusions is considered on geological evidence to be late Permian to early Triassic. Radioisotope age determination (K-Ar on micas) from various intrusives gave an average of 250 m.y., indicating a Middle to Upper Permian age on Kulp's 1961 Time Scale. Stability is indicated by divergence from the present field.

7.40–41 *Permian Sediments from Kenya* (Nairn, 1960*b*) Two results are available: **7.40** from the Maji ya Chumvi Formation (Upper Permian) based on 5 samples (21 specimens) from one site; and **7.41** from the Taru Grit (Lower Permian) based on 8 samples (32 specimens) from 2 sites. The divergence from the present field indicates stability. The mean directions are inconsistent. The statistical values are internally inconsistent and the method of obtaining them is not stated.

7.42 *Upper Marine Latites* Middle to Upper Permian (Irving and Parry, 1963) Forty-three samples (138 specimens) were collected from 12 sites in 5 igneous members. The stratigraphic thickness spanned by the samples is about 400 m and their lateral spread 50 km. Radioisotope age determinations (K-Ar) of 2 members gave 244 and 252 m.y. (Evernden and Richards, 1962). The precision is much improved by magnetic cleaning (150–300 oe (peak)). The divergence from the present field, and the laboratory studies, indicate stability. It is of historical interest to note that the pioneer worker Mercanton (1926*a*) obtained an inclination of +87 from a single sample of these rocks.

7.43 *Lower Marine Basalt* Lower Permian (Irving and Parry, 1963) Six samples (12 specimens) were from a single site in a basalt flow. Small unstable components were removed by magnetic cleaning (150 oe (peak)). Samples were given unit weight in the analysis ($N = 6$).

7.44–46 *Culter Formation* Permian (J. W. Graham, 1955) Two localities: **7.44** Glenwood Springs, Colorado, 2 samples; **7.45** Monument Valley, Utah, 4 samples. Eight additional samples gave directions close to the present field and are rejected in this analysis in which sample directions were given unit weight. Stability is indicated by the divergence from the present field.

7.46 *Combined* Means of directions and poles for **7.44** and **7.45**.

7.47–49 *Abo Formation* Lower Permian (J. W. Graham, 1955) Results from 2 sites in New Mexico: **7.47** Abo Canyon, 16 m coverage, 11 samples, 20 specimens (3 rejected); and **7.48** Zuni Mts., 8 m, 13 samples, 25 specimens. In the analyses unit weight was given to each specimen. Stability is indicated by the divergence from the present field.

7.49 *Combined* Means of directions and poles for **7.47** and **7.48**.

7.50 *Yeso Formation* Lower to Middle Permian (J. W. Graham, 1955) Result based on 26 sedimentary samples (4 results excluded because of wide scatter) spanning a stratigraphic thickness of 10 m from 1 site at Tecolate, New Mexico. The statistics were calculated giving unit weight to each sample ($N = 22$). The mean diverges from the present field indicating stability.

7.51 *Supai Formation* Upper Carboniferous to Permian sediments (Runcorn, 1955*a*, 1956*a*; Doell, 1955; J. W. Graham, 1955; Collinson and Runcorn, 1960) Seven separate determinations were made at 4 localities in Arizona. At 3 of these 2 independent determinations were made by different workers. Each determination is based on many samples spaced through stratigraphic thicknesses ranging between 30 and 300 m. Samples from some determinations probably overlap stratigraphically. Samples at some sites showed smearing towards the present field and were not used in the analyses, but the majority (about 114 samples and 240 specimens) showed good grouping. The mean direction, giving unit weight to each ($N = 7$) determination and without correction for differences in location, is given. The divergence from the present field indicates stability. The pole is calculated by giving unit weight to poles calculated for each determination ($N = 7$, $K = 45$).

7.52 *Sangre de Cristo Formation* Upper Carboniferous or Lower Permian (J. W. Graham, 1955) Nineteen samples from 3 m of sediments at one site gave positive directions indicating stability. The statistics are calculated giving each sample unit weight ($N = 19$).

7.53 *Greenland Sediments* Permian (Bidgood and Harland, 1961) Result based on 10 samples (about 20 specimens) from 2 localities in east Greenland. The divergence from the present field indicates stability.

PERMIAN SUPPLEMENT

7.54 *Volcanics of Nideck-Donon* Permian (Roche, Soucier, and Lacaze, 1962) Thirty-seven samples were collected from 9 sites over a distance of about 12 km. Thermal demagnetization of test specimens and the divergence from the present field indicate the stability of the NRM. In the analysis, unit weight is given to each site ($N = 9$), using the data in p. 62 of the original. The mean direction and pole given in the original are 192, -13 and 47° N, 169° E. See **7.07**.

7.55–56 *Red Beds and Andesites from the Spanish Pyrenees* (Schwarz, 1963) Age cited as "Permo-Triassic." Discordant results were obtained from red sediments (9 samples) and andesites (14 samples) in the same sequence in the Rio Aragón Subordan valley, Huesca province. The NRM of the andesites is considered by Schwarz to be original, but the sediments "acquired a strong, stable magnetization in post-Alpine times; the original magnetization could not be detected." The latter result is entered in brackets. All specimens were magnetically cleaned in 900 oe. Samples were given unit weight in the analyses. Figure 2 of Schwarz shows the NRM directions of the sediments to be close to the present field. See **7.21**.

7.57 *Beloyarsk Suite* Lower Permian sediments (Popova, 1963). This pole result is based on 23 samples (15 negative 8 positive); the divergence from the present pole and the reversal indicate stability. The directions are not reported. Five samples directed near the present field were not used. $H_{cr}' = 70$ oe.

7.58–59 *Permian of China* (Wang, Teng, Li, and Yeh, 1960) Two results. The circles of confidence in both cases are large ($>25°$) and the entries are bracketed. **7.58** is based on about 8 sedimentary samples apparently mostly from Shantung. **7.59** is based on about 10 samples of basalt from the Omei Mts. of Szechwan.

7.60 *Corumbatai Formation* (Creer, 1962d) Age cited as "upper Permian." Samples from the states of Parana and São Paulo gave positive and negative directions, the latter being close to the present field. The direction given is the direction of stable magnetization estimated by Creer from the smeared positive directions. The pole is calculated from this direction.

TRIASSIC (230–180 M.Y.)

8.01–03 *Vosge Sandstone* Early Triassic There are 2 results in which the observations, although widely scattered, have average directions which are approximately opposed to one another. The negative group (Nairn, 1960a) contains 46 specimen observations from 9 samples collected from 3 sites. The positive group (Clegg, Deutsch, Everitt, and Stubbs, 1957) consists of 61 specimen observations from 7 sites. In the latter it is uncertain whether the observations refer to specimens or samples. In the former the weighting used is not stated in the original. The lack of alignment of the means along the same axis is in the right sense to be due to secondary components imposed by the present field, and the effect of these may be nullified by averaging the two irrespective of sign [**8.03**]. The reversal and the divergence from the present field are indicative of the stability of this direction.

8.04 *Bunter Sandstone of Germany* Lower Triassic (Nairn, 1960a) About 5 samples were collected from each of 5 localities spread over a distance of several hundred kilometers (total of 27 samples, 133 specimens). The within-site precision is low (average k is 6) but the agreement between-sites is good. Four localities, low in the sequence, show negative polarization, the other, somewhat higher, is positive. The over-all mean direction calculated giving unit weight for each locality, and uncorrected for the spread of samples, is given. The pole is the average of the locality poles giving unit weight to each ($N = 5$, $K = 64$).

8.05 *Triassic Sandstones from Spain* (Clegg, Deutsch, Everitt, and Stubbs, 1957; Blackett, Clegg, and Stubbs, 1960) Results were obtained from 7 sites, but only 3 (Villaviciosa, Alcolea, and Aguilar) were internally consistent. Stability is suggested by the departure of the *in situ* directions from the present field.

8.06–08 *New Red Sandstone of Britain*

8.06 *Keuper Marls* Upper Triassic (Clegg, Almond, and Stubbs, 1954a and b) Result based on 43 samples (540 specimens) from 9 (5 negative, 4 positive) sites spread over a distance of about 400 km. The between-site dispersion decreases after correction for bedding, but the dips are low ($\sim 10°$) and the test is not decisive. Thermal demagnetization of certain test specimens to within a few degrees of the Curie temperature did not greatly change the intensity (Figure 5.28) or direction of magnetization, and the directions were also unchanged by demagnetization in an ac field of 1000 oe (Leng, 1955). The mean was calculated, irrespective of sign, giving each site unit weight ($N = 9$). Stability is indicated by the good agreement between-sites, the occurrence of reversals, the divergence from the present field, and the laboratory tests.

8.07 *Keuper Marl, Sidmouth* Upper Triassic (Creer, 1957b, 1959) A study of 35 samples (329 specimens) from a section 52 m thick showed smeared directions (Figure 4.1c). Partial demagnetization of 65 specimens (from 26 samples spaced through the section) in ac fields of 850 oe(peak) condensed the directions into two opposed groups with means at 27, +30 and 213, −17. The positive (reversed) directions were confined to an 11 m zone in the middle of the section. The mean direction, irrespective of sign, is given in this entry ($N = 2$). The divergence from the present field, the reversal, and the laboratory tests indicate stability.

8.08 *Arran* Triassic (Leng, 1955) Forty-one specimens (? samples) had scattered directions. The divergence from the present field indicates stability.

8.09–14 *Lower Triassic Sediments U.S.S.R.* Five results are available from widely spread localities. At several localities the directions were considered to be much affected by secondary components imposed by the present field. Corrections were made for these. The presence of both polarities, and the divergence from the present field suggest stability.

8.09 *Vitloosian Sediments* (Khramov, 1958) The directions in 9 samples collected over a lateral distance of 100 km and a thickness of 40 m in the region of the R. Vyatka showed smearing. The mean (NRM) is 235, +21. The direction given is the direction of the "stable" component estimated by rotating the directions along great circles away from the present field.

8.10 *Serebryansk Suite* (Khramov, quoted in Kalashnikov, 1961) Result based on 26 samples from the Donbas. It is stated that stability is determined by use of the "circle of remagnetization."

8.11 *Bashunchak Suite* (Khramov, quoted in Kalashnikov, 1961) Fifty-two samples gave this result.

8.12 *Tananyk Suite* (Khramov, quoted in Kalashnikov, 1961) Fourteen samples gave this result. It is stated that stability is determined by use of the "circle of remagnetization."

8.13 *Buzuluk Suite* (Khramov, quoted in Kalashnikov, 1961) Nine samples gave this result. It is stated that stability is determined by use of the "circle of remagnetization."

8.14 *Combined.* This entry gives the average of poles ($N = 5$, $K = 26$) for entries **8.09–13.**

8.15–20 *Siberian Traps* These traps, from which 5 results are available, are made up of lava flows and sills, the bulk of which were "erupted in the Triassic period, but it is clear that in different regions they are of different age" (Nalivkin, 1960, p. 34). In the originals the age of the different localities sampled was variously specified as Lower or Middle Triassic. Sampling was carried out over a wide area in the Lower Tunguska and Vilui River valleys. The presence of mixed polarities in **8.15** and **8.18,** the strong divergence of the means from the present field in the other 3 cases, and the broad agreement between all 5 results indicate stability.

8.15 (1) Feinberg and Dashkevitson (1960) Cited as Lower Triassic.

8.16 (2) Makarova (1959) Cited as "end of the Lower and beginning of the Middle Triassic." About 50 samples (from each of which many specimens were studied) of "gabbro and gabbro-diabase" were collected from 6 sites spread over a distance of more than 100 km.

8.17 (3) Deutsch and Watkins (1961) Age cited as Lower Triassic. Thirty-two samples (83 specimens) were collected from 5 sites spread over a distance of over 300 km. The results from 1 site (6 samples, 16 specimens) were discarded as anomalous.

8.18 (4) Kochegura, quoted in Kalashnikov (1961) Age cited as T_1. Result based on 92 samples (? specimens).

8.19 (5) Komarov (1957) Age cited as T_1.

8.20 *Combined* An average of the poles in **8.15–19** is given ($N = 5$, $K = 52$).

8.21 *Taimyr Peninsula* Triassic (Gusev, quoted in Kalashnikov, 1961) Result based on 29 samples (? specimens). Stability is indicated by the divergence from the present field and by the improvement in precision after correction for folding.

8.22–25 *Igneous Rocks of the North Siberian Platform* (Gusev, quoted in Kalashnikov, 1961) Three results are available from rocks whose age is cited as Triassic. Stability is indicated by the agreement between results, by the presence of reversals, by the divergence of the means from the present field direction, and by the field tests specified below.

8.22–23 *Dolerites* Two results based on 31 and 34 samples (? specimens). Studies of "pebbles and volcanic bombs" are stated to indicate stability.

8.24 *Dikes* Result based on 25 samples (? specimens) from augitite dikes. Stability is stated to be indicated by "levelling of folds."

8.25 *Combined* The mean of the directions in **8.22–24** is calculated giving unit weight to each ($N = 3$). A pole is calculated from this mean.

8.26 *Cave Sandstone* Upper Triassic (Nairn, 1957c, 1960b) Two sets of samples, 10 in all (52 specimens), from the Kgoma dia Tshaba valley, and from near Debeeti, gave scattered directions which depart systematically from the present or dipole field directions thus indicating stability. In the analysis unit weight was given to specimens ($N = 52$).

8.27 *Rhodesian Sandstone* Upper Triassic (Nairn, 1960b) Directions at 6 sites (21 samples, 99 specimens) gave directions grouped round the geocentric axial dipole field from which their mean does not appear to differ significantly. The result is therefore entered in brackets.

8.28 *Chocolate Shales, Narrabeen Series* Lower Triassic (Irving, 1963) Four sites (32 samples, 32 specimens) were studied, each given unit weight in the analysis ($N = 4$). The thickness spanned exceeds 50 m. The directions show some slight streaking towards the present field, but this is lost after thermal cleaning at 300°C. The values given refer to the directions after heating. The divergence from the present field indicates stability. Between-site precision is not significant. The inclination is confirmed by study of bore core.

8.29 *Brisbane Tuff* Middle Triassic (Robertson, 1963) Twelve samples (36 specimens) were studied from 6 sites. Treatment in *ac* fields improves the precision. The results given are those obtained after magnetic cleaning in 150 oe (peak). In the analysis the two-tier method is used and the precision quoted is the between-site precision. The divergence from the present field and the laboratory studies indicate stability.

8.30 *Chugwater Formation* Permian and Triassic (Collinson and Runcorn, 1960) An average of 10 samples (total 98, and 425 specimens) were collected from each of 10 localities

in Wyoming and Colorado. At each locality a thickness of 20–120 m was spanned. At 7 localities both polarities occurred. At 3 localities only positive polarities occurred. In total 317 specimens were positive and 108 negative. The presence of reversals and the divergences from the present field indicate the stability. The average direction giving unit weight to each polarity group ($N = 17$) is given, no allowance being made for the spread of localities. Poles for each positive and negative group were calculated and the average pole is given ($N = 17$, $K = 57$). See Figure 4.2*d*.

8.31 *Moenkopi Formation* Lower to Middle Triassic (Runcorn, 1956a; Collinson and Runcorn, 1960; Kintzinger, 1957) An average of 11 samples (altogether 92 samples and over 200 specimens) were collected from each of 8 (4 negative and 4 positive) localities in Colorado, Utah, and Arizona. At each locality the samples spanned a thickness of 15–70 m. The presence of reversals, and the large divergences from the present field, indicate stability. The average direction giving unit weight to each locality ($N = 8$) is given without correction for the variation in locality positions. The average of poles for each locality is given ($N = 8$, $K = 32$).

8.32 *Springdale Sandstone* Upper Triassic, Moenave Formation (Runcorn, 1956a) The directions in 8 samples (18 specimens) from 1 locality in Zion National Park show a smeared distribution. The mean direction of the NRM is 350, +39, $k = 17$, $a_{95} = 9°$. The direction of the stable component estimated by choosing a point in the distribution farthest from the present field is given, together with the pole calculated from this.

8.33–40 *Chinle Formation* Upper Triassic Results from about 100 samples (and over 200 specimens) from 7 localities give inconsistent results.

8.33 *Shinarump Formation* (J. W. Graham, 1955) Seventeen samples (20 specimens) from a 1.5 m section at 1 site gave some scattered directions (which were not used in the analysis quoted in this entry) and others smeared between the present field and a northerly direction with low inclination. The latter may be presumed to be an effect of partial instability but no correction for this was made. The result, as it stands, is considered to have no reliability as a Triassic field indicator and is entered in brackets.

8.34 *Las Vegas* (J. W. Graham, 1955) Six samples (8 specimens) from 1.5 m section at 1 site gave scattered directions. The mean obtained from an analysis of 8 specimen directions is apparently just significantly different from the present field, but the method probably underestimates the error. Partial instability is probably present, and since no correction was made for this, the result is considered of no reliability as an indicator of the Triassic field direction and is entered in brackets.

8.35–36 *Colorado National Monument* (Collinson and Runcorn, 1960) The directions at 2 localities (**8.35,** 30 m thickness, 6 samples, 29 specimens; **8.36,** 15 m thickness, 7 samples, 31 specimens) were grouped around the geocentric dipole and present fields respectively, and, in the absence of any special stability tests, no reliability can be placed on these results and they are entered in brackets. Specimens were used as units in the analyses.

8.37 *Romeroville, New Mexico* (J. W. Graham, 1955) Sixteen samples from one site cover a thickness of 5 m. The direction in 1 sample is 180° from that in the others, which are well-grouped, and strongly divergent from the present field indicating stability. In the analysis each sample was given unit weight ($N = 16$).

8.38–39 *Moab, Utah* (Collinson and Runcorn, 1960) Sampling was carried out at 2 localities. At locality **8.38** 14 samples (39 specimens) spaced through a thickness of 67 m showed marked smearing from the present geocentric dipole field direction towards the SSE and gave a mean (NRM) of 160, +44. The estimated stable direction and pole calculated from it is given. At locality **8.39** the directions in 10 samples (60 specimens) spaced through 42 m were distributed along a great circle through the geocentric dipole field both to the NNW and SSE, with a mean (NRM) at 59, +73. The estimated stable axial direction and pole is given. It would appear that at **8.38** the stable directions were positive, whereas at **8.39** both polarities are present.

8.40 *Combined* This entry gives the mean of poles **8.37, 8.38,** and **8.39** being, apparently, the only Chinle results of any reliability.

8.41–44 *Newark Group* Upper Triassic Results are available from the Newark Group of Maryland and New Jersey, and its equivalents in New England.

8.41 *New Oxford Formation* (J. W. Graham, 1955) A total of 14 samples (14 specimens) were collected at one site in Maryland through a stratigraphic thickness of 6 m. The directions are well-grouped and diverge significantly from the present field indicating stability. Samples (1 divergent value not used) were given unit weight in the analysis ($N = 13$).

8.42 *Newark Group, New Jersey* A preliminary study of some Brunswickian red beds was described by P. M. Du Bois, Irving, Opdyke, Runcorn, and Banks (1957), and Collinson and Runcorn (1960). This was followed by a more detailed study (Opdyke, 1961*a*) into which the earlier results were incorporated, and which was extended to include red beds of the Stockton facies, the Watchung flows, and the dolerite intrusives (Palisades, etc.). The sampling sites are toward the top of the group spanning a stratigraphic thickness of more than 1000 m. The radiogenic age of the flows and dolerite has been given as 190 m.y. (Erickson and Kulp, 1960), indicating an Upper Triassic age on Kulp's 1961 Time Scale. The 18 sampling sites (48 samples, 210 specimens) in the sediments cover a stratigraphical thickness of about 800 m. The 5 sampling sites (13 samples, 50 specimens) in the flows are distributed among 3 thick flows which are multiple in character. The 6 dolerite sites (17 samples, 69 specimens) are in 5 intrusive bodies. The NRM of the sediments is very stable—test specimens treated in *ac* fields of 900 oe (peak) suffered no change in direction and only a 5 per cent decrease in intensity, and $H_{cr} = 5400$ oe. The flows and intrusives are less stable (H_{cr} ranges 200–500 oe) and were magnetically cleaned in 150 oe. In the analysis sites were given unit weight. See § 5.03.

8.43 *Connecticut Valley, Lavas and Sediments* Upper Triassic (P. M. Du Bois, Irving, Opdyke, Runcorn, and Banks, 1957; P. M. Du Bois, 1957) Twelve samples (32 specimens —19 negative, 13 positive) were collected from red beds and lavas. The reversal and the divergence from the present field indicate stability.

8.44 *Massachusetts Lavas* Upper Triassic (P. M. Du Bois, Irving, Opdyke, Runcorn, and Banks, 1957; Irving and Banks, 1961) Sixteen samples (32 specimens) from 5 sites in 2 lava members in the Meriden Formation of Massachusetts showed smearing due to viscous components imposed by the present field, and these were removed by magnetic cleaning in 150 oe(peak). The divergence from the present field, and the laboratory tests indicate stability. The two-tier analysis was used and the between-site precision is given.

8.45 *Red Sediments from Kapp Biot* Middle to Upper Triassic (Bidgood and Harland, 1961) Result based on 44 samples (90 specimens) 8 samples being positive and 36 negative. The mean direction irrespective of sign is given, the statistics being calculated giving unit weight to each sample ($N = 44$). The reversals and the divergence from the present field indicate stability.

TRIASSIC SUPPLEMENT

8.46 *Dolerite* (Wang, Teng, Li, and Yeh, 1960) This result, based on about 5 samples from the Western Hills, Peking, is entered in brackets because of the very large circle of confidence ($> 25°$).

8.47 *Las Cabras Formation, Mendoza Province* (Creer, 1962*d*) Age cited as "probably Triassic." Eleven sedimentary samples were each given unit weight in the analysis. Creer states that these samples "are likely to have been remagnetized in recent geological time" and because of this and the large circle of confidence ($>25°$) the result is entered in brackets.

8.48 *Rio Blanco Formation, Mendoza Province* (Creer, 1962*d*) Age cited as "probably Triassic." Sediments.

8.49 *Red Sediments, La Rioja and Salta Provinces* Triassic (Creer, 1962*d*) Results from 13 samples (49 specimens) with positive directions were each given unit weight in this analysis. The pole was calculated from the directions and locality coordinates listed. Stability is indicated by the large departure from the present field directions. In addition results were obtained from 4 samples (13 specimens) with negative directions (mean 42, –33).

8.50 *Giron Beds* (Creer, 1962*d*) Cited as "Triassic?" Twenty-seven sedimentary samples were each given unit weight in the analysis ($N = 27$). Creer states that the samples "are likely to have been remagnetized in recent geological time" and so the result is bracketed.

8.51 *La Quinta Formation* (Creer, 1962*d*) Age cited as Triassic or possibly early Jurassic. Eighteen sedimentary samples were each given unit weight in the analysis ($N = 18$). Creer states that the samples "are likely to have been

remagnetized in recent geological time" and the result is bracketed.

JURASSIC (180–135 M.Y.)

9.01 *Northants Ironstone* Middle Jurassic (Belshé (1957*b*) reporting measurements by R. W. Girdler) No details are reported. The result is entered in brackets.

9.02–09 *Lower Liassic Sands of England* (Girdler, 1959*b*) Five groups were studied, ranging in age from Whitbian to Lower Aalenian. Comments on this work were made by Creer, Irving, and Runcorn (1960) and Girdler (1960). In the analysis specimen observations were given unit weight.

9.02 *Bridport Sands* Seven samples (12 specimens) gave directions close to the dipole field and were considered by Girdler to be unstable. The results are entered in brackets.

9.03 *Yeovil Sands* Ten samples (11 specimens) gave directions close to the present dipole field and were considered unstable by Girdler. The results are entered in brackets.

9.04 *Midford Sands* Twenty samples (42 specimens) from 3 sites gave negative directions whose mean diverges from the present field indicative of stability.

9.05–06 *Cotswold Sands* **9.05,** 17 samples (32 specimens) gave directions close to the present dipole field and were considered unstable by Girdler; the results are entered in brackets. **9.06,** 17 samples (38 specimens) gave positive directions whose mean diverged strongly from the present field indicating stability.

9.07 *Midford and Cotswold* (*positive*) *Sands combined.* The mean, irrespective of sign, of the directions in entries **9.04, 9.06** is given, and the pole calculated from this. Stability is indicated by the reversal.

9.08–09 *Blea Wyke Beds* **9.08,** yellow sediments, 9 samples, 26 specimens. **9.09,** grey sediments, 5 samples, 15 specimens. In both cases the directions cluster around the present dipole field and were considered unstable by Girdler. The results are entered in brackets.

9.10 *Yorkshire Sediments* Lower to Upper Jurassic (Nairn, 1956, 1957*a*) Six samples (36 specimens) were collected from beds ranging from Middle Lias to Lower Corallian. Specimens were given unit weight in the analysis ($N = 36$). The directions were close to the present field and were regarded by Nairn

(1957a) as unstable. The results are entered in brackets.

9.11 *Scottish Sediments* Lower Jurassic (Nairn, 1956, 1957a) This result is based on only 4 samples (14 specimens) and is entered in brackets. Specimens were given unit weight in the analysis ($N = 14$).

9.12 *Pyrenean Tuffs* Lower Hettangian, Lower Liassic (Girdler, 1959b, 1961) Eighteen samples (38 specimens) were collected from 4 sites separated by about 2 km. These beds are dipping but the estimated dip values are subject to an error of ±15° (Girdler, 1959b, p. 360). The directions corrected to bedding are therefore subject to possible errors of this magnitude. The mean direction after correction for the assumed bedding dips is given. This result is bracketed because of the very large uncertainty in the bedding corrections. The directions of the principal susceptibility axes in 11 tuff specimens are randomly oriented, the average susceptibility anisotropy (equation 2.23) is 2.4 per cent.

9.13–15 *Alpine Sediments* Lower and Middle Jurassic (Hargraves and Fischer, 1959) Samples were collected from 2 sites in the North Calcareous Alps. This region has undergone considerable tectonic disturbance since the Jurassic. **9.13,** a stratigraphic thickness of 1 m of red limestone was spanned by 16 samples (30 specimens). **9.14,** 15 samples (21 specimens) were obtained through a thickness of 7 m of radiolarite. In the analyses unit weight was given to specimens. The departure of the directions from the present field indicates stability. Because of their condensed fossil sequences the sediments at each site are considered to have accumulated over a considerable span of time, but this does not necessarily mean that the magnetic record in each case is of comparable length.

9.15 *Combined* The direction given here is the mean of the directions in entries **9.13, 14.** The pole was calculated from this mean direction.

9.16–19 *Armenian Porphyrites* (Akopyan, quoted in Kalashnikov, 1961) Three results are available, but Yanovsky and others (1963) now state that they are not confirmed by Akopyan so the entries are bracketed.

9.19 *Combined* Result obtained by combining the directions listed in **9.16–18** giving each unit weight ($N = 3$). A pole is calculated from this mean assuming a location in central Armenia (40 N, 45 E).

9.20 *Turkmenian Sediments* (Khramov, 1958) Result based on about 10 samples from Middle and Upper Jurassic sediments from the Great Balkhan. The directions are smeared toward the present field and this was corrected by use of the "circle of remagnetization."

9.21–22 *Japanese Intrusives* (Kawai, Ito, Kume, 1961) Ages not closely specified. Localities given unit weight in the analyses. See § 10A.6.

9.21 *Mesozoic Intrusives of NE Japan* Eighty-seven specimens from 9 localities, 2 in serpentine, 3 in gabbro, 3 in granite, and 1 in granodiorite.

9.22 *Late Paleozoic and Mesozoic Intrusives of SW Japan* Sixty-three samples from 7 localities, 3 in serpentine, 2 in gabbro, 1 in granite, and 1 in granodiorite.

9.23 *Rajmahal Traps* (Clegg, Radakrishnamurty, and Sahasrabudhe, 1958) Thirty-three samples were collected from 3 quarries about 12 km apart in Bihar State. The samples came from the upper 75 m of the traps. The lower traps are interbedded with Lower to Middle Jurassic sediments, and the upper traps may be of this age or younger. Samples were given unit weight in the analysis ($N = 33$). The marked divergence of the directions from the present field indicates stability.

9.24–27 *Basalts and Dolerites of the Karroo System* Late Triassic to Lower Jurassic. Four results are available from South Africa and Rhodesia. The dolerites intrude rocks of many ages up to and including Triassic. The basalts, which are at the top of the Stormberg Series, immediately overlie the Cave Sandstone. From the geological evidence this widespread igneous activity is thought to have occurred in the late Triassic to Lower Jurassic, and this has recently been confirmed for some intrusive phases by the radioisotope studies (K-Ar) of McDougall (1963) who obtained ages ranging from 190 to 154 m.y.

9.24 *Karroo Basalts* (Nairn, 1956, 1957c) Eleven samples (44 specimens) were collected from 6 or 7 flows in the Bulawayo area and in the gorge of the Zambezi River below Victoria Falls. The directions diverge from the present field direction indicating stability. The statistics were calculated giving unit weight to each specimen ($N = 44$). Nairn (1960b) has revised this result giving a mean of 338, −40.

9.25 *Stormberg Lavas* (Hales, 1960) The result is based on observations from 119 cores drilled from 14 outcrops spaced through a sequence 1200 m thick containing many flows. With the exception of 1 site, which has a low inclination, the upper part of the sequence is characterized by negative polarizations (8 sites) and the lower part by positive polarizations (5 sites). The occurrence of reversals indicates stability. The calculations were made giving each site unit weight ($N = 14$). Samples from 5 other sites were considered to be affected by lightning. See **9.46–50**.

9.26 *Karroo Dolerite, surface collections* (K. W. T. Graham and Hales, 1957) Samples were collected from 20 sites over a wide area in Natal, Transvaal, Cape Province, and the Orange Free State. Remeasurement of specimens after storage for about 8 months showed changes in excess of 10° in specimens from some localities, and these localities were excluded in the final result, which is based on 33 samples (149 specimens). Most samples were negative, although a few were positive. Stability is indicated by the divergence from the present field. In the analysis unit weight was given to each sample ($N = 33$). K. W. T. Graham (1961) has demonstrated lightning effects in certain surface outcrops (§ 5.13).

9.27 *Karroo Dolerite, collections from mines* (K. W. T. Graham and Hales, 1957) Results are available from underground collections in mines at Winkelhaak (26.5 S, 29.1 E) in the Transvaal, and Estcourt (29.1 S, 29.9 E) in Natal. At Winkelhaak an upper sill (17 samples, 57 specimens) was positively magnetized, and a lower sill (8 samples, 33 specimens) was negative (units 1 and 2). At Estcourt positive (15 samples, 53 specimens) and negative (9 samples, 34 specimens) groups of directions were observed in different dolerite bodies (units 3 and 4). At Estcourt sets of positive (8 samples, 25 specimens) and negative (7 samples, 24 specimens) directions were observed in contact sediments baked by the dolerite at the time of intrusion (units 5 and 6). The unit members refer to Table 1 in the original. Stability is indicated by the divergences from the present field and by the occurrence of reversals. The agreement, irrespective of sign, between contacts and dolerite indicates that the magnetization originated at the time of intrusion. In certain cases the polarities of contact sediment and igneous rock are different (§ 7.8). The direction statistics were obtained by applying Fisher's method to the mean directions for each unit ($N = 6$).

The pole is the mean of poles calculated for each unit ($N = 6$, $K = 25$).

9.28 *Mt. Gibraltar Microsyenite* Lower Jurassic (Boesen, Irving, and Robertson, 1961) This laccolithic body is intrusive into flat-lying Middle Triassic sediments. A radioisotope age determination (K-Ar on hornblende) gave 178 m.y. (Evernden and Richards, 1962), indicating a Lower Jurassic age on Kulp's 1961 Time Scale. Ten samples (20 specimens) were collected from 2 quarries. Stability was checked by *ac* fields. Specimens were given unit weight in the analysis ($N = 20$).

9.29 *Prospect Dolerite* Lower or Middle Jurassic (Boesen, Irving, and Robertson, 1961) This dish-shaped dolerite sheet is intruded into flat-lying Upper Triassic sediments. A radioisotope age determination (K-Ar on biotite from picrite phases) gave 168 m.y. (Evernden and Richards, 1962) indicating a Lower or Middle Jurassic age on Kulp's 1961 Time Scale. Ten samples (18 specimens) from 3 quarries gave negative directions. Stability was checked by *ac* fields. Specimens were given unit weight in the analysis ($N = 18$).

9.30–31 *Tasmanian Dolerites* Lower or Middle Jurassic These dolerites occur as intrusions into basement rocks or, more commonly, into flat-lying or gently dipping Permian and Triassic sediments. Individual bodies may have dike-like or sill-like forms with thicknesses of the order of 500 m and lateral extents of tens of kilometers. Radioisotopes studies (K-Ar on plagioclase and pyroxene from the Red Hill "dyke") yield an average age of 167 m.y. indicating a Lower or Middle Jurassic age on Kulp's 1961 Time Scale (McDougall, 1961). Total TRM directions are parallel to the applied field. Thermal demagnetization gives a single Curie point at 550°C (Robertson, 1962). Anisotropy is negligible (Stacey, 1960a), and there are no detectable stress effects on TRM or IRM (Stott and Stacey, 1959, 1960). Results are available from a general survey of many bodies [**9.30**] and from a study of one dike-like intrusion [**9.31**]. The directions are approximately vertical and very uniform. Vertical directions were recorded in numerous measurements from bore core (Jaeger and Joplin, 1955; Almond, Clegg and Jaeger, 1956).

9.30 *Tasmanian Dolerites, general survey* (Irving, 1956a, 1963) Result based on 132 samples (156 specimens) from 51 sites spread over an area 150 by 250 km. Directions in dolerite boulders in a Lower Tertiary breccia were random. This evidence, and the departure from the present field, indicate stability. Two-tier analysis was used; the between-site precision is given.

9.31 *Tasmanian Dolerite, Red Hill Dike* (Stott, 1963) Result based on 37 samples (92 specimens) from 8 sites. Sites given unit weight in the analysis. *Ac* demagnetization in 750 oe did not change the mean site directions significantly. In some specimens *ac* demagnetization curves of total TRM in the Earth's field and NRM were identical. Baked contacts are parallel to the dolerite.

9.32 *Noosa Head Intrusive Complex* Upper Jurassic (Robertson, 1963) Hypabyssal intrusives of variable composition intrude Triassic and Jurassic sediments. Radiometric results (K-Ar), including concordant values from hornblende and biotite, gave 140 m.y. (Evernden and Richards, 1962) indicating an Upper Jurassic age on Kulp's 1961 Time Scale. Eight bodies were sampled; 3 gave negative directions and 1 was positive, reversed from the others; the precision improved by treatment in *ac* fields of 150–300 oe and the result given here was obtained by applying Fisher's statistics to the mean for each body $N = 4$ (10 samples, 24 specimens). Stability is indicated by the divergence from the present field and by the reversal. In the other 4 bodies the magnetization was unstable.

9.33 *Gingenbullen Dolerite* (Boesen, Irving, and Robertson, 1961) This body rests on Upper Triassic sediments. Radiometric studies indicate a Jurassic age (J. R. Richards, private communication). Eight samples (16 specimens) from 1 quarry showed smearing toward the present field. Partial demagnetization removes this, yielding the mean direction listed, whose stability is indicated by the laboratory evidence, and by the divergence from the present field. Unit weight was given to specimens in the analysis ($N = 16$).

9.34 *Kayenta Formation* Lower Jurassic, Glen Canyon Group (Collinson and Runcorn, 1960) Thirty-nine samples (146 specimens) from 4 localities gave directions which clustered about the present dipole field, with some indication of smearing. The values were obtained by combining the means for localities giving each unit weight ($N = 4$). There is no significant departure from the dipole field and the results are entered in brackets.

9.35 *Carmel Formation* Jurassic (Collinson and Runcorn, 1960) Nine samples (31 specimens) gave directions clustered round the present dipole field. The result is entered in brackets. Specimens were given unit weight in the analysis ($N = 31$).

9.36 *Serra Geral Formation* (Creer, 1958) These lavas form part of the São Bento Series, which consists of the Santa Maria (oldest), the Botucatú, and Serra Geral Formations. The lavas contain interbedded sandstones comparable to those of the Botucatú (called Tacuarembo in Uruguay). It seems to be a matter of definition as to whether the Serra Geral Formation with interbedded sediments is considered to be overlain by the Botucatú (Oliviera, 1956, p. 44), or whether the Serra Geral lavas are regarded as overlying and interbedded with the Botucatú sandstone (Bigarella and Salamuni, 1961). The Botucatú is poorly fossiliferous, but in Rio Grande do Sul it overlies the Santa Maria Formation with "its fauna of vertebrates of early Late Triassic or late Middle Triassic age" (Oliviera, 1956, pp. 42, 43). This would seem to fix a satisfactory lower limit to the age of the Serra Geral lavas. Their upper limit is set by overlying Upper Cretaceous sediments (Harrington, 1956). Almeida (op. cit.) assigns the São Bento to the "Late Triassic." Oliviera (op. cit.) states that "most, if not all, of the deposition of the Serra Geral formation may have occurred in the upper part of Triassic or maybe in the Jurassic." Paleomagnetic samples from lavas (4 sites, 12 samples, 48 specimens) and from baked Triassic Tacuarembo sandstone (4 sites, 12 samples, 81 specimens) gave positive and negative directions. The directions in the lavas were initially scattered and the precision was much improved after partial demagnetization in 250 oe; the directions in the sediments were little affected by 500 oe. The mean directions, irrespective of sign, in the lavas are 351, –42, and in the baked sandstone 356, –43. Stability is indicated by the laboratory studies and by the reversals. The agreement between baked sediments and the lavas which baked them indicates that the magnetization originated at the time the lavas cooled. See **9.53.**

9.37–42 *Results from South Victoria Land* Results were obtained from rocks of many different types and ages. The directions are uniform throughout (§ 7.8), and it is convenient to describe them together although many geological ages are represented.

9.37–38   *Ferrar Dolerites*   These intrusions outcrop extensively to the west of the Ross Sea and the Ross Ice Shelf. Individual members can be traced laterally for hundreds of kilometers. Their age is post-Beacon Group which is Triassic in its younger portions, but the lower age limit is not well defined geologically. A radioisotope age determination (K-Ar on plagioclase) from a sample in the Lower Sill of the Victoria Valley gave 162 m.y. (Evernden and Richards, 1962). Concordant ages were found for micas in granites collected from baked contacts (Evernden and Richards, see McDougall, 1963). Further K-Ar work by McDougall (1963) from samples from the Victoria Valley and Beadmore and Skelton glacier region gave ages ranging from 163 to 147 m.y., indicating a Lower or Middle Jurassic age on Kulp's 1961 Time Scale. See **9.56.**

9.37   (1)   (Turnbull, 1959)   Fifty-seven samples (? specimens) were collected from 5 sites over a distance of 30 km near the Ferrar Glacier. Stability is indicated by the divergence from the present field, and by the result that the directions in test specimens were changed by less than 3° after partial demagnetization in *ac* fields of 500 oe. In the analysis samples were given unit weight ($N = 57$).

9.38   (2)   (Bull and Irving, 1960*a* and *b*; Bull, Irving, and Willis, 1962)   Eighty-three samples (92 specimens) from 46 sites were collected from the Wright and Victoria dry valleys. The aggregate thickness of dolerite in this region is about 750 m made up of 3 thick sheets. The samples span the entire thickness. Very small viscous components aligned along the present field occur, and all specimens were magnetically cleaned in 225 oe (peak). In some specimens the directions were little changed in *ac* fields of 745 oe, and H_{cr} ranges 500–700 oe (Figure 2.15*a*). This evidence, and the divergence from the present field, indicate stability. Baked contacts, when stable, gave directions parallel to those in the dolerites, suggesting that the magnetization of the dolerite originated at the time of cooling. A two-tier statistical analysis was used, the between-site precision being quoted here. See Tables 4.8, 4.9.

9.39   *Beacon Group Sediments*   (Turnbull, 1959; Bull, Irving, and Willis, 1962)   The age of the Group lies within the limits of Devonian to Triassic. Beds of Permian and Triassic age are certainly present. Results were obtained from 5 sites whose distance from dolerite contacts range from 0–140 m. Turnbull obtained 27 observations from 3 sites in a red stratum. The mean site directions are as follows: 233, –77; 252, –67; 243, –76. Bull and others obtained results from 2 sites (4 samples, 9 specimens) with these mean directions: 232, –74; 325, –75. The directions are negative and uniform, parallel to those in the dolerites. Stability is indicated by studies of behavior in *ac* fields and by the departures from the present field. Both originals favor the view that this magnetization is a moderate-temperature VRM acquired at the time of intrusion of the dolerites when general heating of the region may have occurred. On this interpretation the directions relate to Lower Jurassic time. Because of this the results, which were obtained by applying Fisher's statistics to the above site directions giving each unit weight ($N = 5$), are entered in brackets.

9.40   *Basement Dikes*   (Bull and Irving, 1960*a*, *b*; Bull, Irving, and Willis, 1962)   Extensive dike swarms cut the Admiralty granites [**9.41**], but not the Beacon Group sediments or the Ferrar Dolerites. They are therefore Paleozoic, or Precambrian. Forty-eight samples (58 specimens) were collected from 29 dikes (1 site in each). Very small soft components parallel to the present field sometimes occur, and these were minimized in all specimens by magnetic cleaning in 225 oe (peak), but in some test specimens the directions were not systematically changed in 745 oe. H_{cr} usually exceeds 1000 oe. This evidence and the divergence from the present field indicate stability. The two-tier statistical analysis was used, the between-site precision being quoted. The mean direction and precision are indistinguishable from those observed in the Ferrar Dolerites in the same area [**9.38**]. Bull and others consider that the stable magnetization was acquired at a time of general heating during the intrusion of the Ferrar Dolerite. The results are entered in brackets because they are not considered to provide information about the Earth's field at the time of dike intrusion.

9.41   *Admiralty Granites*   (Bull, Irving, and Willis, 1962)   These are overlain by the Beacon Group and cut by the Basement Dikes [**9.40**] and the Ferrar Dolerite [**9.38**]. A radioisotope age determination (K-Ar) from a locality some distance away gave 520 m.y., which indicates an Upper Cambrian age on Kulp's 1961 Time Scale, but samples within

100 m or less of dolerite contacts gave Jurassic ages [**9.37–9.38**]. Five samples (15 specimens) from 5 sites at distances varying from 20–90 m from dolerite contacts gave directions (after magnetic cleaning in 225 oe) parallel to those in the dolerite from this region [**9.38**]. Specimens were given unit weight in the analysis ($N = 15$). Bull and others (1962) consider that the magnetization was acquired at a time of general heating during intrusion of the Ferrar Dolerites. The result is entered in brackets because it is unlikely that information is provided about the paleogeomagnetic field at the time of granite formation.

9.42 *Dolerite Intrusives* (Blundell and Stephenson, 1959) Eight samples were collected from 7 sills and dikes in the region of the Theron Mountains (about 79° S, 25° W), Shackleton Range (about 81° S, 25° W), and Whichaway Nunataks (about 82° S, 25° W) to the E and SE of the Filchner Ice Shelf. It is stated in the original that they "bear petrological affinities with the Karroo Dolerites of South Africa and with the dolerite sills of Tasmania and are thought to be of comparable age." They intrude flat-lying sediments. Three samples were negative and 5 positive. The mean, irrespective of sign, is given. Stability is indicated by the divergence from the present field and by the reversal.

JURASSIC SUPPLEMENT

9.43 *"Dark red hematite"* (Wang, Teng, Li, and Yeh, 1960) This result is based on 7 samples from the Ch'ichiang region of Szechwan, and is entered in brackets because of the very large circle of confidence ($>25°$).

9.44–45 *Sylhet Traps* (Athavale, Radakrishnamurty, and Sahasrabudhe, 1963) Age cited by Krishnan (1949) as "pre-Upper Cretaceous." Basaltic lavas and associated dikes, exposed along the southern foot of the Khasi Hills of Assam, overlie Precambrian basement, and are overlain by Cretaceous sediments. The directions from samples obtained over a distance of about 20 km fall into two groups, and the authors think that this might be due to relative tectonic rotations. Thermal and ac demagnetization were used to diminish scatter. **9.44**, 25 samples, 80 specimens. **9.45**, 11 samples, 20 specimens.

9.46–50 *Stormberg Lavas* (van Zijl, K. W. T. Graham, and Hales, 1962*a* and *b*) These papers greatly extend the preliminary report

[**9.25**] given by Hales (1960). The lavas are regarded as essentially contemporaneous with the Karroo Dolerite which has been dated radiogenically. These lavas contain an important reversal transition, which is described in § 7.6, and the values given here are of the positive and negative sequences at 2 localities below and above the transition. All specimens were magnetically cleaned. Stability is indicated by the reversal, by the laboratory demagnetization tests, and by contact studies (§ 7.8). **9.46**, 33 samples spanning 650 m stratigraphic thickness. **9.47**, 21 samples spanning 550 m. **9.48**, 13 samples spanning 200 m. **9.49**, 7 samples spanning 250 m. Samples given unit weight in the analyses ($N = 33, 21, 13$, and 7 respectively).

9.50 Means of directions (irrespective of sign) and poles ($K = 41$) in entries **9.46–49** giving each unit weight ($N = 4$).

9.51 *Karroo Lavas and Dolerites combined* In this entry the mean pole for the lavas of Southern Rhodesia, the Stormberg Lavas, and the Karroo Dolerite is given. In this calculation, unit weight is given to the poles in entries **9.25, 9.26, 9.46–49**, and to the poles for the Winkelhaak upper and lower sills ($N = 2$), and to the Estcourt positive and negative directions ($N = 2$), making a total $N = 10$ and $K = 36$.

9.52 *Kimmeridgian Sediments, Neuquen* (Creer, 1962*d*) Age stated to be Cretaceous which is inconsistent with the name, which is that of a Jurassic stage. Seven samples (about 45 specimens) each given unit weight in the analysis ($N = 7$). Creer states that these samples "are likely to have been remagnetized in recent geological time" and so the results are bracketed.

9.53 *Serra Geral Formation* (2) (Creer, 1962*c*) Results, which greatly extend those reported earlier [**9.36**], were obtained from 30 sites (about 80 samples and about 250 specimens) in dikes, sills and flows over a wide area (21–31° S, 47–59° W). All specimens were magnetically cleaned. The site polarities are as follows: intrusives, 10 negative and 7 positive; flows, 5 negative and 8 positive. In the analysis unit weight is given to sites and the pole is the average of site poles ($N = 30, K = 23$).

9.54 *Upper Jurassic Volcanic Group* (Blundell, 1962) The directions in 43 samples (64 specimens) from 12 sites in Graham Land and the South Shetland Islands were scattered;

the scatter was not diminished by *ac* demagnetization.

9.55 *Dikes* (Blundell, 1962) Samples (18 samples, 34 specimens) of dike rocks of presumed Jurassic age from 5 sites in Graham Land gave highly scattered results; *ac* demagnetization did not diminish scatter.

9.56 *Ferrar Dolerite* (3) (Briden and Oliver, 1963) Result based on 13 samples (26 specimens) from 9 sites in the Beardmore Glacier region. All specimens were magnetically cleaned in 150 oe. H_{cr} varies in the range 250 to 600 oe. Unit weight given to each site in the analysis ($N = 9$).

CRETACEOUS (134–63 M.Y.)

10.01–10.04 *Wealden Sediments of England* The only results available from the Cretaceous of Europe are from 2 localities in the Wealden beds of England. These are fresh water sediments of Lower Cretaceous age.

10.01 *Wealden Sediments, Isle of Wight* (Wilson, 1959) Forty-six samples were collected from Dorset and the Isle of Wight. "Apparent magnetic stability was found in only nineteen of these samples"—all 19 coming from the Isle of Wight. Ninety-seven specimen measurements were made on these 19 samples. The beds have a variable dip, the angular standard deviation of the sample means with respect to bedding being 9°, and with respect to the horizontal 5°. The mean with respect to the horizontal plane is listed. Samples were given unit weight in the analysis ($N = 19$). The mean appears to depart significantly from the present and dipole field directions; this may be a real effect but it is possible that the precision is artificially high due to the selection of data. Partial demagnetization in *ac* fields, and remeasurement after storage in the Earth's field, indicate the presence of both soft and relatively hard components. It is stated that the decrease in precision after correction for the variable dip "indicates instability of the harder component." The result is therefore entered in brackets.

10.02–04 *Wealden "Iron grit"* (Nairn, 1960*a*) A stratigraphical thickness of "a few inches" was sampled (21 samples, 52 specimens) in the Sussex Weald. Antiparallel directions occur within this thin band (35 specimens negative and 17 positive). It is not stated whether a reversal occurs at a discrete level or whether the negative and positive directions are randomly mixed. The presence of the reversal indicates stability.

10.04 *Combined* The mean of the directions, listed in **10.02, 10.03,** and a pole calculated from this are given.

10.05–06 *Cretaceous Sediments, Turkmenia* (Khramov, 1958) Twelve samples from several levels in the Great and Small Balkhan range in age from Lower to Upper Cretaceous. The sites are spread over a distance of about 100 km. The presence of reversals, the divergences from the present field, and a bedding tilt test indicate stability. **10.05,** Great Balkhan. **10.06,** Small and Great Balkhan.

10.07 *Inkstone Series* Lower to Middle Cretaceous (Nagata, Akimoto, Shimizu, Kobayashi, and Kuno, 1959) About 20 red shale samples were collected at each of 3 sites in Yamaguchi Prefecture. The large departure of the site means from the present field indicates stability. The between-site dispersion is large compared to that within-sites. The locality coordinates given are for Yamaguchi Prefecture and the pole was calculated relative to this from the mean given in the original.

10.08 *Lavas and Dikes* Upper Cretaceous (Roche, Cattala, and Boulanger, 1958; Roche and Cattala, 1959) Age cited as Turonian. This pole, given by Roche and Cattala, is based on observations from 10 sites spread over a distance of about 1000 km. Partial thermal demagnetization experiments indicated stability.

10.09 *Cygnet Alkaline Complex* Late Lower Cretaceous (Robertson and Hastie, 1962) This complex, which outcrops in SE Tasmania, is intrusive into Permian sediments and Tasmanian Dolerite [**9.30**]. Radioisotope (K-Ar) age determinations including concordant ages for sanidine, biotite, and hornblende, gave an average of 104 m.y. (Evernden and Richards, 1962), which is Cenomanian on Kulp's 1961 Time Scale. This result is based on 45 samples (86 specimens) from 15 sites. All specimens were magnetically cleaned in 75 oe (peak). The divergence from the present field indicates stability. The exact agreement, within the errors, between dolerite hybrid rocks, baked sediments, and the intrusions, indicates that the magnetization was acquired at the time of intrusion. The two-tier statistical analysis was used, the between-site precision being quoted here.

10.10 *Mt. Dromedary Igneous Complex* Late Lower Cretaceous (Robertson, 1963) K-Ar age determinations on biotite, hornblende, and pyroxene gave results with a small scatter and a mean of 93 m.y. (Evernden and Richards, 1962) or Cenomanian on Kulp's 1961 Time Scale. At 22 sites ($\simeq$55 samples, $\simeq$180 specimens) in intrusives, lavas, and baked contact rocks, the directions were initially somewhat scattered. After partial demagnetization in either *ac* fields ($\simeq$200 oe) or by heat ($\simeq$400°C) the precision was improved. Magnetic and thermal cleaning was carried out on duplicate specimens from the same samples and a comparison of the 2 procedures suggests that the former is the more efficient as a cleaning method for this material. At one site the directions were positive (§ 7.4). The parallel directions in baked contacts, the divergence from the present field, and the demagnetization studies indicate stability. In the analysis sites were given unit weight ($N = 22$) the mean given in this entry being that derived from magnetically cleaned specimens. The mean for thermally cleaned specimens is 13, –82; $a_{95} = 8°$. See Figures 2.20, 2.22.

10.11 *Igneous Intrusions of the Monteregian Hills* (Larochelle, 1961, 1962) Radioisotope ages (K-Ar) from 3 intrusions (also studied magnetically) gave approximately concordant values from pyroxene and biotite with an average of 111 m.y. This is near the Albian-Cenomanian boundary on Kulp's 1961 Time Scale. Forty-nine samples were collected for magnetic work from 8 intrusive plugs. Ten samples were negative and 39 positive. The means for the polarity groups are given and a combined pole. Magnetic cleaning was used to decrease dispersion. Stability is indicated by the reversal, by demagnetization studies, and by the divergence from the present field.

10.12 *Mt. Megantic* (Larochelle, 1961) Radioisotope ages (K-Ar on biotite) gave 115 m.y., which is Albian on Kulp's 1961 Time Scale. This magnetic result is based on 12 samples from a single intrusion. All specimens were magnetically cleaned in 250 oe. Stability is indicated by the demagnetization studies and by the departure from the present field.

10.13 *Dakota Sandstone* Cretaceous (Runcorn, 1956a) Six samples were collected at Show Low, Arizona, over a lateral spread of about 1 km, and of these 3 were discarded on

grounds of instability. The remaining samples (10 specimens) were positive and the large departure of the mean from the present field is indicative of stability. The values entered are based on these 10 specimen measurements giving each unit weight ($N = 10$). The sampling is considered inadequate and the result is entered in brackets.

CRETACEOUS SUPPLEMENT

10.14 *Volcanics, Georgia* Cretaceous (Vekua, 1961) Ten samples (described as "albitophyric tuffaceous dacites") from Sarkineti gave rather scattered directions. Their mean does not differ significantly from the present or geocentric dipole fields, and no stability tests are reported, so the result is entered in brackets.

10.15 *Lupata Alkaline Volcanics* (Gough and Opdyke, 1963) Age limits, early Jurassic to uppermost Cretaceous. Cores (61) were drilled from 7 sites spanning a thickness >750 m and spread over a distance of 28 km. The within-site precision of NRM is variable, and the wide scatter found at 4 sites is attributed to lightning. After treatment in *ac* fields of between 100 and 500 oe the precision, both within and between sites, becomes very good, and the latter is still further improved (from $k = 162$ to $k = 339$) by correction for the small amount of tilt (up to 10°) which these volcanics are thought to have undergone since formation. The mean direction was obtained from magnetically cleaned samples giving unit weight to each site ($N = 7$); the detailed *ac* demagnetization studies demonstrate the high stability of this magnetization direction. The pole is calculated as a mean of site poles giving each unit weight ($N = 7$).

10.16 *Red Siltstone* (Gough and Opdyke, 1963) The NRM directions at a site (5 samples) in "a succession correlated with the Lupata Series" were highly scattered ($k = 8$), but after demagnetization in *ac* fields of 100 oe became well grouped and their mean is given here.

10.17 *Isachsen Diabase* (Larochelle and Black, 1963) These rocks intrude and cover Lower Cretaceous sediments and have not been observed to intrude Tertiary beds; the probable age is considered to be Lower or Upper Cretaceous. But K-Ar ages on whole rock samples give 241–249 m.y., or Permian on the Kulp 1961 Time Scale, which is inconsistent with the geological evidence. Twenty samples (40 specimens) from 10 sites on Ellef Ringnes Island gave this result after magnetic cleaning in 300 oe. The sites cover an area of about 20 km². The laboratory studies indicate the stability of the magnetization.

10.18 *Granitic Plutons, Sierra Nevada* (Currie, Grommé, and Verhoogen, 1963) Of a collection from 20 sites of about 180 cored samples (about 300 specimens) over one half were rejected because of wide scatter and instability. This result is based on 9 sites (76 samples, 133 specimens) in 3 plutons, for which K-Ar age determinations (Evernden, Curtis, and Lipson, 1957) fall in the range 79–89 m.y. or Upper Cretaceous on Kulp's 1961 Time Scale. Thermal and *ac* demagnetization studies were undertaken, and, in some cases, *ac* demagnetization was used to diminish scatter. The systematic divergence from the present field and the laboratory studies suggest stability.

10.19 *Huitrinian Sediments, Neuquen* Upper Cretaceous (Creer, 1962*d*) Result based on 13 samples (about 90 specimens). Samples given unit weight in the analysis ($N = 13$). Creer states that these samples "are likely to have been remagnetized in recent geological time" and so the results are bracketed.

TERTIARY (63–1 M.Y.)

11.001 *Gergovie Intrusives* Oligocene (Roche, 1950*a*, 1953) The directions in 9 igneous bodies were positive. Calcareous marl baked by one of the dikes gave positive directions in good agreement with the dike itself (Figure 7.23). The divergence from the present field and the contact evidence indicates stability. In the analysis unit weight was given to each body ($N = 9$).

11.002 *Limagne Basalt* (Roche, 1950*b*) Age cited as Aquitanian (Lower Miocene). The positive direction indicates stability.

11.003–005 *Upper Miocene Lavas* (Roche, 1960) Five flows were studied, 3 [**11.003**] from Cantal yield negative directions, and 2 [**11.004**] from the Limagne were positive. This is a very good instance of a 180° opposition of directions. Specimens from one of the Limagne flows were thermally cleaned (300°C). The presence of reversals, and the divergences from the present field indicate stability.

11.005 *Combined* This mean direction was calculated irrespective of sign giving equal weight to each flow ($N = 5$). The pole was calculated from this mean direction.

11.006 *Lavas of Mt. Dore and the Limagne* (Roche, 1951) These lavas are of Miocene and Pliocene age, the oldest flows are cited as Pontian, the 2 youngest as Plaisancian. The direction in 5 flows (about 40 samples) are positive, indicative of stability. Each flow was given unit weight in the analysis ($N = 5$).

11.007 *Bonn Intrusives* (Nairn, 1960*a*) Age cited as Oligocene-Miocene. Positive directions, indicative of stability, were observed in 18 samples (48 specimens). Several observations (5 samples) gave directions close to the present field and were excluded in the analysis.

11.008–010 *Vogelsberg Intrusions and Lavas* Tertiary (Nairn, 1960*a*) Nine samples (29 specimens) gave negative directions [**11.008**]. Sixteen (43 specimens) gave positive directions [**11.009**].

11.010 *Combined* The mean of the directions in **11.008, 009** ($N = 2$) is given and the pole calculated from this. The presence of reversals indicates stability.

11.011 *Vogelsberg Basalt* (Angenheister, 1956) Age cited as Miocene. Directions observed in over 200 samples from 42 flows group themselves into negative and positive sets, the mean directions of which (8, +57; $a_{95} = 8°$ and 188, −60; $a_{95} = 15°$) are, within their errors, 180° apart. This is a very good example of opposed polarities. The mean direction irrespective of sign is quoted, flows being given unit weight in the analysis ($N = 42$). The exact reversal and the divergences from the present field indicate stability.

11.012–026 *Tertiary Igneous Rocks British Isles* Extensive work was carried out on the Tertiary igneous rocks of western Scotland, Northern Ireland and northern England. They form part of the North Atlantic (or Thulean) Tertiary igneous province. They are regarded as of Lower Tertiary age by the Geological Survey (Richey (1948), British Regional Geology, Scotland: The Tertiary Volcanic Districts, p. 4) and they are assumed to be of this age herein.

11.012 *Skye Lavas and Intrusives* (Khan, 1960) The samples studied span a stratigraphic thickness of the order 1000 m. This result is based on observations from 174 samples (488 specimens) from 53 igneous units, unit weight being given to each igneous unit in the analysis (Figure 4.2*a*). Studies of *ac* and thermal demagnetization provide evidence for stability. These tests, and the divergence from the present field, indicate stability. A number of other specimens were magnetically unstable (about 20 per cent), and yet others had apparently been remagnetized by lightning strokes (about 10 per cent), and were not used in the analysis.

11.013 *Ardamurchan Hypersthene Gabbro* (Khan, 1960) Samples were obtained at 3 localities about 5 km apart. About 40 per cent of the samples were thought to have been struck by lightning and were not used in the analysis. This result is based on 15 samples (41 specimens) all showing positive directions strongly divergent from the present field direction. Demagnetization of selected specimens thermally and in *ac* fields indicated stability.

11.014 *Rum Layered Gabbro* (Khan, 1960) This result is based on 8 samples (27 specimens) obtained from 4 beds in a section 500 m thick. The directions were all positive and strongly divergent from the present field. Studies of thermal and *ac* field demagnetization on selected specimens indicated stability. A further 11 specimens were considered to have been remagnetized by lightning strokes.

11.015 *Mull Lavas* (Bruckshaw and Vincenz, 1954) About 7 samples were taken from each of 16 flows at 3 sites with a maximum separation of about 16 km. Only 8 of the flows (53 samples) had stable magnetizations and these "good" flows have the mean direction given here.

11.016 *Mull Intrusives* (Vincenz, 1954) Collections were made from 12 intrusive bodies but most of the specimens were magnetically unstable. The directions in an olivine gabbro, a granophyre, and 3 felsite dikes showed good internal agreement and the average of the means for these ($N = 5$), irrespective of sign, is given. One of the bodies showed positive polarization, the remainder being negative. This result is based on 50 samples.

11.017 *Arran Dikes and Contacts* (Leng, 1955) Seven dikes and their contacts with Triassic sandstones were studied. They are spread over a distance of about 4 km in the south of the Isle of Arran. In 4 cases the dikes have scattered directions and low stability but the contacts are stable. In 3 dikes both contacts and igneous rock are stable, the directions in contact rock being the same as

in the igneous rock which baked it. Five sets of contacts and dikes (where stable) are positive, and 2 sets of contacts and their dike rocks are negative. The values given were obtained by averaging the mean directions, irrespective of sign, for each dike and contact envelope (4), or each contact envelope (3), where the dike rock is unstable ($N = 7$). This result is based on 77 samples.

11.018–024 *Antrim Igneous Suite* The sampling sites cover a distance of about 100 km. The divergence of the directions from the present field, thermal demagnetization, and baked contact studies indicate stability. Studies (Wilson, 1961, 1962*a*) of baked rocks gave these results: (1) the directions in a sill, a dike, and in Triassic sandstones, all baked by a Tertiary intrusion (Scrabo Hill) are parallel to those observed in the intrusion itself; (2) the directions in a Jurassic limestone (Portrush) baked by Tertiary dolerite are parallel to those in the dolerite; (3) Tertiary laterites baked by an overlying Tertiary lava contain a high temperature component with directions parallel to those in the lava itself. In addition to the results listed below Wilson (1963) has recently recorded stable positive directions from rhyolites in this Suite.

11.018–019 *Antrim Lower Basalts*

11.018 (1) Hospers and Charlesworth (1954) Twenty-four flows (72 samples) were sampled at 4 localities spread over a distance of about 50 km. In the analysis unit weight was given to each flow ($N = 24$).

11.019 (2) Wilson (1959) Samples were obtained from 19 flows (35 samples). In the analysis unit weight was given to each flow ($N = 19$).

11.020 *Combined* The mean of the directions in **11.018** and **11.019** is given and the pole is calculated from this.

11.021 *Antrim Upper Basalts* (Wilson, 1959, 1961) Seven samples were obtained from 6 flows. This result was calculated giving unit weight to each flow ($N = 6$). Wilson (1959) calls these "Middle" Basalts, but later (1961) refers to them as "Upper" Basalts, which is the term used here.

11.022 *Antrim Intrusives* (Wilson, 1959) Twenty-five samples were collected from 16 dikes and sills. This result was calculated giving unit weight to each igneous body ($N = 16$).

11.023 *Antrim Nonigneous Rocks* (Wilson, 1961) The result is based on an average of 24 sample observations from lateritized flows. The lateritization occurred between eruptions. Unit weight was given to each sample ($N = 24$).

11.024 *Antrim Igneous Suite combined* (Wilson, 1961) Summary of data from the Antrim Igneous Suite and lateritized lavas. Unit weight was given to each igneous unit (65), and to each sample (24) of lateritized lava ($N = 89$).

11.025 *Northwest Dikes of Northern England* (Bruckshaw and Robertson, 1949) Samples were collected from 7 sites in 4 dikes spread over a distance of about 200 km. This result was calculated, giving unit weight to each site ($N = 7$).

11.026 *Tertiary Igneous Rocks of the British Isles combined* The directions were calculated as a mean, irrespective of sign, of the directions **11.012–017, 11.020–023** and **11.025** giving each unit weight ($N = 11$). The pole is calculated as a mean of the poles in these entries.

11.027 *Lundy Dikes* (Blundell, 1957) These dikes intrude the Lundy Granite, which has been dated radiogenically as 50–55 m.y. (Miller and Fitch, 1962) or Eocene on Kulp's 1961 Time Scale. The upper age limit is not known. Samples were collected from 13 dikes and in some cases from their contact rocks, but the rocks from only 5 dikes and 3 contact rocks were found to be magnetically stable. This result was obtained by giving unit weight to the mean values from 5 dikes and 3 contact zones ($N = 8$).

11.028 *Georgian Igneous Rocks* Upper Pliocene (Vekua quoted by Kalashnikov, 1961) Twenty-five samples gave this pole.

11.029–032 *Georgian Pliocene Igneous Rocks* (Vekua, 1961) Results of mixed polarity are available from the 3 groups listed. The number of samples (? specimens) and localities are as follows: **11.029** Andesiti, 26 samples; **11.030** Mleti, 13 samples; **11.031** Andesiti, 4 samples. Stability is indicated by the occurrence of reversals.

11.032 *Combined* The average, irrespective of sign, of the directions in entries **11.029–031** giving unit weight to each is listed ($N = 3$). The pole is calculated from this mean direction.

11.033–040 *Armenian Eocene Igneous Rocks* Results of Akopyan given by Kalashnikov (1961) are listed here. Yanovsky and others (1963) now say that these have not

been confirmed by Akopyan and so the results are bracketed. In several cases the coordinates of the sampling area given in Kalashnikov (1961) are not consistent with their being in Armenia. In several cases the poles given in this reference are inconsistent with the directions and localities stated. For these reasons directions only, and not poles, are listed.

11.040 *Combined* The mean, irrespective of sign, of the directions in entries **11.033–039**, is given, each result being given unit weight ($N = 7$). A pole is calculated from this mean direction assuming the location to be a central point in Armenia (40° N, 45° E).

11.041 *Armenian Pliocene Lava Flows* (Pospelova, 1959) Result based on 30 samples. The mean direction diverges substantially from both the present and geocentric axial dipole fields indicating stability. Various laboratory experiments (Pospelova, 1960) also indicate stability.

11.042 *Armenian Andesites* Pliocene (Akopyan quoted by Kalashnikov, 1961) The presence of mixed polarity indicates stability. The locality coordinates in the reference cited are not consistent with the position of Armenia; the coordinates given here are for a central place in Armenia and are approximately consistent with the pole cited.

11.043 *Red-colored Sequence* (Khramov, 1958) Age cited as Middle Pliocene. Samples were collected from sequences 360 m and 570 m thick from the Small Balkhan (39.5° N, 55° E) and the Cheleken peninsula (39.5° N, 53° E) respectively. The directions from the Small Balkhan occur in positive and negative groups, and on the Cheleken 4 zones of alternating polarity may be recognized. The mean direction, irrespective of sign, for the whole sequence was computed as an average of 246 sample directions, giving each unit weight ($N = 246$). Stability is indicated by the divergence from the present field and the occurrence of reversals.

11.044–045 *Turkmenian Lower Tertiary Sediments*

11.044 (1) Paleocene to Lower Oligocene (Khramov, 1958) Samples were collected from sequences 400 m and 570 m thick from the Great Balkhan (39.5° N, 54.5° E) and Small Balkhan (39.5° N, 55° E) respectively. Directions corrected for instability by rotating directions along great circles away from the present field. This over-all mean was computed, irrespective of sign, as an average of 26 corrected sample directions giving each unit weight ($N = 26$).

11.045 (2) Oligocene sandstones and clays (Gus'kova, 1959) The reversals and the divergence from the present field indicate stability.

11.046 *North Ferghana Sediments* (Valiev, 1960) Age cited as Oligocene (?) and Miocene. Samples of red silts and clays were collected from the Sumsar River section of the Chutspap anticline.

11.047–051 *North Ferghana Pliocene Sediments* (Valiev, 1960) Results from brown silts and clays at 4 localities in the Chutspap anticline. Stability is indicated by the presence of reversals, and the divergence from the present field. **11.047** (1) Samples from the Sumsar River section; age cited as Middle Pliocene. **11.048** (2) Samples from the Marguzar section; age cited as Middle Pliocene. **11.049** (3) Samples from the Marguzar section; age cited as Upper Pliocene. **11.050** (4) Samples from the Sumsar River section; age cited as Upper Pliocene.

11.051 *Combined* This direction is the mean of those in **11.047–050** giving each unit weight ($N = 4$). The pole is calculated from this mean direction.

11.052 *Khabarovsk Basalts* (Kochegura quoted in Kalashnikov, 1961; Yanovsky and others, 1963) Age cited as Neogene. Result based on 110 samples (specimens?).

11.053 *Primore Oligocene Basalts* (Kochegura quoted in Kalashnikov, 1961) The presence of reversals and the departure from the present field indicate stability. Result based on 19 samples (? specimens).

11.054 *Primore Neogene Basalts* (Kochegura quoted in Kalashnikov, 1961) Result based on 280 samples (? specimens). The presence of reversals indicates stability.

11.055 *Sakhalin Basalts* Pliocene (Kochegura quoted in Kalashnikov, 1961) Result based on 102 samples (? specimens). The presence of reversals indicates stability.

11.056–058 *Kamchatka Sediments and Basalts* (Khramov quoted in Kalashnikov, 1961; Yanovsky and others, 1963) Age cited as Neogene. It is stated that stability is determined by the study of "pebbles," presumably cobbles in a conglomerate. Results are available from sediments (**11.056** based on 11 samples (? specimens)) and basalts (**11.057** based on 36 samples (? specimens)). Stability

is indicated by the agreement between the mean result from sediment and basalt.

11.058 *Combined* The direction is the mean of **11.056** and **11.057**. The pole was calculated from this mean.

11.059 *Kamchatka Andesite-basalts* (Kochegura quoted in Kalashnikov, 1961) Age is cited as Middle Pliocene. This result is based on 64 samples (? specimens). The presence of reversals indicates stability.

11.060–061 *Cenozoic Rocks from Japan* (Kawai, Ito, and Kume, 1961) The age is cited as Tertiary and Quaternary. Samples were collected from 13 localities which are grouped regionally—8 from SW Japan and 5 from NE Japan. The dividing line cuts NW from Tokyo to the Sea of Japan through the *fossa magna* (Figure 10.5). The means for each group were calculated giving unit weight to each locality ($N = 8$ and $N = 5$ respectively). Stability is indicated by the presence of reversals.

11.060 *Cenozoic Rocks of SW Japan* Result based on 182 samples collected from 8 localities (2 basalts, 1 tuff, and 5 andesites). Two localities had positive directions and 6 were negative. The pole is calculated relative to a central point in SW Japan (35° N, 134° E).

11.061 *Cenozoic Rocks of NE Japan* Seventy-one samples were collected from 5 localities (3 andesites, 1 basalt, 1 porphyrite). The pole is calculated relative to a central point in NE Japan (37° N, 140° E).

11.062 *Late Tertiary Volcanics* (Kumagai, Kawai, and Nagata, 1950) This result is based on sampling of 7 lava flows giving unit weight to each flow ($N = 7$). One flow showed positive directions and the remainder were negative. Results from 1 further flow were discarded because of instability (Kawai, 1954). The occurrence of reversals indicates stability.

11.063 *Lavas and Tuffs of the Kinki District* (Kawai, 1951) Detailed sampling of the Osaka Sedimentary Group and the Setouti Volcanic Zone was carried out. The age of both groups is cited as Upper Neogene and Recent. The Azuki Tuff, in the upper part of the Osaka Sedimentary Group, is positively polarized, as are lavas of comparable age in the Setouti Volcanic Zone. Samples from other parts of the sections gave negative directions. No numerical values are available.

11.064–066 *Miocene Igneous Rocks* (Nagata, Akimoto, Shimizu, Kobayashi, and Kuno, 1959) Seven igneous units were studied. Stability is indicated by the occurrence of reversals and by the divergence from the present field direction. "Unstably magnetized rock-samples" were rejected on the basis of certain mineralogical criteria.

11.064 (1) Middle and Upper Miocene. Thirty-two samples were studied from 2 andesite lavas, an andesite sheet, and a dolerite sheet. The flows have positive polarization whereas the sheets are negative. In the analysis sample directions were given unit weight ($N = 32$).

11.065 (2) Lower Miocene. Twenty samples were collected from 2 andesite flows and a dolerite sheet. Two units have negative polarization and 1 is positive. Samples were given unit weight in the analysis ($N = 20$).

11.066 *Combined* The mean pole obtained as an average of 7 poles calculated for each igneous unit is given ($N = 7$, $K = 8$).

11.067–069 *Pliocene Lavas* (Nagata, Akimoto, Shimizu, Kobayashi, and Kuno, 1959) Four igneous units were studied. The directions are close to the present field although the inclinations are often somewhat less. "Unstably magnetized rock-samples" were rejected on the basis of certain mineralogical criteria, and those samples used for analysis were presumed to be stable.

11.067 (1) Twelve samples were obtained from 2 Upper Pliocene basalt flows. Samples were used as units in the analysis ($N = 12$).

11.068 (2) Two andesite lavas of Lower Pliocene age were sampled at 3 sites. In the analysis samples were used as units ($N = 10$).

11.069 *Combined* This pole was calculated as an average of poles calculated for each flow ($N = 4$, $K = 82$).

11.070 *Komoro and Shigarami Volcanic Groups* (Momose, 1958) These groups are approximately of the same age, each covering much of the Pliocene in time. They occur in central Japan. Results are available from basalts, andesites, porphyrites, and welded tuffs from 9 levels in the Komoro group, and 10 in the Shigarami group. South paleomagnetic poles calculated for the oldest levels were near the present north geographic pole, but in the younger levels they moved southwards through Africa to the vicinity of the present south geographic pole; the transition occupied much of Pliocene time. Studies of test specimens showed that the ratio of the intensity of NRM to TRM acquired in the present field ranged between 2.0 and 0.5, and demagnetization in *ac*

fields of 400 oe resulted in a 30 per cent loss of intensity. Hibberd (1961) suggests that the transition is only apparent and is really due to the presence of secondary components of variable magnitude imposed by the present field. He suggests "that in the Lower-Middle Pliocene the pole was near 70° N, 150° W, and that the polarity in the Lower Pliocene was normal and in the Middle Pliocene was reversed." On Hibberd's view the reversal is rapid and is not directly recorded in Momose's data. A new account of studies of these groups has been given recently by Momose (1963).

11.071–077 *Enrei Formation.* Upper Pliocene (Momose, Kobayashi, and Yamada, 1959) Results based on studies of a thick sequence of lava flows in central Japan which are interbedded with tuff-breccias, conglomerates and "mud beds." They are horizontal or gently dipping for the most part. The beds are considered to span much of the Upper Pliocene. Results from 6 groups are listed in entries **11.071–076**. Smearing toward the present field occurs, suggestive of the presence of components imposed by the present field. The *ac* demagnetization curves of intensity are variable in form, some showing an initial increase consistent with such secondary components superposed on a stable positive component. But there is no general magnetic cleaning of all specimens. The large divergences from the present field however indicate the general stability of the directions, but since all are positive there may be some systematic effect due to secondary components imposed by the present field. In order to compensate for this the following procedure is followed in this analysis: the majority of the directions (75 per cent) show a fair grouping around a direction approximately antiparallel to the present field and which, it must be presumed, is little affected by components imposed by the present field. In addition there are scattered directions (about 25 per cent) with positive inclination causing the smearing in individual groups; such directions are not included in the following analyses. A new account of studies of this formation has been given recently by Momose (1963).

11.071 *Enrei Formation (1), Wada-toga Pass* Nineteen samples of andesite, obsidian, and liparite were collected from 7 localities. Ten directions are listed and of these 3 showed positive inclinations; the remainder were averaged giving each unit weight ($N = 7$).

11.072 *Enrei Formation (2), Kawagishi Andesite* Nineteen samples were collected from 6 localities. In the analysis unit weight was given to the mean for each locality ($N = 6$).

11.073 *Enrei Formation (3), Suwa Kankodoro Group* About 33 samples were collected from 7 localities. Two localities (SuI, SuV) gave positive inclinations divergent from the remainder; the statistics were calculated giving unit weight to each remaining locality ($N = 5$).

11.074 *Enrei Formation (4), Fukuzawayama Group* About 30 andesite samples were collected from 6 localities. One locality (Fu IV) gave a positive inclination divergent from the main group; the statistics were calculated giving unit weight to the mean for each of the other localities ($N = 5$).

11.075 *Enrei Formation (5), Mt. Mitsumine Andesite* Six samples from 1 locality gave well-grouped results with this mean direction. Results from 1 other locality (Mu III) have positive inclinations.

11.076 *Enrei Formation (6), Utsukushi-gahara Lavas* Nine samples from 3 localities gave well-grouped directions. The means for these localities were averaged giving unit weight to each ($N = 3$). Results from 2 other localities (UtII, UtIII) gave positive inclinations inconsistent with these and with each other.

11.077 *Combined* These values were obtained by applying Fisher's statistics to those locality directions with upward inclination. Unit weight was given to each locality ($N = 27$). Nine results detailed above were not used. A pole was calculated from the mean direction, Lake Suwa (36° N, 138° E) being the locality assumed.

11.078 *Takaosan Andesite* (Momose, Kobayashi, and Yamada, 1959) This is a volcanic neck whose age is cited as latest Pliocene by Momose (1958). Seventeen samples from 3 localities gave well-grouped directions. Stability is suggested by the slow decrease in intensity in increasing *ac* fields. The mean direction judged by eye from Figure 7 (Momose and others, 1959) is given.

11.079–091 *Deccan Traps* The age of the Deccan Traps is considered to be Upper Cretaceous or Eocene. Their total thickness is about 1800 m. Sampling was carried out at several localities, mostly in the Western Ghats. The relative ages of these localities are not clearly defined. Stability is indicated by the divergences from the present field. Measurements of susceptibility anisotropy have been made (Girdler, 1961b); see § 2.14.

11.079 *Deccan Traps* Reconnaissance survey (Irving, 1954, 1956b) In this first survey 1 sample (2 specimens) was collected from each of 7 sites at different levels over a distance of about 300 km in the Western Ghats. The directions at 5 sites showed positive polarity, the remainder being negative. These results were calculated, irrespective of sign, giving unit weight to the means from each site ($N = 7$).

11.080 *Deccan Traps, Linga Area* (Clegg, Deutsch, and Griffiths, 1956) Samples were obtained from 9 sites over a distance of about 5 km in 4 flows near the base of the Deccan Trap sequence in the Linga area of the Central Provinces. Observations were made on about 70 samples (195 specimens). This result was obtained by giving unit weight to each specimen observation ($N = 195$).

11.081 *Deccan Traps, Khandala Area* (Clegg, Deutsch, and Griffiths, 1956) Result based on 139 samples (233 specimens) from 20 collecting sites in "numerous" flows from the Khandala area of Bombay Province. Specimens were given unit weight in the analysis ($N = 233$). Results from about 40 anomalous specimen observations were not used.

11.082 *Deccan Traps, Kambatki Ghat* (Deutsch, Radakrishnamurty, and Sahasrabudhe, 1958, 1959) Of the 2 flows studied, only 1 was magnetically stable and 5 samples from this gave this mean result ($N = 5$).

11.083 *Deccan Traps, Igatpuri Ghat* (Deutsch, Radakrishnamurty, and Sahasrabudhe, 1958, 1959) Four samples were taken from each of 4 flows. The samples from 1 flow were unstable and the mean direction for the remainder is given.

11.084–085 *Deccan Traps, Nipani Area* (Deutsch, Radakrishnamurty, and Sahasrabudhe, 1958, 1959) The results relate to a single lower flow from which 44 specimens were obtained at 2 sites, and 3 upper flows from which 74 specimens were obtained at 5 sites. In the analysis specimens were given unit weight.

11.086–087 *Deccan Traps, Amba Ghat* (Deutsch, Radakrishnamurty, and Sahasrabudhe, 1958, 1959) At least 5 flows were sampled at 8 sites. The 5 lowest sites, from which 109 specimens were studied, show positive polarization. Several specimens with widely divergent directions were not used in the analysis. The 3 upper sites (54 specimens) have negative polarization. In both cases specimen observations were given unit weight.

11.088 *Deccan Traps, Mt. Pavagadh* (Deutsch, Radakrishnamurty, and Sahasrabudhe, 1958, 1959) Eight flows, below an elevation of 735 m, were sampled (14 samples, 69 specimens). Each specimen observation was given unit weight in the analysis ($N = 69$).

11.089–091 *Deccan Traps combined* Uniform negative polarizations occur only at 1 locality [**11.088**], and at 2 others [**11.084–5** and **11.086–7**] they occur only in the upper levels. Uniform positive polarizations occur at 4 localities, 1 of which [**11.080**] is near the base of the sequence. At 2 other localities [**11.084–085** and **11.086–087**] they occur only in the lower parts of the sections studied. The reversal of magnetization is not exact, the positive inclinations ranging from $+50$ to $+60$, and the negative inclinations from -16 to -32. Where superposition can be demonstrated, beds with negative polarizations always overlie positive beds, suggesting that there is an upper negative level overlying a positive level. The imperfection in the reversal could be due (*a*) to a time variation in the Earth's field between these levels, or (*b*) to a secondary component, or (*c*) to stress during burial. Burial has never been great, and the low anisotropy (§ 2.14) suggests that stress effects are probably negligible (Girdler, 1961). No magnetic cleaning has yet been carried out to check on possibility (*b*).

11.089 *Negative Directions combined* The directions in **11.084, 086,** and **088** were combined without correction for differences in locality and giving unit weight to each entry ($N = 3$). The pole is the average of poles for these entries giving each unit weight ($N = 3$, $K = 78$). These calculations were carried out on the assumption that explanation (*a*) above is correct.

11.090 *Positive Directions combined* The directions in **11.080–083, 085,** and **087** were combined without correction for the spread in localities and giving each entry unit weight ($N = 6$). The pole given is the average of poles for these entries giving each unit weight ($N = 6$, $K = 61$). These calculations were carried out on the assumption that explanation (*a*) above is correct.

11.091 *Over-all combination* The directions in **11.080–088** were combined without correction for the spread in localities and giving each entry unit weight ($N = 9$). The pole is the average of the poles in these entries, each given unit weight ($N = 9$, $K = 28$). These calculations were carried out on the assumption that explanation (*b*) is correct.

11.092 *Mt. Pavagadh Acid Tuffs* (Deutsch, Radakrishnamurty, and Sahasrabudhe, 1959) These beds overlie the Deccan Traps proper and could be as young as Miocene. The tuffs were sampled at 2 sites (8 samples, 15 specimens) at an elevation of more than 755 m. The polarizations are all negative. This result was calculated giving each specimen unit weight ($N = 15$). Stability is indicated by the divergences from the present and geocentric axial dipole fields. Specimens from rhyolite flows associated with the tuffs gave random directions, and laboratory tests indicate that they were unstable.

11.093–095 *Tertiary Basalts of Australia* See also **11.124**.

11.093 *Older Volcanics of Victoria* (Irving and Green, 1957*a* and *b*; Green and Irving, 1958) These basalts are Lower Tertiary probably Eocene in age. Three samples (3 specimens) were collected from each of 15 sites, spread over an area of 65 by 130 km. Four sites have positive polarization, 9 are negative, and 2 have mixed polarity (see § 7.7). The calculations were carried out using the two-tier analysis the precision being the between-site precision. Stability is indicated by the presence of reversals. See **11.124**.

11.094 *Tertiary Basalts of New South Wales* (Green and Irving, 1958; Irving, Stott, and Ward, 1961) These volcanics are cited as Lower Tertiary in the original. Thirty-seven samples (66 specimens) from 8 localities were studied. The localities are spread over a distance of about 700 km. The samples often show marked partial instability and the initial directions are sometimes widely scattered. After treatment in *ac* fields of 100–300 oe (peak) the direction, both within-site and between-sites, are better grouped with a steep inclination and positive polarity. Stability of these directions is indicated by the divergence from the present field, by the good agreement over such a large distance, and by the laboratory studies. The site directions, after partial demagnetization, were lumped together without correction for the geographical spread, and averaged giving each unit weight ($N = 8$). The pole given is the average of poles for each site giving each site pole unit weight ($N = 8$, $K = 9$).

11.095 *Tasmanian Basalt Borecore* (Almond, Clegg, and Jaeger, 1956) Eight samples from 2 cores covering a thickness of 136 m gave an average inclination of 83°. Since the azimuth of the cores was not known, the magnetic declination could not be measured, nor a pole calculated.

11.096 *Tasmanian Basalts* (Green and Irving, 1958) Two samples (2 specimens) from each of 4 sites spaced over about 100 km gave negative directions. The age of the basalts sampled is considered to be Tertiary, and for 1 of the 4 sites a Miocene or older age can be demonstrated. The inclinations in most specimens are steeper than that of the present or geocentric axial dipole field and this would indicate stability.

11.097 *Duchesne River Formation* Tertiary sediments (Collinson and Runcorn, 1960) Twenty-four samples (85 specimens), collected from a 15 m section at Roosevelt, Utah, gave directions whose mean is not significantly different from the present dipole field. In the analysis specimens were given unit weight ($N = 85$). No stability tests were reported and the result is bracketed.

11.098 *Siletz River Volcanics* Early middle to early Eocene age (Cox, 1957) Fifty-seven samples were collected from 8 flows over a lateral distance of 50 km. The flows are interbedded with tilted sediments. The initial directions are widely scattered due to partial instability. All specimens were heated to 225°C and cooled in zero field. After this treatment correction for tilt (deduced from adjacent sediments) decreased the scatter, showing that the high temperature component of magnetization was acquired prior to folding. Five flows are negative and 3 are positive. Flow mean directions given unit weight in the analysis ($N = 8$), the directions being averaged irrespective of sign.

11.099 *Wasatch Formation* Eocene sediments (Torreson, Murphy, and J. W. Graham, 1949) Five samples collected from Gardner, Colorado, showed random directions. Four samples (5 specimens) collected from 1 site (15 m stratigraphic thickness) in Wyoming are negatively polarized and have this mean direction. Statistics were calculated, giving each sample unit weight ($N = 4$). The number of samples is considered too few (less than 5). This direction is not significantly different from

the axial geocentric dipole field or the present field. The result is entered in brackets.

11.100–101 *Green River Formation* Eocene sediments (Torreson, Murphy, and J. W. Graham, 1949) Two results.

11.100 *Green River Formation* Seven samples collected from a 10 m section in Colorado gave negative directions. The statistics were calculated giving unit weight to each sample ($N = 7$). The mean direction departs significantly from the geocentric axial dipole field, and the present field, indicating stability.

11.101 *Green River Formation, Laney Shale Member* Nineteen samples collected from a 30 m section in Wyoming gave negative directions. The statistics were calculated, giving unit weight to each sample ($N = 19$). The direction does not depart significantly from the geocentric axial dipole field and is bracketed.

11.102 *Arikee Formation* Miocene sediments (Torreson, Murphy, and J. W. Graham, 1949) The directions (Figure 4.1*b*) in 21 samples (40 specimens) from a section about 20 m thick were very widely scattered, approaching a random distribution and no significance is attached to the mean which does not differ significantly from the present field. The result is entered in brackets (error exceeds 25°). The statistics were calculated giving unit weight to each sample ($N = 21$).

11.103 *Neroly Formation* Upper Miocene "blue" sandstones of California (Doell, 1956, 1957). Twenty-nine samples were obtained from 3 areas about 80 km apart. The beds dip (50°) in different directions and the directions *in situ* are in good agreement. The folding is later than early Pleistocene so that the magnetization must have been acquired in the Quaternary, not at the time of deposition, and it is attributed to crystallization magnetization developed through the postdeformational growth of magnetic minerals. Detrital magnetite is apparently present, but is not considered to produce the NRM. Heating to 100°C decreased the scatter in the results. In the analysis each sample result was given unit weight ($N = 29$). The result is entered in brackets since it provides no information about the field in Miocene time.

11.104 *Ellensburg Formation* (Torreson, Murphy, and J. W. Graham, 1949) Age cited as Miocene in the original, but stated by Cox and Doell (1960) to be regarded as late Miocene and early Pliocene by the U.S. Geological

Survey. Twenty-three sedimentary samples (25 specimens) were obtained from flat-lying beds in a 25 m section in Washington. One sample had positive polarity, the others being negative. In the analysis, unit weight was given to each sample ($N = 23$). Eight slabs of sedimentary rock in a nearby "Miocene" conglomerate were studied. These slabs are thought to have been derived from the flat-lying beds. The directions within-slabs showed high precision, whereas between-slabs they were highly scattered. Thus the directions of magnetization of the slabs, and presumably also that of the flat-lying beds, have not changed since Miocene time.

11.105 *Payette Formation* (Torreson, Murphy, and J. W. Graham, 1949) The age of these sediments is given as Pliocene in the original, but is stated by Cox and Doell (1960) to be considered Miocene and Pliocene (?) by the U.S. Geological Survey. Thirteen samples collected from a 25 m section in Idaho gave negative directions. In the analysis sample results are given unit weight ($N = 13$). The mean direction is parallel to the geocentric axial dipole field. There is no stability evidence and the result is bracketed. See Figure 4.1*a*.

11.106 *Columbia River Basalts* Miocene (Campbell and Runcorn, 1956) A total of 114 flows, with an aggregate thickness of 345 m, were examined from 7 localities over an area of 480×320 km. Results from 73 flows (138 samples) at 6 localities were considered reliable. At 1 locality negative directions only occurred. At 5 localities both positive and negative directions occurred, the means of opposed groups being 11, +74 and 177, −66. The over-all mean direction, irrespective of sign, is given in this entry the calculations being made giving unit weight to the positive and negative groups at each locality ($N = 11$). Stability is indicated by the presence of reversals. Watkins (1963) has reported briefly on a more extensive study of these basalts and shows that in certain groups of flows departures from the axial field direction found by Campbell and Runcorn, occur; numerical values have not yet been given so it is not clear whether these departures will significantly affect the over-all direction. Cox (1961) has described lightning effects in these lavas.

11.107 *Tertiary Basalts of Yukon and British Columbia* (P. M. Du Bois, 1959*b*) Forty-eight samples were studied from 4 localities over a distance of about 500 km in the Upper Tertiary basalts of the Yukon and British Columbia. The number of flows is not stated. Two samples with widely divergent results were discarded. The polarizations at 2 localities are positive, the remainder being negative. The statistics were calculated (irrespective of sign) by giving each sample unit weight ($N = 46$). Stability is indicated by the presence of reversals.

11.108 *Miocene Lavas of Iceland* (Hospers, 1953–54, 1955) One sample was taken from each of 102 lava flows at 5 localities, the total stratigraphic thickness sampled being about 700 m. Both positive and negative polarizations occur in approximately equal proportions. Four polarity zones of positive and negative polarity were recognized (Table 7.2). There are about 25 flows in each zone. The mean direction, irrespective of sign, obtained by giving unit weight to the single determination from each flow, is given ($N = 102$). Four samples of "interbasaltic lake sediments of probably Miocene age" gave positive polarizations with an average direction of approximately 208, −70 (judged by eye from Hospers (1953–54), Figure 6*f*). Stability is indicated by the presence of reversals, and by the agreement between directions in sediments and lavas.

11.109 *Skaergaard Ferro-Gabbros* Eocene (Girdler, 1961) Basic intrusive complex related to the Thulean Tertiary igneous province. The mean direction was read from Girdler's Figure 4.

TERTIARY SUPPLEMENT

11.110–113 *Igneous Rocks of Rheinland Pfalz* (Nairn, 1962) At all except 3 sites the specimens were magnetically cleaned in *ac* fields between 45 and 400 oe. Unit weight was given to sites in all analyses, the directions being combined irrespective of sign. The demagnetization studies and the reversals indicate stability.

11.110 *Eifel* Age cited as "upper Oligocene or lower Miocene" and Pleistocene. Result based on 15 samples (45 specimens) of basalt, phonolite, etc., from 8 sites (7 negative, 1 positive).

11.111 *Westerwald* Age cited as "upper Oligocene or lower Miocene." Result based on 17 samples (47 specimens) of basalt and trachyte from 6 sites (2 negative, 4 positive).

11.112 *Siebengebirge* Age cited as "upper

Oligocene to lower Miocene." Result based on 21 samples (61 specimens) of basalt, etc., from 8 sites (3 negative, 5 positive).

11.113 Combination of **11.110–112** giving unit weight to each site ($N = 22$).

11.114–115 *Volcanics of Gottingen area* (Schult, 1963) Upper Miocene to Middle Pliocene volcanics (trachy-dolerite, olivine andesine basalt, olivine felspar basalt, and pyroxene andesite). Most samples showed components of viscous magnetization along the present field and these were removed by magnetic cleaning (60–210 oe). Out of a total of 163 samples, 8 (1 site) had anomalous directions and were rejected. The remaining 155 samples were obtained from 15 sites, 12 of which were positive and 3 negative. The sites were spread over a distance of 60 km. Measurement of anomalies in the Earth's field in the vicinity of other volcanic bodies in the area suggested a pattern of positive and negative remanence.

11.114 Values, given by Schult, as an average of 12 positive site directions.

11.115 Mean direction of positive and negative sites irrespective of sign and giving each unit weight ($N = 15$).

11.116 *Tuffs and Lavas, Habichtswald* (Schult, 1963) Eleven samples from 4 sites (1 positive, 3 negative) near Kassel. Viscous components demagnetized by magnetic cleaning (50–100 oe). The mean is calculated, irrespective of sign, giving unit weight to sites ($N = 4$).

11.117 *Volcanics and Sediments, Georgia* (Vekua, 1961) Seventy-five samples from 11 localities gave mixed polarities. The samples comprise a wide variety of volcanics, tuffs and tuffaceous sediments of Eocene age. The reversals indicate stability. In this entry the mean direction is the average of all localities giving each unit weight ($N = 11$). The pole is calculated from this mean direction.

11.118–123 *Tertiary Intrusives of the Fossa Magna* (Ito, 1963) A total of 92 samples were collected from 12 sites at 5 localities; 13 samples showed no detectable NRM and 16 were rejected on the grounds that there were appreciable changes in the remanence after storage in the Earth's field for 5 years. Test specimens selected from the remainder showed a 25 per cent decrease in intensity but negligible change in direction in 300 oe *ac* field and were considered stable. The means for

the bodies are scattered about the axial geocentric dipole field direction, and Ito suggests that this may have arisen from relative tectonic rotations.

11.118 Intrusive into Lower Miocene sediment. Three sites, 20 samples.

11.119 Intrusive into Neogene sediments and overlain by Neogene and Quaternary volcanics. Three sites, 8 samples.

11.120 Intrusive into Miocene beds and overlain by Quaternary volcanics. Four sites, 16 samples.

11.121 Intrusives which "seems to be contemporaneous with . . . the Ichikawadaimon and the Kawaguchi formations." One site, 8 samples.

11.122 Intrusive into early Miocene beds and "appears to be middle Miocene." One site, 11 samples.

11.123 Mean of directions in items **11.118** to **11.122** ($N = 5$) and the pole calculated from this.

11.124 *Older Volcanics of Victoria* Lower Tertiary (Mumme, 1962*a* and *b*, 1963) These lavas were found to contain temporary viscous components which could be removed by treatment in *ac* fields of about 100 oe and all specimens were magnetically cleaned in this way. This result is based on 50 samples from 20 sites (5 positive, 15 negative). Three additional samples from 1 site were found to be completely unstable. The error is calculated using the two-tier analysis. Stability of the components remaining after cleaning is indicated by the detailed laboratory studies and by the occurrence of reversals. See **11.093** and Figure 7.21.

11.125 *Lavas* Tertiary (Creer, 1962*d*) Samples from 4 flows at 1 site. Stability indicated by the departure from the present field.

11.126 *Andean Intrusive Suite* (Blundell, 1962) Age cited as late Cretaceous to early Tertiary. A collection of 77 samples of diorite, quartz diorite, and gabbro from 12 localities (2 positive, 10 negative) spread over about 800 km gave very well grouped directions. The two-tier analysis of directions was used, small corrections being made for the spread of sites; the between-site precision is quoted here. *Ac* demagnetization of test specimens suggested a stable magnetization. This test, the occurrence of reversals, and the good agreement observed over a wide area in different rock types, indicate stability.

QUATERNARY (LESS THAN 1 M.Y.) AND PLIO-PLEISTOCENE

12.01 *Auvergne Lavas* (Roche, 1951, 1953) Samples from 6 flows (4 Villafranchian and 2 younger ones of St. Prestien age) gave positive directions.   Sediments, baked by 3 of the Villafranchian flows, gave positive directions, in good agreement with the flows themselves (Figure 7.23).   The positive directions and the contact evidence indicate stability.   Each flow was given unit weight in the analysis ($N = 6$).

12.02–03 *Pleistocene Lavas of France* (Roche, 1958)   Two groups of lavas were studied, whose magnetization is described as "stable et cohérente, peut être considérée comme thermorémanente."

12.02 *Plateaux Basalts* Early Quaternary Samples from 8 flows gave positive directions indicative of stability.

12.03 *Chaîne des Puys Lavas* Late Pleistocene   Ten flows were sampled.   Their age is estimated to be between -15000 and -6000 years.

12.04 *Roman Kiln near Trêves* (Thellier and Thellier, 1952)   Fourteen samples were collected from a kiln dated archeologically as the latter half of the 4th century A.D.   The scatter of directions is attributed to local field distortion due to the kiln itself but the average direction is considered reliable.   In the analysis samples were given unit weight ($N = 14$).

12.05 See § 8.3.

12.06–08 *Archeomagnetic Studies in Britain* Studies of baked earths in kilns and hearths.

12.06 (1) (Cook and Belshé, 1958)   This result is based on 72 samples from 14 sites. The directions were corrected to Cambridge 52° N, 0° E.   In the analysis sites were given unit weight ($N = 14$).   Stability is indicated by the divergences from the present field, and by the approximate consistency between results from structures of comparable age (see Figure 6.36).

12.07 (2) (Aitken, 1961, p. 148)   Tentative results obtained from 6 sites in Britain dated archeologically as ranging from A.D. 600–1333. Each site given unit weight in this analysis ($N = 6$).   See § 6.13 for a description of more recent work.

12.08 *Combined* The individual site results in **12.06** and **12.07** were lumped together giving unit weight to each ($N = 20$).   The sites range in age from the 1st to 15th centuries, but are not uniformly distributed within this range, there being a notable absence of

data in the last half of the first millennium. The pole was calculated assuming a mean location of sites at 52° N, 1° W.   This is not a rigorous result, but is useful (when taken together with observatory data from London) in indicating the general direction of the field during the past 2000 years in Britain.

12.09 *Mt. Etna Lavas* (Chevallier, 1925) Between 3 and 9 samples (total 81) were collected from each of 11 lava flows.   The flows are dated historically and range from 394 B.C. to A.D. 1911.   See §§ 1.2, 6.13.

12.10–15 *Swedish Varved Clays* Laboratory experiments are described in § 2.12.   Early work by Ising (1943) gave declinations close to that of the present field but with inclinations sometimes as much as 40° less than that of the field.

12.10 *Glacial Varves* (1) (Ising, 1943; Granar, 1958)   Measurements on 39 samples from 8 localities covering the period -3400 to -50 (de Geer's Time Scale) gave directions scattered around the geocentric axial dipole field.   The time span at each locality varied between 35 and 110 years.   The localities are spread over a distance of 800 km.   The direction listed was obtained by averaging the locality directions giving each unit weight ($N = 8$).   The pole is the average of poles for each locality ($N = 8$, $K = 18$).

12.11 *Glacial Varves* (2) (Griffiths, 1955) Result based on a collection of 120 samples from Ragunda covering a period of 100 years about 9000 years ago.

12.12 *Postglacial Varves* (1) (Bancroft, 1951)   Samples obtained from varves at 1 locality (Prästmon) ranging in age from A.D. 0–1000.   The results were arranged by Hospers (1955) into 46 groups and unit weight given to each group in the analysis ($N = 46$).

12.13 *Postglacial Varves* (2) (Griffiths, 1953, 1955)   About 150 samples were collected from 2 localities (Prästmon and Undrom) a few kilometers apart and ranging in age from 1100 B.C.–A.D. 750 (Liden's varve chronology). The samples were arranged into 29 groups, each representing about 100 years, and the mean for each group given unit weight ($N = 29$).   Stability of test specimens was demonstrated in 1000 oe *ac* field.

12.14 *Postglacial Varves* (3) (Granar, 1958)   Varves at Prästmon deposited around A.D. 200 and covering 190 years (mean 296, $+73$), and from a core at Nyland A.D. 1215–1285 (mean 21, +72), gave this over-all mean direction (unit weight to each locality mean, $N = 2$).

12.15 *Postglacial Varves combined* Mean of directions and poles in **12.12–14**, giving each unit weight ($N = 3$).

12.16–19 *Georgian Quaternary Igneous Rocks* (Vekua, 1961) The localities are: **12.16** Kvesheti 5 samples; **12.17** Kazreti 21 samples; **12.18** Pkhelshe 17 samples. Reversals indicate stability.

12.19 *Combined* The average, irrespective of sign, of the directions in **12.16–18** giving unit weight to each ($N = 3$). The pole was calculated from this mean direction.

12.20 *Armenian Plio-Pleistocene Lavas* (Pospelova, 1959) Age cited as Quaternary to Upper Pliocene. Result based on about 60 samples of andesites, andesite-dacites, and dacites. Laboratory studies (Pospelova, 1960) also indicate stability; for instance, ac field demagnetization in 460 oe resulted in only a 10 per cent decrease in intensity in some test specimens.

12.21 *Armenian Quaternary Lavas and Tuffs* (Pospelova, 1959) Result based on about 50 samples of tuffs, andesites, and andesite-dacites. The direction agrees better with the geocentric axial dipole field (0, +59) than with the present field (5, +58), indicating stability over periods of time of the order of the 10^2 years.

12.22–27 *Armenian Quaternary Tuffs and Lavas* (Akopyan quoted in Kalashnikov, 1961, see also Akopyan, 1958, Yanovsky, and others, 1963) In several of the 5 results listed by Kalashnikov the coordinates of the sampling area are not consistent with the localities being in Armenia, and the poles are inconsistent with the directions and localities stated. Because of this confusion the results are entered in brackets.

12.27 *Combined* The mean of the directions listed in **12.22–26** is calculated giving each unit weight ($N = 5$). A pole was calculated from this direction assuming a mean location (40° N, 45° E).

12.28 *Khazar Beds* Quaternary (Khramov, 1958) Result based on 20 sedimentary samples. It is not clear whether the result departs significantly from the present field and the result is entered in brackets.

12.29 *Baku Beds* Quaternary (Khramov, 1958) Result based on 47 samples spanning a 290 m section on the Cheleken peninsula. The directions *in situ* depart systematically from the present field indicating stability, the mean being about 20° away. The beds dip at 10–40° and the mean direction is corrected for this.

12.30 *Akchagylsk and Apsheronsk Stages* (Khramov, 1958) The Apsheronsk Stage overlies the Akchagylsk. A total thickness of more than 1000 m was sampled. The age of these beds is considered to be Upper Pliocene or Lower Pleistocene; Nalivkin (1960) considers both to be Pliocene. The Akchagylsk Stage was sampled at 3 localities: Kiuendag (39° N, 55° E), the Small Balkhan (39.5° N, 55° E), and Cheleken (39.5° N, 53° E). Positive polarizations are more common but negative values occur on the Small Balkhan. In some of the Akchagylsk sediments the directions were corrected for instability by rotation along great circles away from the present field. The Apsheronsk Stage was sampled at 2 localities (Cheleken and Kiuendag). At both places a zone of negative polarization rests on a positive zone. The mean direction is that of 47 samples each given unit weight ($N = 47$). Stability is indicated by the divergences from the present field and by the presence of reversals. See Figure 7.1.

12.31 *Kamchatka Andesite-basalts* (Kochegura quoted in Kalashnikov, 1961) Stability is indicated by divergence from the present field. This result is based on 19 samples.

12.32 *Sheveluch Volcanic Domes* (Pospelova, 1959) Result based on about 17 samples from 2 andesite domes in Kamchatka dating from the 19th and 20th century. Stability is indicated by the divergence of the mean from the present field.

12.33 *Kurile Island Lavas* Quaternary (Pospelova, 1959, 1960; Markhinin and Pospelova, 1959; Yanovsky and others, 1963) Results from about 7 samples gave negative directions. The mean direction appears to be just significantly different from the present field. Results from Plio-Pleistocene lavas were positive but highly scattered.

12.34 *Igneous Rocks from Japan and East Asia* (Matuyuma, 1929a and b) A total of 39 samples (about half positive and half negative) were collected from 36 localities in Honshu, Kyushu, Tyosen, and Manchuria—mostly in Honshu. The values given in this entry were obtained by combining the directions, irrespective of sign, and without correction for the spread in sampling locations. Unit weight was given to each sample ($N = 39$).

The pole was calculated relative to a central place in Honshu (36° N, 138° E).

12.35 *Miocene to Pleistocene Sediments of the Bôsô Peninsula* (Kawai, 1951) A study of sections totaling 4000 m was made. The beds dip to the north at angles increasing from 8° in the Pleistocene to 12° in the Pliocene, but is steeper and less regular in the Miocene. The directions relative to bedding have declinations "nearly the same as that of the present field, while the inclinations gradually decrease from the mean value of 25° in Miocene to 50° in Pleistocene beds." The highest inclination recorded is in sediments of the Narita bed (compare **12.36**). Directions in different pebbles in a conglomerate are magnetized with uniform directions along the present field (Nagata 1953*a*, Figure 5-18; Kawai and Kume, 1959). The magnetization is described as "unstable" by Kawai (1954). The direction given here is the mean of the 4 average directions (based on 147 samples) for Miocene, Lower Pliocene, Upper Pliocene, and Pleistocene beds (Table 1, Kawai, 1951) giving each unit weight ($N = 4$). The result is entered in brackets.

12.36 *Pleistocene Sediments of the Bôsô Peninsula* (Nagata, Hirao, and Yoshikawa, 1950) Detailed sampling through the Narita bed, which is 7 m thick, gave directions close to the present field. The direction given here is the mean judged by eye from Figure 1 (Nagata and others). Radioisotope age determinations for this bed (U-Ra methods) gave 74×10^3 years for the base of the bed and 42×10^3 years for the top. Although, in the original, these results are regarded as reliable indicators of the field direction at the time of deposition, Kawai (who also studied the Narita bed, see **12.35**) in a later paper (1954) classifies the Pleistocene sediments of the Bôsô peninsula as "unstable." This result is therefore entered in brackets. No pole is calculated because of the qualitative nature of the direction estimate.

12.37 *Yamaguchi Basalt* (Domen, 1960) The age is cited as early Pleistocene. This result is based on about 300 samples (about 650 specimens) from 85 sites at 13 localities spaced through a thick sequence and spread laterally over a distance of 90 km. Eight sites show positive polarity, the remainder being negative. The values were calculated, giving unit weight to each site ($N = 85$). Ac field demagnetization of NRM shows that in fields

up to 200 oe there is only a small decrease of magnetization in the positive specimens and also in many negative specimens. Stability is indicated by the presence of reversals and by these studies. Detailed studies of the ferromagnetic minerals are also reported. In earlier work Asami (1954, 1956, 1957) reported results from a single locality at which both positive and negative polarities were found to be intermixed (§ 7.7). The negative group was highly scattered, but the positive group showed high precision. The mean of the positive group is given by Asami (1954) as 167, –56. The result given here is based on Domen's work which is more representative of the group as a whole.

12.38 *North Izu and Hakone Volcanic Rocks* Quaternary (Nagata, Akimoto, Uyeda, Shimizu, Ozima, Kobayashi, and Kuno, 1957; Nagata, Akimoto, Uyeda, Shimizu, Ozima, and Kobayashi, 1957) The sampling region lies about 90 km SW of Tokyo. A study was made of about 300 samples spanning a sequence totaling over 2800 m in thickness, and ranging in age from Lower Pleistocene to Recent. The lateral spread of sites is about 40 km. The sequence is divided in 9 units—each several hundreds of meters thick. Forty-two flows were sampled, 9 near the base having positive polarity, all others being negative. Directions in andesite blocks in a fragmental deposit gave widely scattered directions indicative of stability. Stability is further indicated by the presence of reversals and by laboratory tests. The direction given is the average for the flows, giving each unit weight ($N = 42$). The pole was calculated as a mean of poles for individual flows, giving each unit weight ($N = 42$, $K = 11$).

12.39 *Quaternary Volcanic Rocks* Pleistocene to Recent (Kumagai, Kawai, and Nagata, 1950) This result is based on results from 11 lava flows, the mean for each flow being given unit weight ($N = 11$).

12.40 *Historic Flows* (Kato and Nagata, 1953; Yukutake, 1961) This result is the mean result for 12 lava flows, each given unit weight ($N = 12$). The spread of sites is wide and the directions were corrected to Tokyo (35.7° N, 139.8° E). The flows are dated historically and range from A.D. 325–1779.

12.41 *Archeological Baked Clays* (Watanabe, 1958, 1959) Observations were obtained from 1378 samples of baked clays from kilns, furnaces, and hearths at sites spread over a distance of about 1000 km. The samples are grouped into 174 sets from 55 sites. Each set is from relics of comparable age. Sets at the same site are considered to differ in age. In broad terms the sites range in age from 4000 B.C. to A.D. 1600, but, except at one site, they are not accurately dated. All directions are corrected to Tokyo (35.7° N, 139.8° E). The statistics were calculated giving unit weight to each set ($N = 174$). Stability is indicated by departures from the present field in individual sets.

12.42 *Aden Volcanics* (Irving and Tarling, 1961) These volcanics are probably Quaternary, but they could be older. Fifty-five samples (164 specimens) were collected from 12 sites in trachytic plugs and flows over a distance of 10 km. The directions at 3 sites were negative, and were positive at 9 sites, the means of the 2 groups being, within the statistical errors, opposed to one another. H_{cr} averages 450 oe. One sample (2 specimens) diverged from the axial direction and was rejected. The directions remain unchanged in strong *ac* fields in some cases as high as 900 oe. This evidence, the reversal, and the departures from the present field indicate high stability. These values were obtained from a two-tier analysis, the directions considered irrespective of sign. The precision is the between-site precision. See Figure 2.26.

12.43 *Archeological Baked Clays* (Thellier and Thellier, 1951) Nine samples from the walls of 2 Punic kilns, contemporaneous with the sack of Carthage by the Romans (146 B.C.) gave an average direction 359°30′, +58°0′. Nine samples from a Roman kiln (about A.D. 300) gave 358°45′, +51°0′. The average of these 2 directions is given here. The precision of the results is high and the directions depart systematically from the present field.

12.44 *Ahaggar Basalts* Recent (Roche and Lepêtre, 1955) A study of 61 samples of Recent lava from the Sahara yielded internally consistent directions, but highly scattered directions occurred in Tertiary igneous rocks. The former were described as stable in the original, and the mean of 6 directions from 2 volcanic series (Afilale and Issakarassene) is given here ($N = 6$). The scattered directions in Tertiary rocks is attributed to secondary magnetization.

12.45 *Newer Volcanics of Victoria* (Irving and Green, 1957*a* and *b*; Green and Irving, 1958) These lava fields are predominantly Quaternary in age, but some flows may be Pliocene. Over 100 samples (125 specimens) from 32 quarries spread over an area 300 by 80 km were collected. Thirteen sites were negative and 16 positive (Figures 4.1*d*, 4.2*c*). At 3 sites both polarities occurred. Stability for the volcanics as a whole is indicated by the opposed groups of directions, the means of which are, within the errors, exactly opposed to one another (8, −60 $a_{95} = 8°$ and 177, +60 $a_{95} = 7°$). The analysis was carried out using the two-tier method. The between-site precision is given. Anisotropies are about 2 per cent (Stacey, 1960*a*).

12.46 *Ignimbrites* (Hatherton, 1954*a*, *b*) Age given as Upper Pleistocene (Coombs and Hatherton, 1959) The value given is the mean of directions observed at 3 localities. The result is based on 52 oriented samples and inclination values observed in 62 samples from bore core. The lateral spread of sites is 13 km and the vertical coverage about 140 m. The mean inclination is steeper than the axial dipole field and the declination differs from the present declination. This would seem to indicate stability, but no statistical values are available, and it is not clear whether these departures are significant. The result is therefore entered in brackets.

12.47 *New England Glacial Varves* (Johnson, Murphy, and Torreson, 1948; J. W. Graham, 1949) A total of 1019 samples were collected from 11 sites spread over a distance of 290 km. The localities cover about 5000 years from 15000–9500 B.C. The directions in a disturbed bed were more scattered than those in nearby undisturbed beds indicating stability. The data were arranged in 6 groups each representing approximately 1000 years. The means for groups were averaged unit weight being given to each ($N = 6$).

12.48 *Neuquen Lavas* Quaternary (Creer, 1958) Twenty samples (58 specimens) from 10 lava flows were obtained over an area of 200 by 400 km. The initial directions were scattered, but after magnetic cleaning in *ac* fields of 150 oe (peak) the directions became grouped into 2 sets antiparallel to one another. Forty-six specimens were positive and 12 negative. In the analysis these sets were averaged irrespective of sign giving unit weight to each specimen ($N = 58$). Stability is indicated by the laboratory tests and by the occurrence of reversals.

12.49–50 *Pliocene and Pleistocene Lavas of Iceland* (Sigurgeirsson, 1957) Samples were obtained from "the six latest magnetic groups, three of normal and three of reversed polarity." Thirty-three lavas were sampled from the negative groups, and 26 from the positive groups. In most cases 1 sample was obtained from each flow and each sample was magnetically cleaned in 110 oe which reduced dispersion. No directions but only poles were given. Stability is indicated by the laboratory tests and by the occurrence of reversals.

12.49 *Negative results* The average of poles for 33 lavas ($N = 33$, $K = 19$).

12.50 *Positive results* The average of poles for 26 lavas ($N = 26$, $K = 15$).

12.51 *Early Quaternary Lavas of Iceland* (Hospers, 1953–54, 1955) Beds of glacial origin are intercalated with these lavas. Fifty-one samples were collected from 9 flows at 3 localities spaced over a distance of 120 km. Three samples of associated early Quaternary sediments gave a mean direction (judged by eye from Hospers (1953), Figure 6d) of 160, −75. The divergence from the present field and the good agreement between sediments and lavas indicate stability.

12.52–54 *Post-Glacial Lavas of Iceland*

12.52 (1) Hospers (1953–54, 1955) About 30 samples were studied from 8 flows ranging in age from about 5000 B.C. to A.D. 0. Stability is indicated by the departures from the present field. Five recent flows of Mt. Hekla (1766 to 1947–48) were also studied (26 samples) and gave a mean direction 4, +76.

12.53 (2) Brynjólfsson (1957) Twenty-five flows were investigated. This entry is based on results from 21 flows ranging in age from 3400 B.C. to A.D. 1950. All samples were magnetically cleaned in 110 oe. Poles for each flow not directions were given, and the average of these is listed ($N = 21$, $K = 31$). Stability is indicated by the laboratory studies and by the departures from the present field.

12.54 *Combined* Average pole of **12.52** and **12.53**.

12.55 *Cenozoic Lavas of Cape Hallet* (Turnbull, 1959) Twenty-three samples (31 specimens) were collected—21 samples positive and 2 negative. The number of flows sampled is not stated. Stability is indicated by the reversal and by *ac* demagnetization of test specimens. The weighting procedure used is not stated, but the error and precision cited are consistent with samples being used as units.

12.56–62 *Hawaiian Lavas* Tarling (1962) has identified a sequence of positive and negative polarities in the Hawaiian Islands. Doell and Cox (1961b) have given results from 6 volcanic groups on the youngest island—Hawaii itself. The ages cited for the groups range from Pliocene (?) to Recent. *Ac* demagnetization of test specimens in fields up to 800 oe (peak) yielded significant change of direction. In the analyses flows were given unit weight. The poles are calculated relative to a central point (19.6° N, 155.6° W) in Hawaii.

12.56 *Historic Lavas* Nine flows. Now reported in more detail [**12.68**].

12.57 *Puna Volcanic Series* Late Pleistocene and Recent Seventeen flows spaced through a stratigraphic thickness of 133 m.

12.58 *Kahuku Volcanic Series* Pleistocene Twenty-nine flows spanning 104 m stratigraphic thickness.

12.59 *Hamakua Volcanic Series* Late Tertiary and Quaternary Twenty-three flows spanning 42 m.

12.60 *Pololu Volcanic Series* Pliocene (?) Forty flows spanning 138 m.

12.61 *Ninole Volcanic Series* Pliocene (?) Twenty-five flows spanning 35 m.

12.62 *Combined* Pliocene (?) to Recent A total of 143 flows.

12.63–64 *Samoan Volcanics* Tarling (1963) Magnetic cleaning in 150 oe (peak) used to diminish scatter. Stability indicated by the presence of reversals, and by the departures from the present field.

12.63 *Negative directions* Pleistocene and Recent Thirty samples from 9 sites. Sites given unit weight in the analysis ($N = 9$).

12.64 *Positive directions* Plio-Pleistocene Eighteen samples from 7 sites. Sites given unit weight in the analysis ($N = 7$).

QUATERNARY AND PLIO-PLEISTOCENE SUPPLEMENT

12.65 *Dolerite, Georgia* (Vekua, 1961) Age cited as Upper Pliocene to Lower Pleistocene. Result based on 28 samples from Arakhlo. Reversals indicate stability.

12.66 *Volcanics, South Shetland Islands and adjacent places* (Blundell, 1962) Ages range from ? Miocene to Recent. A collection of 51 samples was made from 12 sites (2 positive, 10 negative) spread over about 200 km. *Ac* demagnetization of test specimens in 200 oe did not cause appreciable direction changes. Stability is suggested by this laboratory test, by the very good grouping of observations, and by the occurrence of reversals. In the analysis the two-tier method is used and the between-site precision is quoted.

12.67 *Volcanics, South Sandwich Islands* (Blundell, 1962) Six "hastily" collected samples from "recent lava flows." The mean differs significantly from the present and axial geocentric dipole field directions and this indicates stability. The accuracy of the sample orientation is described as "doubtful" (yet the between-sample precision is high) and because of this the result is entered in brackets.

12.68 *Historic Lava Flows, Hawaii* (Doell and Cox, 1963) A total of 67 samples were cored from 9 flows extruded in the period A.D. 1750–1955. The spread of sites is about 100 km. All specimens were magnetically cleaned in 100 oe. This mean direction was calculated giving unit weight to each flow ($N = 9$).

12.69 *Pleistocene Silt* (Harrison and Terasmae, 1961) Results from 11 sites (64 specimens) in silts referred to the Kansan, Illinoian, Sangamon, and Wisconsin stages were arranged in 8 groups and the pole given here is the mean of the poles for each group ($N = 8$, $K = 8$). The sites are spread over about 800 km and their mean position is about 41° N, 84° W. The directions are widely scattered and are thought to have been affected by "overconsolidation" due to overriding glaciers and for this reason the result is bracketed. A specimen stressed to 160 kg/cm^2 (equivalent to about 1800 m of overriding ice) had its inclination decreased by 10°.

References

Ade-Hall, J. and R. L. Wilson (1963); Petrology and the natural remanence of the Mull lavas, *Nature,* **198,** 659–660.

Ahlfeld, F. (1956); Handbook of South American Geology (ed., W. F. Jenks), *Mem. Geol. Soc. Amer.,* **65,** 174.

Aitken, M. J. (1961); *Physics and Archaeology,* Interscience, New York, 181 pp.

Aitken, M. J., M. R. Harold, and G. H. Weaver (1964); Some archaeomagnetic evidence concerning the secular variation in Britain, *Nature,* **201,** 659–660.

Aitken, M. J. and G. H. Weaver (1962); Magnetic dating: some archaeomagnetic measurements in Britain, *Archaeometry,* **5,** 4–25.

Akimoto, S. (1954); Thermo-magnetic study of ferromagnetic minerals contained in igneous rocks, *J. Geomag. Geoelec.,* **6,** 1–14.

Akimoto, S. (1955); Magnetic properties of ferromagnetic minerals contained in igneous rocks, *Japan. J. Geophys.,* **1,** 1–31.

Akimoto, S. (1957); Magnetic properties of ferromagnetic oxide minerals as a basis of rock-magnetism, *Phil. Mag. Supp. Adv. Phys.,* **6,** 288–298.

Akimoto, S. and T. Katsura (1959); Magneto-chemical study of the generalised titano-magnetite in volcanic rocks, *J. Geomag. Geoelec.,* **10,** 69–90.

Akimoto, S., T. Katsura, and M. Yoshida (1957); Magnetic properties of $TiFe_2O_4$–Fe_3O_4 system and their change with oxidation, *J. Geomag. Geoelec.,* **9,** 165–178.

Akimoto, S. and I. Kushiro (1960); Natural occurrence of titanomaghemite and its relevance to the unstable magnetization of rocks, *J. Geomag. Geoelec.,* **11,** 94–110.

Akimoto, S., T. Nagata, and T. Katsura (1957); The $TiFe_2O_5$–Ti_2FeO_5 solid solution series, *Nature,* **179,** 37–38.

Akopyan, Ts. G. (1958); Paleomagnetism of volcanic rocks of Armenia, *Akad. Nauk. SSSR Izv. Geophys. Ser.,* 1033–1039.

Almond, M., J. A. Clegg, and J. C. Jaeger (1956); Remanent magnetism of some dolerites, basalts, and volcanic tuffs from Tasmania, *Phil. Mag.,* **1,** 771–782.

Andreeva, O. L. (1961); Paleomagnetic investigation of Krasnotsvet clays of the Gzhelian stage in the Moscow basin, *Akad. Nauk. SSSR Izv. Geophys. Ser.,* 1382–1383.

Angenheister, G. (1956); cited in Cox and Doell (1960).

Aramaki, S. and S. Akimoto (1957); Temperature estimation of pyroclastic deposits by natural remanent magnetism, *Amer. J. Sci.,* **255,** 619–627.

Armstrong, D. (1957); Dating of some minor intrusions of Ayrshire, *Nature,* **180,** 1277.

As, J. A. (1961); Instruments and measuring methods in palaeomagnetic research, *Med. en Verh. Kon. Nederl. Meteor. Inst., De Bilt,* no. 78.

As, J. A. and J. D. A. Zijderveld (1958); Magnetic cleaning of rocks in paleomagnetic research, *Geophys. J.,* **1,** 308–319.

Asami, E. (1954); On the reverse natural remanent magnetism of basalt at Cape Kawajiri, Yamaguchi prefecture, *Proc. Japan Acad.,* **30,** 102–105.

Asami, E. (1956); A paleomagnetic consideration on the remanent magnetism of the basalt lavas at Kawajiri-misaki, Japan, *J. Geomag. Geoelec.,* **8,** 147–155.

Asami, E. (1957); Positional intermixing of the normal and the reverse magnetizations of the Kawajiri-misaki basalt lavas, *J. Geomag. Geoelec.,* **9,** 162–164.

Athavale, R. N., C. Radhakrishnamurty, and P. W. Sahasrabudhe (1963); Paleomagnetism of some Indian rocks, *Geophys. J.*, **7**, 304–313.

Bagin, V. I. (1961); Hematite as a magnetically stable component, *Akad. Nauk. SSSR, Izv. Geophys. Ser.*, 1388–1393.

Bagnold, R. A. (1941); *The Physics of Blown Sand and Desert Dunes*, Methuen, London.

Bain, G. W. (1958); Possible climatic zonation and its implications, *Amer. J. Sci.*, **256**, 596–600.

Balsley, J. R. and A. F. Buddington (1954); Correlation of reverse remanent magnetism and negative anomalies with certain minerals, *J. Geomag. Geoelec.*, **6**, 178–181.

Balsley, J. R. and A. F. Buddington (1957); Remanent magnetism of the Russell belt of gneisses, Northwest Adirondack Mountains, New York, *Phil. Mag. Supp. Adv. Phys.*, **6**, 317–322.

Balsley, J. R. and A. F. Buddington (1958); Iron-titanium oxide minerals, rocks and aeromagnetic anomalies of the Adirondack area, New York, *Econ. Geol.*, **53**, 777–805.

Balsley, J. R. and A. F. Buddington (1960); Magnetic susceptibility anisotropy and fabric of some Adirondack granites and orthogneisses, *Amer. J. Sci.*, **258-A**, 6–20.

Bancroft, A. M. (1951); quoted in Hospers (1955).

Banks, M. R. and N. Ahmed (1962); The Permian System in western Tasmania, *Pap. Proc. Roy. Soc. Tasmania*, **96**, 1–8.

Bean, C. P. (1955); Hysteresis loops of mixtures of ferromagnetic micropowders, *J. App. Physics*, **26**, 1381–1383.

Belshé, J. C. (1957a); Paleomagnetic investigation of Carboniferous rocks in England and Wales, *Phil. Mag. Supp. Adv. Phys.*, **6**, 187–191.

Belshé, J. C. (1957b); Recent magnetic investigations at Cambridge University, *Phil. Mag. Supp. Adv. Phys.*, **6**, 192–193.

Benedikt, E. T. (1943); A method of determination of the direction of the magnetic field of the earth in geological epochs, *Amer. J. Sci.*, **241**, 124–129.

Bidgood, D. E. T. (1961); Differential secondary magnetization in some British Cambrian rocks, *Nature*, **192**, 39–40.

Bidgood, D. E. T. and W. B. Harland (1961);

Paleomagnetism in some east Greenland sedimentary rocks, *Nature*, **189**, 633–634.

Bigarella, J. J. and R. Salamuni (1961); Early Mesozoic wind patterns as suggested by dune bedding in the Botucatú sandstone of Brazil and Uruguay, *Geol. Soc. Amer. Bull.*, **72**, 1089–1106.

Black, R. F. (1963); Palaeomagnetism of part of the Purcell System in Southwestern Alberta and Southeastern British Columbia, *Geol. Survey Canada Bull.*, **83**, 1–31.

Blackett, P. M. S. (1956); *Lectures on rock magnetism*, Weizmann Science Press, Jerusalem, 131 pp.

Blackett, P. M. S. (1961); Comparisons of ancient climate with the ancient latitude deduced from rock magnetic measurements, *Proc. Roy. Soc. London A*, **263**, 1–30.

Blackett, P. M. S. (1962); Paleomagnetism and palaeoclimatology, *J. Geomag. Geoelec.*, **13**, 127–132.

Blackett, P. M. S., J. A. Clegg, and P. H. S. Stubbs (1960); An analysis of rock magnetic data, *Proc. Roy. Soc. A*, **256**, 291–322.

Blundell, D. J. (1957); A palaeomagnetic investigation of the Lundy dyke swarm, *Geol. Mag.*, **94**, 187–193.

Blundell, D. J. (1961a); Rock magnetism applied to some geological problems, *Geol. Mag.*, **98**, 301–312.

Blundell, D. J. (1961b); The palaeomagnetism of some igneous rocks from Antarctica, *Polar Record*, **10**, 349–352.

Blundell, D. J. (1962); Palaeomagnetic investigations in the Falkland Islands Dependencies, *British Antarctic Survey Scientific Report*, no. 39, 1–24.

Blundell, D. J. and H. H. Read (1958); Palaeomagnetism of the younger gabbros of Aberdeenshire and its bearing on their deformation, *Proc. Geol. Assoc.*, **69**, 191–204.

Blundell, D. J. and P. J. Stephenson (1959); Palaeomagnetism of some dolerite intrusions from the Theron Mountains and Whichaway Nunataks, Antarctica, *Nature*, **184**, 1860.

Boesen, R., E. Irving, and W. A. Robertson (1961); The palaeomagnetism of some igneous rock bodies in New South Wales, *J. Proc. Roy. Soc. N. S. W.*, **94**, 227–232.

Bol'shakov, A. S. (1937); The stability of normal rock magnetization, *Izv. Akad. Nauk. SSSR, Ser. Geofiz.*, 595–603.

Bowen, R. (1961); Paleotemperature analyses

of Mesozoic Belemnoidea from Germany and Poland, *J. Geol.*, **69**, 75–83.

Bradley, J. (1957); The meaning of paleogeographic pole, *New Zealand J. Sci. Tech. B*, **38**, 354–365.

Brailsford, F. (1951); *Magnetic materials*, Methuen, London.

Briden, J. C. and E. Irving (1964); Palaeolatitude spectra of sedimentary paleoclimatic indicators, *Problems in Palaeoclimatology*, Interscience, New York.

Briden, J. C. and R. L. Oliver (1963); Paleomagnetic results from the Beardmore Glacier Region, Antarctica, *New Zealand J. Geol. Geophys.*, **6**, 388–394.

Brooks, C. E. P. (1949); *Climate through the ages*, Benn, London.

Bruckshaw, J. M. (1954); Rock magnetism—some recent developments, *Science Progress*, no. 167, 406–418.

Bruckshaw, J. M. and E. I. Robertson (1949); The magnetic properties of the tholeiite dykes of north England, *Mon. Not. Roy. Astr. Soc. Geophys. Supp.*, **5**, 308–320.

Bruckshaw, J. M. and S. A. Vincenz (1954); The permanent magnetism of the Mull lavas, *Mon. Not. Roy. Astr. Soc. Geophys. Supp.*, **6**, 579–589.

Bruhnes, B. (1906); Recherches sur le direction d'aimantation des roches volcaniques, *J. Phys.*, **5**, 705–724.

Brynjólfsson, A. (1957); Studies of remanent magnetism and viscous magnetism in the basalts of Iceland, *Phil. Mag. Supp. Adv. Phys.*, **6**, 247–254.

Bucha, V. (1961); Some results of paleomagnetic investigations of primary igneous rocks in Czechoslovakia, *Izv. Akad. Nauk. SSSR Geophys. Ser.*, 54–59.

Bull, C. and E. Irving (1960*a*); Palaeomagnetism in Antarctica, *Nature*, **185**, 834–835.

Bull, C. and E. Irving (1960*b*); The palaeomagnetism of some hypabyssal intrusive rocks from South Victoria Land, Antarctica, *Geophys. J.*, **3**, 211–224.

Bull, C., E. Irving, and I. Willis (1962); Further palaeomagnetic results from South Victoria Land, Antarctica, *Geophys. J.*, **6**, 320–336.

Bullard, E. C., C. Freedman, H. Gellman, and J. Nixon (1950); The westward drift of the Earth's magnetic field, *Phil. Trans. Roy. Soc. London, A*, **243**, 67–92.

Burlatskaya, S. P. (1962); The ancient magnetic field of the Earth, *Akad. Nauk. SSSR. Isv. Geophys. Ser.*, 524–528.

Campbell, C. D. and S. K. Runcorn (1956); Magnetization of the Columbia River basalts in Washington and Northern Oregon, *J. Geophys. Res.*, **61**, 449–459.

Campbell, K. S. W. (1962); Marine fossils from the Carboniferous glacial rocks of New South Wales, *J. Paleontology*, **36**, 38–52.

Carey, S. W. (1955); The orocline concept in geotectonics, *Proc. Roy. Soc. Tasmania*, **89**, 255–288.

Carey, S. W. (1958); The tectonic approach to continental drift, *Continental Drift—a symposium*, University of Tasmania, Hobart, 1956, 177–358.

Carmichael, C. M. (1959); Remanent magnetism of the Allard Lake ilmenites, *Nature*, **183**, 1239–1241.

Carmichael, C. M. (1961); The magnetic properties of ilmenite-haematite crystals, *Proc. Roy. Soc. London A.*, **263**, 508–530.

Chamalaun, F. H. and K. M. Creer (1963); A revised Devonian pole for Britain, *Nature*, **198**, 375.

Chang Wen-you and A. E. M. Nairn (1959); Some palaeomagnetic investigations on Chinese rocks, *Nature*, **183**, 254.

Chevallier, R. (1925); L'aimantation des laves de l'Etna et l'orientation du champ terrestre en Sicile du XIIᵉ au XVIIᵉ siècle, *Ann. Phys.*, **4**, 5–162.

Chevallier, R. (1951); Propriétés magnétiques de l'oxyde ferrique rhomboédrique (Fe_2O_3a), *J. Phys. Radium*, **12**, 172–188.

Chevallier, R., J. Bolfa, and S. Mathieu (1955); Titanomagnétites et ilménites ferromagnétiques, *Bull. Soc. Franc. Miner. Crist.*, **78**, 307–346.

Chevallier, R. and S. Mathieu (1943); Propriétés magnétiques des poudres d'hematites, *Ann. Phys.*, **18**, 258–288.

Chevallier, R., S. Mathieu, and E. A. Vincent (1954); Iron-titanium oxide minerals in layered gabbros of the Skaergaard intrusion, East Greenland, Part II. Magnetic properties, *Geochim. Coscochim. Acta*, **6**, 27–34.

Clegg, J. A. (1956); Rock magnetism, *Nature*, **178**, 1085–1087.

Clegg, J. A., M. Almond, and P. H. S. Stubbs (1954*a*); The remanent magnetism of some sedimentary rocks in Britain, *Phil. Mag.*, **45**, 583–598.

Clegg, J. A., M. Almond and P. H. S. Stubbs

(1954*b*); Some recent studies of the pre-history of the Earth's magnetic field, *J. Geomag. Geoelec.,* **6,** 194–199.

Clegg, J. A., E. R. Deutsch, C. W. F. Everitt, and P. H. S. Stubbs (1957); Some recent palaeomagnetic measurements made at Imperial College, London, *Phil. Mag. Supp. Adv. Phys.,* **6,** 219–231.

Clegg, J. A., E. R. Deutsch, and D. H. Griffiths (1956); Rock magnetism in India, *Phil. Mag.,* **1,** 419–431.

Clegg, J. A., C. Radakrishnamurty, and P. W. Sahasrabudhe (1958); Remanent magnetism of the Rajmahal traps of north-eastern India, *Nature,* **181,** 830–831.

Coleman, A. P. (1926); *Ice Ages, Recent and Ancient,* New York.

Collinson, D. W. and K. M. Creer (1960); Measurements in palaeomagnetism, *Methods and techniques in Geophysics,* Vol. 1 (edit. S. K. Runcorn), Interscience, New York-London, 168–210.

Collinson, D. W. and A. E. M. Nairn (1960); A survey of palaeomagnetism, *Overseas Geol. Min. Res.,* **7,** 381–397.

Collinson, D. W. and S. K. Runcorn (1960); Polar wandering and continental drift: evidence of paleomagnetic observations in the United States, *Geol. Soc. Amer. Bull.,* **71,** 915–958.

Compston, W. (1960); The carbon isotopic composition of certain marine invertebrates and coals from the Australian Permian, *Geochim. Cosmochim. Acta,* **18,** 1–22.

Cook, R. M. and J. C. Belshé (1958); Archaeomagnetism: a preliminary report from Britain, *Antiquity,* **32,** 167–178.

Coombs, D. S. and T. Hatherton (1959); Palaeomagnetic studies of Cenozoic volcanic rocks in New Zealand, *Nature,* **184,** 883–884.

Cox, A. (1957); Remanent magnetism of Lower to Middle Eocene basalt flows from Oregon, *Nature,* **179,** 685–686.

Cox, A. (1961); Anomalous remanent magnetization of basalt, *U.S. Geol. Surv. Bull.,* 1083-E, 131–160.

Cox, A. (1962); Analysis of present geomagnetic field for comparison with paleomagnetic results, *J. Geomag. Geoelec.,* **13,** 101–112.

Cox, A. and R. R. Doell (1960); Review of paleomagnetism, *Geol. Soc. Amer. Bull.,* **71,** 645–768.

Cox, A. and R. R. Doell (1961); Palaeomagnetic evidence relevant to a change in the earth's radius, *Nature,* **190,** 36–37.

Cox, A. and R. R. Doell (1962); Magnetic properties of the basalt in hole EM7, Mohole project, *J. Geophys. Res.,* **67,** 3997–4004.

Cox, A., R. R. Doell, and G. B. Dalrymple (1963*a*); Geomagnetic polarity epochs and Pleistocene geochronology, *Nature,* **198,** 1049–1051.

Cox, A., R. R. Doell, and G. B. Dalrymple (1963*b*); Radiometric dating of geomagnetic field reversals, *Science,* **140,** 1021–1023. (1963*c*); Geomagnetic polarity epochs: Sierra Nevada II, *Science,* **142,** 382–385. (1964); Geomagnetic polarity epochs: a lesson in correlation, *Science,* **143,** 351.

Creer, K. M. (1955); Thesis, University of Cambridge.

Creer, K. M. (1957*a*); The natural remanent magnetization of certain stable rocks from Great Britain, *Phil. Trans. Roy. Soc. London A,* **250,** 111–129.

Creer, K. M. (1957*b*); The remanent magnetization of unstable Keuper Marls, *Phil. Trans. Roy. Soc. London A,* **250,** 130–143.

Creer, K. M. (1958); Preliminary palaeomagnetic measurements from South America, *Ann. Geophys.,* **14,** 373–390.

Creer, K. M. (1959); A. C. demagnetization of unstable Triassic Keuper Marls from S.W. England, *Geophys. J.,* **2,** 261–275.

Creer, K. M. (1961); Superparamagnetism in red sandstones, *Geophys. J.,* **5,** 16–28.

Creer, K. M. (1962*a*); The dispersion of the geomagnetic field due to secular variation and its determination for remote times from paleomagnetic data, *J. Geophys. Res.,* **67,** 3461–3476.

Creer, K. M. (1962*b*); An analysis of the geomagnetic field using palaeomagnetic methods, *J. Geomag. Geoelec.,* **13,** 113–119.

Creer, K. M. (1962*c*); Palaeomagnetism of the Serra Geral Formation, *Geophys. J.,* **7,** 1–22.

Creer, K. M. (1962*d*); Palaeomagnetic data from South America, *J. Geomag. Geoelec.,* **13,** 154–165.

Creer, K. M. (1962*e*); On the origin of the magnetization of red beds, *J. Geomag. Geoelec.,* **13,** 86–100.

Creer, K. M. (1962*f*); A statistical enquiry

into the partial remagnetization of folded Old Red Sandstone rocks, *J. Geophys. Res.*, **67**, 1899–1906.

Creer, K. M. (1962g); Comment on "An analysis of the positions of the Earth's magnetic pole in the geological past" by F. M. Hibberd, *Geophys. J.*, **7**, 275–278.

Creer, K. M., E. Irving, and A. E. M. Nairn (1959); Palaeomagnetism of the Great Whin Sill, *Geophys. J.*, **2**, 306–323.

Creer, K. M., E. Irving, A. E. M. Nairn, and S. K. Runcorn (1958); Palaeomagnetic results from different continents and their relation to the problem of continental drift, *Ann. Geophys.*, **14**, 492–501.

Creer, K. M., E. Irving, and S. K. Runcorn (1954); The direction of the geomagnetic field in remote epochs in Great Britain, *J. Geomag. Geoelec.*, **6**, 163–168.

Creer, K. M., E. Irving, and S. K. Runcorn (1957); Geophysical interpretation of palaeomagnetic directions from Great Britain, *Phil. Trans. Roy. Soc. London A*, **250**, 144–156.

Creer, K. M., E. Irving, and S. K. Runcorn (1960); The palaeomagnetic poles for the Lower Jurassic of Europe, *Geophys. J.*, **3**, 367–370.

Cristi, J. M. (1956); Chile, Handbook of South American Geology (ed., W. F. Jenks), *Mem. Geol. Soc. Amer.*, **65**, 189–214.

Curnow, C. E. and L. G. Parry (1954); Oxidation changes in natural ilmenite, *Nature*, **174**, 1101.

Curnow, C. E. and L. G. Parry (1956); Ilmenite from beach sands of New South Wales, *J. and Proc. Roy. Soc. N. S. W.*, **89**, 64–72.

Currie, R. G., C. S. Grommé, and J. Verhoogen (1963); Remanent magnetization of some Upper Cretaceous Granitic Plutons in the Sierra Nevada, California, *J. Geophys. Res.*, **68**, 2263–2279.

Curtis, R., G. Evans, D. J. J. Kinsman, and D. J. Shearman (1963); Association of dolomite and anhydrite in the recent sediments of the Persian Gulf, *Nature*, **197**, 679–680.

Daly, L. (1959); Sur l'anisotropie magnétique dans les roches déformées, et la nature de leur animantation rémanente naturelle, *C. R. Acad. Sci. Paris*, **248**, 2614–2616.

David, P. (1904); Sur la stabilité de la direction d'aimantation dans quelques roches

volcaniques, *C. R. Acad. Sci. Paris*, **138**, 41–42.

David, T. W. E. (1950); *The Geology of the Commonwealth of Australia*, ed. and supplemented by W. R. Browne, vol. 1, Arnold, London, 747 pp.

David, T. W. E. and C. A. Sussmilch (1931); Upper Paleozoic glaciations in Australia, *Bull. Geol. Soc. Amer.*, **42**, 482–522.

Davis, G. L., G. R. Tilton, L. T. Aldrich, G. W. Wetherill, and H. Faul (1956); The age of rocks and minerals, *Ann. Rep. Dir. Geophys. Lab., Carnegie Inst.*, 164–171.

Day, A. A. and S. K. Runcorn (1955); Polar wandering, some geological, dynamical, and palaeomagnetic aspects, *Nature*, **176**, 422.

Delesse, A. (1849); Quoted in Chevallier (1925).

Deutsch, E. R. (1958); Recent palaeomagnetic evidence for the northward movement of India, *J. Alberta Soc. Petr. Geol.*, **6**, 155–162.

Deutsch, E. R., C. Radakrishnamurty, and P. W. Sahasrabudhe (1958); The remanent magnetism of some lavas in the Deccan Traps, *Phil. Mag.*, **3**, 170–184.

Deutsch, E. R., C. Radakrishnamurty, and P. W. Sahasrabudhe (1959); Palaeomagnetism of the Deccan Traps, *Ann. Geophys.*, **15**, 39–59.

Deutsch, E. R. and N. D. Watkins (1961); Direction of the geomagnetic field during the Triassic period in Siberia, *Nature*, **189**, 543–545.

Dickson, G. O. (1962a); Thermoremanent magnetization of igneous rocks, *J. Geophys. Res.*, **67**, 912–915.

Dickson, G. O. (1962b); The origin of small, randomly directed magnetic moments in demagnetized rock, *J. Geophys. Res.*, **67**, 4943–4945.

Dickson, G. O. (1963); The palaeomagnetism of Peat's Ridge Dolerite and Mt. Tomah Basalt, *J. and Proc. Roy. Soc. New South Wales*, **96**, 129–132.

Dietzel, G. F. L. (1960); Geology and Permian paleomagnetism of the Merano region, province of Bolzano, N. Italy, Thesis Utrecht, Geologica Ultraiectina, no. 4, 1–57.

Doell, R. R. (1955); Palaeomagnetic study of rocks from the Grand Canyon of the Colorado River, *Nature*, **176**, 1167.

Doell, R. R. (1956); Remanent magnetization

of the Upper Miocene "Blue" Sandstones of California, *Tr. Amer. Geophys. Union,* **37,** 156–167.

Doell, R. R. (1957); Crystallization magnetization, *Phil. Mag. Supp. Adv. Phys.,* **6,** 327–332.

Doell, R. R. and A. Cox (1961*a*); Paleomagnetism, *Advances in Geophysics,* **8,** 221–313; Academic Press, New York.

Doell, R. R. and A. Cox (1961*b*); Palaeomagnetism of Hawaiian lava flows, *Nature,* **192,** 645–646.

Doell, R. R. and A. Cox (1963); The accuracy of paleomagnetic method as evaluated from historic Hawaiian lava flows, *J. Geophys. Res.,* **68,** 1997–2009.

Domen, H. (1958*a*); On the remanent magnetism of the gabbro of Ko-yama, Yamaguchi prefecture, West Japan, *Bull. Fac. Ed., Yamaguchi Univ.,* **7,** 35–39.

Domen, H. (1958*b*); An experimental study of remanent magnetism caused by one-directional high pressure, *Bull. Fac. Ed., Yamaguchi Univ.,* **7,** 41–43.

Domen, H. (1960); Some magnetic properties of the early Pleistocene basalts in the northern part of Yamaguchi prefecture, West Japan, *Bull. Fac. Ed., Yamaguchi Univ.,* **9,** 31–42.

Domen, H. (1961*a*); A note on remanent magnetism caused by impulsive pressure, *Bull. Fac. Educ. Yamaguchi Univ.,* **10,** 71–76.

Domen, H. (1961*b*); A memoir on the space variation of the natural remanent magnetism of rocks, *Bull. Fac. Educ. Yamaguchi Univ.,* **10,** 77–83.

Domen, H. (1962); Piezo-remanent magnetization in rocks and its field evidence, *J. Geomag. Geoelec.,* **13,** 66–72.

Dorman, F. H. and E. D. Gill (1959*a*); Oxygen isotope palaeotemperature measurements on Australian fossils, *Proc. Roy. Soc. Victoria,* **71,** 73–99.

Dorman, F. H. and E. D. Gill (1959*b*); Oxygen isotope paleotemperature determinations of Australian Cainozoic fossils, *Science,* **130,** 1576.

Dott, R. H. (1961); Squantam "Tillite" Massachusetts—evidence of glaciation or subaqueous mass movements? *Geol. Soc. Amer. Bull.,* **72,** 1289–1305.

Du Bois, P. M. (1955); Palaeomagnetic measurements of the Keweenawan, *Nature,* **176,** 506.

Du Bois, P. M. (1957); Comparison of palaeo-

magnetic results for selected rocks of Great Britain and North America, *Phil. Mag. Supp. Adv. Phys.,* **6,** 177–186.

Du Bois, P. M. (1958*a*); Palaeomagnetism and continental drift, *Trans. Roy. Soc. Canada,* **52,** 17–26.

Du Bois, P. M. (1958*b*); Palaeomagnetism and geological correlation, *Ann. Geophys.,* **14,** 509–513.

Du Bois, P. M. (1959*a*); Correlation of Keweenawan rocks of Lake Superior District by palaeomagnetic methods, *Proc. Geol. Assoc. Canada,* **11,** 115–128.

Du Bois, P. M. (1959*b*); Late Tertiary geomagnetic field in northwestern Canada, *Nature,* **183,** 1617–1618.

Du Bois, P. M. (1959*c*); Palaeomagnetism and rotation of Newfoundland, *Nature,* **184,** 63–64.

Du Bois, P. M. (1962); Palaeomagnetism and correlation of Keweenawan rocks, *Geol. Surv. Canada Bull.,* **71,** 75 pp.

Du Bois, P. M., E. Irving, N. D. Opdyke, S. K. Runcorn, and M. R. Banks (1957); The geomagnetic field in Upper Triassic times in the United States, *Nature,* **180,** 1186–1187.

DuBois, R. L. (1961); Remanent magnetism of Carboniferous limestone, *Geophys. J.,* **5,** 230–234.

DuBois, R. L. (1962); Magnetic characteristics of a massive hematitic body, *J. Geophys. Res.,* **67,** 2887–2893.

Du Toit, A. L. (1937); *Our wandering continents,* Oliver and Boyd, Edinburgh, 336 pp.

Egyed, L. (1957); A new dynamic conception of the internal constitution of the Earth, *Geol. Rundschau,* **46,** 101–121.

Egyed, L. (1960); Some remarks on continental drift, *Geofis. pura appl.,* **45,** 115–116.

Egyed, L. (1961); Palaeomagnetism and the ancient radii of the Earth, *Nature,* **190,** 1097–1098.

Einarsson, T. (1957*a*); Magneto-geological mapping in Iceland with the use of a compass, *Phil. Mag. Supp. Adv. Phys.,* **6,** 232–239.

Einarsson, T. (1957*b*); Der paläomagnetismus der isländischen basalte und seine stratigraphische Bedeutung, *Neues Jb. Geol. Paläontol. Mh.,* **4,** 159–175.

Einarsson, T. (1957*c*); Über den Wert alter sedimente für paläomagnetische Zwecke, *Neues Jb. Geol. Paläontol. Mh.,* **5,** 193–195.

Einarsson, T. and T. Sigurgeirsson (1955); Rock magnetism in Iceland, *Nature,* **175,** 892.

Elliot, R. B. and W. D. Evans (1963); A Beacon Sandstone: its petrology and hydrocarbon content, *Nature,* **199,** 686–687.

Epstein, S. and H. A. Lowenstam (1953); Temperature-shell-growth relations of recent and interglacial Pleistocene shoalwater biota from Bermuda, *J. Geol.,* **61,** 424–438.

Erickson, G. P. and J. L. Kulp (1960); Potassium-argon measurements on the Palisades diabase and associated basalts (Abs.), *J. Geophys. Res.,* **65,** 2487–2488.

Everdingen, R. O. van (1960); Studies on the igneous rock complex of the Oslo region, *Skift. Norske Videnskaps-Akad. Oslo,* **1,** 1–80.

Everitt, C. W. F. (1960); Rock magnetism and the origin of the Midland Basalts, *Geophys. J.,* **3,** 203–210.

Everitt, C. W. F. (1961a); The magnetic properties of three Carboniferous sills, *Phil. Mag.,* **6,** 698–699.

Everitt, C. W. F. (1961b); Thermoremanent magnetization(I). Experiments on single domain grains, *Phil. Mag.,* **6,** 713–726.

Everitt, C. W. F. (1962a); Thermoremanent magnetization(II). Experiments on multidomain grains, *Phil. Mag.,* **7,** 583–597.

Everitt, C. W. F. (1962b); Thermoremanent magnetization(III). Theory of multidomain grains, *Phil. Mag.,* **7,** 599–616.

Everitt, C. W. F. (1962c); Self-reversal of magnetization in a shale containing pyrrhotite, *Phil. Mag.,* **7,** 831–842.

Everitt, C. W. F. and J. C. Belshé (1960); Palaeomagnetism of the British Carboniferous System, *Phil. Mag.,* **5,** 675–685.

Everitt, C. W. F. and J. A. Clegg (1962); A field test of palaeomagnetic stability, *Geophys. J.,* **6,** 312–319.

Evernden, J. F., G. H. Curtis, and J. Lipson (1957); Potassium-argon dating of igneous rocks, *Bull. Amer. Assoc. Petroleum Geol.,* **41,** 2120–2127.

Evernden, J. F. and J. R. Richards (1962); Potassium-argon ages in eastern Australia, *J. Geol. Soc. Australia,* **9,** 1–50.

Evison, F. F. (1961); Rock magnetism in western Europe as an indication of continental growth, *Mon. Not. Roy. Astr. Soc. Geophys. Supp.,* **4,** 320–335.

Evison, F. F. (1962); Rock magnetism and low-angle faulting, *Nature,* **194,** 644–646.

Faure, G., P. M. Hurley, H. W. Fairbairn, and W. H. Pinson (1962); Isotopic composition of strontium in Continental Basic Intrusives, *J. Geophys. Res.,* **67,** 3356–3557.

Faure, G., P. M. Hurley, H. W. Fairbairn, and W. H. Pinson (1963); Age of the Great Dyke of Southern Rhodesia, *Nature,* **200,** 769–770.

Feinberg, F. S. and N. N. Dashkevitson (1960); The nature of the magnetization of Traps in the lower reaches of the Angara River, *Akad. Nauk. SSSR Izv. (Siberian Branch) Geol. Geophys. Sec.,* no. 6, 116–122.

Fisher, R. A. (1953); Dispersion on a sphere, *Proc. Roy. Soc. London A,* **217,** 295–305.

Folgerhaiter, G. (1899); Sur le variations séculaires de l'inclinaison magnetique dans antiquité, *J. Phys.,* **8** (3rd ser.), 5–16. (References to earlier publications in Italian journals are given in this paper.)

Fourmarier, P. (1950); *Principles de geologie,* Masson, Paris.

Fuller, M. D. (1960); Anisotropy of susceptibility and the natural remanent magnetization of some Welsh slates, *Nature,* **186,** 791–792.

Fuller, M. D. (1963); Magnetic anisotropy and paleomagnetism, *J. Geophys. Res.,* **68,** 293–309.

Fuller, M. D. and S. Uyeda (1962); Discussion of magnetic anisotropy, *Proc. Benedum Earth Magnetism Symp.,* 117–121.

Gelletich, H. (1937); Uber magnetitfuhrende eruptive Gänge und Gangesysteme im mittleven Teil des südlichen Transvaals, *Beitr. Angew. Geophys.,* **6,** 337–406.

Gilbert, W. (1600); *De Magnete,* trans., P. F. Mottely (1893), Dover, New York, 1958, 368 pp.

Girdler, R. W. (1958); The relationship of the Red Sea to the East African rift system, *Quart. J. Geol. Soc. London,* **114,** 79–105.

Girdler, R. W. (1959a); Possible reversal of the Earth's magnetic field in the Jurassic Period, *Nature,* **184,** 540–541.

Girdler, R. W. (1959b); A palaeomagnetic study of some Lower Jurassic rocks of N. W. Europe, *Geophys. J.,* **2,** 353–363.

Girdler, R. W. (1960); The palaeomagnetic poles for the Lower Jurassic of Europe, *Geophys. J.,* **3,** 371–373.

Girdler, R. W. (1961); Some preliminary

measurements of anisotropy of magnetic susceptibility of rocks, *Geophys. J.*, **5**, 197–206.

Girdler, R. W. (1963); Sur l'application de pressions hydrostatiques a des aimantations thermorémanentes, *Ann. Géophys.*, **19**, 118–121.

Gold, T. (1955); Instability of the Earth's axis of rotation, *Nature*, **175**, 526.

Goldich, S. S., H. Baadsgaard, G. Edwards, and C. E. Weaver (1959); Investigations in radioactivity—dating of sediments, *Bull. Amer. Assoc. Petrol. Geol.*, **43**, 654–662.

Goldich, S. S., H. Baadsgaard, and A. O. Nier (1957); Investigations in A-K dating, *Trans. Amer. Geophys. Union*, **38**, 547–551.

Gorter, E. W. (1957); Chemistry and magnetic properties of some ferrimagnetic oxides like those occurring in nature, *Phil. Mag. Supp. Adv. Phys.*, **6**, 336–361.

Gorter, E. W. and J. A. Schulkes (1953); Reversal of spontaneous magnetization as a function of temperature in LiFeCr spinels, *Phys. Rev.*, **90**, 487–488.

Gough, D. I. (1956); A study of the palaeomagnetism of the Pilansberg dykes, *Mon. Not. Roy. Astr. Soc. Geophys. Supp.*, **7**, 196–213.

Gough, D. I. and C. B. van Niekerk (1959); A study of palaeomagnetism of the Bushveld Gabbro, *Phil. Mag.*, **4**, 126–136.

Gough, D. I. and N. D. Opdyke (1963); The palaeomagnetism of the Lupata Alkaline Volcanics, *Geophys. J.*, **7**, 457–468.

Grabovsky, M. A. and S. Y. Brodskaya (1958); Normal magnetization and thermomagnetization of anisotropic rocks, *Izv. Akad. Nauk. SSSR ser. Geofiz.*, **8**, 977–988.

Grabovsky, M. A., G. N. Petrova, and L. I. Isakova (1956); On the emergence of thermoremanent magnetism of rocks, *Akad. Nauk. SSSR Izv. Ser. Geophys.*, 56–66.

Grabovsky, M. A. and A. H. Pushkov (1954); On the question of the emergence of residual magnetism of reversely polarized rocks, *Akad. Nauk. SSSR Izv. Geofiz. ser.*, 320.

Graham, J. W. (1949); The stability and significance of magnetism in sedimentary rocks, *J. Geophys. Res.*, **54**, 131–167.

Graham, J. W. (1953); Changes of ferromagnetic minerals and their bearing on ferromagnetic properties of rocks, *J. Geophys. Res.*, **58**, 243–260.

Graham, J. W. (1954a); Rock magnetism and the Earth's magnetic field during Paleozoic time, *J. Geophys. Res.*, **59**, 215–222.

Graham, J. W. (1954b); Magnetic susceptibility anisotropy an unexploited petrofabric element, *Geol. Soc. Amer. Bull.*, **65**, 1257–1258.

Graham, J. W. (1955); Evidence of polar shift since Triassic time, *J. Geophys. Res.*, **60**, 329–347.

Graham, J. W. (1956); Palaeomagnetism and magnetostriction, *J. Geophys. Res.*, **61**, 735–739.

Graham, J. W. (1957); The role of magnetostriction in rock magnetism, *Phil. Mag. Supp. Adv. Phys.*, **6**, 362–363.

Graham, J. W., A. F. Buddington, and J. R. Balsley (1957); Stressed-induced magnetizations of some rocks with analyzed magnetic minerals, *J. Geophys. Res.*, **62**, 465–474.

Graham, K. W. T. (1961); The re-magnetization of a surface outcrop by lightning currents, *Geophys. J.*, **6**, 85–102.

Graham, K. W. T. and A. L. Hales (1957); Palaeomagnetic measurements on Karroo dolerites, *Phil. Mag. Supp. Adv. Phys.*, **6**, 149–161.

Graham, K. W. T. and A. L. Hales (1961); Preliminary paleomagnetic measurements on Silurian sediments from South Africa, *Geophys. J.*, **5**, 318–325.

Granar, L. (1958); Magnetic measurements on Swedish varved sediments, *Arkiv. för Geofys.*, **3**, 1–40.

Green, Robert (1961); Palaeoclimatic significance of Evaporites, *Descriptive Palaeoclimatology* (ed., A. E. M. Nairn), Interscience, New York, 61–88.

Green, Ronald (1958); Polar wandering, a random walk problem, *Nature*, **182**, 382–383.

Green, Ronald (1959); Thesis, Australian National University, Canberra.

Green, Ronald (1961); Palaeomagnetism of some Devonian rock formations in Australia, *Tellus*, **13**, 119–124.

Green, Ronald and E. Irving (1958); The paleomagnetism of the Cainozic basalts of Australia, *Proc. Roy. Soc. Victoria*, **70**, 1–17.

Griffiths, D. H. (1953); Remanent magnetism of varved clays from Sweden, *Nature*, **172**, 539.

Griffiths, D. H. (1954); The remanent magnetism of varved clays from Sweden, *J. Geomag. Geoelec.,* **6,** 217–220.

Griffiths, D. H. (1955); The remanent magnetism of varved clays from Sweden, *Mon. Not. Roy. Astr. Soc., Geophys. Supp.,* **7,** 103–114.

Griffiths, D. H. and R. F. King (1954); Natural magnetization of igneous and sedimentary rocks, *Nature,* **173,** 1114.

Griffiths, D. H., R. F. King, and A. E. Wright (1957); Some field and laboratory studies of the depositional remanence of recent sediments, *Phil. Mag. Supp. Adv. Phys.,* **6,** 306–316.

Griffiths, D. H., R. F. King, and A. E. Wright (1958); An assessment of the difficulties involved in using Quaternary varved sediments for palaeomagnetic studies of the secular variation, *Ann. Geophys.,* **14,** 515–518.

Griffiths, D. H., R. F. King, A. I. Rees, and A. E. Wright (1960); The remanent magnetization of some recent varved sediments, *Proc. Roy. Soc. A,* **256,** 359–383.

Grommé, C. S. and R. L. Hay (1963); Magnetization of bed I, Olduvai Gorge, Tanganyika, *Nature,* **200,** 560–561.

Gross, W. H. and D. W. Strangway (1961); Remanent magnetism and the origin of hard hematites in Precambrian banded iron formation, *Econ. Geol.,* **56,** 1345–1362.

Gusev, B. V. (1959); Age of alkaline-ultrabasic rocks of Maymecha-Kotuy region according to paleomagnetic data, *Inf. Bull. Inst. Geol. Arkitiki, Leningrad,* 30–33.

Gus'kova, N. G. (1959); Paleomagnetic studies of sedimentary rocks of southeastern Turkmenia, *Akad. Nauk. SSSR Izv. Geophys. Ser.,* 311–349.

Haigh, G. (1958); The process of magnetization by chemical change, *Phil. Mag.,* **3,** 267–286.

Hales, A. L. (1960); Research at the Bernard Price Institute of Geophysical Research, University of the Witwatersrand, Johannesburg, *Proc. Roy. Soc. London A,* **258,** 1–26.

Hall, J. M. and R. N. Neale (1960); Stress effects on thermoremanent magnetization, *Nature,* **188,** 805–806.

Hallimond, A. F. and E. F. Herroun (1933); Laboratory determinations of the magnetic properties of certain igneous rocks, *Proc. Roy. Soc. London A,* **141,** 302–314.

Hamilton, N. (1963); Susceptibility anisotropy measurements on some Silurian siltstone, *Nature,* **197,** 170–171.

Hanuš, V. and K. Miroslav (1963); Palaeomagnetic dating of hydrothermal deposits in Czechoslovakia, *Geophys. J.,* **8,** 82–101.

Hargraves, R. B. (1959); Magnetic anisotropy and remanent magnetism in hemo-ilmenite from ore deposits at Allard Lake, *J. Geophys. Res.,* **64,** 1565–1578.

Hargraves, R. B. and A. G. Fischer (1959); Remanent magnetism in Jurassic red limestones and radiolarites from the Alps, *Geophys. J.,* **2,** 34–41.

Harland, W. B. and D. E. T. Bidgood (1959); Palaeomagnetism in some Norwegian sparagmites and the late Pre-Cambrian ice age, *Nature,* **184,** 1860.

Harrington, H. J. (1956); Handbook of South American Geology (ed., W. F. Jenks) *Mem. Geol. Soc. Amer.,* Argentina, **65,** 133–165.

Harrison, W. and J. Terasmae (1961); Remanent magnetism in silts of Pleistocene age from North America, *J. Sed. Petr.,* **31,** 448–452.

Harshbarger, J. W. (1949); quoted in Runcorn (1961).

Hatherton, T. (1954*a*); The permanent magnetisation of horizontal volcanic sheets, *J. Geophys. Res.,* **59,** 223–232.

Hatherton, T. (1945*b*); The magnetic properties of the Whakamaru ignimbrites, *New Zealand J. Sci. Techn. B.,* **35,** 421–432.

Hess, H. H. (1956); Discussion, *Amer. J. Sci.,* **254,** 446–451.

Hibberd, F. (1961); Secondary magnetization and the palaeomagnetism of some Pliocene rocks of Japan, *J. Geomag. Geoelec.,* **12,** 222–226.

Hibberd, F. H. (1962); An analysis of the positions of the Earth's magnetic pole in the geological past, *Geophys. J.,* **6,** 221–244.

Hilgenberg, O. C. (1962*a*); Paläopollagen der Erde, *N. Jb. Geol. Palaont. Abh.,* **116,** 1–56.

Hilgenberg, O. C. (1962*b*); Rock magnetism and the Earth's palaeopoles, *Geofis. Pura Appl.,* **53,** 52–54.

Hill, D. (1948); The distribution and sequence of Carboniferous coral faunas, *Geol. Mag.,* **85,** 121–148.

Hill, D. (1950); The Ordovician corals, *Proc. Roy. Soc. Queensland,* **62,** 1–28.

Hill, D. (1957); The sequence and distribution of Upper Palaeozoic coral faunas, *Austr. J. Sci.*, **19**, 42–61.

Hill, D. (1958a); Distribution and sequence of Silurian coral faunas, *J. and Proc. Roy. Soc. N. S. W.*, **92**, 151–173.

Hill, D. (1958b); Sakmarian geography, *Geol. Rundschau*, **47**, 590–600.

Hilten, D. van (1960); Geology and Permian Paleomagnetism of the Val-di-non area, Thesis Utrecht, *Geologica Ultraiectina*, no. 5, 1–95.

Hilten, D. van (1962a); A deviating Permian pole from rocks in northern Italy, *Geophys. J.*, **6**, 377–390.

Hilten, D. van (1962b); Presentation of paleomagnetic data, polar wandering, and continental drift, *Amer. J. Sci.*, **260**, 401–426.

Hilten, D. van (1963); Palaeomagnetic indications of an increase in the Earth's radius, *Nature*, **200**, 1277–1279.

Holmes, A. (1960); A revised geological time scale, *Trans. Geol. Soc. Edinburgh*, **17** (pt. 3), 183–216.

Hood, P. J. (1958); quoted by Cox and Doell (1960).

Hood, P. J. (1961); Paleomagnetic study of the Sudbury Basin, *J. Geophys. Res.*, **66**, 1235–1241.

Hospers, J. (1951); Remanent magnetism of rocks and the history of the geomagnetic field, *Nature*, **168**, 1111–1112.

Hospers, J. (1953–1954); Reversals of the main geomagnetic field I, II, and III, *Proc. Kon. Nederl. Akad. Wet. B*, **56**, 467–476, 477–491; **57**, 112–121.

Hospers, J. (1954a); Rock magnetism and polar wandering, *Nature*, **173**, 1183.

Hospers, J. (1954b); Summary of studies in rock magnetism, *J. Geomag. Geoelec.*, **6**, 172–175.

Hospers, J. (1955); Rock magnetism and polar wandering, *J. Geol.*, **63**, 59–74.

Hospers, J. and H. A. K. Charlesworth (1954); The natural permanent magnetization of the Lower Basalts of Northern Ireland, *Mon. Not. Roy. Astr. Soc. Geophys. Supp.*, **7**, 32–43.

Howell, L. G. (1962); Chemical and crystal controlled magnetization of rocks, *Amer. J. Sci.*, **260**, 539–549.

Howell, L. G. and J. D. Martinez (1957); Polar movement as indicated by rock magnetism, *Geophysics*, **22**, 384–397.

Howell, L. G., J. D. Martinez, A. Frosch, and E. H. Statham (1960); A note on chemical magnetization of rocks, *Geophysics*, **25**, 1094–1099.

Howell, L. G., J. D. Martinez, and E. H. Statham (1958); Some observations on rock magnetism, *Geophysics*, **23**, 285–298.

Humboldt, A. von (1797); Uber die merkwürdige magnetische Polarität einer Gebirgskuppe von Serpentinstein, *Greus neues J. Physik*, **4**, 136–140.

Irving, E. (1954); Thesis, Univ. of Cambridge.

Irving, E. (1956a); The magnetization of the Mesozoic dolerites of Tasmania, *Pap. Proc. Roy. Soc. Tasmania*, **90**, 157–168.

Irving, E. (1956b); Palaeomagnetic and palaeoclimatological aspects of polar wandering, *Geofis. Pura Appl.*, **33**, 23–41.

Irving, E. (1957a); The origin of the paleomagnetism of the Torridonian Sandstone Series of Northwest Scotland, *Phil. Trans. Roy. Soc. London A*, **250**, 100–110.

Irving, E. (1957b); Directions of magnetization in the Carboniferous glacial varves of Australia, *Nature*, **180**, 280–281.

Irving, E. (1957c); Rock magnetism: a new approach to some paleogeographic problems, *Phil. Mag. Supp. Adv. Phys.*, **6**, 194–218.

Irving, E. (1958a); Rock magnetism: a new approach to the problem of polar wandering and continental drift, *Continental Drift—a symposium*, University of Tasmania, Hobart, 1956, 24–61.

Irving, E. (1958b); Palaeogeographic reconstructions from palaeomagnetism, *Geophys. J.*, **1**, 224–237.

Irving, E. (1959); Palaeomagnetic pole positions: a survey and analysis, *Geophys. J.*, **2**, 51–79.

Irving, E. (1960–1962); Palaeomagnetic directions and pole positions, parts I–VII, *Geophys. J.*, **3**, 96–111; **3**, 444–449; **5**, 72–79; **6**, 263–267; **7**, 263–274; (with P. M. Stott) **8**, 249–257; **9**.

Irving, E. (1961); Paleomagnetic methods: a discussion of a recent paper by A. E. M. Nairn, *J. Geol.*, **69**, 226–231.

Irving, E. (1962); An analysis of the positions of the Earth's magnetic pole in the geological past, *Geophys. J.*, **7**, 279–283.

Irving, E. (1963); Paleomagnetism of the Narrabeen Chocolate Shale and the Tasmanian Dolerite, *J. Geophys. Res.*, **68**, 2283–2287.

Irving, E. and M. R. Banks (1961); Paleomagnetic results from the Upper Triassic lavas of Massachusetts, *J. Geophys. Res.,* **66,** 1935–1939.

Irving, E. and J. C. Briden (1962); Palaeolatitude of evaporite deposits, *Nature,* **196,** 425–428.

Irving, E. and T. F. Gaskell (1962); The palaeogeographic latitude of oil fields, *Geophys. J.,* **7,** 54–63.

Irving, E. and Ronald Green (1957a); Palaeomagnetic evidence from the Cretaceous and Cainozoic, *Nature,* **179,** 1064–1065.

Irving, E. and Ronald Green (1957b); The palaeomagnetism of the Kainozoic basalts of Victoria, *Mon. Not. Roy. Astr. Soc. Geophys. Supp.,* **7,** 347–359.

Irving, E. and Ronald Green (1958); Polar wandering relative to Australia, *Geophys. J.,* **1,** 64–72.

Irving, E. and A. Major (1964); Post-depositional detrital remanent magnetization in a synthetic sediment, *Sedimentology,* **3.**

Irving, E. and L. G. Parry (1963); The magnetism of some Permian rocks from New South Wales, *Geophys. J.,* **7,** 395–411.

Irving, E., W. A. Robertson and P. M. Stott (1963); The significance of the paleomagnetic results from Mesozoic rocks of eastern Australia, *J. Geophys. Res.,* **68,** 2313–2317.

Irving, E., W. A. Robertson, P. M. Stott, D. H. Tarling, and M. A. Ward (1961); Treatment of partially stable sedimentary rocks showing planar distribution of directions of magnetization, *J. Geophys. Res.,* **66,** 1927–1933.

Irving, E. and S. K. Runcorn (1957); Analysis of the palaeomagnetism of the Torridonian Sandstone Series of Northwest Scotland I, *Phil. Trans. Roy. Soc. A.,* **250,** 83–99.

Irving, E., P. M. Stott, and M. A. Ward (1961); Demagnetization of igneous rocks by alternating magnetic fields, *Phil. Mag.,* **6,** 225–241.

Irving, E. and D. H. Tarling (1961); The paleomagnetism of the Aden Volcanics, *J. Geophys. Res.,* **66,** 549–556.

Irving, E. and M. A. Ward (1964); A statistical model of the geomagnetic field, *Geofis. Pura Appl.,* **57,** 25–30.

Ishikawa, Y. (1958); An order-disorder transformation phenomenon in the $FeTiO_3$–Fe_2O_3 solid solution series, *J. Phys. Soc. Japan,* **13,** 828–837.

Ishikawa, Y. and S. Akimoto (1958); Magnetic property and crystal chemistry of ilmenite ($MeTiO_3$) and hematite (αFe_2O_3) system; (I) crystal chemistry; (II) magnetic property, *J. Phys. Soc. Japan,* **13,** 1110–1118 and 1298–1310.

Ising, G. (1943); On the magnetic properties of varved clay, *Ark. Mat. Astr. Phys.,* **29A,** 1–37.

Ising, G. (1954); Discussion to Dr. D. H. Griffith's communication, "The remanent magnetism of varved clays from Sweden," *J. Geomag. Geoelec.,* **6,** 221–222.

Ito, H. (1963); Natural remanent magnetism of Tertiary plutonic rocks affected by tectonic movements of land-mass in Japan, *J. Geomag. Geoelec.,* **15,** 37–42.

Jaeger, J. C. (1957a); The temperature in the neighborhood of a cooling intrusive sheet, *Amer. J. Sci.,* **255,** 306–318.

Jaeger, J. C. (1957b); The variation of density and magnetic properties in dolerite sills, *Pap. Proc. Roy. Soc. Tasmania,* **91,** 143–144.

Jaeger, J. C. and Ronald Green (1956); The use of the cooling-history of thick intrusive sheets for the study of the secular variation of the Earth's magnetic field, *Geofis. Pura Appl.,* **35,** 49–53.

Jaeger, J. C. and Ronald Green (1958); A cross-section of a tholeiite sill, *Dolerite, a symposium,* University of Tasmania, Hobart, 26–37.

Jaeger, J. C. and E. Irving (1957); Palaeomagnetism and the reconstructions of Gondwanaland, *C. R. 3rd Congr. Pac. Ind. Oc. Sc. A. Tananarive,* 1957, 233–242.

Jaeger, J. C. and Germaine A. Joplin (1955); Rock magnetism and the differentiation of dolerite sill, *J. Geol. Soc. Australia,* **2,** 1–19.

Jaeger, J. C. and Germaine A. Joplin (1956); Discussion, *Amer. J. Sci.,* **254,** 443–446.

Jaeger, J. C. and R. F. Thyer (1960); Geophysics in Australia, *Geophys. J.,* **3,** 450–461.

Janovsky, B. M. and L. E. Sholpo (1962); Magnetic viscosity of the Far East Upper Tertiary basalts, *J. Geomag. Geoelec.,* **13,** 73–79.

Jeffreys, H. (1959); *The Earth,* Cambridge University Press, 420 pp.

Johnson, E. A., T. Murphy, and O. W. Torreson (1948); Pre-history of the Earth's magnetic field, *Terr. Magn. Atmos. Elec.*, **53**, 349–372.

Joplin, Germaine A. (1957); the problem of the quartz dolerite: some significant facts concerning mineral volume, grain size, and fabric, *Pap. Proc. Roy. Soc. Tasmania*, **91**, 129–143.

Kalashnikov, A. G. (1961); The history of the geomagnetic field, *Akad. Nauk. Izv. SSSR Geophys. Ser.*, 1243–1279.

Kato, Y. and T. Nagata (1953); On the secular variation in geomagnetic declination in the historic time in Japan, *Proc. 7th Pacific Sci. Congr.*, **2**, 562–564.

Kato, Y., A. Takagi, and I. Kato (1954); Reverse remanent magnetism of dyke and basaltic andesite, *J. Geomag. Geoelec.*, **6**, 206–207.

Kawai, N. (1951); Magnetic polarization of Tertiary rocks in Japan, *J. Geophys. Res.*, **56**, 73–79.

Kawai, N. (1954); Instability of natural remanent magnetism of rocks, *J. Geomag. Geoelec.*, **6**, 208, 209.

Kawai, N. (1955); Magnetism of rocks and solid phase transformation in ferromagnetic minerals III, *Proc. Japan Acad.*, **31**, 346–351.

Kawai, N. (1956); Exsolution of titanomagnetite and its time effect on rock-magnetism, III, *Proc. Japan Acad.*, **32**, 464–468.

Kawai, N. (1957); Magnetism of the Earth's crust, *J. Geomag. Geoelec.*, **9**, 140–156.

Kawai, N. (1959); Subsolidus phase relation in titanomagnetite and its significance in rock magnetism, *Congr. Geol. Intern., Mexico 1956*, section 11A, 103–120.

Kawai, N., H. Ito, and S. Kume (1961); Deformation of the Japanese Islands as inferred from rock magnetism, *Geophys. J.*, **6**, 124–130.

Kawai, N., H. Ito, K. Yaskawa, and S. Kume (1959); Chemical-pressure remanent magnetism in sedimentary and metamorphic rocks, *Mem. College Sci. Univ. Kyoto*, **26**, 235–239.

Kawai, N. and Y. Kang (1962); Magnetism of black shales and red sandstone in Japan, *J. Geomag. Geoelec.*, **13**, 80–83.

Kawai, N. and S. Kume (1953); The thermal fluctuation after effect found in the natural remanent polarization of rocks, *J. Geomag. Geoelec.*, **5**, 66–70.

Kawai, N. and S. Kume (1959); Observation of magnetic chronic drag over geologic time, *J. Phys. Radium*, **20**, 258–261.

Kawai, N., S. Kume, and H. Ito (1962); study of magnetization of the Japanese rocks, *J. Geomag. Geoelec.*, **13**, 150–153.

Kawai, N., S. Kume, and S. Sasajima (1954a, b); Magnetism of rocks and solid phase transformation in ferromagnetic minerals I and II, *Proc. Japan Acad.*, **30**, 588–593, and 865–868.

Kawai, N., S. Kume, and S. Sasajima (1956); Exsolution of titanomagnetite and its time effect on rock-magnetism, II, *Proc. Japan Acad.*, **32**, 459–463.

Kawai, N., S. Kume, and K. Yasukawa (1956); Exsolution of titanomagnetite and its time effect on rock-magnetism, I, *Proc. Japan Acad.*, **32**, 455–458.

Kawai, N. and G. W. Massé (1959); Application of rock magnetism to the formation of mountains, *Mem. Coll. Sci. Univ. Kyoto*, **26**, 229–234.

Kern, J. W. (1961a); Effects of moderate stresses on directions of thermoremanent magnetization, *J. Geophys. Res.*, **66**, 3801–3805.

Kern, J. W. (1961b); The effect of stress on the susceptibility and magnetization of a partially magnetized multidomain system, *J. Geophys. Res.*, **66**, 3807–3816.

Kern, J. W. (1961c); Stress stability of remanent magnetization, *J. Geophys. Res.*, **66**, 3817–3820.

Khan, M. A. (1960); the remanent magnetization of the basic Tertiary igneous rocks of Skye. Inverness-shire, *Geophys. J.*, **3**, 45–62.

Khan, M. A. (1962); The anisotropy of magnetic susceptibility of some igneous and metamorphic rocks, *J. Geophys. Res.*, **67**, 2873–2885.

Khramov, A. N. (1958); *Palaeomagnetism and stratigraphic correlation*, Gostoptechizdat, Leningrad, 218 pp. (English translation by A. J. Lojkine pub. Geophys. Dept. Australian National University, Canberra, 1960).

Khramov, A. H., G. N. Petrova, A. G. Komarov, and V. V. Kotchegura (1961); Methods in paleomagnetic investigations, Gostoptechizdat, Leningrad, 130 pp.

Kiersch, G. A. (1950); Small-scale structures and other features of Navajo Sandstone, northern part of San Rafael Swell, Utah, *Amer. Assoc. Petr. Geol. Bull.*, **34**, 923–942.

King, C. A. M. (1951); Depth of disturbance of sea beaches by waves, *J. Sed. Petr.*, **21**, 131–134.

King, L. C. (1958); The origin and significance of the suboceanic ridges, *Continental Drift —a symposium*, University of Tasmania, Hobart, 1956, 62–102.

King, L. C. (1961); The palaeoclimatology of Gondwanaland during the Palaeozoic and Mesozoic Eras, *Descriptive Palaeoclimatology* (ed., A. E. M. Nairn), Interscience, New York, 307–339.

King, R. F. (1955); The remanent magnetism of artificially deposited sediments, *Mon. Not. Roy. Astr. Soc. Geophys. Supp.*, **7**, 115–134.

King, R. F. and A. I. Rees (1962); The measurement of the anisotropy of magnetic susceptibility of rocks by the torque method, *J. Geophys. Res.*, **67**, 1565–1572.

Kintzinger, P. R. (1957); Paleomagnetic survey of Triassic rocks from Arizona, *Bull. Geol. Soc. Amer.*, **68**, 931–932.

Knight, S. H. (1929); Quoted in Runcorn (1961).

Kobayashi, K. (1959); Chemical remanent magnetization of ferromagnetic minerals and its application to rock magnetism, *J. Geomag. Geoelec.*, **10**, 99–117.

Kobayashi, K. (1961); Magnetization-blocking process by volume development of ferromagnetic fine particles, *J. Phys. Soc. Japan*, **17**, 695–698.

Kobayashi, T. and T. Shikama (1961); The climatic history of the Far East, *Descriptive palaeoclimatology* (ed., A. E. M. Nairn), Interscience, New York, 292–306.

Koenigsberger, J. G. (1938); Natural residual magnetism of eruptive rocks, parts I and II, *Terr. Mag. Atmos. Elec.*, **43**, 119–127 and 299–320.

Komarov, A. G. (1957); Residual magnetism of rocks and their age, *Akad. Nauk. SSSR Izv. Geol. Ser.*, 48–60.

Komarov, A. G. (1959); Paleomagnetic investigations of Lower Paleozoic basalts of the Ukraine, *Akad. Nauk. SSSR Izv. Geophys. Ser.*, 1219–1225.

Köppen, W. and A. Wegener (1924); *Die Klimate der geolischen Vorzeit*, Bornträger, Berlin.

Krishnan, M. S. (1949); *Geology of India and Burma*, Madras Law Journal Office, p. 544.

Kruglyakova, G. I. and V. V. Kruglyakov (1960); The influence of the character of a lava flow on the formation of remanent magnetization of rocks, *Akad. Nauk. SSSR Izv. Geophys. Ser.*, 158–160.

Kulp, J. L. (1961); Geologic Time Scale, *Science*, **133**, 1105–1114.

Kumagai, N., N. Kawai, and T. Nagata (1950); Recent progress in Japan, *J. Geomag. Geoelec.*, **2**, 61–65.

Kume, S. (1962); Sur des changements d'aimantation rémanente de corps ferromagnétiques soumis a des pressions hydrostatique, *Ann. Géophys.*, **18**, 18–22.

Larochelle, A. (1961); Application of palaeomagnetism to geological correlation, *Nature*, **192**, 37–39.

Larochelle, A. (1962); Palaeomagnetism of the Monteregian Hills, southeastern Quebec, *Geol. Surv. Canada Bull.*, **79**, 1–44.

Larochelle, A. and R. F. Black (1963); An application of palaeomagnetism in estimating the age of rocks, *Nature*, **198**, 1260–1262.

Leng, J. (1955); Thesis, University of London.

Lin'kova, T. I. (1960); Paleomagnetic studies of Devonian sedimentary layers in the northwest of the Russian platform, *Akad. Nauk. SSSR Izv. Geophys. Ser.*, 868–870.

Lin'kova, T. I. (1961); Laboratory studies of the natural remanent magnetization of direct and reverse magnetized Devonian rocks, *Akud. Nauk. SSSR Izv. Geophys. Ser.*, 91–95.

Lin'kova, T. I. (1963); Some results of paleomagnetic investigations of Devonian sedimentary rocks, *Akad. Nauk. SSSR Izv. Geophys. Ser.*, 318–323.

Long, W. E. (1962); Sedimentary rocks of the Buckeye Range, Horlick Mountains, Antarctica, *Science*, **136**, 319–320.

Lotze, F. (1957); *Steinsalz und Kalisalze*, Bornträger, Berlin, 466 pp.

Lovering, J. F. (1959); The magnetic field in a primary meteorite body, *Amer. J. Sci.*, **257**, 271–275.

Lovering, J. F., L. G. Parry, and J. C. Jaeger (1960); Temperatures and mass loss in iron meteorites during ablation in the Earth's atmosphere, *Geochim. Cosmochim. Acta*, **19**, 156–167.

Lowenstam, H. A. (1957); Niagaran reefs in the Great Lakes Area. *Geol. Soc. Amer. Mem.*, **67** (vol. 2), 215–248.

Lowenstam, H. A. and S. Epstein (1954);

Paleotemperatures of the Post-Aptian Cretaceous as determined by the oxygen isotope method, *J. Geol.,* **62,** 207–248.

Lowenstam, H. A. and S. Epstein (1959); Cretaceous paleotemperatures as determined by the oxygen isotope method, their relations to, and the nature of rudistid reefs, *Congr. Geol. Internacional Mexico, Symposium del Cretacico,* 65–76.

McDougall, I. (1961); Determination of the age of a basic igneous intrusion by the potassium-argon method, *Nature,* **190,** 1184–1186.

McDougall, I. (1963); Potassium-argon age measurements on dolerites from Antarctica and South Africa, *J. Geophys. Res.,* **68,** 1535–1545.

McDougall, I. and Ronald Green (1958); The use of magnetic measurements for the study of the structure of talus slopes, *Geol. Mag.,* **95,** 252–260.

McDougall, I. and D. H. Tarling (1963); Dating of reversals of the Earth's magnetic field, *Nature,* **198,** 1012–1013. (1964); Dating geomagnetic polarity zones, *Nature,* **202,** 171–172.

McElhinny, M. W. and D. I. Gough (1963); The palaeomagnetism of the Great dyke of Southern Rhodesia, *Geophys. J.,* **7,** 287–303.

McNish, A. G. and E. A. Johnson (1938); Magnetization of unmetamorphosed varves and marine sediments, *Terr. Magn. Atmos. Elec.,* **53,** 349–360.

Ma, T. H. (1962); The reliability of palaeomagnetism for research in palaeogeography, *J. Geomagn. Geoelec.,* **13,** 133–149.

Makarova, Z. V. (1959); Location of the magnetic pole during the Triassic period by means of remanent magnetization of basaltic trap rock in the Yenisei region, *Akad. Nauk. SSSR Izv. Geophys. Ser.,* 1520–1521.

Manley, H. (1951); The terrestrial magnetic field, *Research,* **4,** 43–45.

Manley, H. (1954a); The thermo-magnetic properties of the tholeiite dikes of Britain, *Geofis. Pura Appl.,* **29,** 57–70.

Manley, H. (1954b); An estimate of the time taken for a dyke to cool through its Curie point, *Geofis. Pura Appl.,* **27,** 105–109.

Manley, H. (1956); The effects of weathering and alteration on the magnetic properties of a doleritic basalt, *Geofis. Pura Appl.,* **33,** 86–90.

Manley, H. and D. J. Burdon (1955); The thermo-magnetic properties and history of some plutonic rocks from the Leinster Granite, Ireland, *J. Geomag. Geoelec.,* **7,** 37–50.

Manwaring, E. A. (1963); Palaeomagnetism of some igneous rocks of the Sydney Basin, New South Wales, *Proc. Roy. Soc. New South Wales,* **96,** 141-151.

Markhinin, E. K. and G. A. Pospelova (1959); Some results of paleomagnetic investigations in the Kurile Islands, *Akad. Nauk. SSSR. Izv. Geophys. Ser.,* 1517–1519.

Martinez, J. D. and L. G. Howell (1956); Palaeomagnetism of chemical sediments, *Nature,* **178,** 204–205.

Matsuzaki, H., K. Kobayashi, and K. Momose (1954); On the anomalously strong natural remanent magnetization of the lava of Mt. Utsukushi-ga-hara, *J. Geomag. Geoelec.,* **6,** 53–56.

Matuyama, M. (1929a); On the direction of magnetization of basalt in Japan, Tyôsen and Manchuria, *Proc. 4th Pacific Science Congress,* 1–3.

Matuyama, M. (1929b); On the direction of magnetization of basalt in Japan, Tyôsen and Manchuria, *Proc. Imp. Acad. Japan,* **5,** 203–205.

Maurain, C. (1901); Propriétés des dépots électrolytiques de fer obtenus dans un champ magnétique, *J. Physique,* **10** (3rd ser.), 123–125.

Melloni, M. (1853); see Chevallier (1925).

Mercanton, P. L. (1918); État magnétique de quelques terres cuites préhistoriques, *C. R. Acad. Sc. Paris,* **166,** 681 and 949.

Mercanton, P. L. (1926a); Inversion de l'inclinaison magnétique terrestre aux âges geologiques, *Terr. Magn. Atmos. Elec.,* **31,** 187–190.

Mercanton, P. L. (1926b); Aimantation de basaltes groenlandais, *C. R. Acad. Sci. Paris,* **180,** 859–860.

Mercanton, P. L. (1931); Inversion inclinaison magnétique aux âges geologique, *C. R. Acad. Sci. Paris,* **192,** 978.

Mercanton, P. L. (1932); Inversion inclinaison magnétique aux âges geologique, *C. R. Acad. Sci. Paris,* **194,** 1371.

Mikhailova, N. P. (1961); On the natural intensity of magnetization of gabbro-pyroxenites of the October alkaline massif, *Akad. Nauk. SSSR Izv. Geophys. Ser.,* 1599–1606.

Miller, J. A. and F. J. Fitch (1962); Age of the Lundy Granite, *Nature*, **195**, 553–555.

Miller, J. A. and A. E. Musset (1963); Dating basic rocks by the potassium-argon method: the Whin Sill, *Geophys. J.*, **7**, 547–553.

Miller, J. A., K. Shibata, and Mary Monro (1962); The potassium-argon age of the lava of Killerton Park, near Exeter, *Geophys. J.*, **6**, 394–396.

Momose, K. (1958); Palaeomagnetic researches for the Pliocene volcanic rocks in central Japan (1), *J. Geomag. Geoelec.*, **10**, 12–19.

Momose, K. (1963); Studies on the variations of the Earth's magnetic field during Pliocene time, *Bull. Earthquake Res. Inst.*, **41**, 487–534.

Momose, K., K. Kobayashi, and T. Yamada (1959); Palaeomagnetic and geologic researches for the volcanic rocks around Lake Suwa. Palaeomagnetic researches for the Pliocene Volcanic rocks in central Japan (2), *Bull. Earthquake Res. Inst.*, **37**, 433–481.

Morin, J. (1950); Magnetic susceptibility of αFe_2O_3 and αFe_2O_3 with added titanium, *Phys. Rev.*, **78**, 819–820.

Mumme, W. G. (1962a); A note on the mixed polarity of magnetization in Cainozoic basalts in Victoria, Australia, *Geophys. J.*, **6**, 546–549.

Mumme, W. G. (1962b); Stability of magnetization in Cainozoic basalts of Victoria, Australia, *Phil. Mag.*, **7**, 1263–1278.

Mumme, W. G. (1963); Thermal and alternating magnetic field demagnetization experiments on Cainozoic basalts of Victoria, Australia, *Geophys. J.*, **7**, 314–327.

Nagata, T. (1952); Reverse thermo-remanent magnetism, *Nature*, **169**, 704.

Nagata, T. (1953a and 1961); *Rock magnetism* (1st and revised editions), Maruzen, Tokyo, 225 pp., 350 pp.

Nagata, T. (1953b); Self-reversal of thermo-remanent magnetization of igneous rocks, *Nature*, **172**, 850

Nagata, T. (1953c); Ferrimagnetism in nature, *Proc. Int. Conf. Theor. Phys.*, 714–718.

Nagata, T. (1962); Notes on the detrital remanent magnetization of sediments, *J. Geomagn. Geoelec.*, **14**, 99–106.

Nagata, T. and S. Akimoto (1956); Magnetic properties of ferromagnetic ilmenites, *Geofis. Pura Appl.*, **34**, 36–50.

Nagata, T. and S. Akimoto (1961); Outline of ferromagnetism, and magnetic properties of rock-forming ferromagnetic minerals, in Nagata (1961), 1–39.

Nagata, T., S. Akimoto, Y. Shimizu, K. Kobayashi, and H. Kuno (1959); Palaeomagnetic studies on Tertiary and Cretaceous rocks in Japan, *Proc. Japan Acad.*, **35**, 378–383.

Nagata, T., S. Akimoto, and S. Uyeda (1951); Reverse thermo-remanent magnetism, *Proc. Japan Acad.*, **27**, 643–645.

Nagata, T., S. Akimoto, and S. Uyeda (1952); Reverse thermo remanent magnetism (II), *Proc. Japan Acad.*, **28**, 277–281.

Nagata, T., S. Akimoto, and S. Uyeda (1953a); Self-reversal of thermo-remanent magnetism of igneous rocks (III), *J. Geomag. Geoelec.*, **5**, 168–184.

Nagata, T., S. Akimoto, and S. Uyeda (1953b); Origin of reverse thermo-remanent magnetism of igneous rocks, *Nature*, **172**, 630.

Nagata, T., S. Akimoto, S. Uyeda, K. Momose, and E. Asami (1954); Reverse magnetization of rocks and its connection with the geomagnetic field, *J. Geomag. Geoelec.*, **6**, 182–193.

Nagata, T., S. Akimoto, S. Uyeda, Y. Shimizu, M. Ozima, and K. Kobayashi (1957); Palaeomagnetic study on a Quaternary volcanic region in Japan, *Phil. Mag. Supp. Adv. Phys.*, **6**, 255–263.

Nagata, T., S. Akimoto, S. Uyeda, Y. Shimizu, M. Ozima, K. Kobayashi, and H. Kuno (1957); Palaeomagnetic studies on a Quaternary volcanic region in Japan, *J. Geomagn. Geoelec.*, **9**, 23–41.

Nagata, T., Y. Arai, and K. Momose (1963); Secular variation of the geomagnetic total force during the last 5000 years, *J. Geophys. Res.*, **68**, 5277–5281.

Nagata, T., K. Hirao, and H. Yoshikawa (1950); Remanent magnetization of "Pleistocene" deposits, *J. Geomag. Geoelec.*, **1**, 52–58.

Nagata, T. and K. Kobayashi (1958); Experimental studies on the generation of remanent magnetization of ferromagnetic minerals by chemical reactions, *Proc. Japan Acad.*, **34**, 269–273.

Nagata, T. and K. Kobayashi (1961); Measuring instruments for magnetic properties of rocks and minerals, in Nagata (1961), 40.

Nagata, T. and K. Kobayashi (1963); Thermochemical remanent magnetization of rocks, *Nature*, **197**, 476–477.

Nagata, T. and M. Ozima (1955); Anomalous increase in thermo-remanent magnetization of ferromagnetic minerals—magnetic interaction between different constituents in ferromagnetic minerals, *J. Geomag. Geoelec.*, **7**, 105–120.

Nagata, T. and Y. Shimizu (1959); Natural remanent magnetization of pre-Cambrian gneiss of Ongul Islands in the Antarctic, *Nature*, **184**, 1472–1473.

Nagata, T. and Y. Shimizu (1960); Palaeomagnetic studies on Pre-Cambrian gneiss of Ongul Islands, Antarctica, *Antarctic Record Min. Educ. Japan*, **10**, 661–668.

Nagata, T. and S. Uyeda (1955); Interaction of two constituents in ferromagnetic materials showing reverse thermo-remanent magnetism, *Nature*, **175**, 35.

Nagata, T. and S. Uyeda (1956); Production of self-reversal of thermo-remanent magnetism by heat treatment of ferromagnetic minerals, *Nature*, **177**, 179–180.

Nagata, T. and S. Uyeda (1959); Exchange interaction as a cause of reverse thermo-remanent magnetism, *Nature*, **184**, 890–891

Nagata, T. and S. Uyeda (1961); Thermo-remanent magnetization, in Nagata (1961), 145–195.

Nagata, T., S. Uyeda, and S. Akimoto (1952); Self-reversal of thermo-remanent magnetism of igneous rocks (I), *J. Geomag. Geoelec.*, **4**, 22–38.

Nagata, T., S. Uyeda, S. Akimoto, and N. Kawai (1952); Self-reversal of thermo-remanent magnetism of igneous rocks (II), *J. Geomag. Geoelec.*, **4**, 102–107.

Nagata, T., S. Uyeda, and M. Ozima (1957); Magnetic interaction between ferromagnetic minerals contained in rocks, *Phil. Mag. Supp. Adv. Phys.*, **6**, 264–287.

Nagata, T. and M. Yama-ai (1961); Palaeomagnetic studies on rocks on the coast of Lutzow-Holm Bay, *Antarctic Record Min. Educ. Japan*, **11**, 945–947.

Nairn, A. E. M. (1956); Relevance of palaeomagnetic studies of Jurassic rocks to continental drift, *Nature*, **178**, 935–936.

Nairn, A. E. M. (1957a); A palaeomagnetic study of Jurassic and Cretaceous sediments, *Mon. Not. Roy. Ast. Soc., Geophys. Supp.*, **7**, 308, 313

Nairn, A. E. M. (1957b); Observations paléo-magnétiques en France: roches Permiennes, *Bull. Soc. Geol. France*, **7**, 721–727.

Nairn, A. E. M. (1957c); Palaeomagnetic collections from Britain and South Africa illustrating two problems of weathering, *Phil. Mag. Supp. Adv. Phys.*, **6**, 162–168.

Nairn, A. E. M. (1960a); Palaeomagnetic results from Europe, *J. Geol.*, **68**, 285–306.

Nairn, A. E. M. (1960b); A palaeomagnetic survey of the Karroo System, *Overseas Geol. Min. Res.*, **7**, 398–410.

Nairn, A. E. M. (1961a); Palaeomagnetic results from Europe: a reply to E. Irving, *J. Geol.*, **69**, 231–235.

Nairn, A. E. M. (editor) (1961b); *Descriptive palaeoclimatology*, Interscience, New York.

Nairn, A. E. M. (1962); Paleomagnetic investigations of the Tertiary and Quaternary igneous rocks, 1. Preliminary collections in the Eifel, Siebengebirge, and Westerwald, *Notizbl. hess. L-Arnt Bodenforsch*, **90**, 412–424.

Nairn, A. E. M. (1963); Palaeomagnetic measurements on the Great Dyke, Southern Rhodesia, *Phil. Mag.*, **8**, 213–221.

Nairn, A. E. M., D. V. Frost, and B. G. Light (1959); Palaeomagnetism of certain rocks from Newfoundland, *Nature*, **183**, 596–597.

Nalivkin, D. V. (1960); *The Geology of the U. S. S. R.* (English trans. S. I. Tomkeieff), Pergamon, Oxford, 177 pp.

Néel, L. (1949); Théorie du trainage magnétique des ferromagnétiques au grains fins avec applications aux terres cuites, *Ann. Géophys.*, **5**, 99–136.

Néel, L. (1951); L'inversion de l'aimantation permanente des roches, *Ann. Geophys.*, **7**, 90–102.

Néel, L. (1955); Some theoretical aspects of rock magnetism, *Phil. Mag. Supp. Adv. Phys.*, **4**, 191–243.

Nicholls, G. D. (1955); The mineralogy of rock magnetism, *Phil. Mag. Supp. Adv. Phys.*, **4**, 113–190.

Nijenhuis, G. H. W. (1961); A palaeomagnetic study of the Permian volcanics in the Nahe region (S.W. Germany), *Geol. Mijn.*, **40**, 26–38.

Norris, D. K. and R. F. Black (1961); Application of palaeomagnetism to thrust mechanics, *Nature*, **192**, 933–935.

Northrop, J. W. III and A. A. Meyerhoff (1963); Validity of polar and continental movement hypotheses based on paleomagnetic studies, *Amer. Assoc. Petr. Geol. Bull.*, **47**, 575–585.

Oliveira, A. I. (1956); Handbook of South American Geology (ed., W. F. Jenks): Brazil, *Mem. Geol. Soc. Amer.*, **65**, 1–62.

Opdyke, N. D. (1959); The impact of paleomagnetism on paleoclimate studies, *Intern. J. Bioclim. Biomet.*, **3**, 1–6.

Opdyke, N. D. (1961a); The paleomagnetism of the New Jersey Triassic: a field study of the inclination error in red sediments, *J. Geophys. Res.*, **66**, 1941–1949.

Opdyke, N. D. (1961b); The palaeoclimatological significance of desert sandstone, *Descriptive Palaeoclimatology* (ed., A. E. M. Nairn), 45–60.

Opdyke, N. D. and S. K. Runcorn (1956); Remanent magnetization of lava flows in northern Arizona, *Plateau (Museum of N. Arizona)*, **29**, 1–5.

Opdyke, N. D. and S. K. Runcorn (1960); Wind direction in the western United States in the late Paleozoic, *Bull. Geol. Soc. Amer.*, **71**, 959–972.

Parry, J. H. (1954); The interpretation of reversed magnetization in igneous rocks, *J. Geomag. Geoelec.*, **6**, 210–214.

Parry, J. H. (1957); The problem of reversed magnetizations and its study by magnetic methods, *Phil. Mag. Supp. Adv. Phys.*, **6**, 299–305

Parry, L. G. (1960); Thermomagnetic properties of basalt from the Newer Basalts of Victoria, Australia, *J. Geophys. Res.*, **65**, 2425–2428.

Petrova, G. N. (1956); Magnetic stability of rocks, *Akad. Nauk. Izv. SSSR Geophys. Ser.*, 52–61.

Petrova, G. N. (1961); Various laboratory methods of determining the geomagnetic stability of rocks, *Akad. Nauk. SSSR Izv. Geophys. Ser.*, 1585–1598.

Petrova, G. N. and V. A. Koroleva (1959); Determination of the magnetic stability of rocks under laboratory conditions, *Akad. Nauk. SSSR Izv. Geophys. Ser.*, 703–709.

Phillips, F. C. (1955); *The use of stereographic projections in structural geology*, 86 pp., Arnold, London.

Poole, F. G. (1957); Paleo-wind directions in late Paleozoic and early Mesozoic time on the Colorado Plateau as determined by cross-strata (abstract), *Geol. Soc. Amer. Bull.*, **68**, 1870.

Pospelova, G. A. (1959); Remanent magnetization of Tertiary and Quaternary volcanic rocks, *Akad. Nauk. SSSR Izv. Geophys. Ser.*, 1591–1598.

Pospelova, G. A. (1960); Origin of the reversed magnetization of volcanic rocks from Armenia and the Kurile Islands, *Akad. Nauk. SSSR Izv. Geophys. Ser.*, 37–49.

Popova, A. V. (1963); Paleomagnetic investigations of Paleozoic sedimentary rocks in Siberia, *Akad. Nauk. SSSR Izv. Geophys. Ser.*, 444–450.

Powell, D. W. (1960); Stress dependant magnetization in some quartz-dolerites, *Nature*, **187**, 225.

Powell, D. W. (1963); Significance of differences in magnetization along certain dolerite dykes, *Nature*, **199**, 674–676.

Raasch, G. O. (1958); The Baraboo (Wis.) Monadnock and palaeo-wind direction, *J. Alberta Soc. Petr. Geol.*, **6**, 183–187.

Rees, A. I. (1961); The effect of water currents on the magnetic remanence and anisotropy of susceptibility of some sediments, *Geophys. J.*, **5**, 235–251.

Reiche, P. (1938); An analysis of cross-lamination in the Coconino Sandstone, *J. Geol.*, **46**, 905–932.

Rimbert, F. (1958); Thesis, University of Paris.

Rimbert, F. (1959); Contribution a l'etude de l'action de champs alternatifs sur les aimantations remanentes des roches, *Rev. Inst. Francais Petrole et Ann. Combustibles Liquides*, **14**, nos. 1 and 2.

Robertson, W. A. (1962); Thesis, Australian National University, Canberra.

Robertson, W. A. (1963); The paleomagnetism of some Mesozoic intrusives and tuffs from eastern Australia, *J. Geophys. Res.*, **68**, 2299–2312.

Robertson, W. A. and L. Hastie (1962); A palaeomagnetic study of the Cygnet alkaline complex of Tasmania, *J. Geol. Soc. Australia*, **8**, 259–268.

Roche, A. (1950a); Sur les caracteres magnétiques du système éruptif de Gergovie, *C. R. Acad. Sci. Paris*, **230**, 113–115.

Roche, A. (1950b); Anomalies magnétiques accompagnant des massifs de pépérites de la Limagne d'Auvergne, *C. R. Acad. Sci. Paris*, **230**, 1603–1604.

Roche, A. (1951); Sur les inversion de l'aimantation rémanente des roches volcaniques dans les monts d'Auvergne, *C. R. Acad. Sci. Paris*, **233**, 1132–1134.

Roche, A. (1953); Sur l'origine des inversions

l'aimantation constantées dans les roches d'Auvergne, *C. R. Acad. Sci. Paris,* **236,** 107–109.

Roche, A. (1954); Exposé somaire des études relatives à l'aimantation de matériaux volcaniques, *J. Geomag. Geoelec.,* **6,** 169–171.

Roche, A. (1956); Sur la date de la dernière inversion du champ magnétique terrestre, *C. R. Acad. Sci. Paris,* **243,** 812–814.

Roche, A. (1957); Sur l'aimantation des roches volcaniques de l'Estérel, *C. R. Acad. Sci. Paris,* **244,** 2952–2954.

Roche, A. (1958); Sur les variations de direction du champ magnétique terrestre au cours du Quaternaire, *C. R. Acad. Sci. Paris,* **246,** 3364–3366.

Roche, A. (1959); Paléomagnétisme déplacements des poles et dérives des continents, *Revue l'industrie minerale,* **41,** 1–10.

Roche, A. (1960); Sur l'aimantation de laves Miocènes d'Auvergne, *C. R. Acad. Sci. Paris,* **250,** 377–379.

Roche, A. and L. Cattala (1959); Remanent magnetism of the Cretaceous basalts of Madagascar, *Nature,* **183,** 1049–1050.

Roche, A., L. Cattala, and J. Boulanger (1958); Sur l'aimantation de basaltes de Madagascar, *C. R. Acad. Sci. Paris,* **246,** 2922–2924.

Roche, A. and B. Leprêtre (1955); Sur l'aimantation de roches volcaniques de l'Ahaggar, *C. R. Acad. Sci. Paris,* **240,** 2002–2004.

Roche, A., H. Saucier, and J. Lacaze (1962); Étude paléomagnétique des roches volcaniques Permiennes de la région Nideck-Donon, *Bull. Serv. Carte Géol. Alsace Lorraine,* **15,** 59–68.

Rodgers, J. (1957); The distribution of marine carbonate sediments: a review, *Regional aspects of Carbonate Deposition, a Symposium* (ed., R. J. Le Blanc and J. G. Breeding), 2–14.

Roquet, J. (1946); Sur les propriétés magnétiques du sesquioxyde de fer faiblement magnétique, *C. R. Acad. Sci. Paris,* **222,** 727–729.

Roquet, J. (1947); Sur l'aimantation rémanente isotherme du sesquioxyde de fer, *C. R. Acad. Sci. Paris,* **224,** 1418–1420.

Roquet, J. (1954a); Sur les rémanences des oxydes de fer et leur intérêt en géomagnétisme (first and second parts), *Ann. Géophys.,* **10,** 226–247 and 282–325.

Roquet, J. (1954b); Sur les aimantations thermorémanente et rémanente isotherme

du sesquioxyde de fer et de la magnétite, *J. Geomag. Geoelec.,* **6,** 200–205.

Roquet, J. (1955); Étude des propriétés magnétiques de roches volcaniques avec aimantation naturelle inversée, *Ann. Géophys.,* **11,** 461–474.

Roquet, J. and E. Thellier (1946); Sur des lois numériques simples, relatives à l'aimantation thermorémanante du sesquioxyde de fer rhomboédrique, *C. R. Acad. Sci. Paris,* **222,** 1288–1290.

Roy, J. L. (1963); Palaeomagnetism of Prince Edward Island, *Geophys. J.,* **8,** 226–229.

Runcorn, S. K. (1955a); Palaeomagnetism of sediments from the Colorado Plateau, *Nature,* **176,** 505–506.

Runcorn, S. K. (1955b); Rock magnetism—geophysical aspects, *Phil. Mag. Supp. Adv. Phys.,* **4,** 244–291.

Runcorn, S. K. (1956a); Palaeomagnetic survey in Arizona and Utah: Preliminary results, *Geol. Soc. Amer. Bull.,* **67,** 301–316.

Runcorn, S. K. (1956b); Palaeomagnetic comparisons between Europe and North America, *Proc. Geol. Assoc. Canada,* **8,** 77–85.

Runcorn, S. K. (1956c); Palaeomagnetism, polar wandering and continental drift, *Geol. Mijn.,* **18,** 253–256.

Runcorn, S. K. (1956d); Magnetization of rocks, *Handbuch der Physik,* **47,** 470–497.

Runcorn, S. K. (1957); The sampling of rocks for palaeomagnetic comparisons between the continents, *Phil. Mag. Supp. Adv. Phys.,* **6,** 169–176.

Runcorn, S. K. (1959); On the hypothesis that the mean geomagnetic field for parts of geological time has been that of a geocentrical axial multipole, *J. Atmos. Terr. Phys.,* **14,** 167–174.

Runcorn, S. K. (1960); Statistical methods in rock magnetism, *Phil. Mag.,* **5,** 523–524.

Runcorn, S. K. (1961); Climatic change through geological time in the light of the palaeomagnetic evidence for polar wandering and continental drift, *Quat. J. Roy. Met. Soc.,* **87,** 282–313.

Runcorn, S. K. (1962); Palaeomagnetic evidence for continental drift and its geophysical cause, *Continental Drift* (ed., S. K. Runcorn), Academic Press, New York, 1–39.

Russinov, B. Sh. and L. E. Sholpo (1962); Magnetic cleaning of specimens of Kazakhstan effusive rocks, *Akad. Nauk. SSSR Izv. Geophysic Ser.,* 529–533.

Rutten, M. G. (1959); Paleomagnetic reconnaissance of mid-Italian volcanoes, *Geol. Mijn.*, **21**, 373–374.

Rutten, M. G. (1960); Paleomagnetic dating of younger volcanic series, *Geol. Rundschau*, **49**, 161–167.

Rutten, M. G., R. O. v'Everdingen, and J. D. A. Zijderveld (1957); Palaeomagnetism in the Permian of the Oslo graben (Norway) and of the Estérel (France), *Geol. Mijn.*, **19**, 193–195.

Rutten, M. G. and J. Veldkamp (1958); Paleomagnetic research at Utrecht University, *Ann. Géophys.*, **14**, 519–521.

Rutten, M. G. and H. Wensink (1959); Geology of the Hvalfjördur-Skorradalur area (southwestern Iceland), *Geol. Mijn.*, **21**, 172–181.

Rutten, M. G. and H. Wensink (1960); Paleomagnetic dating, glaciations and the chronology of the Plio-pleistocene in Iceland, *Int. Geol. Congr., Session 21, Part IV,* 62–70.

Scheidegger, A. E. (1957); On a new theory of mountain building, *Canadian J. Phys.*, **35**, 1380–1386.

S.heidegger, A. E. (1958); *Principles of Geodynamics,* Springer-Verlag, Berlin, 280 pp.

Schmucker, U. (1959); Examination of the rock magnetism of the Permian Nahe volcanics, *Geol. Rundschau*, **48**, 184–195.

Schreiner, G. D. L. (1958a); Age of a Pilansberg dyke of palaeomagnetic significance, *Nature*, **181**, 1330–1331.

Schreiner, G. D. L. (1958b); Comparison of the $^{87}Rb \rightarrow {}^{87}Sr$ ages of the red granite of the Bushveld complex from measurements of the total rock and separated mineral fractions, *Proc. Roy. Soc. London A,* **245**, 112–117.

Schult, A. von (1963); Über die magnetisierung de basaltvorkommen in der Umgebung von Gottingen, *Zeit. Geophys.*, **29**, 1–20.

Schwarz, E. J. (1963); A paleomagnetic investigation of Permo-Triassic red beds and andesites from the Spanish Pyrenees, *J. Geophys. Res.*, **68**, 3265–3271.

Schwarzbach, M. (1961a); *Das Klima der Vorzeit.,* Enke, Stuttgart, 275 pp.

Schwarzbach, M. (1961b); The climatic history of Europe and North America, *Descriptive Paleoclimatology* (ed., A. E. M. Nairn), Interscience, New York, 255–291.

Shillibeer, H. A. and G. L. Cummings (1956); cited in Cox and Doell (1960).

Shimizu, Y. (1960); Magnetic viscosity of magnetite, *J. Geomag. Geoelec.*, **11**, 125–138.

Shotton, F. W. (1937); The Lower Bunter sandstone of North Worcestershire and East Shropshire, *Geol. Mag.*, **74**, 534–553.

Shotton, F. W. (1956); Some aspects of the New Red Sandstone desert in Britain, *Liverpool and Manchester Geol. J.*, **1**, 450–466.

Sigurgeirsson, Th. (1957); Direction of magnetization in Icelandic basalts, *Phil. Mag. Supp. Adv. Phys.*, **6**, 240–246.

Sopher, S. R. (1963); Palaeomagnetic study of the Sudbury Irruptive, *Bull. Geol. Surv. Canada,* **90**, 34 pp.

Stacey, F. D. (1958a); Thermo-remanent magnetization (TRM) of multidomain grains in igneous rocks, *Phil. Mag.*, **3**, 1391–1401.

Stacey, F. D. (1958b); The effect of stress on the remanent magnetism of magnetite-bearing rocks, *J. Geophys. Res.*, **63**, 361–368.

Stacey, F. D. (1959); A domain theory of magnetic grains in rocks, *Phil. Mag.*, **4**, 594–605.

Stacey, F. D. (1960a); Magnetic anisotropy of igneous rocks, *J. Geophys. Res.*, **65**, 2429–2442.

Stacey, F. D. (1960b); Stress-induced magnetic anisotropy of rocks, *Nature*, **188**, 134–135.

Stacey, F. D. (1962); A generalized theory of thermoremanence, covering the transition from single domain to multi-domain magnetic grains, *Phil. Mag.*, **7**, 1887–1900.

Stacey, F. D. (1963); The physical theory of rock magnetism, *Adv. Phys.*, **12**, 46–133.

Stacey, F. D., Germaine Joplin, and J. Lindsay (1960); Magnetic anisotropy and fabric of some foliated rocks from S.E. Australia, *Geofis. Pura Appl.*, **47**, 30–40.

Stacey, F. D. and J. F. Lovering (1959); Natural magnetic moments of two Chondritic meteorites, *Nature,* **183**, 529–530.

Stacey, F. D., J. F. Lovering, and L. G. Parry (1961); Thermomagnetic properties, natural magnetic moments, and magnetic anisotropy of some chondritic meteorites, *J. Geophys. Res.*, **66**, 1523–1534.

Stehli, F. G. (1957); Possible Permian climatic zonation and its implications, *Amer. J. Sci.*, **255**, 607–618.

Stone, D. B. (1963); Anisotropic magnetic susceptibility measurements on a phonolite and on a folded metamorphic rock, *Geophys. J.*, **7**, 375–390.

Stott, P. M. (1963); The magnetization of the Red Hill dike, Tasmania, *J. Geophys. Res.*, **68**, 2289–2297.

Stott, P. M. and F. D. Stacey (1959); Magnetostriction and palaeomagnetism of igneous rocks, *Nature,* **183,** 384–385.

Stott, P. M. and F. D. Stacey (1960); Magnetostriction and paleomagnetism of igneous rocks, *J. Geophys. Res.,* **65,** 2419–2424.

Strangway, D. W. (1961); Magnetic properties of diabase dikes, *J. Geophys. Res.,* **66,** 3021–3032.

Syono, Y., S. Akimoto, and T. Nagata (1962); Remanent magnetization of ferromagnetic single crystals, *J. Geomagn. Geoelec.,* **14,** 113–124.

Tarling, D. H. (1962); Tentative correlation of Samoan and Hawaiian Islands using "reversals" of magnetization, *Nature,* **196,** 882–883.

Tarling, D. H. 1963); Thesis, Australian National University, Canberra.

Teichert, C. (1952); Fossile riffe als klimazeugen in Australien, *Geol. Rundschau,* **40,** 33–38.

Termier, H. and G. Termier (1952); *Histoire géologique de la Biosphere,* Masson, Paris, p. 721.

Thellier, E. (1936); Aimantation des briques et inclinaison du champ magnétique terrestre, *Ann. de l'institut de phys. du globe, Univ. Paris,* **14,** 65–70.

Thellier, E. (1937*a*); Sur l'aimantation dite permanent des basalts, *C. R. Acad. Sci., Paris,* **204,** 876–878.

Thellier, E. (1937*b*); Recherche de intensité du champ magnétique terrestre dans le passé: premier resultats, *Ann. de l'institut de phys. du globe, Univ. Paris,* **15,** 179–184.

Thellier, E. (1937*c*); Aimantation des terres cuites; application à la recherche de l'intensité du champ magnétique terrestre dans la passé, *C. R. Acad. Sci., Paris,* **204,** 184–186.

Thellier, E. (1938); Thesis, University of Paris.

Thellier, E. (1941*a*); Sur le vérification d'une method permettant de determiner l'intensité du champ magnétique terrestre dans le passé, *C. R. Acad. Sci., Paris,* **212,** 281–283.

Thellier, E. (1941*b*); Sur les propriétés de l'aimantation thermorémanente des terres cuites, *C. R. Acad. Sci., Paris,* **213,** 1019–1022.

Thellier, E. (1946); Sur la thermorémanence et la théorie du métamagnétisme, *C. R. Acad. Sci., Paris,* **223,** 319–321.

Thellier, E. (1951); Propriétés magnétiques des terres cuites et des roches, *J. de Phys. et Radium,* **12,** 205–218.

Thellier, E. and F. Rimbert (1954); Sur l'analyse d'aimantations fossiles par action de champs magnétiques alternatifs, *C. R. Acad. Sci., Paris,* **239,** 1399–1401.

Thellier, E. and F. Rimbert (1955); Sur l'utilisation en paleomagnétisme, de la désaimantation par champs alternatif, *C. R. Acad. Sci., Paris,* **240,** 1404–1406.

Thellier, E. and O. Thellier (1941); Sur les variations thermiques de l'aimantation thermorémanente du terres cuites, *C. R. Acad. Sci., Paris,* **213,** 59–61.

Thellier, E. and O. Thellier (1942); Sur l'intensité du champ magnétique terrestre, en France, trois siècles avant les première mesures directes, *C. R. Acad. Sci., Paris,* **214,** 382–384.

Thellier, E. and O. Thellier (1944); Recherches géomagnétique sur des coulées volcaniques d'Auvergne, *Ann. Géophys.,* **1,** 37–52.

Thellier, E. and O. Thellier (1946); Sur l'intensité du champ magnétique terrestre en France, a l'époque galloromaine, *C. R. Acad. Sci., Paris,* **222,** 905–907.

Thellier, E. and O. Thellier (1949); Sur les propriétés magnétiques des roches éruptives pyrenéennes, *C. R. Acad. Sci., Paris,* **228,** 1958–1960.

Thellier, E. and O. Thellier (1951); Sur la direction du champ magnétique terrestre, retrouvée sur des parois de fours des époques punique et romaine, à Carthage, *C. R. Acad. Sci., Paris,* **233,** 1476–1478.

Thellier, E. and O. Thellier (1952); Sur la direction du champ magnétique terrestre, dans la région de Trèves, vers 380 après J.-C., *C. R. Acad. Sci., Paris,* **234,** 1464–1466.

Thellier, E. and O. Thellier (1959*a*); Sur l'intensité du champ magnétique terrestre dans le passé historique et géologique, *Ann. Géophys.,* **15,** 285–376.

Thellier, E. and O. Thellier (1959*b*); The intensity of the earth's magnetic field in the historical and geological past, *Akad. Nauk. SSSR Izv. Geophys. Ser.,* 1296–1331.

Thellier, E. and O. Thellier (1962); Sur le possibilité de controles précis en archéomagnétisme, *J. Geomag. Geoelec.*, **13**, 120–126.

Torreson, O. W., T. Murphy, and J. W. Graham (1949); Magnetic polarization of sedimentary rocks and the Earth's magnetic history, *J. Geophys. Res.*, **54**, 111–129.

Turnbull, G. (1959); Some palaeomagnetic measurements in Antarctica, *Arctic*, **12**, 151–157.

Uyeda, S. (1955); Magnetic interaction between ferromagnetic materials contained in rocks, *J. Geomag. Geoelec.*, **7**, 9–36.

Uyeda, S. (1956); Magnetic interaction between ferromagnetic minerals contained in rocks (II), *J. Geomag. Geoelec.*, **8**, 39–70.

Uyeda, S. (1957); Thermo-remanent magnetism and coercive force of the ilmenite-hematite series, *J. Geomag. Geoelec.*, **9**, 61–78.

Uyeda, S. (1958); Thermo-remanent magnetism as a medium of palaeomagnetism, with special reference to reverse thermo-remanent magnetism, *Japan. J. Geophys.*, **2**, 1–123.

Uyeda, S. (1962); Thermoremanent magnetism and reverse thermoremanent magnetism, *Proc. Benedum Earth Magnetism Symposium*, 87–106.

Uyeda, S., M. D. Fuller, J. C. Belshé, and R. W. Girdler (1963); Anisotropy of magnetic susceptibility of rocks and minerals, *J. Geophys. Res.*, **68**, 279–291.

Urey, H. C., H. A. Lowenstam, S. Epstein, and C. R. McKinney (1951); Measurement of paleotemperatures and temperatures of the Upper Cretaceous of England, Denmark and the southeastern United States, *Bull. Geol. Soc. Amer.*, **62**, 399–416.

Valiev, V. V. (1960); The position of the poles during the Tertiary period as determined from the remanent magnetization of rocks in northern Ferghana, *Akad. Nauk. SSSR Izv. Geophys. Ser.*, 1213–1215.

Van Houten, F. B. (1961); Ferric oxides in red beds as palaeomagnetic data, *J. Sed. Petr.*, **31**, 296–300.

Vekua, L. V. (1961); Certain results of paleomagnetic studies of effusive rocks of Georgia, *Akad. Nauk. SSSR Izv. Geophys. Ser.*, 1668–1673.

Verhoogen, J. (1956); Ionic ordering and self-reversal of magnetization in impure magnetites, *J. Geophys. Res.*, **61**, 201–209.

Verhoogen, J. (1959); The origin of thermo-remanent magnetization, *J. Geophys. Res.*, **64**, 2441–2449.

Vestine, E. H., L. La Porte, C. Cooper, I. Lange, and W. C. Hendrix (1947); Description of the earth's main magnetic field and its secular change, 1905–1945, *Carnegie Inst. Washington Pub. 578*, 532 pp.

Vincent, E. A., J. B. Wright, R. Chevallier, and S. Mathieu (1957); Heating experiments on some natural titaniferous magnetites, *Min. Mag.*, **31**, 624–655.

Vincenz, S. A. (1954); The magnetic properties of some Tertiary intrusives of the Isle of Mull, *Mon. Not. Roy. Astr. Soc., Geophys. Supp.*, **6**, 590–603.

Vincenz, S. A. and J. McG. Bruckshaw (1960); Note on the probability distribution of a small number of vectors, *Proc. Camb. Phil. Soc.*, **56**, 21–26.

Vlassov, A. Ya and V. P. Aparin (1963); On the late Precambrian paleomagnetism in Sinian deposits of the Yenisei Ridge, *Akad. Nauk. SSSR Izv. Geophys. Ser.*, 451–454.

Vlassov, A. Ya, A. A. Bogdanov, and A. G. Zvegintsev (1963); Changes in the magnetic properties of natural hematites due to temperature, *Akad. Nauk. SSSR Izv. Geophys. Ser.*, 324–328.

Vlassov, A. Ya and G. V. Kovalenko (1963); Magnetism of transitional layers between zones of normal and reversed magnetization, *Akad. Nauk. SSSR Izv. Geophys. Ser.*, 552–560.

Vlassov, A. Ya, G. V. Kovalenko, and Yu. De. Tropin (1961); Effect of compression of artificially deposited sediments upon remanent magnetization, *Akad. Nauk. SSSR Izv. Geophys. Ser.*, 1179–1182.

Vlassov, A. Ya, A. V. Popova, A. G. Zvegintsev, and E. K. Rodicheva (1961); Palaeomagnetic investigation of Devonian sedimentary strata in the central part of the Krasnoyarsk district, *Akad. Nauk. SSSR Izv. Geophys. Ser.*, 1022–1024.

Vlassov, A. Ya and A. G. Zvegintsev (1961); The thermoremanent magnetization stability of magnetite against temperature changes and magnetic field reversal, *Akad. Nauk. SSSR Izv. Geophys. Ser.*, 1522–1524.

Vologdin, A. G. (1961); Stromatoliths, indicators of migration of the poles, *Priroda*, **11**, 102–103.

Wadia, D. N. (1953); *Geology of India* (3rd edit.), Macmillan, London, 531 pp.

Walker, F. (1956); The magnetic properties and differentiation of dolerite sills—a critical discussion, *Amer. J. Sci.*, **254**, 433–443.

Wang, T., H. Teng, C. Li, and S. Yeh (1960); *Acta Geophysica Sinica*, **9**, 125–138.

Ward, M. A. (1963); On detecting changes in the Earth's radius, *Geophys. J.*, **8**, 217–225.

Watanabe, N. (1958); Secular variation in the direction of geomagnetism as the standard scale for geomagnetochronology in Japan, *Nature*, **182**, 383–384.

Watanabe, N. (1959); The direction of remanent magnetism of baked earth and its application to chronology for anthropology and archaeology in Japan, *J. Fac. Sci. Univ. Kyoto*, **2**, 1–188.

Watkins, N. D. (1963); Behaviour of the geomagnetic field during the Miocene period in south-eastern Oregon, *Nature*, **197**, 126–128.

Watson, G. S. (1956a); Analysis of dispersion on a sphere, *Mon. Not. Roy. Ast. Soc., Geophys. Supp.*, **7**, 153–159.

Watson, G. S. (1956b); A test for randomness of directions, *Mon. Not. Roy. Ast. Soc., Geophys. Supp.*, **7**, 160–161.

Watson, G. S. and E. Irving (1957); Statistical methods in rock magnetism, *Mon. Not. Roy. Astr. Soc. Geophys. Supp.*, **7**, 289–300.

Weaving, B. (1962a); The magnetic properties of the Brewster meteorite, *Geophys. J.*, **7**, 203–211.

Weaving, B. (1962b); Magnetic anisotropy in chondritic meteorites, *Geochim. Cosmochim. Acta*, **26**, 451–455.

Weaving, B. (1962c); The effect of heating on chlorophaeite and their importance in rock magnetism, *Proc. Phys. Soc.*, **80**, 1149–1154.

Wegener, A. (1924); *The origin of continents and oceans* (English translation by J. G. A. Skerl), Methuen, London, p. 212.

Wells, A. (1962); Recent dolomite in the Persian Gulf, *Nature*, **194**, 274–275.

Wetherill, G. W., G. L. Davis, and L. T. Aldrich (1957); Age measurements on rocks north of Lake Huron, *Trans. Amer. Geophys. Union*, **38**, 412.

Wilson, M. E. (1958); Precambrian classification and correlation in the Canadian shield, *Geol. Soc. Amer. Bull.*, **69**, 757–774.

Wilson, J. T. (1954); The development and structure of the crust, *The Earth as a Planet* (ed., G. P. Kuiper), 138–214.

Wilson, J. T. (1963); Hypothesis of Earth's Behaviour, *Nature*, **198**, 925–929.

Wilson, R. L. (1959); Remanent magnetism of late Secondary and early Tertiary British rocks, *Phil. Mag.*, **4**, 750–755.

Wilson, R. L. (1961); Palaeomagnetism in Northern Ireland, Part I, The thermal demagnetization of natural magnetic moments of rocks, *Geophys. J.*, **5**, 45–69. Part II, On the reality of a reversal of the Earth's magnetic field, *Geophys. J.*, **5**, 59–69.

Wilson, R. L. (1962a); The palaeomagnetic history of a doubly-baked rock, *Geophys. J.*, **6**, 397–399.

Wilson, R. L. (1962b); The palaeomagnetism of baked contact rocks and reversals of the Earth's magnetic field, *Geophys. J.*, **7**, 194–202.

Wilson, R. L. (1962c); An instrument for measuring vector magnetization at high temperatures, *Geophys. J.*, **7**, 125–130.

Wilson, R. L. (1963); The palaeomagnetism of some rhyolites from Northern Ireland, *Geophys. J.*, **8**, 235–241.

Wilson, R. L. and C. W. F. Everitt (1963); Thermal demagnetization of some Carboniferous lavas for palaeomagnetic purposes, *Geophys. J.*, **8**, 149–164.

Wright, H. E. (1956); Origin of the Chushka Sandstone, Arizona—New Mexico: a structural and petrological study of Tertiary aeolian sediment, *Bull. Geol. Soc. Amer.*, **67**, 413–434.

Yanovsky, B., A. Khramov, G. Petrova, and A. Kalashnikova (1963); *Akad. Nauk. SSSR Izv. Geophys. Ser.*, no. 3.

Yaskawa, K. (1959); Remanent magnetism of dynamo-metamorphic rocks, *Mem. Coll. Sci. Univ. Kyoto*, **26**, 225–227.

Yukutake, T. (1961); Aechaeomagnetic study on volcanic rocks in Oshima Island, Japan, *Bull. Earthqu. Res. Inst.*, **39**, 467–476.

Zavoiski, V. N. and Z. A. Krutikhovskaya (1961); The remanent magnetization of ferruginous quartzites in the southern closure of the Krivoi Rog synclinorium, *Akad. Nauk. SSSR Izv. Geophys. Ser.*, 1150–1157.

Zijl, J. S. V. van, K. W. T. Graham, and A. L. Hales (1962a and b); The palaeomagnetism of the Stormberg lavas of South Africa (I and II), *Geophys. J.*, **7**, 23–39 and 169–182.

INDEX

Authors and subjects are listed together. Author entries are *italicized* and folios are **boldface.** Rock units are listed by name. A listing of rock units by geological age and country of occurrence is given on pp. 296–315.

A

Aberdeenshire, younger gabbros of, 298, 321
Abo Formation, 158, 305, 334
Ade-Hall, J., **176**
Aden Volcanics, 27, 28, 253, 315, 360
Adirondack gneisses, 36–38, 167, 168, 297, 319
Admiralty Granites, 175, 309, 343, 344
Afifale Volcanic Series, 360
Λ group data, 104
Aguilar, sediment from, 335
Ahaggar basalt, 315, 360
Ahlfeld, F., **325**
Ahmed, N., **229, 364**
Aitken, M. J., **149, 357**
Akchagylsk Stage, 156, 157, 314, 358
Akimoto, S., **16, 18–20, 25, 162–164, 285, 345, 350, 351, 359, 373, 377, 378, 381**
Akopyan, Ts. G., **340, 349, 358**
Alaskan orocline, 259
Alcolea, sediment from, 335
Aldan Stage, 299, 323
Aldrich, L. T., **319, 367, 384**
Allard Lake ilmenohematite, 22, 24, 35, 167
Almeida, F., **237**
Almond, M., **32, 56, 166, 325, 329, 335, 341, 354, 365**
Alona Bay Lavas, 298
Amnicon Formation, 298, 321
Amonash Series, 301
Analysis of, magnetization directions, 58–69
 geomagnetic field directions, 45–47
 paleomagnetic poles, 109–113
 virtual geomagnetic poles, 47–49
Anchors, 171
Andean Intrusive Suite, 108, 313, 356
Andreeva, O. L., **331**
Angenheister, G., **347**
Angular Standard Deviation, 68, 69

Anhysteretic remanent magnetization, 21
Anisotropy, *see* Magnetic anisotropy
Antiferromagnetism, 12
Antrim Igneous Suite, 88, 171, 184, 310, 348, 349
Antrim Plateau Basalts, 299, 322
Anzhin Series, 301
Aparin, V. P., **320, 383**
Apparent polar-wandering, 133–143, 257
 hypothesis of, 130, 134
 other tests for, 136
 paleoclimatic test for, 136, 191–196
 relative to Africa, 140
 relative to Antarctica, 140, 141
 relative to Australia, 139, 140
 relative to Europe-northern Asia, 137, 138
 relative to Greenland, 141
 relative to India, 140
 relative to Japan, 141
 relative to North America, 138, 139
 relative to South America, 140, 143
 use in correlating beds, 275, 276
Appekunny Formation, 296, 318, 321
Applecross Group, *see* Torridonian Sandstone Series
Apsheronsk Stage, 156, 157, 279, 314, 358
Arai, Y., **182, 183, 377**
Aramakai, S., **285**
Araucarite Stage, 158, 303, 330
Archeocyathinae, 194, 195, 215, 217, 223, 224, 240
Archeomagnetism, 148, 180–183, 357, 359, 360
 use for dating, 274
Ardnamurchan gabbro, 36, 310, 348
Aretine vases, 7
Arikee Formation, 55, 56, 313, 354
Armstrong, D., **275, 332**
Arran, dikes, 310, 348
 sediments, 336
As, J. A., **21, 89, 331**
Asama volcano, 285
Asami, E., **359, 377**
Asha Stage, 299, 323
Athavale, R. N., **320, 344**
Aultbea Group, *see* Torridonian Sandstone Series

Auvergne lavas, 310, 313, 357
Avilov Stage, 158, 303, 329
Axial geocentric dipole, 2, 3, 40, 42, 43, 130, 136, 243, 244
Ayrshire kylites, 158, 275, 305, 332
Azuki Tuff, 350

Baadsgaard, H., **318, 369, 370**
Bagin, V. I., **363**
Bagnold, R. A., **233**
Bain, G. W., **218**
Baked clays, 313, *see* Archeomagnetism, Hearths, Kilns, and Bricks
Baku Stage, 156, 157, 314, 358
Balkhan, Great, 345, 349
 Small, 345, 349, 358
Balsley, J. R., **34, 36, 37, 168, 319, 370**
Bancroft, Ontario, 319
Bancroft, A. M., **357**
Banded iron formation, 286, 287
Banded sediments, 80, 81, 83, 84
Banks, M. R., **229, 338, 368, 372**
Baraboo monadnock, 235–237
Baraga County Dikes, 127, 276, 297, 318
Barnett Formation, 117, 158, 304, 330
Barrandian, 125, 298, 322
Barron Hill igneous body, 329
Basement Complex, *see* South Victoria Land
Basement Dikes, *see* South Victoria Land
Bashunchak Suite, 306, 336
Bass Limestone, 296, 317
Bathurst Formation, 331
Bauxite, North Urals, 326
Bayfield Group, 321
Beacon Group Sediments, *see* South Victoria Land
Beacon Sandstone, *see* South Victoria Land
Bean, C. P., **15**
Beardmore Glacier, 343
Bedding error, 31
Bedding tilt test, 76, 77, 92
Beloyarsk Suite, 158, 306, 335
Belshé, J. C., **35, 149, 274, 328, 329, 339, 357, 366, 369, 383**
Beltian, 127, 276, 296, 318
Benedikt, E. T., **30**
Berkeley latite, 87
Bidgood, D. E. T., **229, 316, 320, 322, 334, 371**
Bigarella, J. J., **237, 238**
Bijawar Traps, 297, 320
Bingara meteorite, 293
Biscay sphenochasm, 254, 255
B group data, 104

Black, R. F., **98, 251, 252, 318, 320, 375, 378**
Blackett, P. M. S., **97, 127, 131–133, 190, 191, 206, 216, 257, 325, 335**
Blackhead Sandstone, 297, 319, 320
Blea Wyke Beds, 308, 339
Blocking diameter, 15
Blocking temperature, 16
 spectrum, 21, 22
Block-settling hypothesis, 282, 283
Bloomsburg red beds, 98, 99
"Blue" Sandstone, California, 313, 354
Blundell, D. J., **273, 321, 323, 344, 349, 356, 361, 362**
Boesen, R., **68, 341, 342**
Bogdanov, A. A., **383**
Bolfa, J., **365**
Bol'shakov, A. S., **364**
Bolzano quartz-porphyries, 254, 305, 333
Bonaventura Formation, 331
Bonito Canyon Quartzite, 296, 317
Bonn Intrusives, 310, 347
Botucatú Sandstone, 237, 238, 342
Bôzô Peninsula sediments, 33, 93, 311, 314, 359
Boulter Intrusive, 297
Boulanger, J., **345, 380**
Bowen, R., **232**
Bradley, J., **364**
Brailsford, F., **14**
Brewster chondrite, 292, 293
Bricks, magnetization of, 7
Briden, J. C., **204, 215, 217, 218, 226–228, 242, 345, 372**
Bridport Sands, 307, 339
Bright Angel Shale, 299, 323
Brisbane Tuff, 307, 337
British Columbia, lavas of, 355
Brodskaya, S. Y., **36, 370**
Broken ground, 245, 246
Brooks, C. E. P., **191, 224**
Brown, A. D., **223**
Brownstone Series, 300
Bruckshaw, J. M., **63, 348, 349, 383**
Bruhnes, B., **7, 8, 82**
Brunswickian red beds, 338
Brynjólfsson, A., **21, 361**
Bucha, V., **322**
Buddington, A. F., **36, 37, 168, 319, 370**
Buldiva Quartzite, 296, 317
Bull, C., **23, 34, 67, 102, 175, 281, 343**
Bullard, E. C., **41**
Bunter Sandstone, 158, 235, 237, 256, 306, 335
Burdon, D. J., **376**
Burlatskaya, S. P., **182**
Bushveld Gabbro, 126, 296, 316, 317

Buzuluk Suite, 306, 336
Byskar Series, 302
Bystryansk Suite, 331

Caerbwby Sandstone, 298, 322
Caerfai Series, 322
Calciferous Sandstone Series, 328
Campbell, C. D., **355**
Campbell, K. S. W., **226**
Cantal, lavas of, 310, 347
Cape Hallet, lavas of, 313, 315, 361
Carbonates, coral, *see* Coral
    distribution of, 204–214
    dolomite, *see* Dolomite
    organic reefs, *see* Organic reefs
    paleoclimatic indicator, 189
    paleolatitude of, 211, 212, 217, 242
Carboniferous Limestone, U.K., 158, 302, 328, 329
Carey, S. W., **249, 251, 253–256, 259, 263, 264, 270, 271, 290, 292**
Carmel Formation, 308, 342
Carmichael, C. M., **19, 22, 167**
Carthage, kiln, 360
Catombal Formation, 301, 326
Cattala, L., **345, 380**
Casper Sandstone, 234, 235
Cave Sandstone, 174, 307, 337, 340
Châine des Puys lavas, 313, 357
Chamalaun, F. H., **34, 99, 325**
Chang, Wen-you, **324**
Chapman's Peak, 325
Chargin Series, 301
Charlesworth, H. A. K., **69, 348, 372**
Chasovennay Series, 301
Cheleken Peninsula, 349, 358
Chemical remanent magnetization, 4, 28–30, 73
Chequamegon Sandstone, 297, 318, 319
Chergaka Suite, 300, 325
Chevallier, R., **1, 2, 6, 8, 18, 147, 148, 357, 383**
Chinle Formation, 307, 337, 338
Chocolate Shales, *see* Narrabeen Series
Chondrites, 292, 293
Chugwater Formation, 56, 57, 115, 158, 305, 307, 337
Chuska Sandstone, 236, 237
Circle of confidence, 62
Circle of remagnetization, 75
Circular Standard Deviation, 60
Clegg, J. A., **32, 56, 82, 83, 127, 131–133, 140, 166, 256, 257, 325, 328, 329, 335, 340, 341, 352, 354, 363, 364, 369**
Climatic zones, past, 191, 242, 243
    present, 190, 191

Clinton iron-ore, 300, 325
Coal, 220–223
    distribution of, 204–209, 227
    paleoclimatic indicator, 190, 221
    paleolatitude of, 227, 228, 242
Coal Measures, U.K., 328, 329
Coconino Sandstone, 235, 236, 238
Codroy Beds, 158, 304, 331
Coercive force, 14, 91
    spectrum of, 21
Coercivity of, maximum IRM, 23, 91
    NRM, 22
Coleman, A. P., **230**
Collinson, D. W., **11, 57, 138, 276, 317, 318, 323, 324, 331, 334, 337, 338, 342, 354**
Columbia River Basalt, 249, 313, 355
Compaction, 38
Compston, W., **228**
Conglomerate test, 77, 78
Connecticut Valley Triassic, 307, 338
Contacts, *see* Igneous contacts
Continental Drift, 4, 8, 256–259
    hypothesis of, 131–137, 186, 257
    its relation to glaciation, 224
    ocean island drift, 259, 263
    paleoclimatic tests for, 186, 258–262
    paleomagnetic evidence, 144, 145, 227
    paleomagnetic test for, 136, 144, 259, 263–265
    reconstructions of, 259, 263–273
    Red Sea rift, 252
Cook, R. M., **149, 274, 357**
Coombs, D. S., **360**
Cooper, C., **42**
Copper Harbor, beds, 297, 318
    conglomerate, 318
Coral, Ordovician, 213, 219
    paleoclimatic indicators, 188, 189
    reefs, *see* Organic reefs
    southward trend with time, 212, 213, 216
Correga das Pedras, sediments of, 325
Correlating by paleomagnetism, *see* Paleomagnetic correlation
Corumbatai Formation, 158, 306, 335
Cotswold Sands, 308, 329
Cow Springs Sandstone, 236
Cox, A., **40, 41, 44, 47–50, 86, 100, 145, 159, 160, 176, 182, 249, 291, 295, 317, 319, 354, 355, 361, 362, 368**
Creer, K. M., **11, 21, 33, 34, 44–46, 50, 55, 56, 68, 97–99, 137, 238, 316, 321–325, 327, 331, 332, 335, 336, 339, 344, 347, 356, 360, 365, 366**
Cristi, J. M., **238**
CRM, *see* Chemical remanent magnetization

Crystallization, magnetization, 29, 354
  remanence, 29
Cuddapah Traps, 297, 320
Culter Formation, 158, 305, 334
Cummings, G. L., **319, 381**
Curie point, *see* Curie temperature
Curie temperature, 12, 16, 20, 21
Curnow, C. E., **367**
Currie, R. G., 347
Curtis, G. H., **347, 369**
Curtis, R., **212**
Cygnet Alkaline Complex, 101, 276, 309, 345

Dakota Sandstone, 276, 346
Dalrymple, G. B., **159, 160, 176, 366**
Daly, L., **36**
Dashkevitson, N. N., **336, 369**
Dating by paleomagnetism, *see* Paleomagnetic
  correlation
David, P., **7, 8, 76**
David, T. W. E., **195, 226, 228, 229, 262, 276, 330**
Davis, G. L., **319, 322, 384**
Day, A. A., **323**
Deadwood Formation, 299, 323
De Chelly Sandstone, 235, 236
Declination, 11, 39
Deccan Traps, 35, 108, 271, 312, 352, 353
Delesse, A., **6**
Demagnetization, alternating magnetic field, 21,
    87
  self, 13
  steady fields, 22
  thermal, 21, 87, 88
  viscous, 32
Depositional remanent magnetization, 30
Derbyshire, lavas, 303, 329
  sediments, 303, 328
Desert sandstones, distribution of, 207–209, 214,
    262
  paleoclimatic indicator, 189
  paleolatitude of, 235, 237–239, 242
  paleowind directions in, *see* Paleowind direc-
    tions
Destructive field, 22, 91
Detrital remanent magnetization, 30–32
Deutsch, E. R., **140, 256, 328, 329, 335, 336, 352, 353, 365, 366**
Deviation angle, 129
Devonian coral reefs, 214, 222
Diabaig Group, *see* Torridonian Sandstone
  Series
Diabase dikes of Canadian Shield, 297, 298, 319,
    321
Diamagnetism, 12
Dickson, G. O., **95, 96**

Dietzel, G. F. L., **333**
Dikes, contacts, 82, 83, 172, 174, 175, 298, 321
  instances studied, *see* Appendix reference list
  magnetization parallel to internal field of, 319
Dip poles, 39
Dispersion, analysis of, 58, 63–68
  between-sites, 56, 57, 67, 68, 146, 147
  examples of, 55, 56
  of geomagnetic field, 45–47
  of virtual geomagnetic poles, 47–49
  sources of, 57, 58
  within-sites, 55, 57, 67, 68
Divergence angle, 128, 132
Doell, R. R., **30, 40, 41, 44, 49, 86, 101, 145, 159, 160, 176, 182, 291, 295, 317, 319, 334, 354, 355, 361, 362, 366**
Dolaizon lava, 173, 175
Dolomite, distribution of, 204–213
  paleoclimatic indicator, 212
  paleolatitude, 212, 218
Domains, *see* Magnetic domains
Domain walls, *see* Magnetic domains
Domen, H., **36, 100, 172, 176, 359**
Domite pavement, 7
Donbas sediments, 158, 303, 305, 330, 333
Dorman, F. H., **195, 232, 258**
Dott, R. H., **224**
DRM, *see* Detrital remanent magnetization
Du Bois, P. M., **98, 319, 321, 331, 332, 338, 355**
DuBois, R. L., **328**
Duchesne River Formation, 312, 354
Duluth Gabbro, 298, 321
Dumfries Sandstone, 235, 237
Dune-bedded sandstone, *see* Desert sandstone
Duro Porphyry, 300, 325
Du Toit, A. L., **214, 262–265, 271**
Dwyka Series, 258, 259, 303, 330

Edith River Volcanics, 296, 317
Edwards, G., **318, 369**
Egyed, L., **289–291**
Eifel, lavas, 315, 355
  sandstone, 325
Eileen Sandstone, 298
Einarsson, T., **156, 170, 277**
Elder Mountain Sandstone, 100, 299, 322
Eleonore Bay Formation, 320
Ellef Ringnes Island, 347
Ellensburg Formation, 313, 354
Elliot, R. B., **176**
EM 7 basalt, 93
Enrei Formation, 251, 312, 351
Entrada Sandstone, 236
Epstein, S., **230–232, 375, 383**
Equatorial projection, 55

Equilibrium magnetization, 15, 16
Equivalent paleomagnetic pole, 267
Erickson, G. P., **338**
Escourt mine, dolerite of, 341, 344
Esterel rocks, 158, 253, 304, 331
Etruscan vases, 170
Evans, G., **212, 367**
Evans, W. D., **176, 368**
Evaporites, distribution of, 204–214, 238, 240, 262
    paleoclimatic indicators, 189
    paleolatitude of, 206, 210, 215, 216, 242
    southward trend with time, 206, 216
Everdingen, R. O., van, **57, 331, 332, 380**
Everitt, C. W. F., **14, 24, 82, 83, 166, 256, 283, 328, 329, 335, 365**
Evernden, J. K., **101, 228, 330, 334, 341, 342, 345, 346, 347**
Evison, F. F., **128**
Exeter Traps, 158, 305, 332
Expansion of Earth, *see* Paleoradius of the Earth

Fairbairn, H. W., **369**
Farmington chondrite, 293
Faroe Islands, 8
Faul, H., **367**
Faure, G., **320**
F'derick ore body, 286, 287
Feinberg, F. S., **336**
Ferghana sediments, 311, 350
Ferrar Dolerite, 23, 24, 34, 67, 68, 83, 93, 102, 115, 145, 175, 176, 265, 308, 309, 343, 345
Ferrar Glacier, 343
Ferrimagnetism, 12
Ferromagnetism, 12
Fischer, A. G., **340, 371**
Fisher, R. A., **47, 49, 52, 58, 295**
Fisher's Distribution, 58–60
Fitch, F. J., **349, 376**
Fold test, *see* Bedding tilt test
Folgerhaiter, G., **7, 8, 76, 170**
Fossa magna, 250, 251, 350, 356
    intrusives of, 313, 356
Fossil magnetism, 1
Fourmarier, P., **155**
Freda Sandstone, 98, 297, 318
Freedman, C., **41**
Frosch, A., **99, 372**
Frost, D. V., **319, 331**
Fuller, M. D., **34–36, 383**
Fusulinids, *see* Permian Fusulinids

Gaskell, T. F., **287, 372**
Gaspé Peninsula, 331
Gelletich, H., **171**

Gellman, H., **42**
Geocentric axial dipole, *see* Axial geocentric dipole
Geocentric dipole, 2
Geomagnetic, axis, 40
    equator, 39
    latitude, 40
    poles, 40, 44
Geothite, 20
Gergovie rocks, 155, 173, 310, 347
Gibraltar (Mt.) microsyenite, 276, 308, 341
Gilbert, W., **243**
Gill, E. D., **195, 232, 258, 368**
Gingenbullen Dolerite, 276, 308, 342
Girdler, R. W., **34–36, 252, 339, 340, 352, 355, 383**
Giron Beds, 307, 339
Glacial varves, *see* Varved sediments
Glaciation, index, 224, 228
    late Paleozoic, 224, 226, 228, 229, 262
    paleoclimatic evidence for, 189, 224
    Precambrian, 228–230
    Quaternary, 224
    see also Varves and Upper Kuttung sediments
Glen Canyon Group, 236, 342
Gold, T., **132**
Goldich, S. S., **318, 321**
Gondwana beds, 190, 195
Gondwanaland, 257, 263, 265, 271, 272
Gonganda Formation, 230
Gorter, E. W., **16, 17, 162**
Gottingen volcanics, 313, 356
Gough, D. I., **89, 98, 100, 171, 316, 320, 346, 376**
Grabovsky, M. A., **36, 162**
Graham, J. W., **4, 21, 34, 36, 56, 76, 77, 101, 249, 324, 325, 327, 337, 338, 354, 355, 360, 382**
Graham, K. W. T., **100, 101, 168–170, 174, 176, 184, 341, 344, 384**
Graham Land rocks, 344, 345
Graham's conglomerate test, *see* Conglomerate test
Graham's fold test, *see* Bedding tilt test
Granar, L., **30, 34, 36, 357**
Grand Canyon Series, 276, 296, 317
Gravenoire baked clays, 183, 184
Gray Phase, 277, 278
Great Barrier Reef, 215, 222
Great-circle distribution, *see* Smeared distribution
Great Dike of Rhodesia, 127, 297, 320
Great Whin Sill, 93, 158, 248, 254, 305, 332
Green River Formation, 312, 354
Green, Robert, **205, 206**

Green, Ronald, **54, 101, 150, 245, 246, 281, 317, 322, 325–327, 353, 354, 360, 372, 373, 376**

Greenland, Permian sediments, 334

 Precambrian sediments, 297, 320

 Skaergaard, *see* Skaergaard gabbro

 Tertiary lavas of, 8

 Triassic sediments, 339

Grenville rocks, 298, 319, 321

Griffiths, D. H., **30, 151, 152, 352, 357, 366**

Grinnel Formation, 296, 297, 318

Gromme, C. S., **159, 347, 367**

Gross, W. H., **286**

Group *A* data, 104

Group *B* data, 104

Gusev, B. V., **333, 336**

Gus'kova, N. G., **350**

Gzhelian Stage, 304, 331

Habichtswald volcanics, 313

Haigh, G., **29**

Hakatai Shales, 296, 317, 319

Hakone volcano, 285

Hales, A. L., **168–170, 174, 176, 184, 341, 344, 370, 384**

Hall, J. M., **37**

Hallimond, A. F., **100**

Hamakua Volcanic Series, 361

Hamilton, N., **371**

Hanus, V., **371**

Hargraves, R. B., **34, 167, 340**

Harland, W. B., **229, 316, 334, 364**

Harold, M. R., **363**

Harrington, H. J., **238, 342**

Harrison, W., **362**

Harshbarger, J. W., **236**

Hartshill Quartzite, 298, 322

Hastie, L., **75, 99, 101, 345, 379**

Haruna dacite, 160, 162–165, 168

Hatherton, T., **284, 360, 366**

Hawaiian lavas, 159, 315, 361, 362

Hay, R. L., **159**

Hazel Formation, 296, 317

Heard Island, 263

Hearths, baked, 148, 180, 357, 359

Hematite, 12, 16, 17, 18, 35, 36; *see also* Specularite

 powders of, 23–25, 27, 29

Hematite-ilmenite Series, 17, 19, 22, 24, 161, 165, 167

Hendrix, W. C., **42**

Herroun, E. F., **100, 371**

Hess, H. H., **283**

Hibberd, F. H., **145, 351**

Hilgenberg, O. C., **290, 292**

Hill, D., **194, 195, 213, 214, 216, 219, 222, 262**

Hilten, D. van, **254, 255, 265, 292, 333**

Hirao, K., **359, 377**

Homestead chondrite, 293

Hood, P., **101, 246, 319**

Hospers, J., **44, 69, 106, 156, 277, 348, 355, 357, 361**

Howell, L. G., **30, 36, 99, 317, 322, 325, 330, 376**

Huesca rocks, 254, 255, 306, 333, 335

Humbolt, Alexander von, **6**

Hupeh sediments, 302, 327

Hurley, P. M., **369**

Huronian glaciation, 230

Hydrostatic pressure, effect of, 36

Hyolithus Limestone, 322

Hysteresis, of IRM, 22–24

 loop, 14, 15

Iceland, 8

 early Quaternary deposits, 156, 361

 historic lavas, 156, 361

 interglacial deposits, 156

 Mt. Hekla, 361

 Palagonite Formation, 156

 Pliocene and Pleistocene lavas, 315, 361

 Pliocene deposits, 156

 post-glacial lavas, 156, 315, 361

 Tertiary lavas, 93, 156, 311, 355

 transition zones, 168, 171, 184

Igneous contact test for, magnetic stability, 81–83

 reversals, 172–176

 sill or lava?, 283

Illawarra reversal, 158, 159, 279

Ilmenite, 17, 19

Ilmenite-hematite Series, *see* Hematite-ilmenite Series

Ilmenite-magnetite minerals, 19, 20

Inclination, 11, 39

Inclination error, effect on paleolatitude, 240

 field studies, 74, 151

 laboratory studies, 31

Inclined geocentric dipole, 2, 40, 45

Induced magnetization, 10

Inkstone Series, 345

Intensity of geomagnetic field, during a reversal, 184

 in Armenia, 182

 in Basutoland, 183, 184

 in Carthage, 181, 182

 in France, 181–184

 in Iceland, 184

 in Ireland, 183, 184

Intensity of geomagnetic field, in Japan, 182, 183
  in Switzerland, 180, 181
  in U.S.A., 179
Intensity of magnetization, 11
IRM, *see* Isothermal remanent magnetization
Iron formation, Allard Lake, 22, 24, 35, 167
  Clinton, 300, 325
  F'derick, 286
  Grit, 309, 345
  Yenesei Ridge, 320
Iron meteorites, 292, 293
Irregular field of the Earth, 40
Isachsen Diabase, 310, 346
Isakova, L. I., **370**
Ishikawa, Y., **373**
Ising, G., **30, 34, 36, 357**
Isocline, 39
Isodynamic maps, 40
Isogonic line, 39
Isopor, 41, 42
Isothermal remanent magnetization, 13, 22–24
Issakarassene Volcanic Series, 360
Ito, H., **249–251, 340, 350, 356, 374**
Ivanov, N. A., **326**
Ivashikhin Series, 301

Jacadigo Series, 300, 325
Jacobsville Sandstone, 296, 297
Jaeger, J. C., **54, 150, 166, 172, 245, 264, 281–283, 292, 341, 354, 363, 375**
Jan Mayen Island, 8
Janovsky, B. M., **33**; see also *Yanovsky B.*
Jeffreys, H., **132, 249**
Johnson, A. E., **22, 30, 54, 92, 152, 179, 360, 376**
Joints, effect of, 86
Joplin, G. A., **34, 172, 281–283, 341, 373, 381**
Jujuy Province, sediment of, 321, 327
Juniata Formation, 300, 324

Kahuku Volcanic Series, 361
Kalashnikov, A. G., **316, 322–324, 326, 330, 333, 336, 340, 349, 350, 358**
Kalashnikova, A., **384**
Kamchatka, rocks of, 311, 314, 350, 358
Kang, Y., **374**
Kansu red beds, 300, 324
Kapp Biot red beds, 307, 339
Karroo, 237, 340
  basalt, 308, 340; *see also* Stormberg Lavas
  dolerite, 115, 176, 265, 309, 341
Karymov Series, 301
Kato, I., **174, 374**

Kato, Y., **174**
Katsura, T., **18, 363**
Kawai, N., **17, 18, 33, 93, 162, 249, 250, 340, 350, 359, 375, 378**
Kayenta Formation, 308, 342
Kazakhstan Porphyrites, 302, 327
Kazanian, 158, 305, 333
Keele beds, 303, 328
Kennebecassis Formation, 331
Kerguelen Islands, 263
Kern, J. W., **37, 38**
Keuper marls, 306, 335, 336; *see also* New Red Sandstone
Keweenawan, 127, 139, 297, 298, 318, 319, 321
Khabarovsk Basalt, 311, 350
Khan, M. A., **36, 56, 100, 274, 347**
Khasi Hills, rocks of, 344
Khazar Beds, 314, 358
Khramov, A. N., **75, 156, 157, 263, 264, 279, 316, 322–324, 326, 330, 333, 336, 340, 345, 349, 350, 358, 384**
Kiaman Magnetic Division, 158, 280
Kiaman Magnetic Interval, 280
Kiersch, G. A., **235, 236**
Killerton lava, 332
Kilns, 7, 148, 357, 359, 360
King, C. A. M., **85**
King, L. C., **263, 264, 271, 272**
King, R. F., **30, 31, 32, 34, 151, 370, 371**
Kinghorn Lavas, 158, 302, 328
Kinghorn sill, 328
Kinlet igneous body, 329
Kinsman, D. J. J., **212, 367**
Kintla Formation, 296, 297, 318
Kintzinger, P. R., **337**
Kiuendagh, 358
Knight, S. H., **234**
Kobayashi, I., **258**
Kobayashi, K., **11, 29, 30, 100, 345, 350–352, 359, 376, 377**
Koenigsberger, J. G., **6, 11, 29, 179, 180**
Koenigsberger ratios, 11, 93
Ko-Fuji volcano, 285
Komarov, A. G., **323, 324, 336, 374**
Komoro Group, 351
Koninsk Suite, 297, 320
Köppen, W., **224, 257, 263**
Koroleva, V. A., **22, 379**
Kotchegura, V. V., **336, 350, 358, 374**
Kovalenko, G. V., **38, 327, 330, 383**
Krishnan, M. S., **344**
Kruglyakov, V. V., **326, 375**
Kruglyakova, G. I., **322, 324, 326**
Krutikhovskaya, Z. A., **384**
Kulp, J. L., **369**

Kulp's 1961 Time Scale, *see* Appendix Table, 296–315
Kumagai, N., **350, 359**
Kume, S., **17, 18, 33, 36, 249, 250, 340, 350, 359, 374**
Kunguss Series, 301, 302, 327
Kuno, H., **345, 350, 351, 359, 377**
Kurile Island lavas, 314, 358
Kurkuaut Suite, 323
Kushiro, I., **363**
Kuttung, Lower, *see* Lower Kuttung lavas
   Main Glacial Stage of, 330
   Paterson Toscanite, 330
   Upper, *see* Upper Kuttung

Lacaze, J., **335, 380**
Lancashire sediments, 302, 303, 328
Laney Shale, 312, 354
Lange, I., **42**
Laporte, L., **42**
La Quinta Formation, 307, 339
La Rioja Province sediments, 331, 337, 339
La Roche Noir, 173
Larochelle, A., **275, 346**
Las Cabras Formation, 307, 339
Late Paleozoic glaciation, *see* Glaciation
Laterite, as paleoclimatic indicator, 189
   paleomagnetism of, 349
Latitude determinations, *see* Paleolatitude
Latium, volcanics of, 7
Laurasia, 257, 263
Lena Stage, 299, 323
Leng, J., **83, 98, 335**
Lepêtre, B., **360, 380**
Lepidocrocite, 20
Lewis Thrust, 251, 252
Li, H., **327, 331, 335, 339, 344**
Light, G., **319, 331, 378**
Lightning, 77, 99–101, 341, 346, 348, 355
Limagne rocks, 155, 310, 347
Lindsay, J., **34, 381**
Lin'kova, T. I., **326**
Lipson, J., **347, 369**
Little Wenlock lava, 303, 329
Llano uplift, 330
Lloyd, J. L., **32**
Lodore Formation, 299, 323
Logan Diabase, 298, 321
Long, W. E., **224**
Longitude determinations, *see* Paleolongitude
Longmyndian, 296, 316
Lotze, F., **205, 214–216, 262**
Lovat Series, 301
Lovering, J. F., **292, 293, 381**

Lowenstam, H. A., **221, 230–232, 236, 369, 383**
Lower Angara Suite, 297, 320
Lower Kuttung lavas, 158, 226, 304, 330
Lower Marine Basalt, 158, 226, 305, 334
Ludlow Series, 300, 324
Ludwigite, 35
Lugov Suite, 300, 324
Lundy dikes, 311, 349
Lundy granite, 349
Lupata Alkaline Volcanics, 310, 346

Ma, T. H., **376**
McDougall, I., **145, 159, 245, 340, 341, 343**
McElhinny, M. W., **89, 320**
McKinney, C. R., **230, 383**
McNamara Formation, 296, 318
McNish, A. G., **30, 54**
Maghemite, 17, 18, 36
Maghemite-magnetite Series, 18
Magnetic anisotropy, in hematite, 18, 35
   in hemoilmenite, 22, 35
   in magnetite, 17
   in rocks, 34–36, 93
   intrinsic, 34
   magnetocrystalline, 12, 13
   of susceptibility, 34
   of TRM, 35, 93
   shape, 13
   strain, 13
   stress-induced, 34, 37, 38
Magnetic cleaning, 88–90
Magnetic domains, 12, 14
   multidomains, 14
   single-domain theory, 14, 15, 28
   walls, 12, 14
Magnetic minerals, 4, 16–20
Magnetic "noise," 57, 93, 94
Magnetic stability, 7, 21, 22
Magnetic viscosity, *see* Viscous remanent magnetization
Magnetite, 12, 16, 17, 36
   in red beds, 97
   powders of, 23–25, 27, 29
Magnetization, anhysteretic remanent, 21
   anisotropy, *see* Magnetic anisotropy
   chemical remanent, 4, 28–30, 73
   crystallization remanent, 29, 354
   depositional remanent, 30
   detrital remanent, 30–32
   equilibrium, 15
   fossil, 1
   induced, 11
   intensity of, 11
   isothermal remanent, 13, 22–24

Magnetization, natural remanent, 1
 parallel to internal field of dikes, 319
 primary, 5, 72, 73
 remanent, 10
 saturation, 13, 20
 secondary, 5, 72, 73
 self-reversed, *see* Self-reversed magnetization
 stability of, 7, 21, 22
 temporary, 5
 thermoremanent, 4, 24–28, 73
 viscous remanent, 32–34
Magnetocrystalline anisotropy, 12, 13
Magnetogeological mapping, 277
Magnetometer, 11
Magnetostriction, 13
Main Glacial Stage, Upper Kuttung, 330
Maji Ya Chumvi Formation, 305, 334
Major, A., **32, 373**
Makarova, Z. V., **336**
Malani rhyolites, 297
Mamaisne Point Lavas, 298
Manchurian lavas, 8, 358
Manley, H., **99**
Manwaring, E. A., **89**
Marguerite Bay, intrusives of, 323
Markhinin, E. K., **358**
Martinez, J. D., **30, 36, 99, 317, 322, 325, 330, 372**
Martite, 19
Massachusetts lavas, 307, 338
Massé, G. W., **374**
Massif Central rocks, 155, 173–175
Matayuma, M., **8, 358**
Mathieu, S., **18, 365, 383**
Matsuzaki, H., **100**
Mauchline beds, 158, 254, 275, 305, 332, 333
Maurain, C., **29**
Maximum isothermal remanence, 23
Maymecha-Kotuy Ultrabasic rocks, 158, 305, 333
Melloni, M., **7**
Mendecino orocline, 249, 250
Mendoza Province, sediments of, 339
Mercanton, P. L., **8, 137, 171, 280**
Meriden Formation, 338
Meteorites, 292, 293
Method I of pole calculation, 69
Method II of pole calculation, 70
Meyerhoff, A. A., **378**
Midford Sands, 307, 339
Midland Basalts and sills, 158, 283, 303, 329
Mihara Basalt, 20
Mikhailova, N. P., **376**
Milestone Grit, 328, 329
Miller, J. A., **332, 349**

Miller Peak Formation, 296, 318
Minimum intensity, 94–96
Minimum movement, assumption of, 266, 268, 269, 272
Minimum reliability criteria, 102, 103, 295
Minusinsk Basin, 327, 331
Miroslav, K., **371**
Mitu Formation, 304, 331
Models of the geomagnetic field, comparison of, 50
 from field analysis, 45–49
 model *A,* 49, 146, 147
 model *B,* 50
 model *C,* 50
Moderate temperature VRM, 33, 34, 82
Moenave Formation, 337
Moenkopi Formation, 115, 158, 307, 337
Mohole project, basalt core, 93
Mokoia chondrite, 293
Momose, K., **100, 182, 183, 351, 352, 376, 377**
Monro, M., **332, 376**
Montcenis Sandstone, 158, 304, 331
Monteregian Hills intrusives, 275, 309, 346
Moore County eucrite, 293
Morin, J., **19**
Morin transition, 19
Morvan, 332
Mt. Browne chondrite, 396
Mt. Coupet, lavas of, 173, 175
Mt. Dore, lavas of, 310, 347
Mt. Dromedary Intrusive Complex, 26, 28, 166, 167, 309, 346
Mt. Etna lavas, 1, 2, 6, 8, 107, 147, 148, 313, 357
Mt. Gibraltar microsyenite, 276, 308, 341
Mt. Hekla, 361
Mt. Megantic intrusive, 275, 309, 346
Mt. Pavagadh, acid tuffs, 312, 353
 rhyolites, 353
Mt. Wellington sill, 281, 282
Mt. Vesuvius lavas, 7
Mudflows, 285
Mull rocks, 8, 108, 310, 348
Multicolored Series, 297, 322
Mumme, W. G., **95, 101, 172, 356**
Mundwarra Complex, 297
Murphy, T., **22, 30, 56, 92, 152, 179, 249, 354, 355, 361, 373, 382**
Murrumbidgee Series, 301, 326
Musset, A. E., **332, 373**

Naco Formation, 158, 304, 331
Nagata, T., **10, 11, 20, 24–26, 29, 30, 160, 162–164, 182, 183, 324, 345, 350, 351, 359, 363, 375, 381**

Nahe valley rocks, 158, 254, 255, 304, 332
Nairn, A. E. M., **44, 50, 68, 267, 319, 320, 324–326, 328, 330–332, 334, 335, 337, 339, 340, 345, 347, 355, 365–367**
Nalivkin, D. V., **194, 316, 336, 358**
Narita Bed, 359
Narrabeen Series, 158, 226, 241, 307, 337
Natural remanent magnetization, 1
Navajo Sandstone, 235, 236
Neale, R. N., **37, 371**
Néel, L., **14, 16, 24, 159, 161, 162**
Neel temperature, 12
Neroly Formation, 313, 354
Nethercote, basalt, 326
   sediment, 301, 326
Neuquen, lavas, 315, 360
   sediments, 301, 344, 347
Newark Series, 73, 74, 115, 307, 338
Newer Volcanics of Victoria, 55–57, 312, 315, 360
New Oxford Formation, 307, 338
New Red Sandstone, conglomerate, 78
   red beds, 55, 56, 97, 98, 115, 256, 306, 335, 336
Niagaran coral reefs, 214, 221
Nichols, G., **16, 18**
Nideck volcanics, 158, 254, 304, 306, 332, 335
Nier, A. O., **370**
Nierkerk, C. B. van, **316, 370**
Nijenhuis, G. H. W., **332**
Ninole Volcanic Series, 361
Nixon, J., **41**
"Noise," magnetic, 57, 93, 94
Non-dipole field of the Earth, 40
  low values in Pacific, 40, 48
  westerly drift of, 41, 42
Non-dipole "hypothesis," 132, 133
Nonesuch Shale, 318
Nonmagnetic minerals, 3
Noosa Head Intrusive Complex, 308, 342
Normal temperature VRM, 33
Norris, D. K., **251, 252**
North Ferghana, *see* Ferghana
North Izu and Hakone Volcanics, 251, 314, 359
Northants Ironstone, 307, 339
North-west Dikes, U.K., 310
NRM, *see* Natural remanent magnetization
Nuée ardente, 285
Nugere Volcano, 184
Nugget Formation, 235, 236
Nullagine Lavas, 296, 317

Oceanic island drift, 259, 263
Odawara dacite pumice, 20
Oil, 287, 288
Oka-Serpukhov Stage, 303, 330
Okler Series, 168, 301, 302, 327

Old Red Sandstone, Brownstones, 301, 325
  lavas, 301, 325
  sediments, 34, 97, 99, 121, 301, 325, 326
Older Volcanics of Victoria, 101, 172, 312, 353, 356
Olduvai Gorge, 159
Oliver, R. L., **345, 365**
Oliviera, A. I., **258, 342**
Omei Mts., basalt of, 335
Onondaga Limestone, 301, 324, 327
Opdyke, N. D., **74, 98, 234–236, 338, 368**
Ordovician corals, 213, 219
Organic reefs, 213–215, 240
  Archeocyathinae, *see* Archeocyathinae
  Devonian reefs, 214, 222
  modern reefs, 213, 220
  Niagaran reefs, 214, 221
  paleolatitude of, 215, 220, 222
  Permian reefs, 262
  southerly trend with time, 213, 214, 220
Orienta Sandstone, 298, 321
Original magnetization, 5
Orocline, paleomagnetic test for, 249, 250, 259
Osaka Sedimentary Group, 350
Oslo Igneous Complex, 56, 57, 115, 158, 254, 305, 332
"Overconsolidation" of glacial silts, 362
Oxygen-isotopes, *see* Paleotemperatures
Oxyhydroxides of iron, 20, 97
Ozima, M., **359, 377, 378**

Palagonite Formation, 277, 279
Paleoclimatic indicators, 188–190
  distribution atlas of, 204–214, 238
Paleocolatitude circles, 268, 269, 273
Paleogeographic pole, 5
Paleogeomagnetic field, 1
Paleolatitude, 186, 187
  atlas of regional variations, 196–203
  spectra, 4, 188
  variation at Bloemfontein, 258, 261
  variation at Canberra, 193, 195, 258, 261
  variation at Cincinnati, 193, 194
  variation at Curityba, 258, 261
  variation at Krasnoyarsk, 192, 194
  variation at Moscow, 192, 194
  variation at Nagpur, 193, 258, 260
  variation at Paris, 192, 194, 258, 260
  variation at Peking, 258, 260
  variation at Salt Lake City, 193, 194
Paleolongitude, determination of, 266–273
Paleomagnetic correlation, intrusives, 275, 276
  lavas, 274
  sediments, 276
  use of apparent polar-wandering, 275, 276

Paleomagnetic correlation, use of reversals, 277–280
  use of secular variation, 274, 275
Paleomagnetic errors, 57
Paleomagnetic pole, 5, 9, 43–45, 52, 69–71
  analysis of, 109–113
  atlas of, 107–129
  equivalent, 267
  errors in, 69, 70
  method I, 69
  method II, 70
Paleomeridian, 187
  atlas of regional variations, 196–203
Paleoradius of the Earth, estimates of, 288–292
  hypotheses of changes in, 135, 136, 289, 290
Paleosecular variation, *see* Secular variation
Paleotemperatures, 190
  in Cretaceous, 230–233
  in Maestrichtian, 231, 233
  from Belemnites, 231
  oxygen-isotope methods, 230, 231
Paleowind directions, in Africa, 237
  in Europe, 235, 237
  in North America, 235–237
  in South America, 237, 238
  maps of, 235, 238
  method of estimating, 233
  "wheel round," 234, 238
Palisade Sill, 338
Pangaea, 257, 263
Paramagnetism, 12
Parana, red beds from, 321
Parry, J. H., **97**
Parry, L. G., **158, 280, 292, 293, 334, 367, 373, 375, 381**
Partial self-reversal, *see* Self-reversed magnetization
Partial TRM, 26
Paterere ignimbrites, 284, 315
Paterson reversal, 158, 159, 280
Paterson Toscanite, 158, 303, 330
Pavement of domite, 7
Payette Formation, 55, 56, 313, 355
Pendle monocline, 328
Pennant Sandstone, 158, 303, 329
Penov Series, 301
Peperites, 155
Permian Fusulinids, 217–220, 225, 226, 240, 241, 259, 262
Petrova, G. N., **22, 91, 370, 374, 384**
Phillips, F. C., **54**
Phlegraen Fields, lavas of, 7
Pilansberg Dikes, 100, 101, 127, 171, 296, 316
Pinson, W. H., **369**
Pivot points, 267, 268, 273

Planar distribution, *see* Smeared distribution
Plateaux, Basalt de, France, 313, 357
Plotting of directions, 54
Points isolés, 6
Point Peak Shale, 322
Polarity, definition of, 71
Polar projection, 55
Polar-wandering, 3, 4, 8, 264
  hypothesis of, 131, 132, 134, 135, 257
  its relation to glaciations, 224
  paleomagnetic tests for, 136
  sets, 267, 270, 271
  see also Apparent polar-wandering
Pole, paleomagnetic, *see* Paleomagnetic pole
Pole paths, *see* Apparent polar-wandering
Pololu Volcanic Series, 361
Pontfarein lava, 7, 8, 173
Poole, F. G., **234**
Popova, A. V., **323–327, 331, 335, 383**
Popper, K., **133**
Portage Lake Lavas, 297
Portrush baked limestone, 348
Pospelova, G. A., **349, 358, 376**
Pottery, 7, 170, 183
Pouillard, E., **18**
Pouk Hill igneous body, 329
Powell, D. W., **36, 179**
Precambrian glaciation, 229, 230
Precision, Fisher's parameter, 58; *see also* Dispersion
Primary magnetization, 5, 72, 73
Primore basalt, 311
Prince Edward Island red beds, 158
Probable error of the mean, 62
Prospect Dolerite, 276, 308, 341
Puna Volcanic Series, 361
Punti Distinti, 6
Purcell Lavas, 297
Purcell System, 297, 320, 321
Pushkov, A. H., **162, 370**
Pyrenees, andesites and sediments, 254, 255, 333, 335
  compression of, 254, 255
  tuff, 308, 340
Pyrrhotite, 20, 161, 162, 166, 168

Raasch, G. O., **237**
Radhakrishnamurty, C., **140, 340, 344, 352, 353, 363, 366, 367**
Radiolarite, 340
Rajmahal Traps, 115, 265, 271, 340
Randomness, Test for, 63
Rashiehill bore core, 166
Read, H. H., **321, 364**
Red Beds, *see also under particular rock units*
  as paleoclimatic indicator, 189, 190

Red Beds, distribution of, 204–214, 226
  magnetic minerals of, 97
  paleolatitude of, 220, 226, 242
  secondary magnetization in, 97, 98
  superparamagnetism in, 97, 98
  thermal demagnetization of, 98
Red Bed Sequence, Turkmenia, 156, 157, 279, 311, 349
Red Hill dolerite, 342
Red Sea, 251–253
Rees, A. I., **30, 32, 34, 151, 371, 375**
Reference localities, 186, 187
  paleolatitude variation of, 191–196, 258–261
Reiche, P., **236**
Relaxation time, 15, 16
Reliability criteria, 102
Remanence, 10
Remanent magnetism, 10
Remanent saturating field, 23
Reversals of polarity, 3, 8, 71
  igneous contact studies, 7, 8, 173–176
  in California, 160
  in Carboniferous shale, 166
  in France, 155
  in Hawaiian Islands, 159
  in Iceland, 156, 278
  in Mt. Dromedary Intrusive Complex, 166, 167
  in rock units, *see* polarity column in Appendix Table, 296–315
  intermixed polarities, 171, 172
  in Tasmanian tuff, 166
  in Turkmenia, 156, 157
  self-reversal, *see* Self-reversed magnetization
  test for secondary components, 75
  transition zones, 168–171
  use for correlation, 277–280
Rheinland-Pfalz, lavas of, 355
Rhodesian sandstone, 337
Richards, J. R., **101, 228, 330, 334, 341, 342, 345, 346, 369**
Rimbert, F., **21, 33, 100, 382**
Rio Blanco Formation, 307, 339
Ripple marks, 85
Robertson, E. I., **349, 364**
Robertson, W. A., **22, 26, 68, 75, 91, 99, 101, 144, 166, 337, 341, 342, 345, 346, 349, 364, 373**
Robinson dike, 100, 101
Roche, A., **155, 156, 173, 331, 335, 345, 347, 357, 360**
Rodgers, J., **189**
Rodicheva, E. K., **326, 383**
Roquet, J., **23–25, 33**
Rosehill Formation, 77, 300, 325

Rotation angle, 127, 131, 186, 187
Rotliegende, 158, 254, 304, 237, 332
Rowley Regis igneous body, 329
Roy, J. L., **158**
Royat lava, 7, 8
Rum Gabbro, 310, 348
Runcorn, S. K., **44, 57, 69, 71, 84, 85, 96, 97, 101, 130, 132, 138, 144, 234–236, 267, 268, 316, 317, 323, 324, 331, 334, 337–339, 342, 346, 354, 355, 365–368, 373, 378, 379**
Russel Border Belt (gneisses), 319
Russinov, B. Sh., **100, 327**
Rutile, 17
Rutten, M. G., **156, 277–280, 331, 332**
Ryazanova, V. N., **326**
Rybinsk Basin, 327

Sahasrabudhe, P. W., **140, 340, 344, 352, 353, 363, 366, 367**
Saito, T., **165**
Sakhalin Basalt, 311
Salamuni, R., **237, 238, 364**
Salta Province, sediments of, 323, 327, 339
Samoan Volcanics, 315, 361
Sampling schemes, 52, 53
Sandstone Dikes, Keweenawan, 298
Sangre de Cristo Formation, 158, 306, 334
Santa Maria beds, 342
Sao Bento Series, 342
Sasajima, S., **18, 374**
Saturating field, 13, 23
Saturation magnetization, 13, 20
Saucier, H., **335, 380**
Sawatch sandy dolomite, 299, 322
Scheiddegger, A. E., **132, 249**
Schmucker, U., **332**
Schreiner, G. D. L., **316, 317**
Schulkes, J. A., **162, 370**
Schult, A. von, **356**
Schwarz, E. J., **335**
Schwarzbach, M., **194, 220, 230, 237**
Scrabo Hill-intrusion, 348
Secondary magnetization, 5, 72, 73
Secular variation, observatory observations, 3, 41
  at Ascension Is., 41
  at Capetown, 41
  at Hongkong, 41
  at London, 41
  low in Pacific, 41, 42
  westerly drift of, 41
  paleomagnetic observations, 54, 58, 64
  evidence from dispersion, 146, 147
  in Japan, 150

Secular variation, paleomagnetic observations, in Sicily, 147, 148
   in Sweden, 151, 152
   in Tasmania, 150
   in Torridonian sandstone, 149
   in U.K., 148–150
   in U.S.A., 152, 153
   use in correlation problems, 274, 275
Sendai dikes, 174, 175
Self-demagnetization, 12
Self-reversed magnetization, 3, 154, 159–168
  exchange interaction, 160–162
  in Adirondack gneiss, 167, 168
  in Asio pitchstone, 165, 168
  in Haruna dacite, 160, 162–165, 168
  in ilmenite-hematite minerals, 161, 165, 167, 168
  in lithium-chromium spinels, 162
  in pyrrhotite shale, 166, 168
  in Sokota iron sands, 165, 168
  ion migration model, 162
  magnetite-pyrrhotite model, 161, 162
  magnetostatic interactions, 161, 162
  partial, 165, 166
  two constituent models, 160–162
Serebryansk Suite, 306, 336
Serra Geral Formation, lavas of, 237, 265, 308, 309, 342, 344
Setouti Volcanic Zone, 350
Shantung, sediments of, 335
Shape anisotropy, 13
Shatterford intrusive, 329
Shearman, D. J., **212, 367**
Sheveluch Volcanic Dome, 314, 358
Shibata, K., **332, 376**
Shigarami Group, 351
Shikama, T., **258, 375**
Shillibeer, M. A., **319**
Shimizu, Y., **33, 324, 345, 350, 351, 359, 377**
Shinarump Formation, 337
Shinumo Quartzite, 296, 317
Sholpo, L. E., **33, 100, 327, 373, 380**
Shotton, F. W., **237**
Siberian Traps, 158, 306, 336
Sibley Series, 298
Sidorova, E. P., **322, 323**
Siebengebirge lavas, 355, 356
Sierra Nevada granites, 310, 347
Signal Hill Sandstone, 297, 319
Sigurgeirrson, T., **170, 171, 184, 277, 361, 368**
Siletz River Volcanics, 108, 312, 354
Silurian coral reefs, 214, 221
Single-domain theory, 14–16, 28

Sinian sediments, 139, 296, 316
Siyeh Formation, 297, 318
Skaergaard gabbro, 35, 313, 355
Skelton Glacier, 343
Skye igneous rocks, 56, 57, 171, 248, 249, 274, 275, 310, 347
Slump beds, 78–81
  laboratory experiments, 32
Smeared distribution, cause of, 75
  example of, 55, 56, 89
  magnetic cleaning of, 87, 89
  thermal cleaning of, 91
Sopher, S. R., **102, 246–248, 321**
Southdean Basanite, 158, 302, 328
South Sandwich Islands lavas, 315, 362
South Shetland Islands volcanics, 344, 361
South Victoria Land rocks, 342, 343
  Admiralty Granite, *see* Admiralty Granites
  Basement Dikes, 309, 343
  Beacon Group Sediments, 34, 83, 175, 176, 309, 343
  Ferrar Dolerite, *see* Ferrar Dolerite
  secondary magnetization of, 34, 83, 175, 176, 343
Spain, rotation of, 254–256
Sparagmites, 229, 230, 296, 316
Specularite (hematite), 24
  in banded sediments, 24, 80, 81, 84, 85
  in red beds, 97
Spitzbergen, rocks of, 8
Spokane Shale, 296, 318
Spontaneous magnetization, 12
Spot reading of field, 54, 64
Springdale Sandstone, 307, 337
Stability of remanent magnetization, 21, 22
Stacey, F. D., **14, 24, 30, 34, 37, 293, 341, 366, 381**
Standard deviation, angular, 68, 69
  circular, 60
Statham, E. H., **36, 99, 317, 322, 325, 372**
Statistical models of the field, *see* Models of the geomagnetic field
Steady field demagnetization, 22
Stehli, F. G., **217–219, 225, 262**
Stephanian sediments, 158, 254, 302, 328
Stephenson, P. J., **344, 364**
Stockton red beds, 338
Stone, D. B., **34**
Stormberg Lavas, 168–170, 174, 175, 184, 340, 344
Stott, P. M., **22, 23, 37, 89–91, 95, 96, 144, 341, 353, 373**
Strain anisotropy, 13
Strangway, D. W., **286, 319, 371**
Stress effects, 36–38
  on IRM, 37

Stress effects, on NRM, 36, 37
  on TRM, 37, 38, 93
  compaction in sediments, 38
  "overconsolidation" in glacial silts, 362
Stress-induced anisotropy, 37, 38
Stubbs, P. H. S., **32, 56, 127, 131–133, 256, 257, 325, 327–329, 335, 364, 365**
St. Wendel Sandstone, 158, 254, 304, 332
Sudbury Nickel Irruptive, **101, 127, 230, 246–248, 276, 297, 298, 319, 321**
  diabase dikes, 298, 321
Supai Formation, 101, 158, 304, 305, 334
Superparamagnetism, 15, 29, 73
  in red sediments, 97
Surface effects, 6, 73 ; *see also* Lightning, Weathering
Susceptibility, 10
  compared with NRM, 93
Sussmilch, C. A., **226, 367**
Sylhet Traps, 115, 309, 344
Syono, Y., **25**
Szechwan red beds, 344

Table Mountain Series, 300, 324
Tacuarembo Sandstone, 237, 307
Taimyr Peninsula, sediments of, 158, 307, 336
Takagi, A., **174, 374**
Takaosan andesite, 312
Talus, 246
Tananyak Suite, 306, 336
Tapeats Sandstone, 299, 323
Tarling, D. H., **22, 28, 91, 159, 253, 360, 361, 373, 376**
Tartarian, 157, 158, 305, 333
Taru Grit, 305, 334
Tasmanian Basalt, 312
Tasmanian Dolerite, 65, 93, 115, 145, 150, 166, 172, 245, 246, 281–283, 308, 341, 342, 345, 354
Tatysheva Series, 301
Teichert, C., **190, 195, 214, 221**
Temporary magnetization, 5
Teng, H., **327, 331, 335, 339, 344, 383**
Tensleep Sandstone, 234, 235
Terasmae, J., **362, 371**
Terella, 42
Termier, G., **220, 290**
Termier, H., **220, 290**
Tertiary Basalt N.S.W., 23, 24, 89, 90, 312
Thanet Intrusive, 297
Thellier, E., **21, 26, 33, 148, 180, 181, 184, 274, 357, 360, 380**
Thellier, O., **148, 180, 181, 184, 274, 357, 360, 382**
Thermal cleaning, 88, 90, 91, 92
Thermomagnetic analysis, 20, 97, 163, 164

Thermoremanent magnetization, 4, 24–28, 73
Theron Mts., 344
Thulean Igneous Province, 347, 355
Thyer, R. F., **172, 373**
Tideswelldale rocks, 158, 303, 329
Tiles, 180
Tillite Formation, Greenland, 229, 230, 297, 320
Tillites, 189, 320
Tilton, G. R., **367**
Titanomagnetites, 17
Titterstone Clee Hill igneous body, 283, 329
Toadstones, 158, 303, 329
Torreson, O. W., **22, 30, 56, 92, 152, 179, 249, 354, 355, 361, 373**
Torridonian Sandstone Series, 23, 24, 30, 61, 77–81, 84, 85, 93, 97, 98, 126, 127, 150, 151, 168, 276, 296, 316
Total thermoremanent magnetization, 24
Transient variations, 40, 41
Transition, of axis, 276
  polarity, 168–171
Tremadocian sediments, 299, 323
Trenton Group, 300, 324
Trêves, kiln, 313, 357
Tropin, Y. D., **38, 383**
TRM, *see* Thermoremanent magnetization
Tudor Intrusive, 297
Tula horizon, 158, 303, 330
Turnbull, G., **34, 102, 343, 361**
Tyosen lavas, 358

Ufimian, 158, 305, 333
Ukrainian Basalt, 299, 323
Ulvospinel, 17
Ulvospinel-magnetite series, 17, 18
Umfraville Intrusive, 297
Uniaxial stress, 36
Upper Kuttung sediments, 66, 90, 91, 92, 158, 226, 259, 303, 330
Upper Marine Latites, 87, 93, 158, 280, 305, 334
Upper Marine Series, 226, 228
Ural Mts., bauxites of, 326
  rocks of, 324, 330
  peridotites of, 300, 324
Urey, H. C., **230–232**
Ust-Kutsk Stage, 324
Uyeda, S., **19, 24, 25, 35, 160–165, 359, 369, 377, 378**

Valiev, V. V., **350**
Van der Lingen, **333**
Van Houten, F. B., **97**
Varved sediment, 54
  Australia, *see* Upper Kuttung
  Canada, 315, 362

Varved sediment, Dwyka Series, 258, 259, 303, 330
  Iceland, 151
  Rhodesia, *see* Dwyka Series
  Sweden, 151, 152, 313, 314, 357
  U.S.A., 152, 153, 179, 315, 360, 362
Vekua, L. V., **346, 349, 356, 358, 361**
Veldkamp, J., **380**
Verhoogen, J., **14, 24, 162, 347, 367**
Verkolensk Suite, 299, 322
Vestine, E. H., **42**
Victoria Falls, basalt of, 340
Victorian red beds, 301, 327
Villaviciosa, sandstone of, 335
Vincent, E. A., **18**
Vincenz, S. A., **63, 348**
Virtual geomagnetic pole, 43–45
Viscous demagnetization (or decay), 32
Viscous remanent magnetization, 32–34, 73
  stress-aided, 37, 73
Vitloosian, 306, 336
Vlassov, A. Ya., **38, 320, 326, 327, 330**
Vogelsberg igneous rocks, 310, 347
Vologdin, A. G., **233**
Vosges Sandstone, 158, 256, 306, 335
VRM, *see* Viscous remanent magnetization

Wadia, D. N., **224**
Walker, F., **283**
Wang, T., **327, 331, 336, 341, 344**
Ward, M. A., **22, 23, 49, 59, 60, 63, 89, 90, 91, 95, 96, 146, 291, 292, 353, 373**
Wasatch Formation, 312, 354
Watanabe, N., **359, 360**
Watchung Flow, 338
Waterton Formation, 297
Watkins, N. D., **336, 355, 367**
Watson, G. S., **60, 62, 63, 67**
Wealden, 309, 345
Weathering, 29, 333
  ancient, 88
  recent, 99, 100
Weaver, C. E., **318, 369**
Weaver, G. H., **363**
Weaving, B., **292, 293**
Weber Sandstone, 234, 235
Wegener, A., **224, 257, 263, 375**
Wells, A., **212**

Welsh sediments, 303, 329
Wensink, H., **156, 277–280, 380**
Westerly drift, 41, 42
Western Ghats, lava of, 352
Western Hills Peking, rocks of, 331, 339
Western Tiers Tasmania, talus of, 246
Westerwald lavas, 313, 355
Wetherill, G. W., **318, 319, 367**
"Wheel round," 234, 238
Whichaway Nunatak, dolerite of, 344
Whin Sill, *see* Great Whin Sill
Whitewater volcanics and sediments, 246, 247
Wilberns Formation, 299, 322
Willis, I., **23, 34, 67, 102, 175, 281, 343, 365**
Wingate Sandstone, 235, 236
Winkelhaak mine, dolerite of, 341, 344
Wilson, J. T., **249, 263**
Wilson, M. E., **319**
Wilson, R. L., **22, 68, 69, 88, 176, 183, 184, 243, 328, 345, 348, 349**
Wright, A. E., **30 151, 370, 371**
Wright, H. E., **236**
Wright, J. B., **18, 383**

Yalwal Stage, basalts, 301, 326
  sediments, 301, 326
Yama-ai, M., **324, 378**
Yamada, T., **351, 352, 377**
Yamaguchi Basalts, 172, 251, 314, 359
Yanovsky, B., **316, 326, 330, 340, 349, 350, 358;** see also *Janovsky, B. M.*
Yaskawa, K., **374**
Yasukawa, K., **17, 374**
Yeh, S., **327, 331, 335, 339, 344, 383**
Yeovil Sands, 308, 339
Yeso Formation, 158, 305, 334
Yoshida, M., **18, 363**
Yoshikawa, H., **359, 377**
Younger Gabbros Aberdeenshire, 298, 321
Yukon, basalts of, 355
Yukutake, T., **150, 359**

Zavoiski, V. N., **384**
Zijderveld, J. D. A., **21, 89, 331, 332, 363, 380**
Zijl, J. S. V. van, **168–170, 174, 176, 184**
Zvegintsev, A. G., **326, 383**